# GEOTECHNOLOGY

# IN

# MASSACHUSETTS

PROCEEDINGS OF A CONFERENCE IN MARCH 1980

O. C. FARQUHAR, *Editor*

GRADUATE SCHOOL

UNIVERSITY OF MASSACHUSETTS

1982

The conference was supported in part by the National Science Foundation under grant no. EAR-7927089. This support is acknowledged also in the preface, together with other sources of support for the conference.


Any opinions, findings, and conclusions or recommendations expressed in this publication are those of the authors and do not necessarily reflect the views of the National Science Foundation.


ISBN 0-9604712-0-0        LC 82-70207


Published by the Graduate School, University of Massachusetts at Amherst


Inquiries to:   Department of Geology and Geography
                University of Massachusetts
                Amherst, MA 01003

1982        003033452

Printed in the United States of America

# GEOTECHNOLOGY IN MASSACHUSETTS

The upper reservoir of the Northfield Mountain pumped storage hydroelectric project in western Massachusetts. The top view was taken looking up and the bottom view looking down the intake channel when it was under construction in August 1972. The rock benches are cut in gneiss. (Courtesy: Northeast Utilities Service Company, and the Stone & Webster Engineering Corporation.)

for people in
Massachusetts,
and places beyond

# VOLUME ABSTRACTS

This volume contains papers presented in March 1980 at a conference on Geotechnology in Massachusetts. The conference was held at the Boston campus of the University of Massachusetts. It provided a forum for the reporting of geotechnical activities in the Massachusetts area, as well as some areas bordering Massachusetts and beyond. These activities are solving a variety of important problems concerned with energy, the environment, and natural resources, including water resources. More than 300 people attended the two-day conference. Reports and abstracts include: 1 dealing with bedrock geology; 2 with surficial geology; 9 with hydrogeology; 3 with geophysics; 4 with siting of critical facilities; 13 with soils engineering and rock mechanics; 8 with underground space; 2 with energy and the geosciences; 3 with industrial rocks; 5 with mineral resources; 12 with environmental and geochemical problems; 5 with tectonics; 4 with nearshore zones; and 6 with the marine boundary.

تكنولوجيا الارض في ماساتشوستس : ملخص المجلّد . يتضمن هذا المجلّد بحثا قدم في مارس (اذار) ١٩٨٠ في مؤتمر عن تكنولوجيا الارض في ماساتشوستس . اقيم المؤتمر في حرم جامعة ماساتشوستس في بوسطن . وقد وفر هذا المؤتمر برنامجا لمناقشة نشاطات خصائص التربة في منطقة ماساتشوستس وكذلك بعض المناطق المتاخمة لماساتشوستس وما وراءها . وعملت هذه النشاطات على حل مشاكل هامة تتعلق بالطاقة والبيئة والموارد الطبيعية ، بما فيها الموارد المائية . وقد حضر ما يزيد على ٣٠٠ شخص هذا المؤتمر الذى استغرق يومين . ان التقارير والملخصات تتضمن : ١ يتناول جيولوجيا صخور القاعدة ، و ٢ عن جيولوجيا السطح ، و ٩ عن جيولوجيا الماء ، و ٣ عن الجيوفيزيقيا ، و ١٣ عن تحديد الموقع والتسهيلات النووية ، و ١٣ عن الطاقة والعلوم الارضية ، و ٣ عن الصخر الصناعي ، و ٥ عن الموارد المعدنية ، و ١٢ عن مشاكل البيئة والكيمياء الارضية ، و ٥ عن التكتونية ، و ٤ عن المناطق القريبة من الشاطئ ، و ٦ عن الحدود البحرية .

麻萨诸塞州的地质技术：集刊摘要

这本集刊汇集了1980年3月麻州地质技术讨论会所发表的文献。该会议是在麻州大学波斯顿校园举行，为麻州及麻州边境和周围地区的地质活动提供一次交流机会。这些活动正在解决一系列有关能源、自然环境、天然资源（包括水源）等重要课题。这次的两天会议共吸引了300多人，所发表的技术报告和论文摘要包括（文献数量示于括弧内）：基岩地质学（1）；地表地质学（2）；水文地质学（9）；地质物理学（3）；临界地质构造的探寻（4）；土壤工程与土壤力学（13）；地下空隙（8）；能源与地质科学（2）；工业岩石（3）；矿物资源（5）；环境与地球化学问题（12）；构造地质学（5）；近海地质（4）及海洋境界（6）。

GEOTECHNOLOGIE AU MASSACHUSETTS : RESUME DE L'OUVRAGE.  Ce volume
réunit les communications présentées en mars 1980 lors de la
conférence intitulée "Géotechnologie au Massachusetts" et
organisée sur le campus Boston de l'Université du Massachusetts.
Conçue comme un forum, cette conférence a permis  de faire le point
sur les activités géotechniques dans l'Etat du Massachusetts
ainsi que dans certaines régions plus ou moins limitrophes.
Ces activités portent sur la résolution d'un certain nombre
de problèmes de première importance concernant l'énergie,
l'environnement et les ressources naturelles, et notamment les
ressources hydrauliques. Plus de 300 personnes ont participé à
cette conférence de deux jours et les rapports et résumés re-
produits dans l'ouvrage se répartissent comme suit : 1 sur la
géologie du soubassement, 2 sur la géologie des formations
superficielles, 9 sur l'hydrogéologie, 3 sur la géophysique,
4 sur l'implantation des installations critiques, 13 sur la
pédologie et la mécanique des roches, 8 sur l'espace
souterrain, 2 sur l'énergie et les sciences de la terre, 3
sur les roches industrielles, 5 sur les ressources minérales,
12 sur les problèmes écologiques et géophysiques, 5 sur la
tectonique, 4 sur les zones littorales et 6 sur la limite marine.

GEOTECHNOLOGIE IN MASSACHUSETTS:   BANDZUSAMMENFASSUNG.

Dieser Band enthält Vorträge, die im März 1980 auf einer geotechnologischen Tagung in Massachussetts gehalten wurden. Die Tagung fand auf dem Gelände der Universität von Massachussetts in Boston statt. Sie war ein Forum für die Berichterstattung über geotechnologische Aktivitäten in Massachussetts sowie in einigen angrenzenden Gebieten und darüber hinaus. Diese Aktivitäten tragen zur Lösung verschiedener wichtiger Probleme in bezug auf Energie, Umwelt und Naturschätze, u.a. Wasser, bei. Zu der zwei-tägigen Tagung kamen mehr als 300 Teilnehmer. Die Berichte und Zusammenfassungen beziehen sich auf folgende Bereiche: 1 auf Kernfelsgeologie; 2 auf Oberflächengeologie; 9 auf Hydrogeologie; 3 auf Geophysik; 4 auf die Situierung kritischer Atomareinrichtungen; 13 auf Erdbau und Felsme-chanik; 8 auf unterirdische Hohlräume; 2 auf Energie und die Geowissenschaften; 3 auf Industriegestein; 5 auf Mine-ralienquellen; 12 auf umwelttechnische und geochemische Probleme; 5 auf Tektonik; 4 auf Flachwasserzonen und 6 auf die Meeresgrenze.

GEOTECNOLOGIA IN MASSACHUSETTS:   COMPENDIO DEL VOLUME.   Questo volume

contiene le relazioni presentate nel mese di marzo 1980 ad un convegno

sulla Geotecnologia in Massachusetts.   Il convegno si è tenuto nella

città universitaria dell'università del Massachusetts a Boston ed ha

offerto la possibilità di riferire sull'attività geotecnica nella

zona del Massachusetts, così come in alcune zone limitrofe e oltre.

Quest'attività sta risolvendo diversi problemi importanti relativi

ad energia, ambiente, e risorse naturali, tra cui le risorse idriche.

Più di 300 persone hanno partecipato al convegno durato due giorni.

Le relazioni ed i riassunti includono: 1  geologia del basamento;

2  geologia della superficie;  9  idrogeologia;  3  geofisica;

4  ubicazione di attrezzature critiche;   13  tecnica dei terreni e

meccanica della roccia;  8  spazio sotterraneo; 2  energia e

scienza geologica;  3  rocce industriali;  5  risorse minerali;

12  problemi ambientali e geochimici;  5  tettonica;  4  zone costiere;

e 6  la delimitazione marina.

ГЕОЛОГИЧЕСКАЯ НАУКА В МАССАЧУСЕТСЕ - РЕЗЮМЕ ТОМА.  В данный том включены доклады, прочитанные в марте 1980 г. на конференции, посвященной геологической науке в Массачусетсе.  Конференция проводилась на территории Массачусетского Университета в Бостоне.  Конференция обеспечила форум для обсуждения работ в области геотехники, проводимых в Массачусетсе, а также в некоторых граничащих с Массачусетсом районах и за их пределами.  Эти работы направлены на разрешение различных важных проблем, связанных с энергией, окружающей средой и природными ресурсами, включая водные ресурсы.  Свыше 300 человек участвовали в двухдневной конференции.  Доклады и рефераты посвящены следующим темам: 1 - геология коренных пород; 2 - поверхностная геология; 9 - гидрогеология; 3 - геофизика; 4 - размещение атомных установок; 13 - техника грунтов и механика горных пород; 8 - подземные хранилища; 2 - энергия и геологические науки; 3 - промышленные горные породы; 5 - минеральные ресурсы; 12 - проблемы окружающей среды и геохимические проблемы; 5 - тектоника; 4 - прибрежные зоны; 6 - границы моря и суши.

GEOTECNOLOGIA EN MASSACHUSETTS: RESUMEN DEL VOLUMEN.  Este volumen
contiene ponencias presentadas en marzo de 1980 en una conferencia
sobre la Geotecnología en Massachusetts.  La conferencia tuvo lugar
en las aulas de Boston de la Universidad de Massachusetts.  Dio una
oportunidad de informar sobre las actividades geotécnicas en el área
de Massachusetts, y en algunas áreas limítrofes e incluso más lejanas.
Estas actividades están resolviendo una serie de importantes problemas
relacionados con la energía, el ambiente, y los recursos naturales,
incluso los recursos hidráulicos.  Más de 300 personas asistieron a
la conferencia que duró dos días.  Los informes y resúmenes incluyen:
1 tratando de la geología de la roca subyacente;  2 de geología super-
ficial;  9 de hidrogeología;  3 de geofísica;  4 sobre la ubicación de
facilidades nucleares críticas;  13 de ingeniería de suelos y mecánica
de rocas;  8 sobre espacio subterráneo;  2 sobre la energía y las
ciencias geológicas;  3 sobre rocas industriales;  5 sobre recursos
minerales; 12 sobre problemas geoquímicos y del ambiente;  5 sobre la
tectónica;  4 sobre zonas cerca de la costa y 6 sobre el contorno
marino.

from the world of government

# FOREWORD BY EVELYN MURPHY

AS INCREASING DEMANDS ARE MADE ON THE NATURAL RESOURCES OF MASSACHUSETTS, WE ARE BEGINNING TO REALIZE THE IMPORTANCE OF GEOTECHNOLOGY IN MANAGING THOSE RESOURCES AS A MEANS OF STRENGTHENING THE ECONOMIC BASE OF THE COMMONWEALTH. WE ARE WITNESSING INTERNATIONAL, NATIONAL AND REGIONAL TRENDS THAT PLACE INCREASINGLY CHALLENGING TASKS BEFORE THE GEOTECHNICAL COMMUNITY IN MASSACHUSETTS. THE DEGREE OF SUCCESS IN MEETING THOSE CHALLENGES WILL HAVE MUCH TO DO WITH HOW ECONOMIC GROWTH IN MASSACHUSETTS WILL FARE AS WE APPROACH THE NEXT CENTURY.

THE IMPORTANCE OF GEOTECHNOLOGY TO OUR ECONOMIC GROWTH HAS ALREADY BEEN MADE EVIDENT IN SEVERAL WAYS. FOR EXAMPLE, MANY OF OUR COMMUNITIES HAVE SUFFERED SEVERE WATER SHORTAGES IN RECENT YEARS, AND LARGE-SCALE PLANNING IS UNDERWAY TO AUGMENT THE STRAINED METROPOLITAN DISTRICT COMMISSION SYSTEM THAT SUPPLIES MUCH OF THE BOSTON METROPOLITAN AREA. SINCE ADEQUATE WATER SUPPLIES ARE ESSENTIAL TO SUPPORT GROWING POPULATIONS AND AN EXPANDING INDUSTRIAL SECTOR, GEOTECHNOLOGISTS MUST PLAY AN IMPORTANT ROLE IN LOCATING PRODUCTIVE AQUIFERS IN MASSACHUSETTS WHERE ADDITIONAL WATER SUPPLIES MAY BE FOUND.

ANOTHER EXAMPLE OF GEOTECHNOLOGY'S EMERGING CONTRIBUTION TO ECONOMIC GROWTH IN MASSACHUSETTS IS THE EFFORT TO BUILD LOW-HEAD HYDROELECTRIC FACILITIES TO SUPPLEMENT OIL-FIRED ELECTRICAL GENERATION. THE LAWRENCE HYDROELECTRIC PROJECT WILL HELP, IN A SMALL WAY, TO KEEP MASSACHUSETTS CAPITAL AT HOME, AVOIDING ITS TRANSFER TO THE OIL-EXPORTING NATIONS. BUILDING A NUMBER OF LOW-HEAD HYDROELECTRIC FACILITIES MAY HELP TO REDUCE THE HIGH COST OF BUSINESS IN MASSACHUSETTS, THUS ENCOURAGING RENEWED GROWTH IN THE INDUSTRIAL SECTOR.

FINALLY, GEOPHYSICAL STUDIES OF THE SEAFLOOR ON THE CONTINENTAL SHELF OFF

MASSACHUSETTS ARE HELPING IN THE DEVELOPMENT OF ENVIRONMENTALLY ACCEPTABLE METHODS OF OFFSHORE OIL EXPLORATION.

NEW CHALLENGES AWAIT GEOTECHNOLOGY IN ITS CONTRIBUTIONS TO ECONOMIC GROWTH. WE MUST FIND THE SITES FOR AND THE METHODS OF ACCEPTABLY DISPOSING OF TOXIC WASTES, FOR EXAMPLE, A DILEMMA IGNORED IN POLITICAL CIRCLES UNTIL RECENTLY. ADDITIONALLY, EXPLORATION OF COAL RESOURCES IN SOUTHEASTERN MASSACHUSETTS MAY PROVIDE ENERGY BENEFITS TO A STATE IN NEED OF MORE OPTIONS.

OTHER CHALLENGES WILL ARISE AS GEOTECHNOLOGY BECOMES AN EVER MORE VISIBLE AND VALUABLE FACTOR IN ECONOMIC GROWTH. THE PROCEEDINGS OF "GEOTECHNOLOGY IN MASSACHUSETTS" WILL HELP TO HIGHLIGHT THESE CONTRIBUTIONS AND TO EDUCATE OUR CITIZENS TO GEOTECHNOLOGY'S VALUABLE ROLE IN THE FUTURE.

EVELYN F. MURPHY
SECRETARY OF ENVIRONMENTAL AFFAIRS, 1975-1979
THE COMMONWEALTH OF MASSACHUSETTS
BOSTON

from the world of industry

# FOREWORD BY DENNIS MOHAN

Geotechnology as an endeavor has always acted as a bridge between engineering and geology, engineering and construction, and regulatory bodies and industry, as well as between itself and other disciplines.

The credibility of the practitioners of geotechnology, although presently high, now rests on a threshold. It is from these experts that rational site development concepts must come. Their unique intimacy with the nature they must bend to meet human needs and yet lovingly protect creates an ever-growing challenge to ensure proper environmental balance.

It is from these same experts that solutions to the horrendous national waste disposal problem, both hazardous and benign, must come. These solutions involve technologies as yet undeveloped, site characterizations, and performance verification techniques, as well as the common-sense application of presently available methods.

It is from these same experts that solutions to pressing environmental problems must come. This work requires an understanding of the forces of nature that shape the areas in which we live, assuring the preservation and proper utilization of vital but sensitive groundwater supplies, forests, wetlands and croplands. New approaches to environmental renewal, with regard to timing and to the setting of realistic goals, are critically needed.

Finally, it is from these same experts that the solution of many of our energy needs must come. Mineral exploration, seismicity research, safe foundation design and proper environmental characterization, as well as energy-related waste treatment, handling, and disposal, are critical items for consideration

BOTH TODAY AND, TO AN EVEN GREATER EXTENT, IN THE NEAR FUTURE.

GEOTECHNOLOGISTS MUST SUPPLY THE SOLUTIONS. THEY WILL BE ABLE TO DO SO ONLY THROUGH COOPERATION AMONG THE VARIOUS SCIENCES AND DISCIPLINES INVOLVED. GEOLOGISTS, HYDROGEOLOGISTS, GEOTECHNICAL ENGINEERS AND ENVIRONMENTAL ENGINEERS WILL EXCHANGE IDEAS AND COMPARE RESULTS. MORE SOPHISTICATED SUBSURFACE EXPLORATION TECHNIQUES, TOGETHER WITH IN SITU TESTING METHODS, WILL BE DEVELOPED AS REQUIRED TO INSTILL CONFIDENCE IN THE DATA AND PROPOSED SOLUTIONS. WITH THESE ADVANCES WILL COME NEW AND MORE SOPHISTICATED TECHNOLOGIES.

FULL COOPERATION AMONG THE GEOTECHNOLOGISTS OF INDUSTRY, GOVERNMENT AND EDUCATIONAL INSTITUTIONS MUST CONTINUE IF THESE COMMON GOALS ARE TO BE ACHIEVED. SUPPORTIVE INSTITUTIONAL RESEARCH WILL BE FUNDED BY GOVERNMENT AND INDUSTRY. TECHNOLOGIES WILL EVOLVE, ALONG WITH PERFORMANCE EVALUATION TECHNIQUES, THAT WILL RESTORE PUBLIC CONFIDENCE IN THE ABILITY OF THE GOVERNMENT TO SAFEGUARD THE ENVIRONMENT WITHOUT HINDERING THE INDUSTRIAL PROGRESS REQUIRED TO PRODUCE A HEALTHY ECONOMY. COOPERATION AND IMPROVED CHARACTERIZATION AND PERFORMANCE MONITORING WILL LEAD TO MORE REASONABLE AND ENFORCEABLE GOVERNMENT REGULATIONS.

FORUMS SUCH AS "GEOTECHNOLOGY IN MASSACHUSETTS" FOSTER THIS KIND OF DISSEMINATION OF INFORMATION AND INTERDISCIPLINARY COOPERATION. THE PROCEEDINGS WILL BE A VALUABLE DOCUMENT OF THIS COMMITMENT BY GEOTECHNOLOGISTS, DEMONSTRATING AWARENESS OF THE IMPORTANCE OF THEIR ROLE IN PROVIDING A BRIDGE TO THE FUTURE.

DENNIS J. MOHAN
GEOTECHNICAL ENGINEERING
UNITED ENGINEERS & CONSTRUCTORS, INC.
PHILADELPHIA, PENNSYLVANIA

from the academic world

# FOREWORD BY GERALD FRIEDMAN

Geotechnology rates high among the most important fields of applied geology, and yet in academia its importance is not given its due. Although aspects of geotechnology are included in several courses, such as sedimentology, rock mechanics, geophysics, engineering geology, and economic geology, few departments of geology provide separate geotechnology courses. This kind of relegation to benign neglect of a mature and creative science is at variance with current social and economic needs.

Consider the following scenario: An offshore drilling platform slides downslope as an integral part of a mud or debris flow. What do we know about the geotechnical behavior of the sediment involved? Probably very little. Certainly, geology students normally will have received no training in the processes and products concerned and the geotechnical characteristics of the kind of sediment responsible for such an accident. Not long ago, in fact, an offshore drilling platform vanished in the depths of the ocean under circumstances similar to these. Fortunately, the people aboard the platform were rescued. My message is in the form of a question: Should not research and training be commensurate with the importance of the field of geotechnology to prepare for the eventualities and risks we will face in the future?

As a member of the academic community, I consider this volume to be a lucky break and say "hats off" to the convener who organized the original conference and then saw the publication through to completion. The volume focuses on issues involving geotechnology, and academic faculty can use its contents in developing parts of courses, and even full-scale courses, in geotechnology. Much of what has been written here can serve as important readings for students. Inspired by the conference, a new journal, NORTHEASTERN ENVIRON-

MENTAL SCIENCE*, WAS BORN. THIS WILL EMPHASIZE FUNDAMENTAL ASPECTS OF GEO- AND RELATED TECHNOLOGIES, AND IT IS HOPED THAT IT WILL BE A VALUABLE SOURCE OF SUCH INFORMATION.

FOR THE NORTHEASTERN UNITED STATES, AND ESPECIALLY FOR MASSACHUSETTS, THE CONFERENCE ON GEOTECHNOLOGY AND THIS VOLUME OF PROCEEDINGS ARE IMPORTANT STEPPING STONES TO THE FUTURE.

---

*P.O. BOX 746
TROY, NY 12181

GERALD M. FRIEDMAN
DEPARTMENT OF GEOLOGY
RENSSELAER POLYTECHNIC INSTITUTE
TROY, NEW YORK

# PREFACE

This volume contains papers presented at a conference on March 20 and 21, 1980, at the Boston Campus of the University of Massachusetts, overlooking the city harbor at Dorchester. In some cases only abstracts or titles are available. More than 300 people were at the daytime meetings, and about 75 attended a dinner in downtown Boston on Thursday, March 20.

GEOTECHNOLOGY IN MASSACHUSETTS

The conference provided a forum for reporting geotechnical activities in Massachusetts, as well as in areas bordering Massachusetts and beyond. These activities are solving a variety of important problems concerned with energy, the environment, and natural resources including water resources.

VOLUME CONTENTS

The conference proceedings were divided into these 14 technical sessions.

1. Bedrock Geology
2. Surficial Geology
3. Hydrogeology
4. Geophysics
5. Siting of Critical and Other Facilities
6. Soils Engineering and Rock Mechanics
7. Underground Space

8. Energy and the Geosciences
9. Industrial Rocks
10. Mineral Resources
11. Environmental and Geochemical Problems
12. Tectonics
13. Nearshore Zones
14. The Marine Boundary

The closing session was chaired by Joseph S. Fitzpatrick, Secretary of the Massachusetts Executive Office of Energy Resources, and was addressed by Duane Day, Region I, United States Department of Energy. Mr. Day discussed the general subject of energy resources and the economic future, mainly in reference to current programs of the Department of Energy in the New England region.

FINANCIAL SUPPORT

Financial support for the conference, which came from several sources, is gratefully acknowledged.

    Academic
        University of Massachusetts at Amherst
            College of Arts and Sciences
            Department of Geology and Geography
            Graduate School
            Remote Sensing Center

    Professional
        Association of Engineering Geologists, New England Section
        Boston Society of Civil Engineers, Geotechnical Section

    Government
        United States Department of Energy, Region 1

Foundation
    National Science Foundation

Industry
    Anderson-Nichols & Co., Inc.
    Camp Dresser & McKee, Inc.
    Dunn Geoscience Corporation
    Geotechnical Engineers, Inc.
    Haley & Aldrich, Inc.
    Arthur D. Little, Inc.
    Lycott Environmental Research, Inc.
    C.E. Maguire, Inc.
    Chas. T. Main, Inc.
    Metcalf & Eddy, Inc.
    Shell Oil Company
    Skanska (USA), Inc.
    Stone & Webster Engineering Corporation
    Storch Engineers

## ADVISORY GROUP

Members of an advisory group met with me during the summer of 1979 to discuss plans for the conference.  The efforts of these members are appreciated.

    Frank Bellini, Yankee Atomic Electric Company
    Brian Fowler, Pike Industries, Inc.
    Deborah Gevalt, Haley & Aldrich, Inc.
    Janice Hight, Haley & Aldrich, Inc.
    Andrew Lacroix, McClelland Engineers, Inc.
    William Mallio, Resources Engineering, Inc.
    John Peck, Stone & Webster Engineering Corporation
    William Pitt, Geotechnical Engineers, Inc.
    Henry Russell, Parsons, Brinckerhoff Quade & Douglas, Inc.
    Richard Sherman, Metcalf & Eddy, Inc.
    Carol Sweet, Metcalf & Eddy, Inc.
    David Woodhouse, Goldberg, Zoino & Associates, Inc.

## SESSION MODERATORS

The names of moderators at the various sessions are noted on the pages introducing those sessions.  Their help was invaluable.

## EXHIBITS

Provision was made for the following display tables.

| | |
|---|---|
| Geological publications | Department of Geology and Geography<br>University of Massachusetts<br>Amherst, MA 01003 |
| Hydrogeological investigations | Ground Water Associates, Inc.<br>Arlington, MA 02174 |
| Analytical systems | K-V Associates, Inc.<br>Falmouth, MA 02541 |
| Geothermics (Journal) | Pergamon Press, Inc.<br>Elmsford, NY 10523 |
| Geotechnical instrumentation | Walter Nold Company<br>Natick, MA 01760 |

## CONFERENCE ARRANGEMENTS

Officials at the University of Massachusetts at Amherst who made this 1980 conference activity possible included:  Henry Koffler, Chancellor; Samuel F. Conti, Dean of the Graduate School; Frederick W. Byron, Jr., Dean of Natural Sciences and Mathematics; and George E. McGill, Head of the Department of Geology and Geography.

A year earlier, when the conference was in the planning stage, those positions were held by:  Randolph W. Bromery, Chancellor; Eugene B. Piedmont, Acting Dean; Seymour Shapiro, Dean; and Charles W. Pitrat, Acting Head while the present incumbent was on leave.  To each of them sincere thanks are due. The new Vice Chancellor for Academic Affairs is Loren Baritz.

As noted later, the President of the University, David C. Knapp, attended the conference banquet in Boston on Thursday, March 20, at which former chancellor Randolph Bromery was the principal speaker. Dr. Bromery's presentation is included in these proceedings.

Permission to hold the conference at the University's Boston campus was given by Chancellor Robert A. Corrigan. Chancellor Corrigan opened the conference with a welcoming address, also reproduced here.

Holding the conference depended to an important extent on many other individuals including: Arthur Clifford, Donald S. Farquhar, Shirley Hill, R. Huguenin, James Johnson, Harold Keohane, John Larner, Vincent Murphy, Joseph Pecoraro, Ronald Reid, Roger Roche, Carolyn Schneider, Joseph Sinnott, Mark Spengler, and Allan Wicklund.

## CLERICAL AND EDITORIAL ASSISTANCE

For clerical services thanks are due to Lillian Forguites, Mary Lou Fortier, Bernadette McDonald, Camille St. Onge, Carol Vreeland and, chiefly, Karen Thatcher. Jeanne Masson-Douglas undertook a number of useful tasks. Marie Litterer drafted or redrafted several of the figures. The contributions of those who reviewed the manuscripts are also acknowledged.

## UNITS OF MEASUREMENT

Although highway distances in Canada have been measured in kilometers rather than miles for several years, the United States has not yet completed its planned conversion to metric scales. For instance, the length of the space shuttle Columbia was reported recently by the media as 122.2 feet, rather than being expressed in meters.

If all the English-unit papers in this volume had been converted to metric, or vice versa, or all to both, the publication date would have receded, and receded. Rather, a table of conversion factors has been included in case it should be required.

## TRANSLATION OF THE VOLUME ABSTRACT

The volume abstract is translated into other languages because the geological sciences have always advanced on an international front, especially in mineralogy, global tectonics, and rock mechanics. As a specific example, session 7 deals with the use of underground space, and the People's Republic of China is one of many nations with interests in this sphere of activity. Under the People-to-People Program, an Underground Space Project was planned in 1981 to send about 35 U.S. delegates to observe current developments in underground space in China. These delegates were to visit sites in the Shansi, Honan, and Konsu provinces. What is done there and what is done in North America are certainly of long-term mutual interest.

## NOTE ABOUT PUBLICATION

Although, gratifyingly enough, a noncommercial organization in the geotechnical field expressed interest in publishing this volume, the final arrangements for publication by the University of Massachusetts adhere to the original plan. The conference was, above all, an activity of the University of Massachusetts, which appreciates the contributions of those who participated and is now pleased to make as much as possible of the printed record available.

## AN EARLIER CONFERENCE

An earlier conference, covering similar topics and entitled "Economic Geology in Massachusetts," was held on the Amherst campus of the University of Massachusetts in 1966. The proceedings were published the following year.

## OVERALL OBJECTIVES

Briefly stated, the overall objectives of the 1980 conference and these proceedings are to discuss some aspects of geotechnical practice in a limited region and to consider the future of geotechnology as a factor in economic growth.

Amherst, Massachusetts                                                        O.C.F.
December 14, 1981

# CONTENTS

# LATE CHANGES

The drawing on page 626 is from a recent issue of Water Power and Dam Construction.

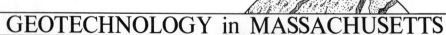

# GEOTECHNOLOGY in MASSACHUSETTS

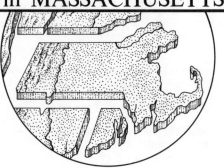

The circle on the cover shows parts of states adjacent to or near Massachusetts, diagrammatically separated along their common borders. Clockwise from the west they are New York, Vermont, New Hampshire, Maine, Rhode Island, and Connecticut. The hook of eastern Massachusetts is Cape Cod.

# WELCOME

The campus of the University of Massachusetts at Boston, located on Dorchester Point on the waterfront south of the city center. This branch of the University was opened in the early 1970's, whereas the much larger campus of the University at Amherst, beginning as the Massachusetts Agricultural College, has been in existence since 1863. The medical school, established in the late 1960's, is in Worcester. Since the Boston campus was completed, the John F. Kennedy Library also has been built on Dorchester Point, about one mile to the east. This photograph looking northwest includes a number of unrelated buildings beyond the campus perimeter road. (Courtesy, The Boston Globe.)

# Opening address

ROBERT A. CORRIGAN
Chancellor
University of Massachusetts at Boston

I am delighted to welcome you to the Harbor Campus of the University of Massachusetts at Boston. We are, as you may know, the urban campus of the University, although we are set out here overlooking the largely uninhabited harbor islands. The University is committed to a mission which will be of some interest to you. We are part of a land-grant institution founded in the 19th century. This means we have responsibility in the public sector for research and service of value to the Commonwealth and to our urban area. We serve over 8,000 students in three colleges with a faculty of 500 at two locations--our downtown Park Square campus and the Harbor campus where we occupied a 150 million dollar site six years ago. We are in our 15th year as a campus of the University.

In practical terms, we are keenly aware of our environment--the immediate site on which we sit and the largely urban environment which we affect. The campus is on filled land--a former city dump, in fact--a situation that we must deal with each time we construct a new building or plant a tree. The only rock-built structure on campus, namely the sea-wall which rings our peninsula, came to us much as our students come to us, from different parts of the greater Boston area. If you have a chance to walk along our dike, you will see that it is made mainly of pieces of granodiorite, a rock which, I am told, characterizes the region north of us. A closer look, however, will reveal samples of Roxbury pudding stone among the boulders, the conglomerate which dominates the areas west and south of the campus. It could even be argued, if you did not look too closely, that the small rise of land between us and the Kennedy Library is our own campus drumlin, soon to become the site of the new State Archives Building.

Some members of our academic community work in areas directly connected or analogous to your concerns. For example, the Biology Department is in the process of completing its Master's level program in applied marine ecology. This program will work closely with environmental firms in Boston and will focus on man's effects on the adjacent waters, using our field station on relatively unspoiled Nantucket Island as a source of baseline data for purposes of comparison. At the same time, our campus governance bodies are currently reviewing a proposal for a Center for Environmental Sciences, which will build upon and broaden our strength in marine ecology. The proposed center will involve undergraduates as well as Master's candidates and will cross disciplinary boundaries to the other sciences, mathematics, and our management program.

Of course, everyone is at least partially involved in their lives with the implications of many of the topics which will be raised at this conference: energy, the factors affecting safety in the siting of critical facilities, the use of underground space, and the appropriate disposal of contaminated materials and hazardous waste, to mention but a few.

As the Chancellor of a University which is committed to the ideals of research and service, I can think of few ways in which we can fulfill these roles better than by hosting conferences such as this. The material you are discussing is of great importance to our futures. We are pleased to be able to welcome such a distinguished group of specialists in the geotechnological field. We know you will learn from one another, but I also wish to thank you for this opportunity for us to learn from you. You have given us the chance to increase our awareness of your very important work and we thank you.

*Hors-Texte

Nimbus III photograph showing the east coast
of North America from Florida to Newfoundland.  Massachusetts is one-third of the
distance from the top corner to the bottom
corner.  The Gulf of Mexico, the Great
Lakes, and the Gulf of St. Lawrence
are plainly visible. "On a clear
day you can see forever."
(HRIR (Daytime), Orbit
2056, 14 September
1969, Goddard
Space Flight
Center.)

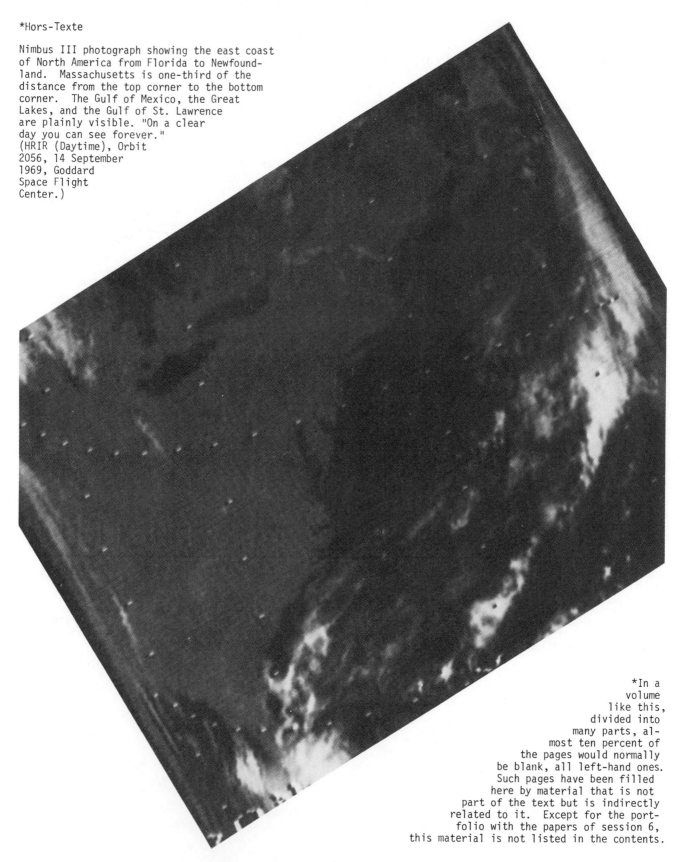

*In a
volume
like this,
divided into
many parts, al-
most ten percent of
the pages would normally
be blank, all left-hand ones.
Such pages have been filled
here by material that is not
part of the text but is indirectly
related to it.  Except for the portfolio with the papers of session 6,
this material is not listed in the contents.

# 1

# BEDROCK GEOLOGY

Session moderators

J. F. Hubert
Department of Geology and Geography
University of Massachusetts at Amherst

J. B. Thompson, Jr.
Department of Geological Sciences
Harvard University

# The bedrock geologic map of Massachusetts

P. ROBINSON
Department of Geology and Geography
University of Massachusetts at Amherst

ABSTRACT

In March 1980 the reviewed draft of the Bedrock Geologic Map of Massachusetts at 1/250,000 was submitted to Chief, Branch of Eastern Environmental Geology, U.S. Geological Survey, for approval and transmission to publication units. The team effort, begun in 1976, was led by E-an Zen (U.S.G.S.), and the map was compiled by N. M. Ratcliffe (C.C.N.Y. and now U.S.G.S.) for western Berkshires, R. S. Stanley (University of Vermont) for eastern Berkshires, Peter Robinson for Connecticut Valley and central Massachusetts, and R. M. Goldsmith (U.S.G.S.) for eastern Massachusetts, requiring the cooperation of many geologists. The map, the first since Emerson's of 1916, will show 370 labelled rock units in 120 colored patterns. Due to press size, it will come out in two sheets --one with the entire map, correlation chart, and credit map, the other with six cross sections, descriptions of rocks, tectonic map, and metamorphic map. After color printing 1 1/2 years from now, sheets will be reprinted in black only to assist in future specialized compilations. In New England, only Massachusetts bridges the Northern Appalachians from Grenvillian North America to the Avalon "Platform". To aid global tectonic thinking, the stratigraphy of the oldest rocks is divided into five zones: 1) TACONIC-BERKSHIRE ZONE, the deformed eastern margin of Cambro-Ordovician North America, 2) ROWE-HAWLEY ZONE, remanents of Cambro-Ordovician ocean, 3) BRONSON HILL ZONE, remanents of east margin of ocean or islands within it, 4) NASHOBA ZONE, uncertain, and 5) MILFORD-DEDHAM ZONE, modestly to weakly deformed, highly faulted, eastern margin of ocean, with anorogenic plutons and local basins of Siluro-Devonian, Carboniferous, and early Mesozoic; and Cretaceous-Cenozoic coastal plain. Superimposed on older zones 1-4 are two others of Siluro-Devonian marine rocks: 6) CONNECTICUT VALLEY SYNCLINORIUM and 7) MERRIMACK SYNCLINORIUM. Closing of 7) produced the culminating Acadian orogeny and metamorphism. Finally, 8) CONNECTICUT VALLEY MESOZOIC BASINS marked early stages of the present Atlantic.

REFERENCE (added in proof)

Bedrock geologic map of Massachusetts, edited by E-an Zen; compiled by R. Goldsmith, N.M. Ratcliffe, P. Robinson, and R.S. Stanley; assisted by N.L. Hatch, Jr., A.F. Shride, E.G.A. Weed, and D.R. Wones, 1981, 40 p., 3 over-size sheets, scale 1:250,000 (1 inch = about 4 miles), Open-File Report 81-1327, microfiche and paper. Prices in "New publications of the Geological Survey," December 1981. When ordering, please use the open-file report number and the full title. Available from: Open-File Services Section, Western Distribution Branch, U.S. Geological Survey, Box 25425, Federal Center, Denver, CO 80225.

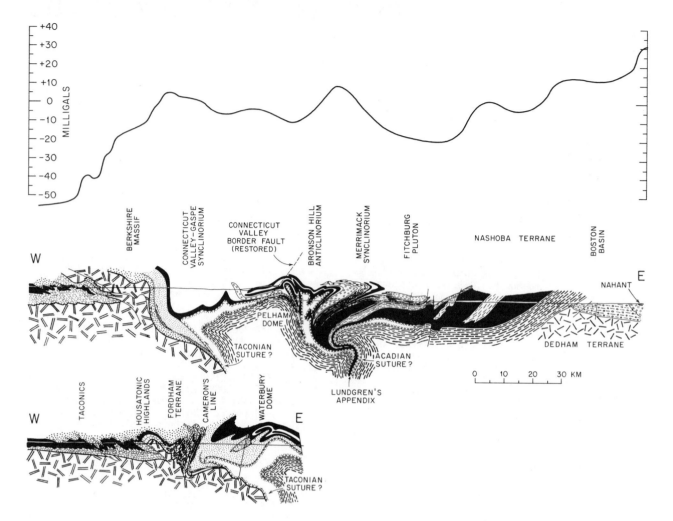

Geophysical and geological sections across Massachusetts
from longer reports by the author of this abstract.  ed.

# 2

# SURFICIAL GEOLOGY

Session moderators

J. B. Thompson, Jr.
Department of Geological Sciences
Harvard University

J. F. Hubert
Department of Geology and Geography
University of Massachusetts at Amherst

# The Massachusetts state surficial geologic map

B. D. STONE
U.S. Geological Survey
Reston, Virginia

## ABSTRACT

Compilation of the new Massachusetts State surficial geologic map is the culmination of 42 years, and more than 80 person-years, of detailed quadrangle mapping by the U.S. Geological Survey in cooperation with the Massachusetts Department of Public Works. Upper Wisconsinan till covers 63 percent of the State. Upper Wisconsinan meltwater deposits cover 37 percent of the map area and are described by more than 200 map units. Glaciolacustrine units, which constitute three-fourths of the total meltwater deposits by area, cover 28 percent of the map area, and glaciofluvial units cover 7 percent. Map overprint patterns illustrate the distribution of sedimentary lithofacies within glaciolacustrine units and can be used to infer the vertical sequence of facies. A typical vertical section in a glaciolacustrine unit coarsens upward from lake-bottom silt and clay, to delta-foreset sand, to fluvial delta-topset sand and gravel. Glaciofluvial units do not commonly show an overall change in grain size or structure in vertical section. Map units of meltwater deposits and moraines are correlated in a time-stratigraphic framework to deduce patterns of ice retreat across the State. Preliminary results show that major topographic features strongly influenced the size and rate of retreat of glacial lobes that formed during thinning and melting back of the ice sheet. A second State surficial map, to be published at a larger scale, shows the distribution of sand and gravel, sand, and fine sediments. Both maps provide a base for future topical and applied studies, as well as an inventory of a major mineral resource of the State.

## INTRODUCTION

The present compilation of the Massachusetts State surficial geologic map is the culmination of 42 years of mapping in a cooperative project between the U.S. Geological Survey (USGS) and the Commonwealth of Massachusetts Department of Public Works (MDPW). During this period, more than 80 person-years were expended in detailed mapping of the surficial geology at 7 1/2 minute quadrangle scale. The project aimed at the compilation of the State surficial geologic map began in 1976. Since then, one-third of the State has been mapped in detailed reconnaissance fashion in areas where detailed mapping had not been done previously.

The State surficial geologic map, to be published in color at a scale of 1:250,000, will summarize the information gathered during detailed geologic mapping and the reconnaissance mapping. It will present 1) a regional synthesis of litho-logic and chronologic relations based on our present knowledge of the distribution and depositional environments of the material, and 2) a regional chronology based on radiometric dates. Many quadrangle maps have been reinterpreted, and map units have been lumped together in State map units that are mappable and meaningful at regional scale. In addition to the State surficial geologic map, a second map showing surficial materials classified according to texture and with minimum geologic interpretation is being compiled and will be published at a scale of 1:125,000. The State maps are being compiled by five geologists who actively participated in the detailed quadrangle mapping program. The compilers are: Byron D. Stone, Robert N. Oldale, Charles R. Warren, and John D. Peper, USGS, and Frederick D. Larsen, Norwich University and USGS.

The mapping cooperative spanned a time of major construction throughout the State. Turnpike and Interstate road construction and urbanization preempted many of the sand and gravel resources of the State, especially around the Boston metro-politan area. During the life of the project, production of sand, gravel, and clay increased by more than one order of magnitude (Fig. 1A) to a total annual value of more than $30 million by 1977 in industries that employ more than 1,200 persons throughout the Commonwealth (Barton and Sinnott, 1975).

## HISTORY

In July 1938, the Commonwealth of Massachusetts Department of Public Works entered into a formal agreement with the U.S. Geological Survey for a continuing program of geologic investigations (Currier, 1939; Page, 1967; L.R. Page and C.T. Hildreth, written commun., 1972). The geologic cooperative project, as planned in July 1938 by the Chief Engineer of the Highway Division, MDPW, and the USGS Chief Geologist, with advice from Professor Kirtley Mather of Harvard, called for immediate mapping of a strip along a proposed highway route in the Lowell 15-minute quadrangle. The map was to show the areal distribution of all sand, gravel, and till deposits and bedrock exposures. Studies were designed for determining depths to bedrock in buried valleys and for collecting groundwater data. In the same year, requests for three more strip maps, a study of flood damage to major highways, and a general

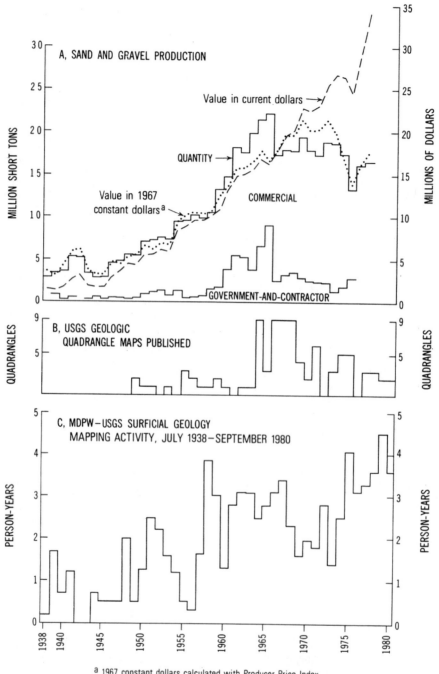

a 1967 constant dollars calculated with Producer Price Index
(all commodities) of U.S. Department of Labor, Bureau of Labor
Statistics

Figure 1.  MDPW-USGS surficial geology mapping activity,
publication record, and State sand and gravel production,
1938-1980.  Sand and gravel production data from U.S.
Bureau of Mines Minerals Yearbook, 1938-1978.

report of the geology of Cape Cod were received. As part of the general geologic survey, areal mapping was begun in the Blue Hills and Norwood quadrangles. The cooperative project funded Robert Balk to map the geology of the area to be flooded that year by Quabbin Reservoir. Professor Kirk Bryan of Harvard was asked to act as a field consultant on physiographic and glacial features. Thus, in the initial planning of the cooperative project, surficial geologic studies constituted a major part of a program directed by immediate needs of the State.

Both local construction-related studies and general geologic mapping were carried out in the surficial program from 1939 to 1941. Areal mapping was completed in the Blue Hills quadrangle, in the Cape Cod-Buzzards Bay area, and in the Greenfield quadrangle. More highway strip maps, areal mapping of gravel deposits available for road building, and studies of shoreline erosion factors characterized the program for immediate needs. At the end of this period, the USGS-MDPW cooperative project had established goals by design and practice: 1) areal mapping, 2) economic studies, 3) engineering studies, and 4) water-resources studies. No definite plans were made for publishing results of the general geologic survey. Suggestions were made that engraved (colored) maps would be published at adequate scales for the reports that they accompanied. Quadrangle maps could be reduced to convenient scales in some areas, and large-scale maps would illustrate outstanding features or complex geology. One long-term goal was to publish, at a preferred scale of 1:125,000, State bedrock and surficial geologic maps based on results of quadrangle mapping.

Following World War II, during which the surficial program was limited to highway strip maps, the program continued at a modest rate (Fig. 1C) as quadrangles were mapped in the western highlands, Nashua River basin, and south-shore coastal areas. The first map products published in the 1950s by the USGS were colored geologic maps (standard Geologic Quadrangle Map, GQ, series of USGS). These early maps were based on detailed field work and showed geologic information on topographic base maps having 10-foot contours; they were the first maps of their kind published for southern New England.

Although surficial map units and interpretations reflected the individual author's philosophy and mapping style, the early quadrangle maps illustrated superposition of, and cross-cutting relationships among, meltwater deposits and thus illustrated the complex nature of the glacial record. R.H. Jahns, in particular, showed how glacial meltwater deposits could be divided into different mappable units, which he called sequences because each deposit contained a sequence of morphologic features deposited contemporaneously in and in front of a stagnant ice zone marginal to the retreating active ice front. Ideally, each deposit ranged from ice-contact forms, such as eskers and kames at the proximal end, to kame terraces, kame plains, and finally outwash plains at the distal end. Jahns' early field work in

1938-1940 in the Westford and Tyngsboro (Nashua South) quadrangles (Jahns, 1941), a Friends of the Pleistocene meeting in 1946 (Jahns and others, 1977), and publication of the Ayer GQ Map (Jahns, 1953) established the principles of the morphologic sequence concept and the attendant concept of deglaciation of southern New England by stagnation zone retreat (Currier, 1941). Koteff, drawing on Jahns' work and earlier work in Massachusetts by W.O. Crosby, F.G. Clapp, J.W. Goldthwait, and others, expanded the concept to include glacial lake deposits (Koteff, 1964, 1966). He later adopted a less ambiguous term, "morphosequence," (Mahaney, ed., 1976) for meltwater depositional units (Koteff, 1980; Koteff and Pessl, in press).

By the late 1950s, the surficial program was focused with the cooperative project toward five goals: 1) preparation of 7 1/2-minute quadrangle maps of the entire State, 2) study of the mineral resources of the State, 3) preparation of State geologic maps, 4) shallow seismic investigations and research, and 5) answering miscellaneous requests for information. The USGS accepted additional responsibilities of publication costs, administrative expenses, capital equipment, rent on offices, and laboratory analyses.

Special projects expanded the general surficial program in the early 1960s (Fig. 1C). From 1962 to 1964, the USGS, MDPW, and U.S. Federal Bureau of Public Roads undertook seismic research and an inventory of sand and gravel and other highway construction materials in the western part of the State. Reconnaissance maps of surficial materials in 25 quadrangles were produced (for example, Holmes, 1964). At about the same time, two projects carried out by the USGS Engineering Branch, urban studies of Boston (Kaye, 1961) and shoreline studies concentrated on the Martha's Vineyard area (Kaye, 1964a/b), contributed to the general mapping program.

From 1964 to 1967, the surficial mapping program concentrated on outer Cape Cod as a target area in conjunction with establishment of the Cape Cod National Seashore (Hartshorn, Koteff, and Oldale, 1967). All of the cape, to the edge of Pocasset and Falmouth quadrangles mapped by Mather, Goldthwait, and Theismeyer in 1940, was mapped in eight years. Another special project in 1962 was the study of cores from three wells that penetrated the entire Pleistocene section on outer Cape Cod (Koteff and Cotton, 1962).

Geologists from the USGS Water Resources Division (WRD) continued their program of ground- and surface-water investigations in the State's river drainage basins in the 1960's and early 1970's. Results of followup groundwater studies are presented by M.H. Frimpter and D.R. LeBlanc in this volume. A notable report for basins in southeastern Massachusetts (Williams and Tasker, 1974) contains a regional compilation of surficial geology. WRD geologists contributed four surficial GQ maps to the program during this time.

The ongoing program of seismic studies continued to define seismic properties of surficial materials. A noteworthy result (Tuttle, 1962) was the recognition that the older, finer grained drumlin till has a higher seismic speed (5,000-8,000 feet per second) than the sandy surface till (2,000-4,500 feet per second).

Operating funds of the cooperative were doubled in 1969, and the rate of areal mapping, chiefly bedrock mapping, was increased. Target areas included the Connecticut-Massachusetts border, southwestern and western Massachusetts, and the Boston Metropolitan region. Several bedrock geologists completed surficial geologic maps in these areas. In 1971, total funds again increased with expansion of the program to offshore areas in work carried out by the USGS Branch of Marine Geology at Woods Hole. This program is aimed at assessing offshore mineral resources, potential dredge-spoil disposal sites, and potential geologic hazards. Maps that show distribution and thickness of marine and glacial deposits and older rocks are closely tied to the onshore glacial and post-glacial record. C.J. O'Hara and R.N. Oldale report results of the offshore program in this volume.

The Connecticut Valley Urban Area Project, a special project funded by the USGS, was closely related to the surficial program from 1971 to 1976. This special project was designed as a pilot project in response to the need for geologic data to be used in making land-use decisions in the urbanizing Connecticut River valley. The project produced the first regional map of surficial materials in the State at a scale of 1:125,000 (Stone, London, and Langer, 1979). Other single-factor map products show thickness of principal clay units, contours of the bedrock surface and additional information.

In 1976, the focus of the USGS-MDPW cooperative project was redirected toward producing two State geologic maps, bedrock and surficial, at a scale of 1:250,000. The project schedule called for reconnaissance mapping of unmapped quadrangles, compilation of the State maps from quadrangle maps, and synthesizing results of the mapping in a regional framework. A second surficial materials map, at a scale of 1:125,000, was planned in recognition of the need for information about sand and gravel resources of the State. The bedrock map, edited by E-an Zen, is in the final stage of review, as reported by Peter Robinson in this volume. Fieldwork in remaining quadrangles for the surficial map will be completed by September 1980. The surficial map will be submitted for review in 1981.

PUBLICATION AND MAPPING STATUS

Figure 2 shows the current status of publications and mapping of surficial geology in the State under the USGS-MDPW cooperative project and includes quadrangle maps produced by students and professors from two academic institutions. The publication record of the surficial quadrangle mapping program is summarized in Figure 1B. As of September 1980, field mapping was complete in 162 of the 187 quadrangles wholly or partly within the State. In all, colored geologic maps of 62 quadrangles had been published in the USGS GQ and I series and the Geological Society of America Bulletin. USGS Open-File or MF (Miscellaneous Field Studies) maps had been released for 26 other quadrangles. Maps of 6 quadrangles were in final preparation for publication. Published quadrangle maps and reports were listed by McIntosh and Eister (1973) and by the U.S. Geological Survey (1977). The USGS List of New Publications will include all future USGS publications of the Massachusetts surficial mapping program.

STATE SURFICIAL GEOLOGIC MAP

Figure 3 is a small-scale condensed version of the surficial geologic map of Massachusetts; it illustrates several features that will be included on the final State map. Upper Wisconsinan till covers 63 percent of the map area. The till, which averages 3-5 m in thickness, is shown as a single time-transgressive unit. Areas of numerous bedrock outcrops, where the till averages less than 3 m in thickness, will be shown on the surficial-materials map. Drumlin map symbols on the surficial geologic map will indicate areas of thick till in drumlin cores. Map symbols will show deep exposures of pre-upper Wisconsinan drumlin till. Upper Wisconsinan meltwater deposits cover 37 percent of the map area. More than 2,000 meltwater depositional units (morphosequences) mappable at quadrangle scale are lumped together in more than 200 map units that form the basis of the regional chronostratigraphic framework north of the coastal moraines. Upper Wisconsinan moraines cover 2 percent of the State, and glacio-marine beds cover another 2 percent.

Meltwater deposits are broadly divided into two groups. The largest group consists of glacio-lacustrine sediments deposited in or graded to the many ephemeral glacial lakes and ponds that formed between the edge of the retreating Laurentide ice sheet and the underlying topographic basins. These deposits compose 76 percent of all meltwater deposits in the State and are characteristic of the glacial geology of most of southern New England. Included in these map units are three lithofacies: 1) lake-bottom silt, sand, and clay (locally varves), 2) delta foreset and bottomset silt, sand, and gravel, deposited subaqueously, and 3) delta topset fluvial beds, chiefly mixed sand and gravel (Fig. 4). Coarse glaciofluvial valley fills, which supplied sediment to the glacial lake deltas, are included in glaciolacustrine map units. Glaciolacustrine units are found in all north-draining basins. Large glaciolacustrine deposits were laid down in south-draining basins, for example, the Connecticut and Taunton River basins, where glacial lakes were impounded behind drift and buried ice dams. The histories of glacial lakes in major drainage basins, outlined by workers of two generations ago (Crosby, 1899; J.W. Goldthwait, 1905; Clapp, 1901; Emerson, 1898; Grabau, 1900; Taylor, 1903), are largely confirmed by quadrangle mapping.

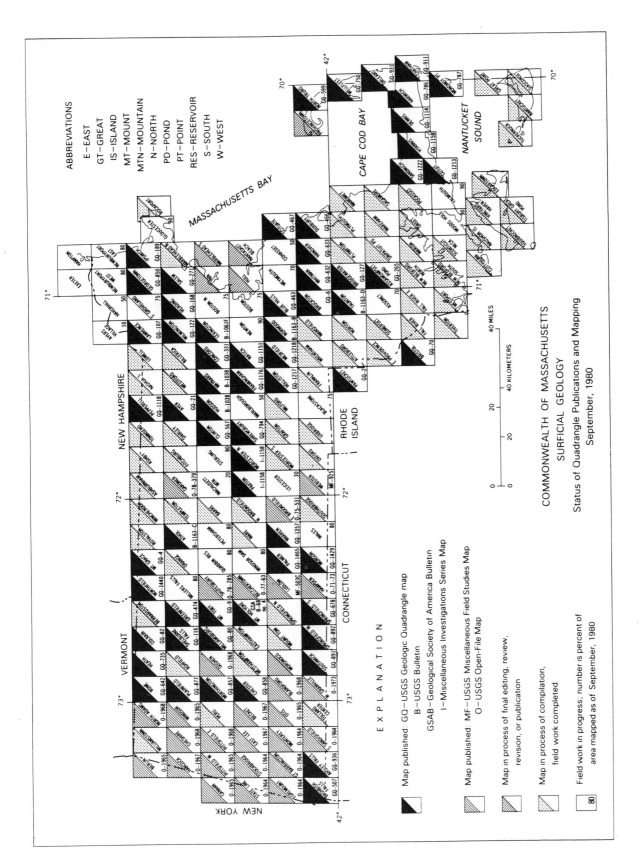

Figure 2. Index map of USGS 7 1/2-minute quadrangle maps showing status of publications and surficial geologic mapping, September 1980.

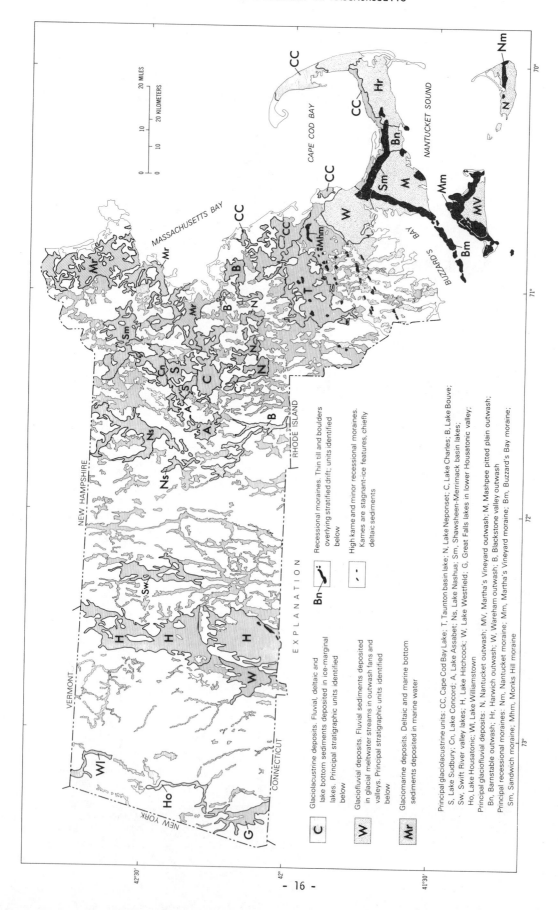

EXPLANATION

Recessional moraines. Thin till and boulders overlying stratified drift; units identified below

High kame and minor recessional moraines. Kames are stagnant-ice features, chiefly deltaic sediments

Glaciolacustrine deposits. Fluvial, deltaic and lake bottom sediments deposited in ice-marginal lakes. Principal stratigraphic units identified below

Glaciofluvial deposits. Fluvial sediments deposited in glacial meltwater streams in outwash fans and valleys. Principal stratigraphic units identified below

Glaciomarine deposits. Deltaic and marine bottom sediments deposited in marine water

Principal glaciolacustrine units: CC, Cape Cod Bay Lake; T, Taunton basin lake; N, Lake Neponset; C, Lake Charles; B, Lake Bouve; S, Lake Sudbury; Cn, Lake Concord; A, Lake Assabet; Ns, Lake Nashua; Sm, Shawsheen-Merrimack basin lakes; Sw, Swift River valley lakes; H, Lake Hitchcock; W, Lake Westfield; G, Great Falls lakes in lower Housatonic valley; Ho, Lake Housatonic; Wl, Lake Williamstown

Principal glaciofluvial deposits: N, Nantucket outwash; MV, Martha's Vineyard outwash; M, Mashpee pitted plain outwash; Bn, Barnstable outwash; Hr, Harwich outwash; W, Wareham outwash; B, Blackstone valley outwash

Principal recessional moraines: Nm, Nantucket moraine; Mm, Martha's Vineyard moraine; Bm, Buzzard's Bay moraine; Sm, Sandwich moraine; Mhm, Monks Hill moraine

Figure 3. Generalized surficial geologic map of Massachusetts, showing recessional moraines, high kames, and stratified drift of late-Wisconsinan age.

Figure 4.  Delta topset, foreset, and bottomset facies of glaciolacustrine deposits.  (A) Delta topsets and foreset beds, Blood Pond delta, Bridgewater quadrangle; topsets have been mined for coarse sand and gravel.  (B) Delta topsets and foresets, glaciomarine delta, Scott's Hill, Ipswich quadrangle.  (C) Rhythmically interbedded fine sand and silt, delta bottomset beds, Westport quadrangle.

Figure 5.  Glaciofluvial, braided stream facies.  (A) Head of Martha's Vineyard outwash plain, Vineyard Haven quadrangle.  (B) Distal portion of Carver outwash plain, Plympton quadrangle.

Glaciofluvial units compose the second broad group of meltwater deposits, chiefly the outwash plains of the islands and southeastern coastal Massachusetts. These units cover 18 percent of the total meltwater deposit area, or 7 percent of the State. Coarse, proximal facies, and sandy distal facies are included within the map units (Fig. 5).

Thus, two basic subdivisions of meltwater deposits are distinguished State-wide by litho-stratigraphic criteria of texture, sedimentary structures, and recognition of fluvial and lacustrine depositional environments. Typically, glaciolacustrine deposits coarsen upward from lake-bottom silt and clay, to delta bottomset and foreset sand, to fluvial topset sand and gravel (Fig. 6). Glaciofluvial units consist of alternating coarse- and fine-grained beds in vertical section.

Meltwater deposits are further divided on the State map by the depositional basin in which they are found. These broad subdivisions correspond to gross compositional differences of the deposits derived from different bedrock terranes that underlie the basins. Sediments of glacial Lake Hitchcock and smaller glacial lakes within the Connecticut valley, for example, contain various proportions of Triassic and Jurassic rocks, just as sediments from the Housatonic and Hoosic Valleys are characterized by the presence of clasts of marble and Cheshire Quartzite. Compositional differences were used to distinguish different depositional units on Cape Cod (Mather, Goldthwait, and Theismeyer, 1940; Koteff, Oldale, and Hartshorn, 1967).

Within topographic (depositional) basins, depositional units (morphosequences) used on quadrangle maps are grouped in State map units according to the glacial lake or glaciofluvial system in which they were deposited. The contact between map units is a mappable feature. Many gravel pits expose an unconformable contact between stratigraphic units. A common relationship is a fluvial gravel facies, that lies on the eroded surface of bottomset or foreset beds of an older delta. The younger gravel can be traced continuously from an ice-contact head of outwash to a lower lake basin where it makes up the surface of a deltaic package. In summary, the criteria by which regional map units are established and differentiated locally at quadrangle scale include recognition of the depositional environment of the deposit and sedimentary facies involved, lateral and vertical continuity (mappability) of facies and map units, altitude and position of facies and units (altitude of topset/foreset contact as a close approximation of the level of a glacial-lake water plane), downstream gradients, fining of grain size and decrease of collapse topography (mapping tools), and presence of clast indicator species.

The map pattern of lacustrine units deposited in different stages (levels) of a large glacial lake illustrates how retreat of the ice margin is related to the uncovering of successively younger and lower drainage paths, or lake spillways. Classic examples of the use of these principles of correlation are the histories of glacial lakes Nashua and Bouvé, documented by W.O. Crosby (1899) and his student A.W. Grabau (1900). The Massachusetts map will include a correlation chart of moraines and meltwater deposits, based on these principles of correlation, that will show a regional deglaciation chronology across the State. The deduced pattern of glacial retreat in major ice lobes, controlled by physiographic features, derives from these correlations.

Other map units include terminal and recessional moraines of the islands, Cape Cod, and southeastern Massachusetts; the Fresh Pond and Hardwick moraines; isolated high kame deposits that mark retreat positions of the ice margin in the Taunton and Connecticut valleys; glaciomarine deltas and marine bottom silt and clay; and Holocene alluvial and marine units. Map symbols will show orientations of drumlins and striae, paleo-wind directions, localities of older pre-Upper Wisconsinan drifts, radiocarbon-dated localities, archeological sites, and fossil localities.

STATE SURFICIAL MATERIALS MAP

The map of surficial materials of Massachusetts will be published in color at a scale of 1:125,000. The map is chiefly a map of textures of stratified glacial deposits. Map units are: gravel (mixed sand and gravel), sand, fine sediments, flood-plain alluvium, swamp deposits, and till. Superposed units, gravel-over-sand, for example, will clearly illustrate deltaic sequences, which cover much of the area of stratified drift. Fine sediments known to exist below coarser units will also be shown by superposed units. This map may prove to be the principal tool of engineering geologists, engineers, planners, local and State governments, and citizen groups.

PRELIMINARY SYNTHESIS

Preliminary synthesis of regional correlations, based on chronology of meltwater deposits and moraines, ice flow-direction indicators, distribution of erratics, and composition of drift, shows that major topographic features strongly influenced the pattern of retreat of the Laurentide ice sheet across the State. Five glacial lobes formed in broad lowland areas during thinning and melting back of the ice.

Chronologic relationships of deposits derived from the Buzzards Bay lobe, Cape Cod Bay lobe, and Great South Channel lobe demonstrate an overall younging of deposits to the east, according to compilation by Oldale (1976). Successive overlap of younger deposits to the east indicates that the Great South Channel lobe, which occupied the lowest and largest basin, produced sediments that were deposited in plains of the outer cape, after

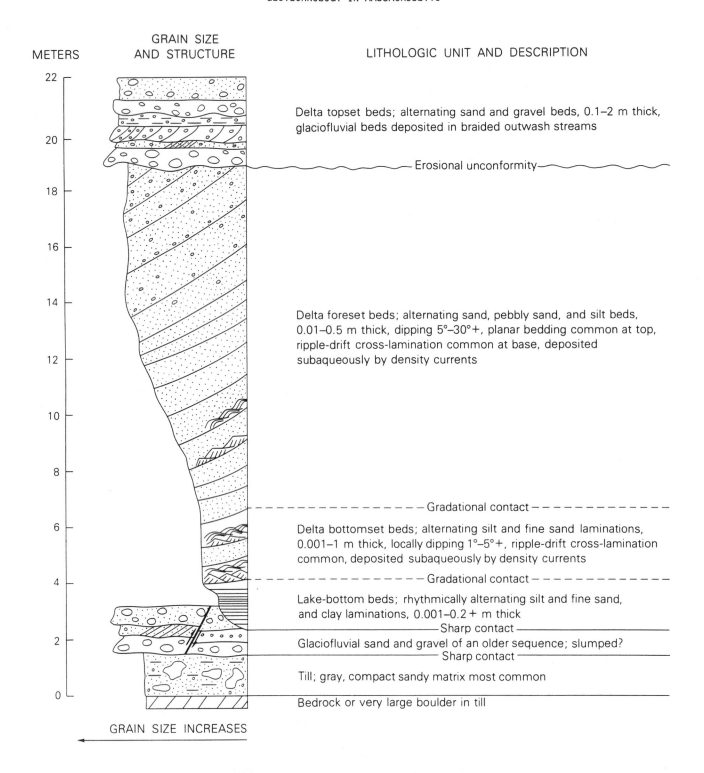

GRAIN SIZE
AND STRUCTURE

METERS

LITHOLOGIC UNIT AND DESCRIPTION

22

20

Delta topset beds; alternating sand and gravel beds, 0.1–2 m thick, glaciofluvial beds deposited in braided outwash streams

Erosional unconformity

18

16

14

Delta foreset beds; alternating sand, pebbly sand, and silt beds, 0.01–0.5 m thick, dipping 5°–30°+, planar bedding common at top, ripple-drift cross-lamination common at base, deposited subaqueously by density currents

12

10

8

Gradational contact

6

Delta bottomset beds; alternating silt and fine sand laminations, 0.001–1 m thick, locally dipping 1°–5°+, ripple-drift cross-lamination common, deposited subaqueously by density currents

4

Gradational contact

Lake-bottom beds; rhythmically alternating silt and fine sand, and clay laminations, 0.001–0.2 + m thick

Sharp contact

2

Glaciofluvial sand and gravel of an older sequence; slumped?

Sharp contact

Till; gray, compact sandy matrix most common

0

Bedrock or very large boulder in till

GRAIN SIZE INCREASES

Figure 6.  Idealized columnar section of a glaciolacustrine deltaic deposit showing vertical coarsening-upward trend of grain size, and associated sedimentary structures.  Deltaic deposit overlies coarse fluvial sand and gravel of an older morphosequence which overlies till.

the Cape Cod Bay lobe had retreated from most of the bay. The deltaic nature of the plains of the outer cape, first noted by Grabau (1897), is re-affirmed by quadrangle mapping. Regional corre-lation of accordant deltas shows that the Cape Cod Bay lake extended to the west side of the bay as far north as Cohasset (Fig. 3).

The retreat of the Buzzards Bay lobe is being traced across southeastern Massachusetts by Peper (Stone and Peper, 1980). Successive retreatal stands of the ice margin are marked by small moraine segments, isolated high-level kames, and heads of meltwater deposits. These features are aligned in a series of east-northeast-trending lines marking ice-front positions; these lines are spaced at 5-10-km intervals from Buzzards Bay to the middle of the Taunton River basin. The spac-ing between lines increases to the west away from the interlobate area along the west side of Cape Cod Bay, indicating a more rapid retreat of the western side of the lobe which extended to the west side of Narragansett Bay. The compilation shows the extent of a major glacial lake in the Taunton basin and a separate higher lake in the Norton area to the west. The regional extent of these units indicates that the Cape Cod Bay lobe blocked drainage of the Taunton basin lake to the east while the Buzzards Bay lobe retreated to the northern end of the lake near Brockton.

Deglaciation north of the Taunton basin was characterized by stagnation-zone retreat and sed-imentation in numerous glacial lakes in intercon-nected drainage basins of the eastern Massachu-setts lowland. Positions and chronologic rela-tionships of ice-marginal lakes in east-draining tributary valleys along the east margin of the Worcester Plateau indicate that these lakes were systematically dammed by the west edge of a broad lobe of ice that occupied the eastern Massachu-setts lowland. Orientations of striae and re-molded drumlins record systematic glacial movement to the south-southwest during retreat of the ice front along the edge of the plateau from the Rhode Island State line to the area west of glacial Lake Nashua (Fig. 3). Clast lithologies and erratic boulders, notably andalusite schist from Redstone Hill, Sterling, further illustrate late-glacial movement to the south-southwest. To the east, rapid retreat of the Great South Channel and Cape Cod Bay lobes, probably caused by marine erosion in the Gulf of Maine, allowed marine waters to invade the isostatically depressed crust north of Quincy where marine clays and glaciomarine deltas are mapped.

The ice margin retreated as an active lobe within the Connecticut River valley, as detailed by Larsen and Hartshorn in this volume. The size, shape, and rate of retreat of the lobe are shown by successive convex-down valley retreatal posi-tions of the ice margin, and by map relationships of local glacial lake deposits and facies of gla-cial Lake Hitchcock, the large, long-lived lake in the valley. The pattern and chronologic rela-tionships of successive ice-marginal lakes in the Mount Tom, Easthampton, Westhampton, and Shutes-bury areas illustrate how the valley ice lobe was related to broad ice fronts that extended over the uplands to the west and east of the valley. Thick sequences of glacial lake sediments in the Quaboag, Swift, and Ware River valleys attest to glacial erosion and local meltwater deposition in narrow valleys of the Worcester Plateau.

Similarly, chronologic relationships between high-level lakes on the east side of the Housa-tonic River valley and major glacial lakes in the Housatonic and Hoosic valleys illustrate retreat of the Hudson valley ice lobe in western Massa-chusetts. Charles Warren, using positions and altitudes of lacustrine and fluvial deposits, has described a complex deglaciation chronology that shows local lobation of ice in principal and tributary valleys (Warren and Harwood, 1978). Similar patterns of successively lower glacial lakes in Hop and Greenwater Brooks, and in the area of the Dalton embayment, trace the retreat of the ice margin from the upland to the Housa-tonic valley. The principal stratigraphic prob-lems are correlation of events between the Hudson lobe and the Connecticut valley lobe over the Berkshire Hills, and determining the history of the interlobate area.

SUMMARY

The Massachusetts State surficial geologic map, to be published in color and at a scale of 1:250,000, summarizes detailed lithologic infor-mation and chronologic relationships of Quaternary deposits gathered in more than 80 person-years of quadrangle mapping. Major emphasis of the State map will be the complex and highly detailed nature of Upper Wisconsinan glacial deposits and the de-glaciation chronology presented on published quadrangle maps. The State map updates data from surficial and bedrock quadrangle maps to show areas of thin till and numerous bedrock outcrops, and to show areas of thick till in drumlin cores. North of the coastal moraines, glacial meltwater deposits form the framework for the deglaciation chronology. Detailed mapping techniques evolved during the mapping program to the point where individual map units, morphosequences, are dis-tinguished on the basis of textural, morphologic, and compositional criteria, inferred depositional environment, and cross-cutting relationships among deposits. Morphosequences are lumped together in more than 200 State-map units that describe major glacial lake and glacial stream depositional sys-tems. Chronologic relationships among units, deduced from cross-cutting relationships and inferred ice margin retreatal positions, illus-trate that major topographic features influenced the mode of deglaciation and the rate of retreat of five ice lobes that formed during thinning and melting back of the Laurentide ice sheet.

A second State map of textures of surficial materials, to be published in color at a scale of 1:125,000, will emphasize the textural character-istics and three-dimensional distribution of sur-ficial materials. This map is aimed at presenting information needed for resource (sand and gravel, clay) planning, land-use decisions, water-resource studies, and construction alternatives. When used together, the two maps provide a regional lithostratigraphic and chronostratigraphic framework by which on site information can be interpreted.

As observed in drill cores, a coarsening-upward sequence of glacial meltwater deposits is typical of most of the area (28 percent of the State) mapped as glaciolacustrine deposits. Study of the surficial geologic and materials maps and the new bedrock map of Massachusetts, which includes descriptions of lithology and metamorphic grade of stratigraphic units, yields inferences of gross composition of the glacial materials, inferences that are related to suitability of gravel for aggregate, for example.

Future work on surficial materials of Massachusetts might include quantitative correlation of geotechnical properties, such as permeability, cohesive and shear strength, and even standard penetration test results, with surficial map units shown on the State maps. Such properties may ultimately be related to the depositional environment of the surficial material and the lithologic characteristics of the local bedrock source. The study of drift composition, both till and stratified deposits, could lead to differentiation of related bedrock source terranes and closely associated glacial deposits and definition of contacts (sharp or gradational) between them. Ultimately, such a field-oriented approach could lead to increased understanding of glacial erosional and transport mechanisms and the effects of topography and climate change on a continental glacier.

## REFERENCES

Barton, W.R., and Sinnott, J.A., 1975, The mineral industry of Massachusetts: U.S. Bureau of Mines, Minerals Yearbook, v. 2, p. 365-373.

Clapp, F.G., 1901, Geological history of the Charles River: Technical Quarterly, v. 14, p. 171-201, 255-269.

Crosby, W.O., 1899, Geological history of the Nashua valley during the Tertiary and Quaternary periods: Technical Quarterly, v. 12, p. 288-324.

Currier, L.W., 1939, Cooperative geologic work in Massachusetts [1938]: Massachusetts Department of Public of Works [U.S. Geological Survey] Cooperative Geology Project Progress Report, 13 p. See also Mather.

Currier, L.W., 1941, Disappearance of the last ice sheet in Massachusetts by stagnation zone retreat [abstract]: Geological Society of America Bulletin, v. 52, p. 1895.

Emerson, B.K., 1898, Geology of old Hampshire County, Massachusetts: U.S. Geological Survey, Monograph 29, 790 p.

Goldthwait, J.W., 1905, The sand plains of glacial Lake Sudbury: Harvard College Museum of Comparative Zoology Bulletin, v. 42, p. 263-301.

Grabau, A.W., 1897, The sand plains of Truro, Wellfleet, and Eastham, Massachusetts [abstract]: Science, new series, v. 5, p. 334-335.

Grabau, A.W., 1900, Lake Bouvé, an extinct glacial lake in the southern part of the Boston basin: Boston Society of Natural History Occasional Papers IV, pt. III, p. 564-600, map.

Hartshorn, J.H., Koteff, C., and Oldale, R.N., 1967, Preliminary report on the geology of the Cape Cod National Seashore, in Farquhar, O.C., ed., Economic geology in Massachusetts: Graduate School, University of Massachusetts, p. 49-58.

Holmes, G.W., 1964, Preliminary materials map, Massachusetts portion of the Egremont quadrangle, Massachusetts-New York: U.S. Geological Survey Open-File Map, scale 1:24,000, 11 data sheets.

Jahns, R.H., 1941, Outwash chronology in northeastern Massachusetts [abstract]: Geological Society of America Bulletin, v. 52, p. 1910.

Jahns, R.H., 1953, Surficial geology of the Ayer quadrangle, Massachusetts: U.S. Geological Survey, Geology Quadrangle Map GQ-21, scale 1:31,680.

Jahns, R.H., Willard, M.E., White, W.S., Currier, L.W., and White, S.E., 1977, Overlay map of the glacial geology of parts of the Tyngsboro and Westford, Massachusetts, quadrangles: U.S. Geological Survey Open-File Map 77-641, 1:31,680.

Kaye, C.A., 1961, Pleistocene stratigraphy of Boston, Massachusetts: U.S. Geological Survey, Professional Paper 424-B, p. B73-B76.

Kaye, C.A., 1964a, Outline of Pleistocene geology of Martha's Vineyard, Massachusetts: U.S. Geological Survey, Professional Paper 501-C, p. C134-C139.

Kaye, C.A., 1964b, Illinoian and early Wisconsin moraines of Martha's Vineyard, Massachusetts: U.S. Geological Survey, Professional Paper 501-C, p. C140-C143.

Koteff, C., 1964, Surficial geology of the Concord quadrangle, Massachusetts: U.S. Geological Survey, Geology Quadrangle Map GQ-331, scale 1:24,000, 4 p. text.

Koteff, C., 1966, Surficial geologic map of the Clinton quadrangle, Worcester County, Massachusetts: U.S. Geological Survey, Geology Quadrangle Map GQ-567, scale 1:24,000, 4 p. text.

Koteff, C., 1980, Patterns of Late Wisconsinan

deglaciation in New England [abstract]: Geological Society of America, Abstracts with Programs, v. 12, no. 2, p. 67.

Koteff, C., and Cotton, J.E., 1962, Preliminary results of recent deep drilling on Cape Cod, Massachusetts: Science, v. 137, no. 3523, p. 34.

Koteff, C., Oldale, R.N., and Hartshorn, J.H., 1967, Geologic map of the North Truro quadrangle, Barnstable County, Massachusetts: U.S. Geological Survey, Geology Quadrangle Map GQ-599, scale 1:24,000.

Koteff, C., and Pessl, F., Jr., Systematic ice retreat in New England (in press): U.S. Geological Survey, Professional Paper 1179.

Mahaney, W.C., ed., 1976, Quaternary stratigraphy of North America: Stroudsburg, Pennsylvania, Dowden, Hutchinson, and Ross, preface.

Mather, K.F., Goldthwait, R.P., and Theismeyer, L.R., 1940, Preliminary report on the geology of western Cape Cod, Massachusetts: U.S. Geological Survey and Massachusetts Department of Public Works, Cooperative Geology Project Bulletin 2, 53 p. See also Currier.

McIntosh, W.L., and Eister, M.E., 1973, Geologic map index of Massachusetts, Rhode Island, and Connecticut, 1952-1971: U.S. Geological Survey, Geology Map Index.

Oldale, R.N., 1976, Generalized geologic map of Cape Cod: U.S. Geological Survey Open-File Report 76-765, 23 p., 1 pl., scale 1:125,000.

Page, L.R., 1967, The role of the United States Geological Survey in Massachusetts, in Farquhar, O.C., ed., Economic geology in Massachusetts: Graduate School, University

of Massachusetts, p. 9-28.

Stone, J.R., London, E.H., and Langer, W.H., 1979, Map showing textures of unconsolidated materials, Connecticut valley urban area, central New England: U.S. Geological Survey, Miscellaneous Investigation Series Map I-1074-B, 3 sheets, scale 1:125,000.

Stone, B.D., and Peper, J.D., 1980, Topographic control of the deglaciation of eastern Massachusetts: ice lobation and marine incursion [abstract]: Geology Society of America Abstracts with Programs, v. 12, no. 2, p. 85.

Taylor, F.B., 1903, The correlation and reconstruction of recessional ice borders in Berkshire County, Massachusetts: Journal of Geology, v. 11, p. 323-364.

Tuttle, C.R., 1962, Seismic high-speed till in Massachusetts [abstract]: Geological Society of America Special Paper 68, p. 288-289.

U.S. Geological Survey, 1977, List of Geological Survey geologic and water-supply reports and maps for Massachusetts, Rhode Island, and Connecticut, 47 p.

Warren, C.R., and Harwood, D.S., 1978, Deglaciation ice fronts in the South Sandisfield and Ashley Falls quadrangles, Massachusetts and Connecticut: U.S. Geological Survey Miscellaneous Field Studies Map MF-1016, scale 1:24,000.

Williams, J.R., and Tasker, G.D., 1974, Water resources of the coastal drainage basins of southeastern Massachusetts, Plymouth to Weweantic River, Wareham: U.S. Geological Survey Hydrological Investigation Atlas HA-507.

Hors-texte

Flood plain of the Connecticut River between
Rocky Hill and Glastonbury in Connecticut.

# Deglaciation of the southern portion of the Connecticut Valley of Massachusetts

### F.D. LARSEN
Department of Earth Science
Norwich University, Vermont

### J. H. HARTSHORN
Department of Geology and Geography
University of Massachusetts at Amherst

## ABSTRACT

During retreat of the last ice sheet, the Connecticut Valley of Massachusetts was occupied by an active lobe of ice that readvanced several times. That the lobe was active in late-glacial time, as opposed to being stagnant, is shown by the radial pattern of striations that defines the last glacial movement throughout the length of the Connecticut Valley in Massachusetts. Erratics of Jura-Triassic rocks derived from the lowland and found on the higher crystalline uplands both east and west of their source area similarly define the latest movement. There are no moraines in the Connecticut Valley, but the shape of the ice margin during retreat can be determined from ice-contact slopes associated with kame terraces, kame deltas, and kames. Some ice-contact slopes are arcuate in plan view and can be extrapolated across the valley in a loop-like manner. Readvance occurred several times during northward retreat of the glacier margin. The occurrence of till overlying deformed stratified drift is the most common evidence for readvance. Bodies of stratified drift such as gravel or clay may underlie readvance till and may constitute a potential hazard at critical construction sites if borings are not deep enough to reveal them.

East of the Holyoke Basalt ridge, glacial Lake Hitchcock expanded northward with the retreating ice. West of the ridge, time-transgressive Lake Westfield, which was graded to Harts Pond gap, filled with sediments almost as fast as the ice margin retreated. Diversion of east-flowing drainage from Harts Pond gap to Westfield gap occurred when the ice margin was in the northern part of the Mt. Tom quadrangle, and marked the end of Lake Westfield. When diversion occurred, short-lived proglacial Lake Manhan formed between the retreating ice and the Timberswamp spillway in the west-central part of the Mt. Tom quadrangle. Retreat of ice from the Holyoke Narrows permitted Lake Manhan to drop to the level of Lake Hitchcock, which expanded north of the Holyoke Range with the retreating ice margin.

Mapping of stratified-drift deposits as parts of morphosequences shows that the retreating ice margin was lobate and had more than 16 stillstands during deglaciation of the southern part of the Connecticut Valley of Massachusetts.

## INTRODUCTION

This paper results from a compilation of part of the surficial geologic map of Massachusetts to be published at a scale of 1:250,000. The original data were compiled on 7-1/2-minute topographic quadrangles published by the U.S. Geological Survey at a scale of 1:24,000 and reduced photographically. The study area (Fig. 1) consists of the southern half of the Connecticut Valley Lowland of Massachusetts, which is bordered on both the east and the west by crystalline rocks of the New England physiographic province (Fenneman, 1938).

The Connecticut Valley Lowland is underlain by igneous and sedimentary rocks of Late Triassic to Early Jurassic age (Cornet and others, 1973; the term Jura-Triassic is used to refer to the age of these rocks in the remainder of this paper). The area is split into two smaller lowlands by a hogback held up by the resistant Holyoke Basalt. The bedrock in the western lowland is the New Haven Arkose, while the eastern lowland is underlain from west to east by the East Berlin Formation, the Hampden Basalt (and associated volcanic rocks), and the Portland Arkose.

All surface drainage in the study area passes to the Connecticut River, which flows south through the middle of the area and eventually into Long Island Sound. Major tributaries of the Connecticut River include the Chicopee and Westfield Rivers. Altitudes range from 39 ft ASL where the Connecticut River crosses the Massachusetts-Connecticut state line to 1,238 ft ASL at the summit of Mt. Lincoln in the Belchertown quadrangle.

## ACKNOWLEDGMENTS

This work was carried out under the auspices of the Massachusetts Cooperative Project supported jointly by the U.S. Geological Survey and the Massachusetts Department of Public Works. We acknowledge the work of many geologists, too numerous to name here, for their work in the Connecticut Valley and adjacent areas. We especially thank Byron D. Stone for reviewing the paper.

## DIRECTION OF ICE MOVEMENT DURING MAXIMUM GLACIATION

At the time of maximum extent of the last ice sheet, all of central and western Massachusetts was covered by ice. The general direction of ice movement in upland areas at the time of maximum glaciation was south-southeast to southeast. This is shown by regional compilations of striations

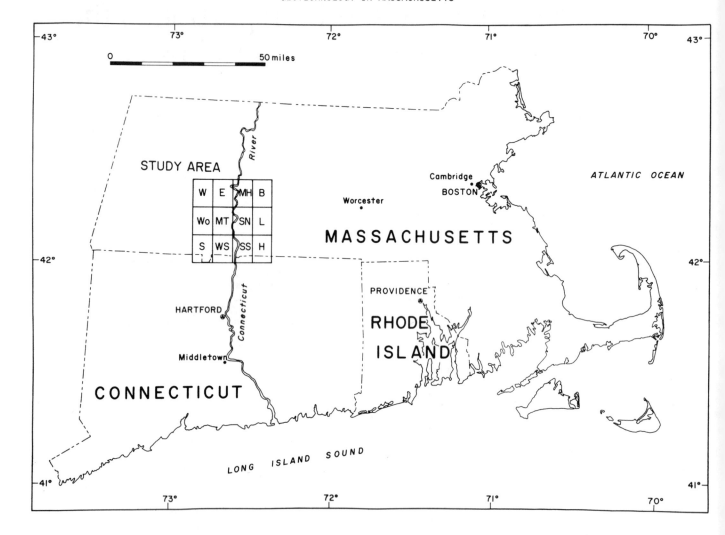

Figure 1. Location of the study area in relation to the southern New England states. Small rectangles are U.S. Geological Survey 7.5-minute quadrangles: W, Westhampton; E, Easthampton; MH, Mount Holyoke; B, Belchertown; Wo, Woronoco; MT, Mount Tom; SN, Springfield North; L, Ludlow; S, Southwick; WS, West Springfield; SS, Springfield South; H, Hampden.

by J.W. Goldthwait (in Flint, 1957, p. 60) and of indicator fans by R.F. Flint (1971, p. 178). B.K. Emerson (1898) noted the distribution of erratics of Cheshire Quartzite in western Massachusetts and recognized that they had been transported southeast from a source area on the west side of the Green Mountains. Evidence found during the present study that supports the generally accepted southeast movement of ice during maximum glaciation is derived from the distribution of erratics of Monkton Quartzite, found both west and east of the Connecticut Valley (Fig. 2). The source area of Monkton Quartzite erratics is in the Vermont Valley and lies on the west side of the Green Mountain anticlinorium. For erratics of this lithology to reach their present locations, they had to be carried southeast across the north-south trend of the Green Mountains, presumably at the time of maximum glaciation.

## RETREAT OF THE LAST ICE SHEET

During retreat of the last ice sheet the Connecticut Valley Lowland of Massachusetts was occupied by an active lobe of ice that, on occasion, readvanced. In its early history, when the ice margin was at the Massachusetts-Connecticut

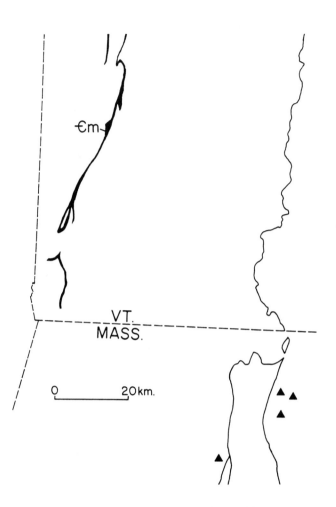

Figure 2. Distribution of erratics of Monkton Quartzite (triangles) transported southeast from source area (Cm, Cambrian Monkton Quartz- ite, solid black) in western Vermont.

state line, the lobe was split by the Holyoke Basalt ridge into two sublobes. The sublobe on the west was about 10 km wide, while that on the east was 20 to 22 km wide. Because the Connecti- cut Valley of Massachusetts is shaped like an inverted funnel, the width of the lobe decreased as the ice margin retreated northward up the valley. When the ice margin retreated north of the Holyoke Range, the ice was no longer split into two sublobes but consisted of a single lobe 19 km wide, which decreased to a width of 10 km when the ice margin was just south of Greenfield.

STRIATIONS

That the Connecticut Valley lobe was active and moving, as opposed to being stagnant, is shown

by a radial pattern of striations formed by both sublobes east and west of the Holyoke Basalt ridge. Striations in the southern half of the Connecticut Valley define two separate lobes dur- ing the last stage of glaciation (Fig. 3). The eastern sublobe is defined by a radial pattern of striations that trend due west in the east-central part of the Mt. Tom quadrangle to S 73° E in the Ludlow quadrangle. A radial pattern from S 60° E in the northeast part of the Mt. Tom quadrangle to S 80° W in the southwest part of the Easthampton quadrangle shows the extent of radial flow of the western sublobe. Overlapping sets of striations occur at several separate localities. In each case, the direction of the older set is close to the trend of the Connecticut Valley, whereas the younger set cuts the trend of the Connecticut Valley at a high angle. This is taken as evidence that early ice movement was parallel to the val- ley, and the last ice movement was oblique to the main valley just prior to deglaciation of the site. The radial movement of ice within the lobe was maintained as the ice retreated by melting northward up the Connecticut Valley at least as far as the Vermont-Massachusetts state line.

INDICATOR FANS

The presence of erratics of Jura-Triassic rocks on crystalline bedrock both east and west of the Connecticut Valley (Fig. 4) is taken as evidence, together with that from striations, for a well-developed lobate movement of ice in late- glacial time. Erratics of Jura-Triassic rocks found east of the Connecticut Valley are not sig- nificant in that they could have been transported southeast during maximum glaciation. However, erratics of Jura-Triassic rocks found up to 4 km west of their source area in the northern part of the Connecticut Valley, and up to 7 km west of the source area in the central part of the valley, must have been transported in late-glacial time.

The dispersal pattern of erratics of Belcher- town Quartz Monzodiorite (Ashwal and others, 1979) derived from the Hatfield pluton is shown in Fig- ure 5. The largest erratics from the Hatfield pluton are in a zone that trends due south from the pluton and cuts obliquely across the Holyoke Basalt ridge at Mt. Tom. A 1.2-meter erratic that lies on the boundary between the Easthampton and Mt. Tom quadrangles is at an elevation of 1,100 feet. Because the bedrock surface between the Hatfield pluton and the present location of the 1.2-meter erratic is below sea level, we know that this erratic has been lifted through a verti- cal distance of at least 1,100 feet. It seems reasonable to assume that this erratic was uplift- ed to its present location during maximum glacia- tion when ice moving due south in this portion of the Connecticut Valley produced the due south trend of the largest erratics. Erratics of the Belchertown Quartz Monzodiorite are also found due west and southwest of the Hatfield pluton. If we accept at face value the above-mentioned radial pattern of striations for the western sub- lobe, it appears that erratics located west and southwest of the Hatfield pluton were transported

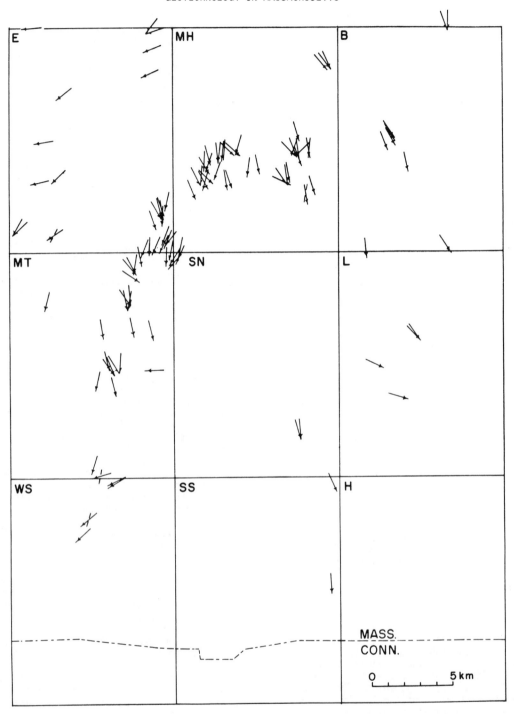

Figure 3. Map of striations in the southern part of the Connecticut Valley of Massachusetts. High concentrations of striations occur on the Holyoke Basalt ridge and on crystalline rocks in the northwest and the east. Striations occur at point of arrow. (See Fig. 1 for quadrangle names.)

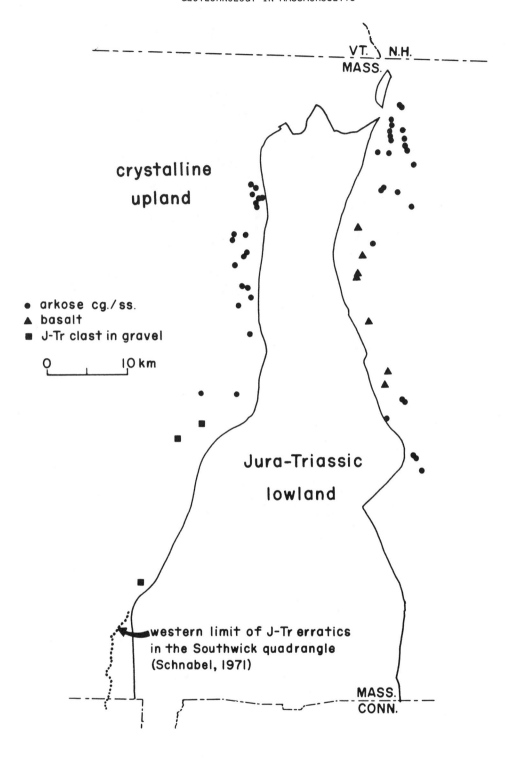

Figure 4. Distribution of erratics of Jura-Triassic rocks transported east and west from their source area in the Connecticut Valley in late-glacial time.

- 33 -

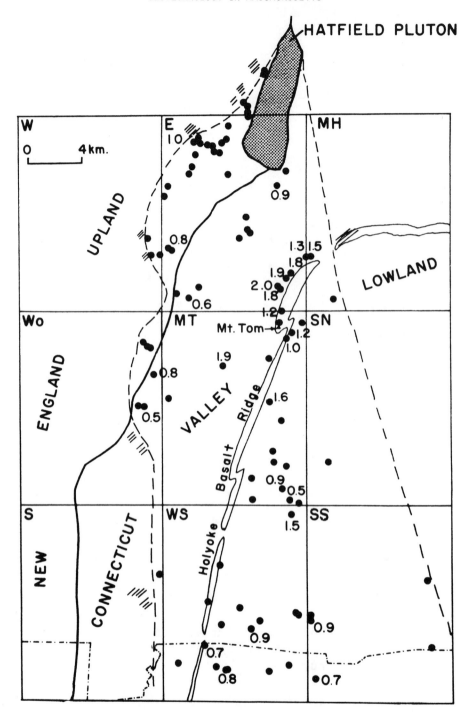

Figure 5. Erratics of Belchertown Quartz Monzodiorite (solid circles) derived from the Hatfield pluton. Dashed line is outline of indicator fan. Diagonal-ruled pattern indicates areas where no erratics of monzodiorite were found after a careful search. Numbers refer to average diameter in meters of erratics greater than 0.49 m in diameter.

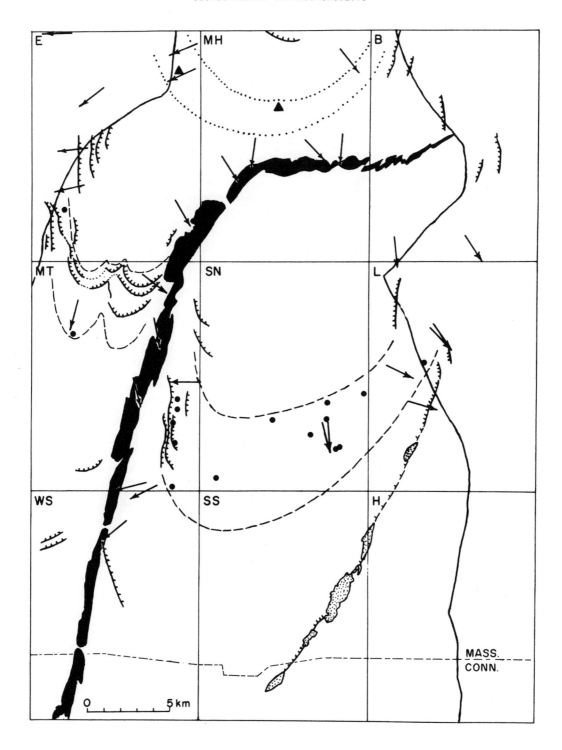

Figure 6. Map of selected striations (arrows), ice-contact slopes
(hachured lines; hachures on side of ice), and readvance localities
(solid circles, Chicopee readvance; solid triangles, Camp Meeting
Cutting readvance). Dashed lines enclose area of Chicopee readvance;
dotted lines enclose area of Camp Meeting Cutting readvance. Ice-
contact deposits shown in stippled pattern. (See Fig. 1 for quadrangle names).

to their final resting place in late-glacial time when the margin of the western sublobe was retreating through the Mt. Tom and Easthampton quadrangles.

## ARCUATE DRIFT BORDERS

Another line of evidence that the Connecticut Valley was occupied by an active lobe, or sublobes, in late-glacial time consists of the location, shape, and orientation of ice-contact slopes associated with kame deltas, kame terraces, and kames (Fig. 6). Deposits of stratified drift with north-south ice-contact slopes indicate that tributary valleys were clear of ice while the Connecticut Valley was filled with ice. As the ice margin retreated downslope away from the main-valley wall, successively lower deposits of stratified drift were formed. This is well illustrated in the Easthampton and Mt. Tom quadrangles, where the ice margin retreated downslope to the east, and in the Belchertown and Ludlow quadrangles, where the ice margin retreated downslope to the west.

The arcuate shape of the former ice margin is clearly shown in some localities, for example in the north part of the Mt. Tom quadrangle and the east-central part of the Springfield South quadrangle (Fig. 6). At each of these localities it is possible to extrapolate the position of the ice margin in a loop-like manner across the valley to the head of deposits of the same approximate age and elevation.

## READVANCE

When the southern edge of the eastern sublobe was located near the center of the Springfield North quadrangle, the ice margin readvanced about 3 or 4 km to a position just south of the quadrangle (dashed lines, Fig. 6). The main evidence for readvance consists of reddish-brown, compact, lodgement till overlying deformed stratified drift, which in turn overlies till of the main ice advance. Glaciotectonic features such as thrust faults, overturned folds of lacustrine sediments, and exotic blocks of deformed lacustrine sediment occur at the outer limit of the readvance. At the edge of the Jura-Triassic lowland in the southwest part of the Easthampton quadrangle, 1 m of reddish-brown, compact till derived from Jura-Triassic rocks overlies 2 m of deformed lacustrine sediment, which in turn rests on gray till derived from crystalline rocks. The older gray till was formed by ice moving southeast off the crystalline upland, and the younger reddish-brown till formed when the ice margin readvanced southwest across lacustrine sediments.

Evidence for the Chicopee readvance is found at 14 localities east of the Holyoke Basalt ridge and in a 3- to 4.5-km wide zone that loops across the Connecticut Valley from the Ludlow quadrangle on the east to the Mt. Tom quadrangle on the west (Fig. 6). Readvance localities west of the basalt ridge in the southwest part of the Easthampton

quadrangle and the northwest part of the Mt. Tom quadrangle are correlated with those east of the ridge.

Following the Chicopee readvance, the two sublobes retreated north of the Holyoke Range, forming a single lobe when the ice was no longer influenced by the Holyoke Basalt ridge. When the ice margin was located in the north part of the Mt. Holyoke quadrangle the lobe readvanced, producing at least two readvance tills at the Camp Meeting Cutting (Emerson, 1898) in the northeast corner of the Easthampton quadrangle. The Camp Meeting Cutting, located along the present interstate highway, I-91, 4 km north of Northampton, is no longer available for study. However, highly contorted and sheared lacustrine sand, silt, clay, and a possible readvance till can be observed in borrow pits east of I-91.

W.R. McIlvride (pers. comm., 1980) reports till over outwash sand in a stream bank north of the Holyoke Range in the Mt. Holyoke quadrangle (solid triangle, Fig. 6). This possible readvance may correlate with the readvance at the Camp Meeting Cutting 7.0 km to the west-northwest.

Other possible readvance sites occur farther north in the Connecticut Valley and, together with the evidence from striations and indicator clasts, indicate that the entire Connecticut Valley of Massachusetts was deglaciated by an active, spreading lobe of ice.

## GLACIAL LAKES

As the margin of the ice sheet retreated north of the Massachusetts-Connecticut state line, the sublobes on both sides of the Holyoke Basalt ridge were accompanied by northward-expanding glacial lakes. The eastern sublobe bordered glacial Lake Hitchcock (Lougee, 1939; Jahns and Willard, 1942; Hartshorn and Koteff, 1967a), while the sublobe on the west bordered a smaller lake, glacial Lake Westfield (Larsen, 1972) that drained eastward into Lake Hitchcock through a gap (Harts Pond gap) in the basalt ridge just north of the state line (Fig. 7a).

## LAKE HITCHCOCK

Lake Hitchcock formed during deglaciation when a large body of stratified drift was deposited across the preglacial course of the Connecticut River at Rocky Hill, Connecticut. The initial spillway for the lake was across the drift dam at an altitude of 125 ft at the present site of Dividend Brook (Hartshorn and Koteff, 1967a). A separate lake developed to the west at an altitude of 100 feet and was controlled by a bedrock-defended spillway at New Britain. Northward retreat of ice from the divide separating the two lakes permitted the higher lake to drop to the level of the second and to abandon the higher threshold at Dividend Brook (Hartshorn and Koteff, 1967a).

As the ice margin retreated past major tributaries to the Connecticut Valley, large deltas were formed in Lake Hitchcock. In addition, shoreward bottom deposits, beaches, and other shoreline features developed in response to the open lake. Studies by Jahns and Willard (1942) indicate that, when the elevations of deltas and shoreline features are plotted on a north-south profile, they define a tilted water plane that rises to the north at a slope of about 80 cm/km (dashed line, Fig. 8). The tilt of the former shoreline of Lake Hitchcock can best be explained by isostatic uplift due to the removal of the weight of the continental ice sheet.

During the present study, a water plane about 8 ft higher than that described by Jahns and Willard (1942) also was determined to rise to the north at 80 cm/km in the study area (solid line, Fig. 8). This second water plane is based on four data points, three of which were carefully measured by transit on the maximum elevation of foreset beds in deltas formed by streams flowing directly into Lake Hitchcock. This higher water plane represents a minimum elevation for Lake Hitchcock in the study area at the time these foreset beds were deposited. The water plane mentioned here extended from the Massachusetts-Connecticut state line northward only 50 km. At present, the evidence is not clear as to whether this same water plane extended even farther north or whether Lake Hitchcock had dropped 10 ft in elevation by the time deltas were formed at the north end of the Jura-Triassic lowland.

Lake Hitchcock, about 9 km wide at the Massachusetts-Connecticut state line, narrowed gradually to 6 km in the area of the Chicopee readvance and to 4 km at the latitude of Holyoke. The lake was only 1 km wide at the Holyoke Narrows and reached its greatest width, 19 km, just north of the Holyoke Range (Fig. 7c).

The bottom deposits of Lake Hitchcock have been described in detail by Ashley (1972) and Gustavson and others (1975) and will not be discussed here.

LAKE WESTFIELD

As soon as the ice margin retreated north of Harts Pond gap, meltwater drainage from the western sublobe flowed eastward through the gap and into Lake Hitchcock (Fig. 7a). As the western

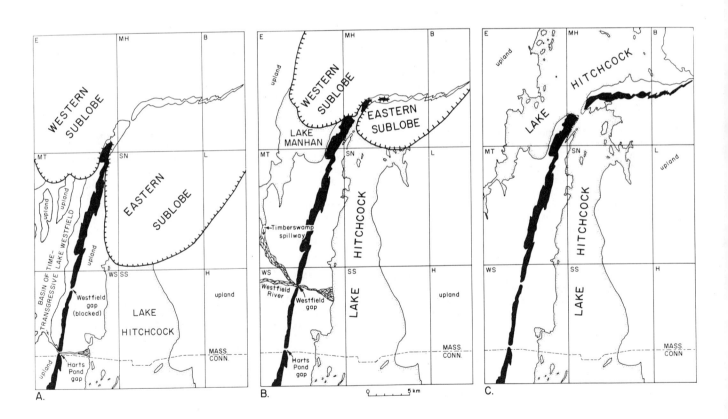

Figure 7. Glacial lakes of the study area: (a) maximum extent of Lake Westfield basin, (b) Lake Manhan, and (c) Lake Hitchcock. Linear black area is Holyoke Basalt ridge. Glacier is outlined by hachured line.

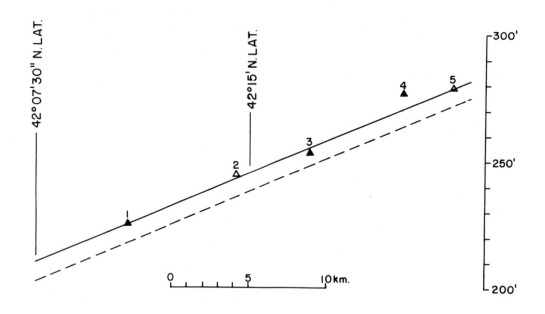

Figure 8. North-south projected profile showing tilted water planes of Lake Hitchcock.
Solid line, this study; dashed line, from Jahns
and Willard (1942); solid triangles (1, 3, 4),
maximum elevation of foreset beds measured by
transit; open triangles (2) beach deposits in
northwest part of Springfield North quadrangle
and (5) break in slope of ice-contact delta in
north-central part of Mount Holyoke quadrangle.

sublobe retreated northward, glacial Lake Westfield formed between the retreating lobe and Harts
Pond gap (Larsen, 1972). Lake Westfield was a
time-transgressive lake that filled with deltaic
and lacustrine sediments almost as fast as the ice
margin retreated. This was probably due to the
fact that the drainage of the Westfield River
basin was added to the meltwater drainage from
the western sublobe and flowed through a narrow
valley to Harts Pond gap.

An interesting point about the history of
deglaciation in this area concerns the gap of the
Westfield River through the Holyoke Basalt ridge
in the north-central part of the West Springfield
quadrangle (Fig. 7a). Westfield gap was blocked
by stratified drift, or possibly by ice, preventing east-flowing drainage, while the margin of
the western sublobe retreated 12 to 14 km north
of Westfield gap (Larsen, 1972). Readvance of
the western sublobe then took place, as shown by
evidence in the southwest part of the Easthampton
quadrangle and the northwest part of the Mt. Tom
quadrangle (Fig. 6). When the western sublobe
was located 2.5 km south of the border between
the Mt. Tom and Easthampton quadrangles, a large
depositional landform, the Barnes delta-outwash
plain (Fig. 9, $Cw_e$), was built southward into
Lake Westfield, which still drained through Harts
Pond gap.

Whatever the cause of the blockage of east-
flowing drainage at Westfield gap, it was removed
at the same time that the western sublobe retreated 1 km north of the head of the Barnes delta-outwash plain. This diversion of drainage from Harts
Pond gap to Westfield gap resulted in a general
lowering of base level west of the basalt ridge
and was accompanied by the development of a small
glacial lake (Lake Manhan) in the valley of the
Manhan River.

LAKE MANHAN

Glacial Lake Manhan (Fig. 7b) formed between
the western sublobe and the Timberswamp spillway,
a spillway over stratified drift in the west-central part of the Mt. Tom quadrangle (Larsen,
1972). Water flowed southeast from the Timberswamp spillway and after joining with drainage
from the Westfield River flowed eastward through
Westfield gap and into Lake Hitchcock. Lake Manhan was short-lived and existed only until the
western sublobe retreated from the Holyoke Narrows, at which time Lake Manhan dropped 30 to 35
ft, thereby merging with Lake Hitchcock and causing abandonment of the Timberswamp spillway.

Lake Hitchcock expanded north of the basalt
ridge with the retreating ice and reached its

greatest east-west width just north of the Holyoke Range (Fig. 7c). Eventually, Lake Hitchcock extended up the Connecticut Valley of Vermont and New Hampshire and at its greatest extent was 240 km long (Schafer and Hartshorn, 1965).

## THE MORPHOSEQUENCE CONCEPT, CHRONOMORPHS, AND THE DEGLACIATION HISTORY OF THE AREA

The history of glacial lakes Hitchcock, Westfield, and Manhan, briefly described above, owes much to detailed mapping of deposits of stratified drift and to the interpretation of those deposits as part of a morphologic sequence, hereafter referred to as a morphosequence.

A morphosequence consists of all the stratified deposits formed by one meltwater stream system deposited in a given depositional basin defined by a particular ice margin and outlet from that basin. A change in the position of the ice margin or the outlet from the basin ends the development of one morphosequence and often initiates the development of a second. Morphosequences were especially well formed in southern New England during the general retreat of the ice sheet, and they mark ice retreatal positions caused by either climatic conditions or topographic controls or both.

Elements of the morphosequence concept as applied to the glacial history of New England are inherent in the work of several early geologists, for example W.M. Davis (1890), J.B. Woodworth (1898), J.W. Goldthwait (1905), and W.C. Alden (1924). However, the concept was first developed and stated by Jahns (1941, 1953) and Currier (1941). Since the 1940's, the concept has been used by the U.S. Geological Survey in mapping surficial deposits in southern New England at a scale of 1:31,680 and 1:24,000. The forthcoming surficial geologic map of Massachusetts will be the first regional-scale map to make extensive use of the morphosequence concept. It is our purpose here to give a general example of the morphosequence concept as it relates to the history of deglaciation in the southern part of the Connecticut Valley of Massachusetts, and to show how the concept can be used to deduce chronological relationships and to indicate the pattern of retreat in a basin through time. For more examples of the morphosequence concept in southern New England, the reader should refer to Koteff (1974) and Koteff and Pessl (1980).

In our example we omit many details and some well-marked morphosequences and start when the ice margin on the Holyoke Basalt ridge was located 6 km north of Harts Pond gap and the eastern sublobe still extended south of the Massachusetts-Connecticut state line (Fig. 9). The ice margin maintained a stationary position in the Springfield South quadrangle while meltwater issuing south between the ice and the valley wall built a long triangular delta, the East Longmeadow delta, southward into Lake Hitchcock. This delta is designated morphosequence $Ah_e$ in Figure 9 (the

A stands for the first identified morphosequence in this area north of the Massachusetts-Connecticut border, the h for Lake Hitchcock, and the e for the east side of the basin). The surface of $Ah_e$ slopes to the south and is underlain by fluvial deposits that grade from coarse on the north to fine on the south. The northwest side of the delta ($Ah_e$) is marked either by an ice-contact slope or by stratified-drift deposits that stand higher than the delta surface.

Apparently these older, higher deposits were formed in elongate depressions parallel to the ice front and between stagnant ice on the southeast and active ice on the northwest (Hartshorn and Koteff, 1967b). The former ice margin can be extrapolated westward across the valley to similar outwash deposits (another morphosequence, $Ah_w$; w stands for west) in the center of the West Springfield quadrangle. The surface of these deposits ($Ah_w$) rises to the north at 3.1 m/km and required a meltwater source at an elevation of 260 ft at the time of their formation. The source of meltwater and sediment at this elevation probably was the western margin of the eastern sublobe as it impinged against the Holyoke Basalt ridge. The lobate form of the eastern sublobe has been documented above by ice-direction indicators and ice-contact slopes. The two morphosequences, $Ah_e$ and $Ah_w$, which were formed in the same depositional basin (Connecticut Valley) and which were graded to the outlet from glacial Lake Hitchcock, are related to one particular ice-marginal position (Fig. 9) and are chronologically equivalent. Therefore, the stratified drift of the East Longmeadow delta (morphosequence $Ah_e$) and the outwash deposit in the center of the West Springfield quadrangle (morphosequence $Ah_w$) are placed in the same <u>chronomorph</u> (a new term, Larsen, 1980).

A chronomorph consists of two or more morphosequences formed at the same time and related to the same ice margin position. The time interval we envisage for some chronomorphs to have formed in the Connecticut Valley may have been as short as one year or as long as several tens of years. In some circumstances, as when morphosequences are very small and probably deposited in one or two meltwater seasons, a chronomorph may contain only two morphosequences. However, in practice a chronomorph should consist of many morphosequences in a band running parallel to the former ice margin. Areas between well-defined bands may contain small or uncorrelated morphosequences. Also, bands containing morphosequences may change width and even pinch out.

We do not know the exact position of the ice margin west of the basalt ridge while morphosequences $Ah_e$ and $Ah_w$ were being formed east of the ridge. Meltwater from the western sublobe formed several bodies of stratified drift in Lake Westfield, which drained eastward through Harts Pond gap. Colton and Hartshorn (1971) show four separate morphosequences in this area that we have placed in two morphosequences, $Aw_{e1}$ and $Aw_{e2}$

| | WESTERN SUBLOBE | | EASTERN SUBLOBE | |
|---|---|---|---|---|
| | (west side) | (east side) | (west side) | (east side) |
| CHRONOMORPH D | Dm | Dp | $Dh_{w2}$ / $Dh_{w1}$ | |
| CHRONOMORPH C | $Cw_w$ | $Cw_e$ | | |
| CHRONOMORPH B | $Bw_w$ (not shown) | $Bw_e$ | | |
| CHRONOMORPH A | | $Aw_{e2}$ / $Aw_{e1}$ | $Ah_w$ | $Ah_e$ |

Figure 9. Morphosequences in the southern part of the Connecticut Valley of Massachusetts. Each box represents a morphosequence. Each horizontal row of morphosequences represents a chronomorph, and each vertical column represents sequential deposition by a particular meltwater drainage system from the ice sheet.

(w stands for Lake Westfield, e for east margin of sublobe), with the same approximate ages as $Ah_e$ and $Ah_w$.

Morphosequence $Bw_e$ consists of an ice-contact delta built into Lake Westfield while the margin of the western sublobe was located in the southwest corner of the Mt. Tom quadrangle. Unit $Bw_e$ includes delta foreset beds that rise to an elevation of 245 ft, or 35 ft above Lake Hitchcock at this latitude. This indicates that the Westfield gap was blocked to east-flowing drainage at the time $Bw_e$ was formed, and that meltwater deposits west of the basalt ridge were graded to Lake Westfield, the level of which was controlled by Harts Pond gap. No clearly defined morphosequences of the same age as $Bw_e$ are known east of the basalt ridge, although outwash deposits in the northeast part of the Springfield South quadrangle may be correlative.

Both the eastern and western sublobes retreated northward to positions on the north side of the Chicopee-readvance zone, then both lobes readvanced 3 to 4 km to the south side of that zone (Fig. 6). If any morphosequences had been formed in that zone, they were destroyed by the readvancing ice. We consider the Chicopee readvance to be an important time-stratigraphic event because it locates the ice margin on opposite sides of the Holyoke Basalt ridge at a given time.

Following readvance, the western sublobe was stationary 2.5 km south of the Easthampton quadrangle while the Barnes delta-outwash plain (discussed above under the heading Lake Westfield) was formed. The Barnes delta-outwash plain is designated morphosequence $Cw_e$ (Fig. 9) and was graded to Harts Pond gap while Westfield gap was still blocked. A small delta that was formed during the same time interval in the northwest part of the Mt. Tom quadrangle is designated morphosequence $Cw_w$.

Retreat of the western sublobe northward from the head of the Barnes delta-outwash plain occurred at the same time that the Westfield gap was opened to east-flowing drainage. Meltwater from

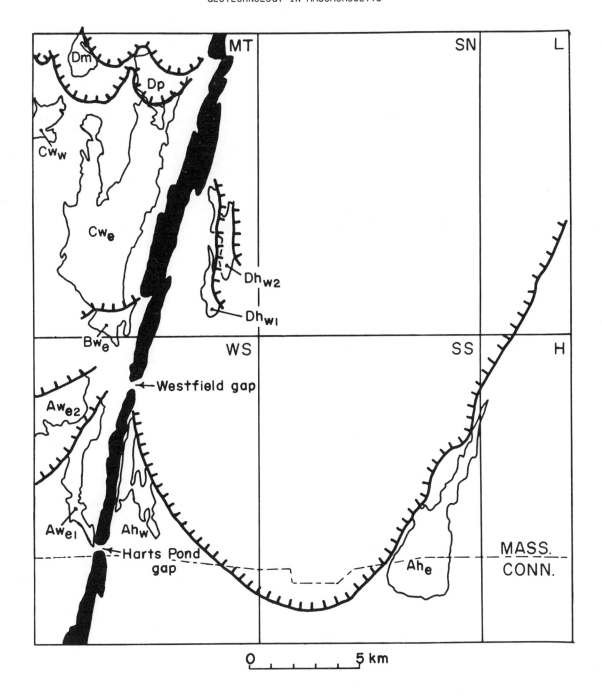

the western sublobe no longer flowed over the Barnes delta-outwash plain but instead flowed south through Lake Manhan and drained south over the Timberswamp spillway (Fig. 7b), a threshold of sand and gravel that was eroded down about 15 ft during its brief history. Meltwater moving south from the Timberswamp spillway cut terraces in both $Bw_e$ and $Cw_e$, and after joining with the Westfield River flowed east through Westfield gap onto the Agawam delta (Fig. 7b) then being built eastward into Lake Hitchcock.

During a stillstand 1.5 km north of the Barnes delta-outwash plain, morphosequences Dm and Dp were formed. Dm is a classic ice-contact delta built directly into Lake Manhan, and Dp is a delta formed in a temporary lake (glacial Lake Pomeroy) trapped behind a till ridge that extends north of Whiteloaf Mountain. At this time at least six separate morphosequences formed east of the basalt ridge in the southeast part of the Mt. Tom quadrangle; the last four are ice-contact deltas graded to Lake Hitchcock. These features are designated $Dh_{w1}$, $Dh_{w2}$, etc., to denote a possible correlation with Dm and Dp.

As stated above, we have omitted many details in our example of the morphosequence concept. Our example is incomplete at this time and is open-ended. Older morphosequences occur to the south in Connecticut, and younger morphosequences occur to the north. Through the use of ice-contact slopes and directional features such as striations and indicator fans it should be possible to extend chronomorphs both east and west from our field area. We hope the reader will compare our example with the surficial geologic map of Massachusetts when it is published.

## SUMMARY

A compilation of ice-directional features such as striations and indicator fans shows that the last movement of ice in the Connecticut Valley of Massachusetts was radial in two active sublobes of the Connecticut Valley lobe. The distribution of ice-contact slopes also indicates that the ice was lobate in plan view.

That the ice was active, as opposed to stagnant, is documented by the occurrence of readvance till overlying deformed stratified drift or lacustrine sediments, which in turn overlie till of the main ice advance. Readvance occurred on at least two occasions, first when the ice margin was in the vicinity of Chicopee and second when the ice margin was at the site of the Camp Meeting Cutting north of Northampton.

Glacial Lake Hitchcock grew northward through the field area with the retreating ice margin in late-glacial time. The approximate former shoreline of Lake Hitchcock rises to the north with a slope of 80 cm/km as based on transit measurements of the maximum elevation of foreset beds of deltas built directly into the lake. Two small temporary glacial lakes, Lake Westfield and Lake Manhan, formed west of the Holyoke Basalt ridge and drain-

ed eastward through the ridge into Lake Hitchcock east of the ridge. When the ice margin retreated north of the Holyoke Narrows, Lake Manhan dropped to the level of Lake Hitchcock, which extended northward and reached its maximum width, 19 km, just north of the Holyoke Range.

The morphosequence concept used in the mapping of stratified-drift deposits elsewhere in southern New England is useful and can be applied to the mapping of similar deposits in the Connecticut Valley of Massachusetts.

## REFERENCES

Alden, W.C., 1924, The physical features of central Massachusetts: U.S. Geological Survey Bulletin, 760-B, p. 13-105.

Ashley, G.M., 1972, Rhythmic sedimentation in glacial Lake Hitchcock, Massachusetts-Connecticut: University of Massachusetts, Amherst, Geology Publication 10, 148 p.

Ashwal, L.D., Leo, G.W., Robinson, P., Zartman, R.E., and Hall, D.V., 1979, The Belchertown Quartz Monzodiorite pluton, west-central Massachusetts: a syntectonic Acadian intrusion: American Journal of Science, v. 279, p. 936-969.

Colton, R.B., and Hartshorn, J.H., 1971, Surficial geology of the West Springfield quadrangle, Massachusetts-Connecticut: U.S. Geological Survey, Map GQ-892.

Cornet, B., Traverse, A., McDonald, N.G., 1973, Fossil spores, pollen, and fishes from Connecticut indicate early Jurassic age for part of the Newark Group: Science, v. 182, p. 1243-1247.

Currier, L.W., 1941, Disappearance of the last ice sheet in Massachusetts by stagnation zone retreat: Geological Society of America Bulletin, v. 52, p. 1895. Abstract.

Davis, W.M., 1890, Structure and origin of glacial sand plains: Geological Society of America Bulletin, v. 1, p. 195-202.

Emerson, B.K., 1898, Geology of Old Hampshire County, Massachusetts, comprising Franklin, Hampshire, and Hampden counties: U.S. Geological Survey, Monograph 29, 790 p.

Fenneman, N.M., 1938, Physiography of Eastern United States: McGraw-Hill, New York, 714 p.

Flint, R.F., 1957, Glacial and Pleistocene geology: New York, John Wiley, 553 p.

Flint, R.F., 1971, Glacial and Quaternary geology: New York, John Wiley, 892 p.

Goldthwait, J.W., 1905, The sandplains of glacial Lake Sudbury: Harvard College Museum of Comparative Zoology Bulletin, v. 42 (geology series 6), p. 263-301.

Gustavson, T.C., Ashley, G.M., and Boothroyd, J.B., 1975, Depositional sequences in glaciolacustrine deltas, in Glaciofluvial and glaciolacustrine sedimentation: Society of Economic Paleontologists and Mineralogists, Special Publication no. 23, p. 264-280.

Hartshorn, J.H., and Koteff, C., 1967a, Lake-level changes in southern glacial Lake Hitchcock, Connecticut-Massachusetts: Geological Society of America Program, Annual Meeting, Northeastern Section, p. 32. Abstract.

Hartshorn, J.H., and Koteff, C., 1967b, Geology of the Springfield South quadrangle, Massachusetts-Connecticut: U.S. Geological Survey, Map GQ-687.

Jahns, R.H., 1941, Outwash chronology in northeastern Massachusetts: Geological Society of America Bulletin, v. 52, p. 1910. Abstract.

Jahns, R.H., 1953, Surficial geology of the Ayer quadrangle, Massachusetts: U.S. Geological Survey, Map GQ-21.

Jahns, R.H., and Willard, M.E., 1942, Late Pleistocene and Recent deposits in the Connecticut Valley, Massachusetts: American Journal of Science, v. 240, p. 161-191, p. 265-287.

Koteff, C., 1974, The morphologic sequence concept and deglaciation of southern New England, in Coates, D.R., ed., Glacial geomorphology: Proceedings of 5th annual symposia series, Binghamton, N.Y., p. 121-144.

Koteff, C., and Pessl, F., Jr., 1980, Systematic ice retreat in New England: U.S. Geological Survey, Professional Paper 1179.

Larsen, F.D., 1972, Surficial geology of the Mt. Tom quadrangle, Massachusetts: U.S. Geological Survey, open file series, no. 1794, 273 p.

Larsen, F.D., 1980, Glacial history of the Northfield-Randolph area, Vermont: Vermont Geological Society guidebook, 7th annual fall field trip, Northfield, VT, 22 p.

Lougee, R.J., 1939, Geology of the Connecticut watershed: New Hampshire Fish and Game Department, Biological Survey of the Connecticut watershed, Survey Report 4, p. 131-149.

Schafer, J.P., and Hartshorn, J.H., 1965, The Quaternary of New England, in Wright, H.E., Jr., and Frey, D.G., eds., The Quaternary of the United States: a review volume for the VIIth Congress of the International Association for Quaternary Research, Princeton, N.J., Princeton Press, p. 113-128.

Schnabel, R.W., 1971, Surficial geology of the Southwick quadrangle, Massachusetts-Connecticut: U.S. Geological Survey, Map GQ-891.

Woodworth, J.B., 1898, Some glacial wash plains of southern New England: Essex Institute Bulletin, v. 29, p. 71-119.

Hors-texte

Connecticut River between Middletown
and Portland in Connecticut.

# 3

# HYDROGEOLOGY

Session moderators

J. H. Hartshorn
Department of Geology and Geography
University of Massachusetts at Amherst

D. T. Clark
Dunn Geoscience Corporation

# Engineering problems related to the development of groundwater supplies on Cape Cod, Massachusetts

S. L. DEAN
Whitman & Howard, Inc.

## ABSTRACT

The importance of ground water to Cape Cod cannot be overemphasized. All communities which have public water systems, with the exception of one, utilize groundwater sources exclusively. Similarly, shallow groundwater wells constitute the vast majority of the individual private water supplies. The maintenance of water table levels is also of prime importance to the very existence of the many ponds and streams as well as for the prevention of salt water encroachment beneath the cape.

## GEOLOGY OF CAPE COD

Cape Cod is composed of unconsolidated material derived from glacial activity. The last advances of ice over this portion of North America occurred some 11,000 years ago, when at its southernmost extension the Laurentide ice sheet formed the cape and the islands of Martha's Vineyard and Nantucket. Along what are now the northern shorelines of the islands and again along the northern and western shorelines of the cape can be found the terminal moraines which are the accumulations characteristic of temporarily stagnated ice sheets. Here, forming a rough and segmented topography, the ice has deposited a predominantly unsorted mixture of materials ranging from fine silts and clays to coarse sands, gravels and cobbles generally referred to as glacial till. However, to the south lie the broad, smooth outwash plains which are composed of silts, sands and gravels washed from the glacier itself or its terminal moraine by meltwater streams emanating from the ice front. Like most water-laid sediments these materials tend to be rather well sorted locally, though their uniformity can change dramatically as one moves either vertically or laterally.

Throughout both the terminal moraine and the outwash plain are many bowl-shaped depressions or kettleholes, which were formed when large blocks of ice broken from the glacier were covered by till or outwash material and subsequently melted, allowing the overlying material to collapse into the resultant hole. Many of these depressions extend below the water table. They have become ponds and small lakes which are usually an accurate indication of groundwater levels. At times, however, these ponds may be the result of underlying impermeable materials which locally perch the water table at an artificially high elevation.

Bed rock is quite deeply buried beneath the cape, as is evidenced by seismic surveys and a few deep wells which place it at about 100 feet below sea level near the Cape Cod Canal and as deep as 900 feet below sea level beneath Truro farther to the east (Fig. 1).

## NATURAL GROUNDWATER PROBLEMS

### Saltwater Intrusion

Because Cape Cod is a peninsula and is surrounded by salt water it is not surprising to find that it is also underlain in certain areas by salt water in the ground. Fresh water is supplied to the cape in the form of rain and snowfall. Precipitation that does not run off through the rivers and streams or is lost to evapotranspiration infiltrates through the ground and due to differing densities forms a lens of fresh water on top of the underlying salt water. Many studies have been performed and much has been written about fresh water/salt water interaction. It is generally accepted that in a static, homogeneous situation the differing densities would result in a lens of fresh water, extending to a depth of 40 feet below sea level for each foot above sea level to which the groundwater table rose (Fig. 2a).

Obviously, ground water is not static nor is the material through which it flows homogeneous. Therefore, the 1:40 ratio is not a hard-and-fast rule of nature. Instead, groundwater movement and the variation of materials lead to a zone of diffusion between the fresh and salt waters.

On the outer cape where the water table elevations are generally lower and the depth to bedrock is greater, the thickness of the fresh water lens is a factor that must be dealt with. Provincetown has had to develop water wells in Truro 10 miles to the south in order to locate them in a thicker portion of the fresh water lens. Farther back on the cape, where the water table levels are higher and the bed rock shallower, the probability of salt water encroachment is quite remote (Fig. 2b). Indeed, a well drilled to bed rock in Yarmouth indicated that water from a depth of 266 feet below sea level had a chloride content of only 18 ppm, in spite of the fact that the water table elevation was only 5 feet above mean sea level. The exception to this would, of course, be near the coastlines themselves, where the water table elevations are lower and the lens is thinner. Here wells drilled deeply or pumped heavily can readily become contaminated by salt water.

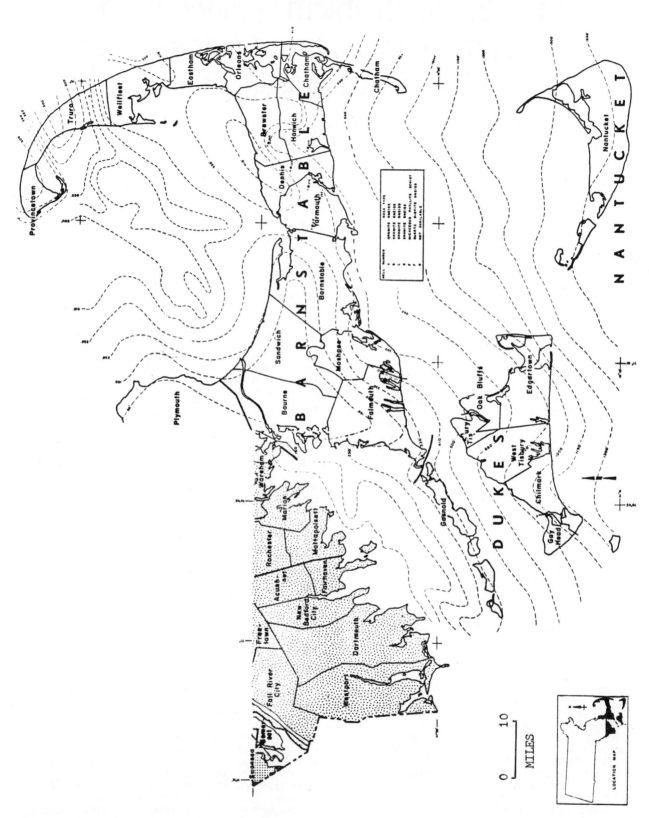

Figure 1. Bedrock topography of Cape Cod.

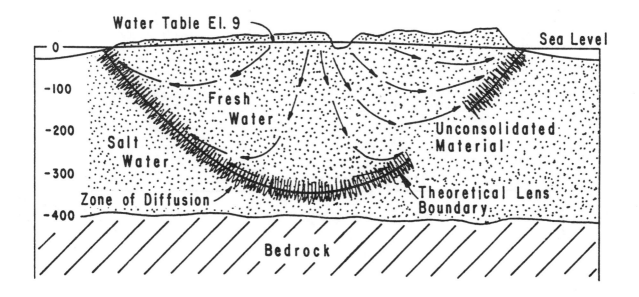

## 2a. OUTER CAPE

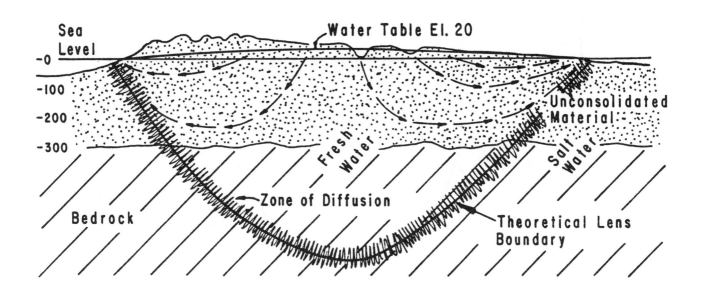

## 2b. INNER CAPE

Figure 2.  Fresh water - salt water
interaction beneath Cape Cod.

Tidal Fluctuation of Ground Water

The mere proximity of a well to the coastline and salt water does not necessarily render it a saline well. However, a different problem can arise which must be overcome when evaluating the water production capabilities of the site. The problem is groundwater levels which fluctuate with the tidal effect on nearby surface water bodies. Typical of this phenomenon is the continuous pump test drawdown curve for a well located approximately 700 feet from the Cape Cod Canal (Fig. 3). The drawdown curve clearly indicates a tidal effect on the water levels. However, at this particular site there is a sufficient hydrologic gradient in the fresh ground water leading past the well site and on toward the canal that the well continues to produce water with acceptable salinity levels.

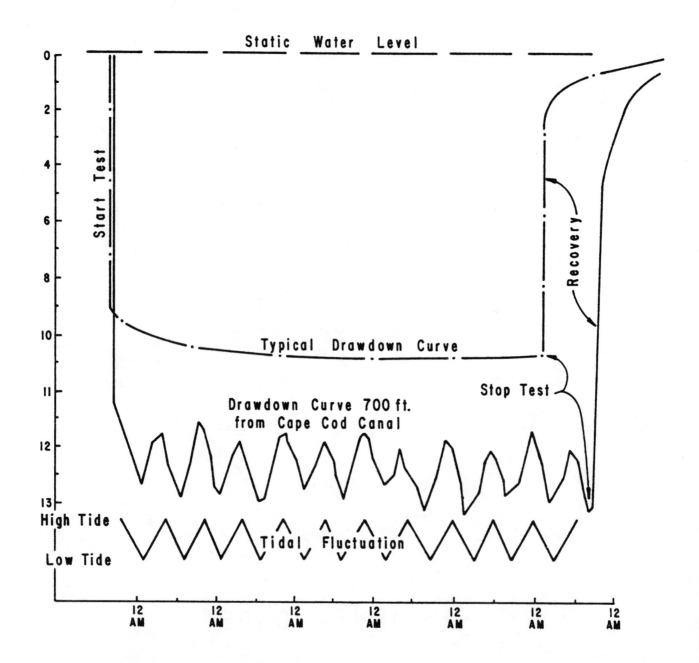

Figure 3. Tidal effect on drawdown curve.

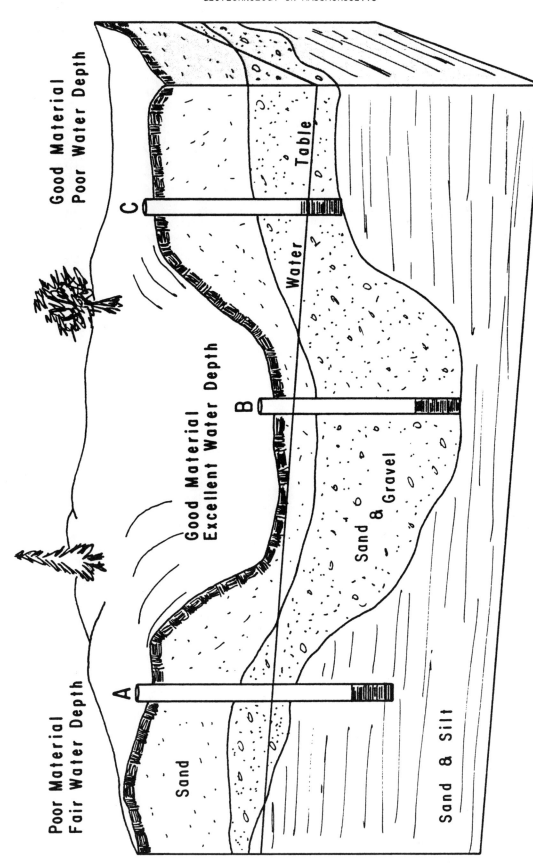

Figure 4. Test well exploration near kettleholes.

## The Influence of Kettleholes

As previously mentioned, the Cape Cod landscape includes numerous kettleholes. They represent an area originally filled with an ice block which acted as an obstruction, causing the rushing melt waters to slow their pace and drop some of their sediment load, mainly the coarser materials. Later, after the ice had melted, the depression collected additional sediments, sometimes coarse sands and gravels, and at other times silts, clays and organic material. Their unique mode of origin, permeable strata, and layered composition make many kettleholes suitable areas for water well development. Nonetheless, kettleholes pose some significant problems to water development. When filled with water, the resultant ponds usually provide an indication of groundwater levels. When attempting to tap nearby permeable sand and gravels, careful attention to the results of continuous pumping tests is necessary to ensure that the design yield of the well will not dewater such a pond.

The bottoms of dry kettleholes have long been favored locations for well exploration for a number of reasons. In addition to the increased potential for finding favorable material, just being down in these depressions puts the driller that much closer to the water table. Small diameter exploration wells can be readily test pumped with simple portable suction pumps. A similar well out of the hole and starting 30 to 40 feet higher in elevation would require a suction lift that would rule out such standard methods. The reduced well depths from inside the kettleholes also significantly reduce exploration costs as well as those for construction of the final gravel-packed wells.

It has also been found that in many cases the more permeable sediment layers will be thicker or at least have greater depth beneath the depressions as in Figure 4. The resultant greater depths at which the well screen can be set often substantially increase the depth of available water that can be utilized, thereby increasing the safe yield of the well.

Unfortunately, the depressions also act as natural collecting bowls for organic deposits. In some instances thick deposits of peat are encountered which affect the pump station footings or give rise to iron and manganese rich waters that would require treatment if developed. In other instances bacteria seem to collect at the base of the kettleholes as a result of precipitation filtering through the decaying vegetation on the side slopes of the depression. This bacteria problem has prompted the Commonwealth of Massachusetts to urge municipalities either to move the wells up the side slopes or fill in the kettleholes and extend the well casings up to the new ground elevation.

## Natural Water Quality

The most frequently encountered natural water quality problem on the cape is that of high iron and manganese concentrations. This problem is generally linked to waters being drawn from or through surface swamps, buried peat deposits or the gray unoxidized sands that usually underlie the near surface materials. The latter are brown in color as a result of iron oxidation. Occasionally a well encounters water that is rich in sulfides. However, this problem is not nearly as widespread as is that of iron and manganese.

In some instances these quality problems can be significantly reduced by prolonged pumping. Unfortunately, more often the reverse is true. Prolonged pumping draws waters into the well from areas farther away than normal, eventually tapping deposits having waters with high iron, manganese and sulfide concentrations.

Another natural characteristic of ground water on Cape Cod is that many areas exhibit relatively low pH values and as such are corrosive to various metals. This results in shorter life expectancies and higher maintenance costs for items such as well screens, pump bowls and columns.

## PROBLEMS GENERATED BY MAN

### Storage and Application of Road Salts

The problem of wintertime salting of highways and storage of the salt before application has plagued the cape as it has most other communities in the Commonwealth. The water supply wells located near the mid-cape highway are especially vulnerable to increased sodium and chloride levels due to the large quantity of salt used to keep this critical artery open to traffic.

Large sheds now cover most salt storage piles on the cape. However, before this safety measure was implemented, rain and snow melt leached salt from these piles into the underlying ground water. In 1972 a public water supply well located approximately 700 feet from a salt storage area in Yarmouth exhibited a dramatic increase in both chloride and sodium. Subsequently, the well was shut down and a shed was constructed to cover the salt pile. The well is still unusable.

### Cranberry Bogs

Though not as abundant on Cape Cod as in other areas of southeastern Massachusetts, cranberry bogs do exist, and when an adjacent area is being considered as a potential site for a large volume water supply well certain factors need to be taken into consideration. Of primary importance are the questions of dewatering the bog and the potential for pesticide or fertilizer contamination of the water supply. Aquifer evaluations based on prolonged pump tests must be designed to delineate the extent, if any, to which the water at the bog is hydrologically connected to the well.

## Landfill and Waste Disposal

Certainly one of the prime concerns shared by all water supply related professionals today is that of waste disposal and the subsequent effect on groundwater quality. Cape Cod is no exception to the rule. With the high permeabilities found in some sands and gravels of the cape, even the one-half mile zone of protection, mandated by the Commonwealth, between public water supply wells and landfills may not be sufficient. Existing landfills and waste disposal areas are known to have well-established contaminant plumes which may one day force the abandonment of nearby wells. In addition, the problem of delineating new waste disposal sites is a complex issue with many physical, financial, political and emotional factors.

Presently, only three communities on the cape are served by centralized sewage collection, and only two of these have sewage treatment facilities. The remainder of the homes, industries, businesses, and institutions presently utilize onsite waste disposal facilities. This situation presents very real contamination problems, particularly where onsite septic facilities and private water wells must both be located on lots that are often undersized due to poorly planned zoning codes or grandfather clause variances. Decentralization of waste disposal also inhibits the ability of towns to realistically enforce aquifer protection regulations once they become adopted.

## Lack of Aquifer Protection

Presently, little is being done on the local level to get involved with the process of protecting aquifers and the quality of the waters that they yield. The Commonwealth itself is just awakening to the fact that aquifer protection means more than the 400-ft radius of ownership now required around most public water supply wells. Such limited areas provide a reasonable degree of safety when the suspected contaminant is organic bacteria derived from household sewage. However, in the case of sewage contamination from road salting, leakage from buried petroleum tanks or dumping of synthetic organic contaminants, the potential travel distances and active lives of the pollutants are much greater.

The rapidly expanding pressures of both residential and commercial development on Cape Cod,

when coupled with inadequate waste treatment facilities and a lack of ordinances designed to protect groundwater quality, can only further limit the availability of potential water supply sites. To a large degree the engineers, geologists, and hydrologists have been at fault for failing to communicate to the public at large and to their elected representatives on the local, state, and federal levels. The average citizen of Cape Cod, the remainder of Massachusetts, and the country in general cannot be expected to intuitively understand the problem. He must be educated by those who do. Planning board members and town selectmen must be shown the rationale and need for protective regulations for known aquifers, as well as the wisdom of identifying and preserving others presently unknown.

There are many natural factors that severely limit the number of sites capable of yielding high quality water in quantities sufficient for public use. We need not further restrict these potential supply areas with ill-planned development or lack of legislative protection. We as professionals in the water supply field must do all that we can to insure the continued management of our groundwater resources not only on Cape Cod, but throughout the country.

REFERENCES (not cited)

Fessenden, F.W., Ayres, J.E., Dean, S. L., 1975, A summary of the geology of eastern Massachusetts: U.S. Army Corps of Engineers, Planning Document.

Dean, S.L., 1974; Water resource investigation for Madaket, Nantucket Island, Massachusetts: M.S. Thesis, University of Vermont, 81 p.

Oldale, R.N., Seismic investigations on Cape Cod, Martha's Vineyard, and Nantucket, Massachusetts, and a topographic map of the basement surface from Cape Cod Bay to the Islands: U.S. Geological Survey Professional Paper 650-B, B122-127.

Strahler, A.N., 1972, The environmental impact of ground water use on Cape Cod: Association for the Preservation of Cape Cod, Inc., 68 p.

Whitman & Howard, Inc., Numerous reports on projects located on Cape Cod.

Hors-texte

Pratt & Whitney Aircraft plant on the bank of the Connecticut
River at Middletown, Connecticut, formerly the Connecticut
Advanced Nuclear Engineering Laboratory (CANEL).

# Hydrogeology of the Lawrence Swamp aquifer system, Amherst, Massachusetts

W. S. MOTTS
Department of Geology and Geography
University of Massachusetts at Amherst

ABSTRACT

The Lawrence Swamp, located near Amherst, is one of the more distinctive wetlands of western Massachusetts because of its size, diversity of flora and fauna, and environmental and aesthetic value. The swamp belongs to the lakebed category of wetlands characterized by surficial sand and gravel containing an unconfined shallow aquifer, a confining bed of silt or clay deposited in a Pleistocene lake, and a lower sand and gravel zone containing an artesian aquifer. At several localities in the swamp, the transmissivity of the productive lower artesian aquifer ranges from 25,000 to 35,000 gpd/ft, and the aquifer supplies Amherst at present with an average of 1.4 mgd. Plans have been made to increase the production, in steps, to a maximum of 3 mgd, depending upon the results of further monitoring.

Negligible amounts of water move through the thick clay confining bed from the artesian aquifer to the shallow aquifer near the center of the swamp. However, larger quantities of water move between the aquifers along the margin of the swamp where the clay is thin or missing. In places along the swamp margin the shallow aquifer recharges the artesian aquifer. The shallow and artesian aquifers are hydrologically connected to the primary recharge area, which is underlain by sand and gravel of kame terrace and kame delta origin. The secondary recharge area, underlain by till and bed rock, generally surrounds the primary area and extends to the topographic and groundwater divide of the Lawrence Swamp basin. Long-term stresses on the Lawrence Swamp aquifer system and swamp ecology are (1) natural climatic variations such as summer low flow and drought conditions, (2) pumping of the artesian aquifer, and (3) increased building and development on the recharge area. Water management plans should include ways of protecting the recharge areas from excessive development and ways of increasing the artesian aquifer yield by artificial recharge and salvage of excessive water lost by evapotranspiration.

Abstract of - Motts, W.S., 1981, The Lawrence Swamp and Lawrence Swamp aquifer system, Amherst, Massachusetts, in Motts, W.S., and O'Brien, A.L., Geology and hydrology of wetlands in Massachusetts: Water Resources Research Center, University of Massachusetts, Amherst, Massachusetts, Publication 123, Chapter 6, p. 72-110. Part of the location map is reproduced on the next page.

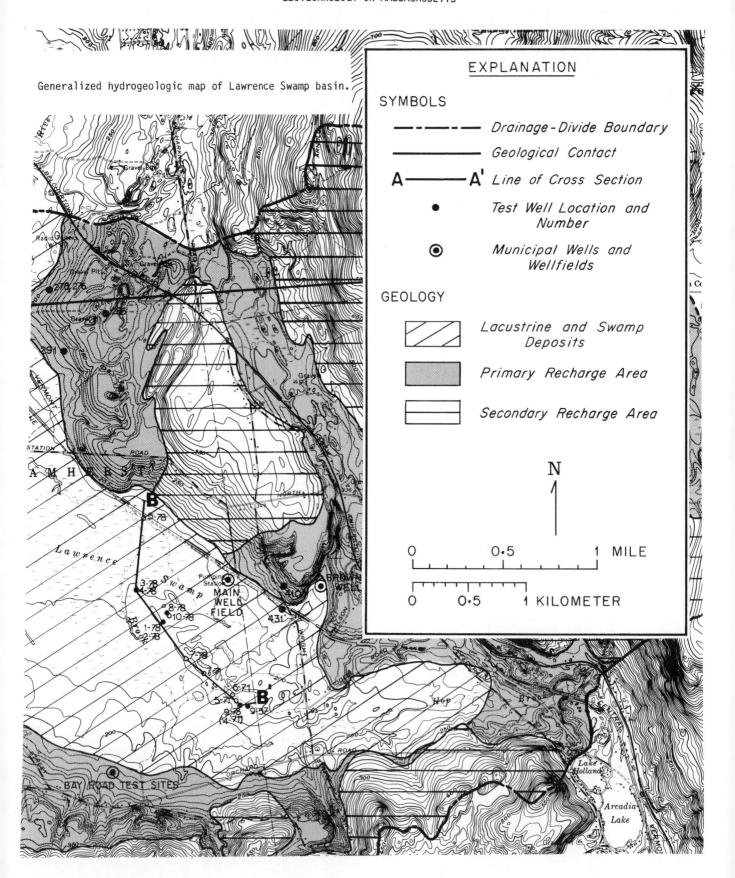

Generalized hydrogeologic map of Lawrence Swamp basin.

EXPLANATION

SYMBOLS

— · — · — · — · —  Drainage-Divide Boundary

————————  Geological Contact

A————A'  Line of Cross Section

•  Test Well Location and Number

⊙  Municipal Wells and Wellfields

GEOLOGY

Lacustrine and Swamp Deposits

Primary Recharge Area

Secondary Recharge Area

N

0          0.5          1  MILE

0          0.5          1  KILOMETER

# Groundwater protection–
# Legal mechanisms, institutions,
# attitudes, and the geologist

## J. J. BALCO
## U.S. Water Resources Council

ABSTRACT

There is growing recognition of the need to
"do something" about protection of groundwater
quality. The development of a comprehensive system of groundwater protection which is thoughtful,
creative, and both technically and administratively sound will be difficult. In order for the
geologist to provide the necessary technical guidance in developing such a system, an overview of
the legal mechanisms available is needed, as well
as knowledge of the institutions and attitudes
which will influence their application.

Although there is a general lack of a comprehensive protection policy or strategy, there
are several legal mechanisms available that can
be packaged to protect groundwater quality. These
mechanisms and examples of their application are
reviewed. Their use in groundwater protection,
particularly in the Northeast, is a recent phenomenon, and their effectiveness has not been fully
evaluated.

"Pluralism, fragmentation, uncertainty, and
indifference are the fundamental starting points"
(Brooks, 1979) in describing the institutional
setting. There is a need to develop a conceptual
framework for protection strategies which is not
technically elegant but presents a timely response
to problems in a way that deals with uncertainty.
If groundwater protection strategies are to be
based on knowledge rather than on emotion or tradition, the geologist must take the initiative to
become involved in the decision-making process
early enough to make a difference.

INTRODUCTION

The hydrologic basis for protecting groundwater systems has developed rapidly. Some states
have developed legal and institutional mechanisms
for groundwater management programs. On a national scale these programs have been oriented toward
groundwater quality with little emphasis on the
protection of groundwater quality (Spencer, 1979).
In the humid Northeast, however, there has been
little action to protect groundwater quality or
quantity. The institutional response has been
slow.

Despite constraints, the reluctance to take
action to protect groundwater quality is changing.
In 1978-79 groundwater supply sources for 26 communities in Massachusetts were temporarily closed
because of contamination (Special Legislative Com-

mission, 1979). Over 250,000 people were directly
affected at a cost yet to be determined. Increased public understanding of the need to secure
a safe and reliable water supply has resulted in
pressure to take action, particularly with respect
to hazardous wastes.

There is a variety of federal, state, and
local legal mechanisms which can be used to protect groundwater quality. While many of these
mechanisms were not designed specifically for
such purposes, they can be used or packaged to
achieve groundwater quality protection goals.
Legal mechanisms available to protect groundwater
quantity in the Northeast are very limited.

The application of available techniques has
been sporadic, generally in response to immediate
problems. The constraints of local autonomy, the
magical image of groundwater, lack of knowledge
of groundwater systems by program managers, difficulty in dealing with uncertainty, and limited
planning horizons must be regarded as influential
factors in decision-making.

LEGAL MECHANISMS - FEDERAL INVOLVEMENT

The federal government has a long history of
supporting basic research, data gathering, and
assessment of groundwater resources. With an
equally long history of primacy in water allocation decisions by state governments, there has
been no strong federal role in developing institutional or legal arrangements to maintain groundwater quality or quantity. However, in recent
years the federal government has become involved
in the protection of groundwater quality in
indirect ways.

- The Resources Conservation and Recovery
  Act (RCRA) of 1976 seeks to encourage recycling and recovery and to reduce contamination of water due to leachate from
  dumps and landfills.

- The Toxic Substances Control Act (TOSCA)
  of 1976 regulates the testing, manufac-
  ture, and distribution of toxic chemicals.
  Implementation of this statute has been
  slow.

- The Safe Drinking Water Act (SDWA) was
  enacted in 1973. This statute attempts
  to control contaminants in public drinking water supplies and is of immediate

interest when considering Federal potential for groundwater protection. Program emphasis has been on establishing drinking water standards and maintaining water quality "at the tap."

The SDWA provides for designation of "sole source aquifers" and the regulation of underground injection. While EPA has published proposed regulations on underground injection, the sole source aquifer feature is of immediate regional interest.

If an area is designated as a sole source aquifer, federal actions must be reviewed to insure the maintenance of groundwater quality. To be designated a sole source aquifer requires that more than 50 percent of an area's water supply must come from the aquifer, contamination of the aquifer would result in a significant hazard to public health, an alternative acceptable water supply is not available, and the aquifer must be multi-county (Federal Register, 1977). There have been four areas designated as sole source aquifers: the Edwards Plateau (Texas), Rathdrum Valley (Washington), Nassau and Suffolk County (New York), and the northern island of Guam (Environmental Protection Agency, 1979).

In Massachusetts, the Old Colony Regional Planning Council has recommended the designation of the "Pembroke - Hanson Aquifer" as a sole source aquifer (Old Colony Planning Council, 1978). While there is interest in the possibility of designating Cape Cod as a sole source aquifer area, there has been reluctance to consider valley aquifers of the Northeast for such designation. This may be due to a lack of recognition of the importance of such groundwater supplies to the region or an avoidance of increased burdens of administering multiple, relatively small-scale, dispersed areas.

## ASSESSMENT OF FUTURE FEDERAL ACTIONS

While increased federal involvement can be predicted in responding to contamination of water supplies resulting from improper disposal of hazardous wastes, it is unlikely that a truly comprehensive groundwater protection strategy will be developed. State water laws, fragmentation of responsibilities, emphasis on establishing groundwater quality standards, and limited authority will constrain action. In addition, President Carter's water policy reform efforts repeatedly assured the states that they, not the federal government, have primary responsibility for water management.

## LEGAL MECHANISMS - STATE INVOLVEMENT

The eastern states follow the common law rule (or modifications thereof) which provides for absolute ownership of ground water by overlying landowners. The legal technicalities are adequately described in available literature. Of particular interest is a publication entitled "Ground water and groundwater law in Massachusetts" published

by the Massachusetts Water Resources Commission (1978).

Recent cases of groundwater contamination have resulted in legal action to seek relief from alleged polluters. The outcome of these actions may result in changes in case law or specific legislation which will establish a new legal framework. Given the vagaries of such actions, it would not be profitable to speculate on future scenarios.

While state programs do not have specific groundwater protection goals per se, the states have wide-ranging programs to address public health aspects of water supply, including ground water. Emphasis has tended to be on the quality of particular sources and the steps needed to limit the risk of deterioration of those sources. Few states have established control measures designed to protect groundwater quality. Pennsylvania is an exception. It has established a groundwater protection and pollution detection program (Spencer, 1979). The program was authorized under water pollution control legislation, as opposed to water supply legislation. It is one of the few water pollution control programs which recognizes ground water as an area of concern or approaches groundwater pollution issues from a perspective other than the traditional surface water pollution control approach. One of the most notable features of the program is a staff of hydrogeologists. While involving hydrogeologists in groundwater protection programs would appear to be obvious, this is not always the case, nor may it be administratively possible.

New York and Maryland have promulgated groundwater quality standards using an approach similar to that of surface water pollution control programs (Spencer, 1979). Connecticut has also proposed to establish groundwater quality standards under the authority of state and federal water pollution control statutes (State of Connecticut, undated).

The strongest role played by state government in groundwater protection is in insuring the quality of drinking water. In Massachusetts, the state approves sources of supply, establishes maximum allowable contamination levels, establishes analytical methods for testing, certifies treatment works operators, and establishes standards for the protection of supplies. Despite these broad responsibilities, the orientation of state programs has been the approval of specific supplies and does not have the objective of aquifer protection.

There is a wide variety of control mechanisms that relate to pollution sources, rather than the resource itself. These include: installation of septic tanks (111 M.G.L.A. 31D), landfills (16 M.G.L.A. 18-21), oil spills (21 M.G.L.A. 59A), salt storage (85 M.G.L.A. 57-58) and pesticide use (132B M.G.L.A. 6). The Water Pollution Control Act (21 M.G.L.A. 26 et seq.) contains language that could be interpreted as allowing strong state control and leadership in groundwater protection.

## ASSESSMENT OF FUTURE STATE ACTIONS

It is unlikely that there will be strong leadership from the state level for aquifer protection programs. Some of the limitations to action are: financial constraints, and administrative concerns (hiring and maintaining a staff of hydrogeologists), the reluctance to change from traditional program approaches, prevailing anti-regulatory mood and intergovernmental conflicts. The latter is significant and may be the greatest barrier to a state or regional groundwater protection program. An illustration is in the response to the problems of hazardous waste disposal. It is widely recognized that the management of hazardous waste is a public problem of major significance--of much greater short-term significance than the related problem of groundwater protection. Yet, there is strong resistance to any state program without local approval. It is difficult to foresee the circumstances under which a local community may grant such approval. Thus, it is even more unlikely that local government will agree to state controls over a problem area of less immediate severity.

## LEGAL MECHANISMS - LOCAL INVOLVEMENT

Although the orientation of New England government toward strong local control makes it difficult to formulate regional groundwater quality protection programs, the structure does allow for opportunities for action. Perhaps because of this flexibility, local approaches to groundwater protection, although few, are more wide-ranging, directive and comprehensive than those at the federal or state levels of government.

### Application of Zoning

The zoning approach generally establishes land-use restrictions, but in some cases may be prohibitive. Restrictions can limit land to certain uses or can provide for a case-by-case review of land-use alternatives. Zoning options implemented by local communities are wide-ranging.

A central issue in zoning is the application of zoning powers and the taking of land. This issue can be emotion-packed and can often frustrate attempts to devise protection strategies. It is of no little significance that a Federal Court recently upheld a Long Island, New York, community zoning by-law which restricted housing density to protect groundwater quality (EDF Letter, 1980). While the issue has not been tested in Massachusetts, the legal status of floodplain zoning is a strong analogy whereby local communities can establish substantial land use restrictions.

Some examples of zoning in Massachusetts include the following.

- Lincoln has established a "Watershed and Wetland Protection District." One of the purposes of the by-law is to protect against contamination of the water supply. The District is a so-called overly district. Activities allowed by the basic zoning ordinances are by special permit. A permit can be granted only after an evaluation of the specific activity is performed and it is determined that the proposed activity is not significant to the broadly defined protection purposes of the by-law.

- Amherst officials proposed an aquifer protection by-law, which did not succeed at a town meeting. The proposal is the most comprehensive and specific in defining prohibitions and design criteria. It was put forward in the context of an overall protection strategy and would regulate fuel storage, earth removal, runoff and recharge.

- Falmouth has established a watershed protection district which prohibits certain land uses that could pollute water supplies. These uses include: sanitary landfills, junk yards, bulk storage of chemicals, pesticides, herbicides and fertilizers, coin-operated laundries, major transportation terminals, subsurface oil and gasoline storage in non-fiberglass containers, and uses which produce potentially hazardous wastes.

### Local Administration of State Statutes

State statutes may give local communities special powers to establish standards for activities which may impact upon groundwater quality. These mechanisms can be used with no new authorizing legislation. Examples are sanitary codes, protection zones around wells, gasoline storage, and wetlands protection.

- Sanitary Codes - Local health departments are responsible for administering State statutes and regulations on the siting and operation of septic systems. They can impose stricter standards than those contained in state regulations. This is probably the most powerful tool available, although there are pressures to eliminate the ability of local health boards to establish stricter standards than the state itself. Some examples are:

  - Tisbury has identified special areas of concern for wells and disposal systems. Higher engineering standards are required within these zones to prevent pollution and salt water contamination. Among the requirements are a minimum separation distance of 200 feet between a well and salt water body and/or a sanitary disposal facility, 5 to 7 feet separation between the lowest portion of the disposal field and seasonal high water table, and optional provisions for annual inspection and monitoring.

- The Cape Cod Planning and Economic Development Commission (1978) has suggested several model ordinances for local health boards.

- The Martha's Vineyard Planning Commission (1977) has suggested an alternative method of calculating disposal areas and lot size requirements based on soils, system loading, infiltration rates, evapotranspiration, and flows.

- Protection Zones Around Wells - The Department of Environmental Protection Engineering regulates the conditions of water supply development to insure the maintenance of drinking water quality. A minimum protection zone of 400 feet around tubular wells with diameters 2 1/2 inches or less is required. Regulations provide that "The Department may order greater distances or permit lesser distance as deemed sufficient to protect public health" (Department of Environmental Quality Engineering, 1977). While there has been reluctance to allow expansion of protective zones, communities can do so if justified on a hydrologic basis.

  - Based on hydrologic studies, the Town of Peperell enacted a local by-law which restricts activities within 1,400 feet of a particular well.

  - The Martha's Vineyard Planning Commission has suggested a methodology for determining distances between waste disposal sites and individual wells.

- Gasoline Storage - The storage of gasoline in large quantities is under the control of the local Board of Selectmen in most Massachusetts towns. Decision-making in most communities centers around fire safety. However, some communities have used the authority to establish standards or limit storage of gasoline. Raynham has enacted a by-law which establishes engineering design standards for the storage of fuel within one-half mile of a public water supply.

- Wetlands Protection - Local conservation commissions grant permits for alteration of wetlands to insure the protection of certain interests under the Massachusetts Wetlands Protection Act. Standards can be established to control wetlands development as it may relate to groundwater protection. The Town of Chelmsford has established such standards (Chelmsford Conservation Commission, 1978). Modifica-

tions to wetlands overlying saturated sand and gravel deposits of 20 feet or more must meet these standards. Examples are: fuel oil storage in excess of 500 gallons to be in non-corrosive tanks; density limits for on-site septic disposal; limits on the application of salt on roads; pipelines carrying materials that could cause pollution to meet certain specifications; excavation limits to maintain specified distances between the surface and water table; and groundwater monitoring program requirements. Some activities are prohibited, such as: fuel storage in excess of 10,000 gallons; activities which produce hazardous wastes; land fills and junk yards; bulk storage of chemicals, pesticides, herbicides and fertilizers; salt storage; and car washes and laundromats.

## ASSESSMENT OF FUTURE LOCAL ACTIONS

On balance, local implementation of groundwater protection programs is the best short-term alternative. There is a variety of mechanisms available, and the institutional constraints are fewer than those at other levels of government. More sophisticated and future-oriented communities will recognize the risks associated with groundwater pollution and will take action. Communities with short-term perspectives and those reluctant to act without extensive legal or technical backup, or those simply having other priorities, will wait until a major problem arises. It is unlikely that local communities will take steps to protect groundwater quality on a large scale basis without external leadership.

## DEVELOPING GROUNDWATER PROTECTION STRATEGIES - INSTITUTIONS AND ATTITUDES

To develop a groundwater protection strategy, the constraints on the application of various techniques must be understood. The constraints are formative. In a recent presentation, Richard O. Brooks, Director of the Environmental Center of the Vermont Law School, suggested that "pluralism, fragmentation, uncertainty and indifference are the fundamental starting points that we should begin with in examining the problems of ground water" (Brooks, 1979). The constraints must be understood, if not accepted, if the geologist is to contribute to the development of groundwater protection strategies. These constraints suggest that there is a need for a conceptual framework for developing protection strategies, that action does take place in a crisis atmosphere, and that programs will be locally oriented.

There are several institutional characteristics and attitudes that must be considered.

- Water, Water Everywhere - The Northeast is water-rich. The water supply industry has provided a safe, reliable and inexpensive source of water. It is difficult for people to accept the possibility of a water crisis. A recent article entitled "The water crisis is almost here" suggested that water will surpass energy as a national concern before the end of the century (Congressional Record, 1979). Yet there is little effort to address the problem now.

- Out-of-Sight, Out-of-Mind - Closely aligned with the abundance syndrome is the difficulty in visualizing ground water and groundwater movement. Relying on charts and graphics may be helpful, but it is still difficult to understand. Difficulty in visualizing the problem unique to groundwater systems will result in postponed action. By analogy, there are many urban water supply systems that are suffering from years of postponed maintenance. Investment is made in the visible structures, but not in underground distribution systems. If communities place a low priority on water distribution systems that are deteriorating, how can they be expected to place a high priority on ground water?

- "If it isn't broken, don't fix it" - There is an institutional bias toward solutions to problems as they arise - the quick-fix syndrome. While the technical and financial obstacles to overcoming a problem may be formidable, experience suggests that a short term solution will always be available. There is thus little payoff for long-term problem identification and solutions. However, things become topsy-turvy with ground water. When a groundwater system is contaminated, it is virtually lost. It is difficult for decision-makers to understand that, when a problem (such as contamination) is detected, it may already be too late to do anything about it!

- It's Unconstitutional - There is a long tradition in the Northeastern states of the common law rule of absolute ownership. Laws have not caught up with science. Attitudes develop which prevent rational discussion of alternatives. Some view any discussion of groundwater protection techniques as an invasion of rights. There is reluctance to consider the possibility of changing the law! Failure to recognize the option of a modified legal framework focuses on today's constraints and shifts attention from solutions to problems.

- Money Talks - The emphasis of water pollution control systems has been on surface water pollution. In large measure this is because federal programs supply large sums for such purposes. Without placing a value judgment on this allocation of money, agencies have responded to sources of federal monies. The concern, however, is not that there have been limited re-

sources devoted to groundwater protection. There are subtle implications in developing such systems. The agencies most likely to be given groundwater protection responsibilities are those responsible for surface water programs. There is a risk that the same approaches to surface water pollution will be taken with ground water because of the training and experience of program administrators. Lack of technical expertise in ground water may result in the adoption of strategies that may be inappropriate to achieve groundwater protection strategies (e.g., groundwater quality standards).

- Groundwater Black Magic and Dealing with Uncertainty - The technical basis for groundwater protection may be presented as too technical, and there may be too much emphasis on uncertainty. There are few who question flood elevation projections to the one-foot contour. However, the calculations of flood heights include many assumptions and untested standards. Flood elevations are best estimates. The basis for defining areas for groundwater protection is also based on many assumptions, yet it is presented as much less certain.

    Decision-makers differ in their attitudes in dealing with uncertainty. These attitudes must be appreciated in developing groundwater protection strategies. While not suggesting that uncertainty be ignored, too much emphasis on what is not known may be counterproductive and may not produce the level of confidence needed for making decisions that have serious land use and economic impacts. The hydrologic basis for devising protection schemes must be more clearly articulated and placed on a par with surface-water hydrology in the eyes of the decision-maker if protection programs are to be accepted.

- "The Pursuit of the Ideal is the Enemy of the Better" - When decisions are needed they are needed now! Lack of data may be viewed as being unresponsive to the problem at hand. More research, more time, more money are responses that are not acceptable. This is not to suggest that decisions be made with no data. However, the propensity for the scientist to need more data to refine conclusions presents roadblocks to effective communication. There must be recognition of a range of accuracy and uncertainty in any decision. We should be able to answer the question - "If the additional information were available, how much different would the decision be?"

- Turf - Most government organizations have mission responsibilities that are based on statutes aimed at particular problems.

Agencies tend to be program-oriented, not resource-oriented. While people have accepted a relationship between ground water and surface water quantity and quality, and the need to manage the resource in total, it is unlikely that a single agency has the authority to move forward with an aggressive groundwater management program. It is further unlikely that this responsibility will be given to a single agency. Local action thus may be the only option.

- Not in My Backyard - Strong tradition in New England stresses local control and encourages resistance to any solution that involves more than one community. A protection system that attempts to apply standards on a regional scale, such as aquifers, may be technically pure, but will provoke negative reactions. Unless there is sufficient understanding and support built at the local level, regional actions are unlikely.

- Public Participation vs. Public Relations - There is a tendency to confuse "public participation" with "public relations." By the time a proposed action is ready for review, there may have been considerable thought given to the issues by a few individuals. Approaches to a problem and assumptions may have been defined, albeit implicitly. There is a risk that a review by others, even hydrogeologists, which challenges those implicit assumptions will be ignored.

## THE INFLUENCE OF THE GEOLOGIST

In order for informed decisions to be made on groundwater protection strategies, both related to groundwater quality and quantity, the hydrogeologist must become more closely involved in decision-making. In order to make the connection between the technical professional and decision-makers, the lead must be taken by the technical professional. Here are some suggestions:

- There is a Chinese proverb - "The art of leadership can be described in two sentences: In crisis act with calm. In times of calm, think ahead of a crisis." The technical community, buffered from the pressures of today's crisis, is uniquely qualified to "act with calm." Since any action will probably be taken in time of crisis, now is the time to think out the characteristics of a groundwater management system and develop the needed conceptual framework. The system must be comprehensive, but be able to be implemented incrementally. It must be conceptually sound, but technical elegance should be avoided.

- The hydrogeologist must ask to participate in the decision-making process. There is a high risk that professionals outside the established system will not be asked to participate until it is too late. Now is not soon enough to begin working with officials. By achieving visibility, credibility, and a responsive image the professional will be asked to participate when the crisis occurs. Now may be the time to seriously discuss the establishment of a state professional organization of geologists to begin this networking effort.

- Roll with the punches. There are constraints which must be recognized - not too early in the process yet demanding action. It may not be the perfect solution - but it may be the only solution. Understand fully what can, and cannot, be compromised.

- See things through the other person's eyes. Ground water is only one of the many problems a decision-maker has to face. Most do not have a technical background. It is the responsibility of the scientist to translate the science into terms the decision-maker can understand. If the scientist is unwilling to perform this role, then he shouldn't complain that he is not part of the process.

There are problems crying for solutions. If the scientific community applies leadership and understanding, in addition to professional competence, we will be far along the road to solutions.

## REFERENCES

Brooks, R.O., 1979, Legal and institutional tools needed to protect, develop and use groundwater resources: New England River Basins Commission Report, v. 7, issue 4, November.

Cape Cod Planning and Economic Development Commission, 1978, Water quality plan - environmental impact statement for Cape Cod: March.

Chelmsford Conservation Commission, 1978, Operating procedures of the Wetlands Protection Act, Chapter 131, Section 40, as amended: September.

Congressional Record, 1979, The water crisis is almost here: Forbes Magazine, p. S116651-116653, November 14.

Department of Environmental Quality Engineering, 1977, Drinking water regulations of Massachusetts: June 23.

EDF Letter, 1980, Rezoning to protect aquifers upheld by Federal Court: Environmental Defense Fund, New York, New York, January/February.

Environmental Protection Agency, 1979, Water supply - wastewater treatment coordination study - report to Congress: public comment and review draft, Contract No. 68-01-5033, 352 p.

Federal Register, 1977, 40 CFR 148: v. 42, no. 189, September 29.

Martha's Vineyard Planning Commission, 1977, Water quality management plan for Martha's Vineyard: p. 368-385.

Massachusetts Water Resources Commission, 1978, Ground water and groundwater law in Massachusetts: 72 p.

Old Colony Regional Planning Commission, 1978, Toward clean water - alternatives for action

- v. 1: Draft environmental impact assessment.

Special Legislative Commission on Water Supply, Massachusetts General Court, 1979, Chemical contamination: 72 p., September.

Spencer, J.C., 1979, Protection of groundwater quality and quantity - legal and administrative alternatives: Massachusetts Water Resources Commission, 119 p., August 31.

State of Connecticut, Connecticut water quality standards and criteria: draft revision, Connecticut Department of Environmental Protection, Water Compliance Unit, 34 p. Undated.

# Aquifer protection—
# Concepts, conflicts, and compromise

L. FELDMAN
Goldberg, Zoino & Associates, Inc.

# Groundwater hydrology
# of Martha's Vineyard Island, Massachusetts

J. L. WILSON
A. A. G. SA DA COSTA
Ralph M. Parsons Laboratory
Department of Civil Engineering
Massachusetts Institute of Technology

## ABSTRACT

Martha's Vineyard lies off the south coast of Cape Cod, Massachusetts. Its main industry is summer tourism, when the population of the island increases almost ten fold. All water supplies on the island come from ground water, and in particular the Wisconsin-age groundwater aquifer underlying Edgartown, Oak Bluffs, Tisbury and West Tisbury. This phreatic aquifer receives over 40 MGD in recharge of which less than 5 percent is captured in water supply wells, before it discharges underground to the sea. Nevertheless, given the location and timing of these withdrawals, it is clear that existing wells cannot supply much additional water. These and other developmental scientific questions concerning the island are discussed, and the use of simulation modeling is suggested to help answer them.

## INTRODUCTION

The Ralph M. Parsons Laboratory for Water Resources and Hydrodynamics of the Massachusetts Institute of Technology has recently completed the development and testing of a computer simulation model of sea water intrusion in coastal or island groundwater aquifers. SWIM, an acronym for Sea Water Intrusion Model (Sa da Costa and Wilson, 1979), is being tested further by an application to Martha's Vineyard Island, located off the southern shore of Cape Cod, Massachusetts (Fig. 1). This paper describes some of the basic features of the groundwater system on the island, and points to a number of potential problem areas of future concern. Many of these problems will be evaluated in later papers, with the help of the SWIM computer code.

Martha's Vineyard was also the subject of a recent United States Geological Survey groundwater study, the results of which are available in open file format in Boston (Delaney, 1979). Coordinated with similar efforts on Cape Cod and Nantucket Island, the purpose of this U.S.G.S. field investigation was to provide the data required for making fundamental decisions about long range plans for the island. We will attempt to summarize some of these data and draw some conclusions. However, the reader who wishes to understand the whole picture as we know it should also refer to Delaney (1979), and to the results of the MIT computer simulation study which are expected to be available in February 1981.

## GEOLOGY-GEOHYDROLOGY

Any discussion of Martha's Vineyard Island must inevitably refer to the island's geologic history, and this is particularly true when the subject is groundwater hydrology. The island is a creature of glaciation and subsequent modification by marine processes. It has experienced as many as five separate glacial advances and retreats (Kaye, 1964). The present triangular shape of the island represents the junction of two different ice fronts and terminal moraines. Figure 2 is a plan view map of Martha's Vineyard,

Figure 1. Geographic location of Martha's Vineyard Island.

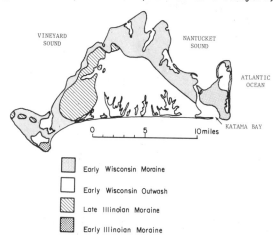

Figure 2. Surface geology. (Source: Kaye, 1964).

showing major coastal lakes and surficial geology (Kaye, 1964).

As seen in the figure the westernmost portion of the island is covered by the "Gay Head" terminal moraine, which is actually composed of three moraine deposits from the Early Illinoian, Late Illinoian and Early Wisconsin periods. This total deposit is made up of an extremely complex arrangement of sands, silts, clays, till, rubble, lignite, peat, etc. On a regional scale it is an aquiclude. Locally there are many small non-connected "aquifers," but finding a home water supply is a risky business. Much of the rainfall on the Gay Head moraine runs off, some of it to the east where it recharges the Wisconsin outwash, a large phreatic aquifer unit 100 to 200 feet thick of very pervious interbedded sand and gravel.

The source of the Wisconsin outwash is the glacial front on the north side of the island. The outwash thins to the north and northwest, where it pinches out at the contact with the Illinoian moraine, and probably thickens to the south. The upper part of the outwash is mostly medium to coarse sand with some beds of gravel. Directly to its north is the Early Wisconsin moraine (Fig. 2). This terminal moraine is composed of horizontally stratified sand with some inter-bedded gravel. According to Kaye (1964; personal communication, 1970) the moraine is similar to the sand and gravel found in the outwash plain, which spreads out from the foot of the moraine to the south. Together with the outwash it forms the principal aquifer of the island (Fig. 3), and all

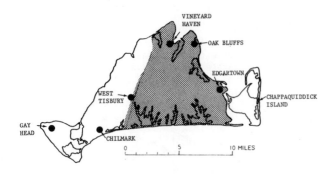

Figure 3. Wisconsin aquifer and relation to local island communities.

municipal water supply wells are in it (Fig. 4). It is separated from its smaller cousin beneath Chappaquiddick only by subsurface salt water.

## GROUNDWATER FLOW

The aquifer is recharged by precipitation from above, and runoff from the hills of the Gay Head moraine to the west. The groundwater flow

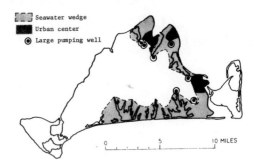

Figure 4. Location of municipal wells, urban population centers, and anticipated extent of sea water intrusion.

pattern, shown in Figure 5, reflects these sources of recharge; an underground water table ridge extends west to east from West Tisbury to Edgartown. The elevation of the ridge decreases to the east, indicating that water flows north, east and south toward the sea. A small portion of the groundwater discharge is captured by two fresh water streams, Mill Brook and the Tiasquam River in West Tisbury, and groundwater pumping operations.

Water table elevations at three points within the aquifer are plotted against time in Figure 6. Those points farthest from the sea exhibit a higher water table elevation, as expected from the contour map. What is surprising is the magnitude of the temporal fluctuation shown. For well OBW-15, near the center of the island, the fluctuation is 5 feet out of a total elevation above sea level of 15 to 20 feet. The time series exhibits both a high frequency component and a trend of increasing water table elevation over the two year period of the plot. The latter can be explained by the fact that Martha's Vineyard underwent a drought over the previous five years and was recovering during the period of observation. The high frequency variation is associated with recharge and thus with precipitation. Note the strong correlation of the precipitation and water table fluctuation. The explanation for this can be found in the fast hydraulic response of the aquifer. A typical response time for a phreatic aquifer (Gelhar and Wilson, 1974) can be written as:

$$\tau = \frac{nL^2}{4KB}$$

where n is the porosity or specific yield, B is the average saturated thickness, L is the horizontal length scale of the aquifer, and K is the horizontal hydraulic conductivity. For the island representative values of these parameters are: n = 0.1, B = 200 feet, K = 200 ft/day, L = $10^4$ feet. This results in a response time of 2 months, which is consistent with the data observed in the figure. This fast response time is somewhat surprising, considering the size of the aquifer, but no doubt the sea water wedge responds much more slowly.

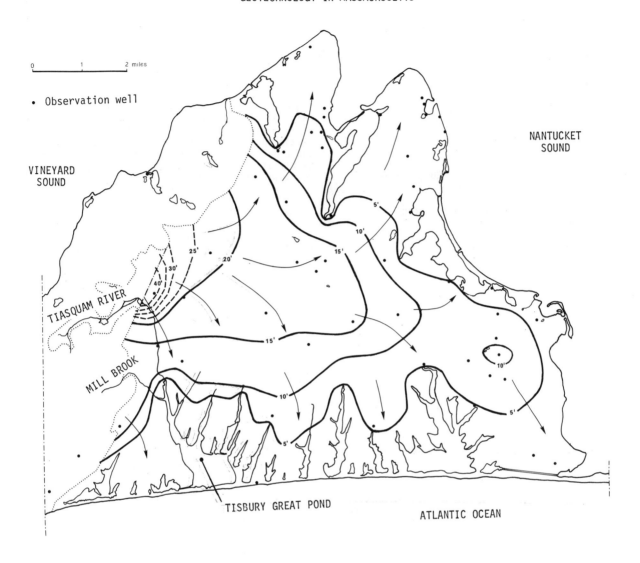

Figure 5.  Groundwater equipotentials and flow pattern, based on observations made by the U.S. Geological Survey, December 1977.

Consider a simple water balance for the island.  Average annual recharge is roughly 16-18 inches, based on similar experiences with Long Island and Cape Cod.  The area of the aquifer shown in Figure 3 is approximately 53 square miles.  Therefore, the average total annual recharge for the aquifer is, say, 2.2 x 10$^9$ ft$^3$/year, or in more convenient terms, 45.4 MGD (million gallons per day).  •Note that we have neglected the contribution of runoff from the Gay Head moraine.  Metcalf and Eddy (1972) estimated the entire island recharge as 57.6 MGD.  The two major streams crossing the outwash plain, Mill Brook and the Tiasquam River, drain the east slope of the Gay Head moraine and discharge to Great Tisbury

Pond in the southwest corner of the outwash.  The total annual "base" flow of these streams, contributed to by ground water, is approximately 2.5 MGD (Martha's Vineyard Commission/EPA, 1977).  Although these streams are locally important to the groundwater system, they provide for removal of only 5 percent or less of the groundwater discharge.  From October 1, 1977, through the end of September 1978 the total pumpage for municipal water supply was 466 million gallons, or 1.28 MGD on average.  Another 0.25 MGD may have been pumped from private wells.  Entering all of these estimates into a budget gives the solution for the remaining variable, groundwater discharge to the sea.  Assuming no change in aquifer storage the water balance equation for the aquifer is:

$$Q_{NR} + Q_{LI} = Q_{SO} + Q_{LO} + Q_P$$

where

$Q_{NR}$ = natural recharge $\simeq$ 45.4 MGD (annual average)

$Q_{LI}$ = lateral inflow from Gay Head moraine $\simeq$ 0 (assumed)

$Q_{SO}$ = base flow to streams $\simeq$ 2 MGD (remaining 0.5 MGD from moraine)

$Q_P$ = pumping $\simeq$ 1.5 MGD (neglect septic tank recycling)

$Q_{LO}$ = lateral outflow to sea

therefore

$$Q_{LO} = Q_{NR} + Q_{LI} - Q_{SO} - Q_{LO}$$

$$= 41.9 \text{ MGD}$$

Unquestionably, a large amount of fresh water is being discharged to the sea. However, it is not necessarily "lost" water. It helps to maintain an appropriate salinity level in the coastal ponds and tidal marshes of the island, and most importantly it works to push back the underground intrusion of sea water.

SEA WATER INTRUSION

The aquifer is subject to sea water intrusion along its contact with Vineyard Sound, Nantucket

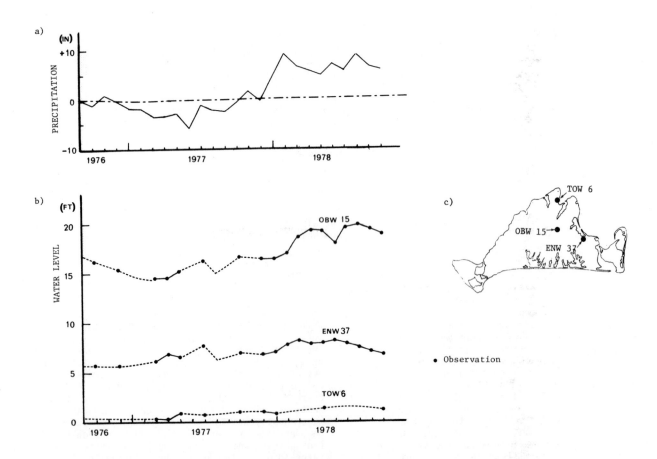

Figure 6.   a) Edgartown precipitation showing cumulative departure from the monthly mean.  b) Water table fluctuation at three observation wells.  c) Location of wells.

Sound, Katama Bay and the Atlantic Ocean. A generalized cross sectional view of the island, taken from north to south, is shown in Figure 7. The

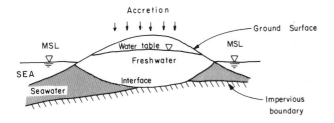

Figure 7. Highly idealized north-south section through Wisconsin aquifer.

measured intrusion at one location in Edgartown is shown in Figure 8 (Delaney, 1979). The sea water is held in dynamic equilibrium by roughly 42 MGD of subsurface fresh water discharge to the sea. Using the Ghyben-Herzberg approximation (Bear, 1979), the water table contour map can be converted into a map of depth to the fresh water-sea water interface. If

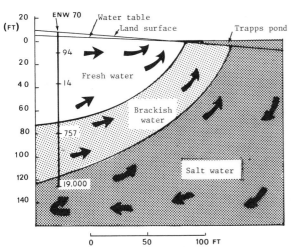

Concentration along boring are Cl⁻ in mg/l

Figure 8. Measured sea water intrusion at Trapps' Pond in Edgartown, November 10, 1977. (Source: Delaney, 1979).

$h$ = water table elevation

$\zeta$ = depth below MSL to the interface

$\Delta \rho / \rho$ = normalized density difference between fresh water and sea water

then the depth to the interface is given by

$$\zeta = \frac{h}{\Delta \rho / \rho} \cong 40\, h$$

Thus, given a twenty foot water table thickness at the center of the aquifer (Fig. 4), the depth to sea water should be approximately 40 x 20 ft = 800 ft, providing that the aquifer is at least that thick. However, the average aquifer thickness is actually between 100 to 200 feet; the only test boring to actually discover the clay layer lining the bottom of the aquifer found it at 160 feet below MSL. Thus, only along the edges of the island, as shown in Figure 7, does the sea water intrude. Assuming that the bottom of the aquifer is at 200 feet below sea level, then the landward extent of intrusion, called the sea water wedge toe, would be identified by the five foot water table contour line. Using this contour from Figure 5 gives the intrusion zone shown in Figure 4. Most of the municipal water supply wells on the island are located within this zone, or close to it.

WATER SUPPLY WELLS

The locations of the municipal water supply wells on the island are shown in Figure 4. These wells are found near their demand centers of Oak Bluffs, Vineyard Haven, and Edgartown, which are all seaports. Also, the wells are located in areas with a minimum depth to the water table. This last criterion means that the wells are near the coastline, as it is near the coastline that the water table comes closest to the land surface (Fig. 7). But it is precisely in this zone, near the coastline, that the propensity for well contamination by sea water intrusion is the greatest.

Provincetown, on Cape Cod, has had a long history of problems with salinity intrusion into its public water supply wells (Delaney and Cotton, 1972). In fact all of their current wells are found in the adjacent town of Truro for this reason, and even some of these wells experience significant increases in the chloride level during the summer when demand peaks.

It is important to realize that the demand on Martha's Vineyard Island is seasonally dependent. The island population is less than 10,000 in the winter (7,900 in 1975) and up to 70,000 in the summer (55,000 to 60,000 in 1975) (Martha's Vineyard Commission/EPA, 1977). In Edgartown this translates into a winter (1972-1976) demand of 0.1 to 0.2 MGD and a summer (1972-1976) peak demand of 0.8 to 1.0 MGD. The pumping rate from the Oak Bluffs well field during 1977-1978 is shown in Figure 9.

Although the total yearly water supply demand is less than 5 percent of the total aquifer recharge, as shown by the water balance above, its spatial and temporal distribution can lead to problems. The easternmost well in Edgartown, called "Shortlift," is used only in the summer time and only at restricted rates in order to avoid high chloride levels. The drawdown near well OBW-19 in Oak Bluffs (Fig. 9) actually takes the water table below sea level from time to time. Clearly, in light of the anticipated increase in population on the island, the situation deserves some scrutiny.

## GROUND WATER AND DEVELOPMENT

As the population of the island increases, there is some concern that ground water will be affected, both quantitatively and qualitatively. Clearly, there is a limit to how much more water existing wells can pump before their water quality is impaired, but what are some of the other concerns?

### Land Waste Water Treatment in Vineyard Haven

Vineyard Haven and surrounding communities presently depend on a number of wells for water supply and septic tanks for wastewater disposal. How would a centralized land waste treatment facility, such as proposed recently by the Martha's Vineyard Commission/EPA (1977) affect the ground water flow pattern? The choice is between diffuse sources of recharge (septic tank) and concentrated recharge (land waste disposal and sewering).

### New Town Concept

A major engineering consulting firm has proposed the creation of a new town in the northeast part of the island, away from the coast. The proposal has stirred up the concept of centralized growth inland, rather than along the beaches. Where will such a community get its water supply, and how will this affect the municipal wells in adjacent communities? Where and how will they dispose of waste water, and what effect on ground water will there be?

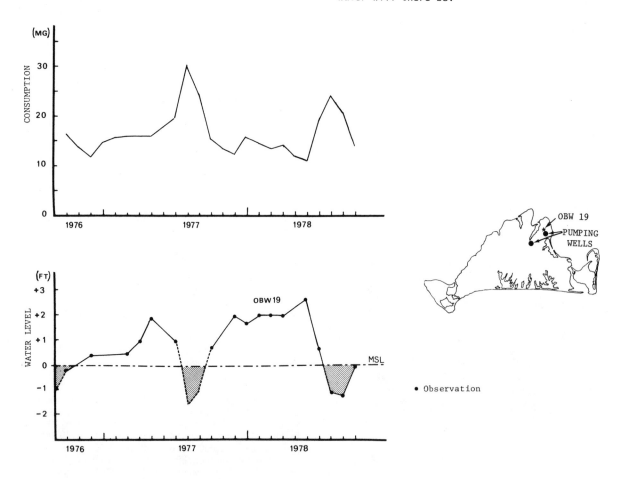

Figure 9. Monthly pumping and water level fluctuations in Oak Bluffs, 1972-1976.

## Dispersed Growth versus Centralized Growth

This refers to the status quo, which is the construction of individual dwellings with their own well and septic tank. What effect will this have on ground water? What happens if water supplies are centralized and distribution systems installed or expanded, as in Edgartown? Will the increased demand on municipal wells near the coast induce sea water intrusion?

## Concentrated Industrial Growth at the Airport

If a large water user(s) is installed at the airport, in the middle of the outwash plain, what will be the effect on others?

## Shoreline Development of Varying Density

Certain shoreline areas are under significant development pressure. The new homes built in these areas depend on their own wells for water supply. Often located only a few hundred feet from the coast, they risk sea water intrusion.

Of particular concern is the development of large shoreline apartment/hotel complexes using ground water.

These issues will be addressed in the continuing MIT Sea Grant study of the island's ground water. But there remain a number of other scientific questions to be addressed first.

## MODELING GROUND WATER

To provide a simulation model capable of making reasonable predictions of the aquifer's response to the stresses of these proposed projects, we must understand the hydrology of the island better than we do at present. Fortunately, the simulation model can help in this task by providing the means to synthesize available data. Along these lines there are several features of the aquifer system that deserve close examination.

## Natural Recharge

The aquifer receives roughly 16-18 inches per year of natural recharge. This recharge varies with the season, due to the effects of evapotranspiration and precipitation. Furthermore, as indicated in Figure 6, there are long term trends in precipitation and thus in the amount of annual recharge that takes place. How important is the seasonal variation? How much recharge occurs? How important is the long term trend?

## Aquifer Bottom

The bottom of the aquifer is defined by a horizontal clay layer, almost 200 feet below sea level. We have only one measurement of the location of this layer, which we assume is extensive. What is the strike and dip of the layer? Is it as extensive as we suppose? How will sea water intrusion be affected by these assumptions?

## Aquifer Properties

Few adequate pump tests have been conducted in the aquifer, and thus there are almost no measurements of the aquifer properties of hydraulic conductivity and specific yield. Similar materials on Cape Cod have a hydraulic conductivity of 100-200 feet/day and a specific yield of 0.2. Are these appropriate estimates for the island aquifer? How sensitive are predictions to these estimated values? Is there any recognizable and significant spatial variability of properties?

As can be seen, despite the level of effort already expended these features still require more definition. A future paper will address them.

## SUMMARY AND CONCLUSIONS

The major aquifer of Martha's Vineyard Island is composed of Wisconsin-age outwash and moraine. It is a phreatic aquifer recharged by roughly 16-18 inches/year of natural recharge and by groundwater runoff from the Gay Head moraine. The aquifer has a subsurface discharge to the sea of over 40 MGD of water. Only a few MGD are recovered by pumping wells or are lost to streams.

Even though pumping on the island withdraws only a small percentage of average annual recharge, there is a potential problem with the security of future water supplies, due to the near coastal location of the wells and their seasonal pumping pattern. Other developments under consideration also threaten the viability of what should otherwise be an abundant storage reservoir.

To better understand the function of the aquifer system, and to evaluate the effects of future projects, a computer simulation model of the aquifer's hydrology is useful. The SWIM code is being applied for this purpose by the authors in cooperation with the Martha's Vineyard Commission and the U. S. Geological Survey. Results of this study will be available in February 1981.

## ACKNOWLEDGMENTS

This paper is based on research sponsored by the MIT Sea Grant Program, supported by NOAA's Office of Sea Grant, U. S. Department of Commerce, under Grant No. NA79AA-D-00101. The authors gratefully acknowledge the comments of David Delaney of the U. S. Geological Survey. The authors also thank the Martha's Vineyard Commission for their cooperation in this study.

## REFERENCES

Bear, J., 1979, Hydraulics of ground water: McGraw-Hill, New York.

Delaney, D.F., 1979, Groundwater hydrology of Martha's Vineyard, Commonwealth of Massachusetts: U.S. Geological Survey Open File Report 79-917, Boston.

Delaney, D.F., and Cotton, J.E., 1972, Evaluation of proposed groundwater withdrawal, Cape Cod National Seashore, North Truro, Massachusetts: U.S. Geological Survey Open File Report, Boston.

Gelhar, L., and Wilson, J.L., 1974, Groundwater quality modeling: Ground Water, v. 12, no. 6, p. 399-408.

Kaye, C.A., 1964, Illinoian and Early Wisconsin moraines of Martha's Vineyard, Massachusetts: U.S. Geological Survey Professional Paper 501-C, C140-143.

Martha's Vineyard Commission/EPA, 1977, Water quality management plan for Martha's Vineyard:  Oak Bluffs, Massachusetts, August.

Metcalf and Eddy, 1972, Comprehensive water and sewerage plan for Martha's Vineyard.

Sa da Costa, A.A.G., and Wilson, J.L., 1979, A numerical model of sea water intrusion in aquifers:  Ralph M. Parsons Laboratory for Water Resources and Hydrodynamics, Report 247, Massachusetts Institute of Technology, Cambridge, November.

# Estimating high groundwater levels from observed water levels in Massachusetts

M. H. FRIMPTER
Water Resources Division
U.S. Geological Survey

ABSTRACT

Water-level records from an observation-well
network are analyzed for utility in estimating
high groundwater levels in three different geohydrologic environments in Massachusetts. Analyses
were made of 83 observation wells with between 8
and 37 years of record. Maximum annual water
levels occur most frequently in March and April.
The maximum range of recorded water levels equaled
or exceeded at 10 percent of the observation-well
sites is estimated to be 16 feet in till, 9.2
feet in sand and gravel on terraces, and 4.0 feet
in sand and gravel in valleys.

A method of estimating high groundwater levels at construction sites is suggested. An estimate of high water level at a site may be derived
by solving the proportion in which the ratio of
potential water-level rise (maximum water level
minus current water level) to expected water-level
range at the test site equals the ratio of potential water-level rise to maximum historical water-
level range at an observation well in a similar
geohydrologic environment. Assuming that the data
are representative of the future, estimates would
not be expected to be exceeded at more than 1 in
10 sites over a period of 20 years or longer.

Hors-texte

Northfield Mountain pumped storage project beside the
Connecticut River in Massachusetts during construction
in 1969.  (Courtesy, Aerial Photos of New England.)

# Distribution of dissolved substances in ground water resulting from infiltration of treated sewage through sand filter beds

D. R. LEBLANC

Water Resources Division

U.S. Geological Survey

ABSTRACT

Secondarily treated sewage has been dis-charged by rapid infiltration through sand-filter beds at Otis Air Force Base, Cape Cod, Massachu-setts, since 1941. The treated waste water re-charges a sand and gravel aquifer where the aqui-fer is about 250 feet thick and where the water table slopes to the south at about seven feet per mile.

A plume of sewage-affected ground water ex-tends to at least 9,000 feet south (down gradient) from the disposal site. At 3,000 feet down gradi-ent, the plume is about 2,500 feet wide, is 100 feet thick, and is more than 35 feet below the water table.

The plume contains elevated levels of spe-cific conductance and nitrogen, detergents (MBAS), boron, and other dissolved solids. MBAS concen-trations as high as 2.6 mg/L (milligrams per liter), boron concentrations as high as 0.4 mg/L, and specific conductance as high as 405 umhos/cm (micromhos per centimeter) have been found in ground water from 1,000 feet to 9,000 feet south of the disposal site. The MBAS concentration is usually below detectable limits, and the boron concentration and specific conductance are usually less than 0.05 mg/L, and 80 umhos/cm, respective-ly, in uncontaminated ground water in the area.

The core of the plume is a reducing environ-ment and contains no dissolved oxygen and no nitrate. Ammonia nitrogen as high as 20 mg/L has been detected 3,000 feet down gradient from the disposal site. Surrounding the core is a zone of sewage-affected ground water containing nitrate nitrogen instead of ammonia nitrogen. The oxida-tion of the ammonia to nitrate occurs where ground water containing ammonia mixes with the indigenous ground water, which contains 3 mg/L to 11 mg/L dissolved oxygen.

Phosphorus is absorbed by aquifer materials close to the disposal site and does not exceed 0.20 mg/L (as P) in the plume beyond 2,000 feet from the disposal site. Concentrations of other dissolved constituents, such as sodium, chloride, and boron, seem to be attenuated with distance only as a result of dilution.

Hors-texte

The City of Boston, looking across the islands of
Massachusetts Bay to the south shore and Cape Cod.
(Courtesy, Aerial Photos of New England.)

# Geoscience in municipal groundwater exploration

P. BEAL
Hanover Water Department
Massachusetts

T. F. SEXTON
E. N. LEVINE
Weston Geophysical Corporation

ABSTRACT

The Town of Hanover, Massachusetts, has used the geosciences to provide state-of-the-art techniques and tools for exploring and planning their municipal water resources. A systematic relatively long-range approach insures the proper development of the groundwater resources picture of an area and involves a critical interfacing of geologic reconnaissance, geophysical exploration, and test drilling. Most groundwater studies involve an evaluation of the surface geology with the subsurface conditions determined by geophysics and test wells. The exploration effort is governed by such factors as the subsurface complexity of the area and the rate and extent of development required or allowed.

## INTRODUCTION

Although some municipalities in New England obtain water from surface supplies, the majority of communities depend on ground water for much, if not all, of their water needs.

Ground water in quantities sufficient for municipal development has become increasingly difficult to find since the most obvious sources are already being used. Also, in many cases, candidate sites for ground water have been preempted by municipal development, such as for sewage treatment and solid waste disposal, and by housing and commercial development. These developments compound the problem because they may not only occupy potential groundwater resource (and recharge) areas, but they also increase demands on existing water supplies while contributing to the contamination of those supplies.

For municipalities to adequately plan future development--both community development and groundwater development--the planners must know their groundwater resources in order to protect them from depletion and contamination.

Groundwater exploration should follow a carefully planned sequence of stages, including: (1) the collection and assimilation of all surface and subsurface data available; (2) a reconnaissance level survey of surficial geology; (3) geophysical exploration of potential groundwater sources; and (4) test drilling of candidate sites.

## BACKGROUND

The Town of Hanover is 25 miles south of Boston and approximately 7 miles inland. In 1932 the town, with a population of 1,200, established its first public water supply system in the Pond Street area.

This water supply system consisted of a well field of 24 2-1/2" wells each approximately 30 feet deep which provided 600 gallons per minute. The town used 35,000 gallons per day and, until 1940, pumping for two hours at 300 gallons per minute was sufficient. During the hurricane of 1938 the well field area was flooded, and overnight surface water infiltrated the well field. For six to eight weeks the color of the water varied from that of weak tea to a slight tinge, but the color finally went away. After 1938, whenever there was flooding from precipitation, a slight tinge of the color was noticeable.

In 1939 the local fireworks plant got a contract for munitions from Britain and water usage for that plant alone immediately went to 50,000 gallons per day. By 1942 water consumption by the town and munitions plant was 700,000 gallons per day and increasing. Exploration for a new well site was started, and a location was tested 300 feet north of the well field resulting in a 750 gallons per minute (gpm), 24" x 48", gravel-packed well. This well was 65' deep with a 20' screen.

At the peak of WWII, usage was up to 1.2 million gallons per day (mgd). Color in the well field continued to increase and by 1947 was increasing in the gravel-packed well. By 1950 the color in the well field was up to 60 and iron was 3 to 5 parts per million (ppm). To replace the well field, a 12" gravel-developed well 65' deep was contructed 300' north of the 24" gravel-packed well. Its initial capacity of 750 gpm quickly decreased to 250 gpm as the well silted in.

By 1952, another source of water had to be found. Over the next five years approximately 150 2-1/2" test wells were drilled to explore for a water source and, by 1958, two locations had been found. One of these, known as the Hanover Street wells, was developed by constructing two 24" x 48" gravel-packed wells 700' apart, each having a capacity of 300 gpm. These were placed in service in 1960. The 12" well was then placed on a standby basis, and the use of the original 24" x 48" well was continued but at a reduced pumping rate at which there was less color.

Using 2-1/2" test wells, exploration continued up to 1965 but no additional supplies were discovered, and in 1966 the second of the two locations discovered in the 1952 to 1958 exploration program was developed. Again, two 24" x 48" gravel-packed wells were constructed, 1,200' apart in an area known as the Broadway well area. Each had a capacity of 300 gpm. At this point, all wells at Pond Street, with the exception of a 200 gpm test well, were discontinued. The 24" x 48" gravel-packed well was pumped overboard weekly to keep it available on a standby basis, as color had reached 40 at a reduced pumping rate.

Facing an ever increasing demand for water, the town turned its attention to the Pond Street well site as it was a proven site for a least 1 mgd. The idea of a treatment process to remove the color, iron, and manganese was explored. In 1969 and 1970 a pilot treatment operation confirmed a process that could make this water usable. The treatment plant was a major undertaking, and it was decided that the volume of water available would have to be established and more exploring would have to be undertaken throughout the town for additional supplies. By 1970, the town was under a water restriction preventing the use of water for anything other than use within a building or for life support, sanitation, or fire protection. The safe yield of the the Hanover Street and Broadway wells was overextended even by the above limited use in the town, which had grown from 4,500 to 10,000 population in 15 years.

## ASSEMBLY OF PERTINENT DATA

There is usually a wealth of experience in every town that involves negative as well as positive knowledge of importance to a groundwater investigation. In some cases, the information is documented in the form of boring logs for foundation studies, construction records, existing profiles, etc. Where the information is undocumented, interviews with townspeople whose jobs involve them with underground conditions are often fruitful. For example, public works officials often can identify areas of the town where rock had to be blasted for utilities, and fire department personnel may have records of blasting for building foundations. This is all negative data that can make a very positive contribution to a water resources study; if the town knows where there is no possibility of finding water, they can proceed more readily with alternative planning strategies.

Such data must be carefully evaluated to assure their reliability. For example, in some instances, the rock blasted may have consisted only of boulders. Where drilling has brought no water, proper efforts may not have been made to determine exact subsurface conditions. Based on seismic data, some sites have been successfully redrilled with 8 inch or larger diameter drilling equipment. In other cases, drilling resulted in water that did not meet the quality standards that the town specified, records were not kept, and a prejudice against the area may persist. Present-day demands make water treatment facilities feasible, and such areas warrant renewed study.

Unfortunately, some municipalities have made no effort to integrate available subsurface data into a comprehensive format that can be used in future planning and can be updated as additional information becomes available.

The exploration work of the 1952 to 1965 period was reviewed. Available records were severely lacking in data, and only 120 of the test well sites could be located. Logs of the test wells had little information, and there were many 2-1/2" test well logs within 100 feet of the producing Hanover Street, Broadway, and Pond Street wells that had refusal depths of less than 20 feet. Persons who had been involved with the exploration work over the years were contacted, and every avenue of information was searched. After a full review, it was evident that the available data from the previous exploration with 2-1/2" test wells were accurate for each test well.

After reviewing the available methods of data collection, the services and expertise of Weston Geophysical Engineers were selected to accomplish these goals:

- to establish and carry out a comprehensive data-gathering program,

- to determine additional well sites in the Pond Street well area,

- to locate new well sites in the town, and

- to determine any interconnection between present and new well sites.

This program was started in the fall of 1970.

In 1975 two additional goals were added to the program:

- to determine the suitability of a 200 acre unoccupied parcel for groundwater development of a reservoir, and

- to further delineate the extent of each of the producing well areas for future groundwater protection.

These changes were the result of recognition by those responsible for the town's water supply that groundwater contamination could result in a loss of the supply. The alternative would be the development of a surface supply.

## GEOLOGIC RECONNAISSANCE

In many areas an assessment of broad topographic features will quickly focus the groundwater search on areas of lower surface elevation. However, this must be done judiciously because some features may mask the preglacial drainage system which is the source for many aquifers throughout New England (Howard, 1967).

For studies of a regional scope, reconnaissance mapping is cost-effective. The best mapping base consists of the United States Geological Survey 7.5 minute quadrangle sheets. Initial surficial studies may be limited to what can be observed within sight of roads, trails, power line rights of way, or other cultural features that appear on the topographic sheets. The occurrence of such features usually provides an excellent random sampling basis and allows for sufficiently accurate locations of geologic features. When available, air photos are helpful in tracing land forms between observation points. However, the mapped contours are often sufficiently accurate to determine generalized boundaries as a prelude to seismic refraction surveys.

The surficial geologic investigation in Hanover was limited to areas of glacial sands and gravel deposits distinct from areas of shallow bedrock or shallow glacial till. In most instances, for groundwater surveys, there is no justification for detailed geologic studies to differentiate between types of till, nor is there any need to distinguish ice-contact sands and gravel from outwash deposits or glacio-fluvial from recent deposits. Bedrock mapping is only necessary (for groundwater studies) in those relatively few areas where large bedrock yields are known to exist.

The overall investigation was related to the previous exploration program. A seismic study was planned and implemented for those areas of the town which were determined to have the best indications of providing a new well site.

SEISMIC SURVEYS

Seismic surveys have proven to be an effective technique for groundwater investigations. When properly integrated with surficial geology and test borings, they provide an insight into subsurface conditions not attainable otherwise. Seismic surveys enjoy a long history of success in New England. Linehan and Keith presented their paper "Seismic reconnaissance for groundwater development" to the New England Water Works Association in 1949 and had described groundwater surveys as early as 1941.

Seismic results of significance to groundwater exploration are the velocity with which a sound wave is transmitted through overburden and bedrock, and profiles of the bedrock surface, as well as discontinuities detected in the overburden (Fig. 1).

The seismic velocity for overburden ranges from a few hundred feet per second (fps) to over 7,000 fps. Occasionally, velocities as high as 9,000 fps are recorded, but these are not common. However, we have found that municipal-size water supplies are found only in the very narrow range of 4,800 fps to 5,300 fps (Murphy and Sexton, 1967).

Accordingly, seismic data can favorably in-

fluence the drilling program, thereby eliminating nonproductive holes due to unsaturated materials, shallow till, and shallow rock.

TEST DRILLING

After a seismic survey had outlined deep areas of favorable seismic velocities, test borings were placed at candidate sites to determine the nature of the 4,800 to 5,300 fps material. Silts and clays have seismic velocities in this critical range. Seismic coverage was then extended to outline the thickness and lateral extent of the favorable material. Seismic depths to bedrock or till are also used to determine the minimum depth that the borings should penetrate. We have experienced many cases where the drilling effort had been insufficient to penetrate to the aquifer that existed.

It should be noted that the well contractor who had done the exploration work and constructed the Hanover Street and Broadway gravel-packed wells had brought to the attention of the Water Commissioners the limitations of exploration with 2-1/2" test wells. He had suggested drilling 8" test holes in particular areas where his experience indicated that the test holes were shallow because of refusal from large boulders. He considered that by using a larger drilling machine and casing (8") this problem could be overcome and full depths accomplished. The town officials involved at that time were unwilling to gamble on the expensive 8" test wells.

From the results of the Pond Street area seismic surveys, locations for 8" test wells were determined, and two of those sites were pump-tested. It was determined that the Pond Street well area could conservatively provide 3 mgd. Both of the producing sites had been explored with 2-1/2" test wells in the 1952 to 1965 period and eliminated for lack of depth, refusal being from 22' to 25'.

Two 24" x 48" gravel-packed wells were constructed in the Pond Street area in 1973 with developed safe yields of .9 mgd and 1.1 mgd which, combined with the 24" x 48" well constructed in 1943, provided a 3 mgd supply for the new treatment plant.

Seismic exploration of other areas (Fig. 1) resulted in the discovery of a new well site: one 8" test well was drilled, and a subsequent pump test determined that an additional supply of .7 mgd could be developed. This location will also require iron removal treatment.

Because the immediate supply needs for the next 15 years have been met, the seismic program has been directed to prove out the most promising new well site areas and determine any interconnection between proven sites.

It should be pointed out that our concern was to locate groundwater supplies regardless of water quality, treatment technology having reached the

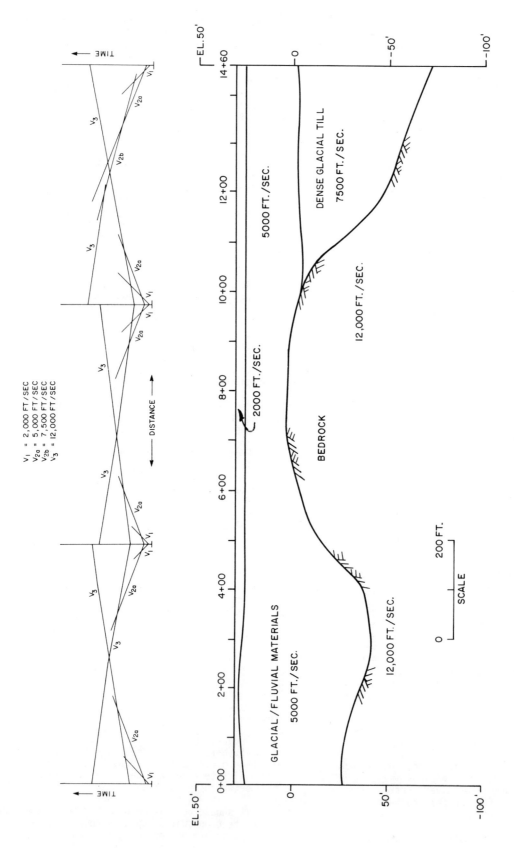

Figure 1. Seismic time distance plot and interpreted sub-surface profile in a new area of potential municipal groundwater supply for Hanover, Massachusetts. The velocity of 5,000 ft/sec is typical for saturated sand and gravel. Subsequent drilling near Station 3+00 resulted in 700,000 gallons per day supply.

point that there were few quality problems that could not be overcome. We could not rule out a supply because of quality if we were to fulfill the town's water supply needs. In considering future water supplies in general, this approach is now the rule rather than the exception that it has been in the past.

As a result, in part, of the data gathered by 1978, a moratorium was placed on all construction within the area which had to that date been determined to be contributing to the town's groundwater supply. The moratorium was for a period of two years during which two studies were made. One study was a complete evaluation of the town's present supply and a determination of the needs to 1995. The second study was to determine the steps necessary to protect the town's groundwater supply in view of the extraordinary development planned and forecasted in the recharge area. At the May 1980 town meeting an aquifer recharge and well protection overlay zone was to be proposed for the townspeople to act upon to protect the present water supply.

Without the seismic data which had been properly collected and interpreted, both of these studies would have taken considerably more time, as the investigation and data collected were essential to the credibility and confirmation of the geologists' and hydrogeologists' findings.

CONCLUSION

Seismic data gathering will continue to be used to locate additional supplies and interconnections of groundwater. We have found it to be an essential part of collecting accurate data for water supply exploration, development, and protection.

REFERENCES

Howard, P.F., 1967, Use of geology in the development of groundwater supplies in New England, in Farquhar, O.C., ed., Economic geology in Massachusetts: University of Massachusetts Graduate School, p. 487-495.

Linehan, S.J., D., and Keith, S., 1949, Seismic reconnaissance for groundwater development: Journal of New England Water Works Association, v. 63.

Murphy, V.J., and Sexton, T.F., 1967, Seismic surveys for groundwater investigation in Massachusetts, in Farquhar, O.C., ed., Economic Geology in Massachusetts: University of Massachusetts Graduate School, p. 450-454.

Hors-texte

Martha's Vineyard off the Cape Cod shore of Massachusetts, looking west to the Elizabeth Islands,
Buzzards Bay, Narragansett Bay, and New Bedford.

# Solute transport in New England's unconsolidated aquifers— Recommended techniques for data gathering and analysis

R. W. HEELEY
Lycott Environmental Research, Inc.

## ABSTRACT

A computer program for solute transport developed by U.S. Geological Survey hydrologists has numerous options which allow the user to simulate nature very closely. Initial solute concentrations and initial conditions in the aquifer can be specified as constant throughout the modeled area, or they can be mapped on a grid. Numerous pumping or injection wells can be specified, and the cumulative effects of several pumping (injection) periods can be simulated. Head changes, groundwater velocities, and simulated solute concentrations are calculated and displayed at each node of the model. Cross-sectional models as well as plan-view models can be run. In particular, the model can be used as a screening device to determine whether additional data are needed by running the model under "worst possible case" assumptions to determine whether the results fall within acceptable limits.

As an example of computer modeling of groundwater quality and flow patterns, subsurface data from a large proposed housing development with on-site sewage disposal were fed into the U.S.G.S. solute transport model. The computer simulation showed that nitrate-nitrogen values would remain considerably below the Safe Drinking Water Act standards. Nearby proposed wells would not be seriously affected by the waste loading, and mounding beneath individual septic systems would be minimal. Cross-sectional modeling by a hydrologist reviewing the project revealed that a considerable amount of flow is channeled through ponds and lakes down-gradient of the project. However, sewage flows are diluted by water from approximately half the saturated thickness of the aquifer prior to discharging into the ponds. The question of whether eutrophication of these ponds will be accelerated by the project cannot be directly answered by the solute transport modeling, but the modeling provides information useful to limnologists studying this type of problem.

Hors-texte

Erosion studies, Corps of Engineers — Gay Head Cliffs project, Martha's Vineyard, Massachusetts. (Courtesy, Woodward-Clyde Consultants; presented to those attending the 1976 Annual Meeting on Onshore and Offshore Problems and Hazards at Cherry Hill, New Jersey, of the Association of Engineering Geologists.)

# 4

# GEOPHYSICS

Session moderator

L. M. Hall
Department of Geology and Geography
University of Massachusetts at Amherst

# Use of geophysics in groundwater exploration in Massachusetts

D. H. BRUEHL
Metcalf & Eddy, Inc.

ABSTRACT

In general, coarse-grained stratified glacial drift deposits make up the most productive aquifers in Massachusetts. Because they are often hidden by finer-grained, less productive deposits and are of limited lateral extent, considerable subsurface exploration must be conducted to locate these aquifers. Geophysical surveys can often reduce the amount of expensive test drilling in such investigations. The use of the gravity method in combination with electrical resistivity depth soundings on a project in Manchester, Massachusetts, is demonstrated. Investigations on sites in Cedar Swamp and adjacent to Round Pond are described.

On the Cedar Swamp site the gravity method outlined a buried bedrock valley system with a computed thickness of overburden of up to 90 feet. Electrical resistivity depth soundings were used to locate test well sites on this anomaly.

The gravity method was also used to detect and map a buried bedrock valley system on the Round Pond site. A maximum overburden thickness of 83 feet was computed for this site. Electrical resistivity depth soundings were then used to locate test well sites. Small-diameter test wells confirmed the presence of thick sand and gravel deposits under as much as 20 feet of swampy muck.

## INTRODUCTION

Much of Massachusetts is underlain by shallow bed rock and moderately thick glacial till which together yield only small amounts of water to wells. Small but important occurrences of coarse-grained stratified glacial drift are the source of most of the larger municipal and industrial underground water supplies. Locating and defining thick deposits of stratified drift requires extensive subsurface investigations. The investigations can include test drilling and geophysical surveys. Geophysical surveys, if properly conducted, can reduce the amount of expensive test drilling.

Methods used frequently by Metcalf & Eddy are seismic refraction, electrical resistivity, and gravity. On regional projects, satellite imagery and air photos are often used. Where the geology permits, magnetic or aeromagnetic surveys can be useful. Thermal surveys have been used recently by others to define high yield well sites in suitable situations. Borehole geophysics are used to define the vertical occurrence of water-bearing materials more precisely. Here, we will deal with the combined use of gravity and electrical resistivity techniques in the Town of Manchester, Massachusetts, as an example of applied geophysics. The geophysical surveys were conducted for Metcalf & Eddy by Dr. John F. Kick, consulting geophysicist.

The use of the gravity method in groundwater exploration is a fairly new development. Until recently the gravity method has been used to define the subsurface portion of large bedrock structures such as salt domes, large scale folds, and faults. The method makes use of small differences in the earth's gravitational field, caused by differences in bedrock and overburden densities. The density differences that generally exist between the overburden and the underlying bed rock are the basis of the successful application of the gravity method to groundwater exploration. In general, bed rock has a substantially higher density than overburden. When the densities are known, it is possible to compute the depth of bed rock.

## SELECTION OF EXPLORATION SITES

To reduce the cost of exploration, potential areas are first screened to eliminate sites having a poor potential for groundwater development. All existing data are obtained first and evaluated. Such data often include the following.

- Soil maps.
- Groundwater favorability maps.
- Well logs.
- Property maps.

Here, we use our town-wide groundwater exploration as an example. A plot of the soil type shows that most of the town is underlain by bed rock at shallow depths and poorly permeable till. Small areas of stratified sand and gravel and glaciolacustrine or marine deposits occur in the valley bottoms. Much of the valley bottom area is overlain by swampy wetlands, lakes, and streams. This made field investigations difficult in places.

The U.S. Geological Survey Water Resources Division was consulted for their assessment of Manchester. They provided water well and test boring information and information from an unpublished hydrologic atlas. Included in the atlas and important in the initial stages of our study was a map of estimated transmissivity.

Property availability was then investigated. Large undeveloped tracts of property are controlled by the town in several areas that showed some promise for groundwater development. In other areas permission for testing was obtained from private property owners.

GEOPHYSICAL INVESTIGATIONS

An initial geophysical investigation was conducted during the winter. Frozen ground limited the choice of methods. The gravity method was selected because it is not affected by frozen ground, as the seismic and resistivity methods are. Also, because explosives are not involved, the method can be used more widely than the seismic method.

Gravity profiles were first conducted along lines of easy access such as roads and trails. Although profiles were conducted in all promising areas throughout Manchester, here we will use surveys conducted in Cedar Swamp and adjacent to Round Pond as examples.

Cedar Swamp Site

Gravity profiles conducted along the roads and trails on the Cedar Swamp site showed distinct anomalies of low gravitational attraction. The low anomalies were on the order of 0.5 milligal below what the gravity measurement should have been on a bedrock outcrop. Maximum-minimum computations indicated probable depths to rock for the three major anomalies of 68 to 80, 60 to 65, and 63 to 68 feet, respectively.

The three anomalies were then explored with 2.5-inch diameter test wells which showed depths of refusal of 66, 56, and 78 feet, confirming the gravity results. Permeable materials, however, were thin and near the surface. Fine, silty sands were found at depth.

A second series of gravity measurements was made north of the first survey in a pattern that could be used to map the water saturated sediments to the town line with Essex and along Sawmill Brook east of Cedar Swamp (Fig. 1). These data indicate a relatively deep northward draining valley. They also show a bedrock divide along the Sawmill Brook Valley east of Cedar Swamp.

Resistivity soundings were conducted on eight selected points in the Cedar Swamp area. A profile of four soundings was conducted along the axis of the buried bedrock valley shown by the gravity survey (Fig. 2). A second profile was conducted over shallower rock west of the buried valley, and a single sounding was conducted along the Sawmill Brook Valley east of Cedar Swamp.

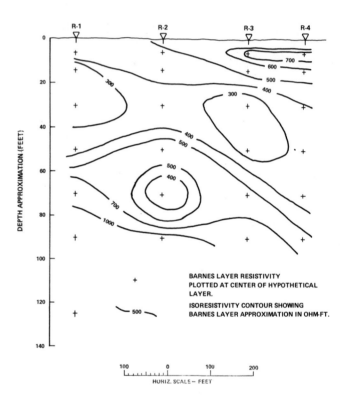

Figure 2. Resistivity profile, Cedar Swamp area, Manchester.

The first resistivity profile shows an area of relatively high resistivity at the surface under soundings R-3 and R-4, indicative of permeable sand and gravel deposits shown in test wells farther south. Under soundings R-1 and R-2 higher resistivities at depth indicate probable sand and gravel deposits which are to be verified by test drilling. Higher resistivities of 1,000 ohm feet or more are believed to represent the underlying crystalline bed rock.

The second resistivity profile in Cedar Swamp is similar, in part, to the first in that a high

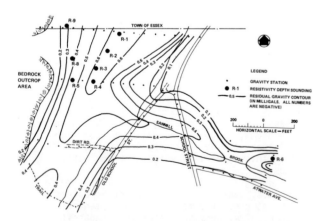

Figure 1. Residual gravity map, Cedar Swamp, Manchester, Massachusetts.

resistivity anomaly is shown at shallow depth in the south end (in R-5). The top of the bed rock is indicated by dipping 700 and 1,000 ohm-foot contours. Below the near-surface sand and gravel, relatively low overburden resistivities are believed to indicate silty, fine-grained, poorly permeable overburden. The single sounding conducted along Sawmill Brook indicated a shallow thickness of low resistivity (poorly permeable) overburden.

Round Pond Site

Our investigation of the Round Pond site was initiated by conducting a gravity traverse along Chebacco Road. It started opposite a bedrock outcrop, crossed a flat swampy area, then ended on an upgrade. The gravity profile indicates that bed rock remains near the surface from the outcrop westward about halfway across the swamp, where it dips downward sharply. It remains deep, even where the land surface rises at the west end of the profile.

Additional gravity measurements were then made to define the location of the buried valley on Town-owned property between Chebacco Road and Round Pond. The map is a Bouguer gravity map rather than a residual gravity map (Fig. 3). This type of map was made because there is little or no regional trend across this site. The map shows a deep bedrock trend that deepens to the northwest. Crossing a divide to the east, another deep trend is encountered. This trend deepens eastward toward Round Pond. Another bedrock low trend angles off the major deep trend in a southwestward direction.

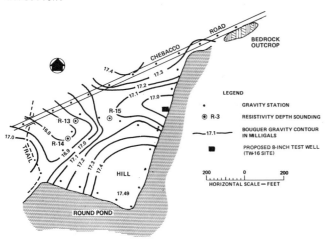

Figure 3. Bouguer gravity map, Round Pond site, Manchester.

Maximum-minimum computations were made for the two major anomalies. The depth of the northwest trending anomaly was computed at 73 to 94 feet. The depth of the eastward trending anomaly was computed at 57 to 68 feet.

Three electrical resistivity soundings were conducted along the low swampy area parallel with Chebacco Road. Sounding R-14 was conducted over the deep northwest trending gravity low, R-13 on a flank of the low and R-15 on the east trending low. The three soundings plotted in cross section show certain resistivity trends (Fig. 4). The low resistivity pocket at the surface at R-14 is believed to indicate mucky swamp deposits. Below the relatively low near-surface resistivities, relatively high values are encountered at fairly shallow depths (small "a-spacings"). There is no clear-cut bedrock resistivity change, but a gradational change from overburden to bed rock. The cross-section is believed to represent relatively coarse-grained (permeable) overburden resistivities. These values are considerably higher than those in Cedar Swamp, except for those that represent coarse-grained materials at shallow depths.

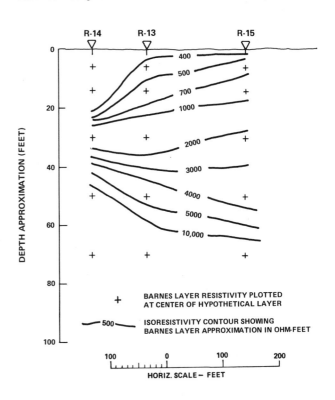

Figure 4. Resistivity profile, Round Pond site, Manchester.

Three 2.5-inch test wells were then drilled to refusal on points that were selected on the basis of the geophysical surveys. All showed predominantly granular materials except at the surface, where varying thicknesses of organic swamp deposits were logged. At test well 15 near Chebacco Road, it is suspected that refusal may have been in coarse granular outwash or bouldery till, as the gravity data indicated a greater depth to bed rock.

## AQUIFER TESTING

Exploration on the Cedar Swamp site will be completed by drilling two 2.5-inch diameter test wells to investigate the gravity and resistivity anomalies at the sites of resistivity soundings R-1 and R-2. If favorable materials are found, a larger diameter well and observation wells would be drilled, and test pumping would be undertaken to establish the long-term safe yield of the aquifer.

Exploration of the Round Pond site will be completed by installing an 8-inch diameter test well and observation wells on the site of TW-16. Test pumping would then be conducted to establish the long-term safe yield for a permanent production well.

## CONCLUSIONS

In an areawide groundwater exploration program such as that which was conducted in the Town of Manchester, Massachusetts, the amount of expensive test drilling can be reduced by appropriate use of geophysics. The geophysical surveys also increase the chances of drilling the best sites by providing subsurface information over complete areas of exploration.

## REFERENCES

Kick, J.F., 1979, Gravity and resistivity investigations, Manchester, Massachusetts: Consulting report prepared for Metcalf & Eddy, Inc., January.

Metcalf & Eddy, 1979, Town of Manchester, Massachusetts: Town-wide groundwater supply investigations, Consulting report prepared for Town of Manchester, Massachusetts, Board of Water and Sewer Commissioners, May 4.  □

Hors-texte

Bhutan postage stamp of Saugus, Massachusetts. New England has a long history of geological exploration, initially involving a search for minerals. In Connecticut copper was first produced near Simsbury in 1709. The bibliography of Maine geology began in 1672. And in New Hampshire mica was first taken from the Ruggles land near Grafton around 1803.

In Massachusetts the Saugus iron works eight miles northeast of Boston were established in 1643, as depicted in this stamp, which is from a set of 12 called the "History of Steel Making." The stamps were printed on steel foil by United States Steel, inscriptions on the reverse reading .001 USS Steel Foil. The set was issued on June 2, 1969, by Bhutan, an 18,000 square mile kingdom that adjoins Tibet in the eastern Himalayas, half way around the northern hemisphere from Massachusetts. The stamp is the 3 ngultrums airmail version and shows the Ironmaster's House, now restored and serving as a museum.

"The exploration of North America, 1630-1776" is the title of a recent book by W. P. Cumming and others (1974, 272 p., Putnam). It was within the period documented that geological surveys in New England, including some of those recounted above, were begun. The subsurface of the region has been under investigation for over 300 years, and at this time a number of new uses are proposed including the underground storage of compressed air.

# Application of the gravity method in Massachusetts

## J. F. KICK
### Dunstable, Massachusetts

## ABSTRACT

This paper outlines the type of gravity data available or obtainable for Massachusetts and their use for geotechnical purposes. Gravity data useful for geological investigations in Massachusetts have been available since at least as early as the late 1930's. Early maps based on pendulum data exhibited the major regional anomalies of New England but are now mainly of historical interest, having been superseded by maps with much denser coverage permitted by development of the modern gravity meter.

Gravity meter data collected during the 1950's and 1960's has been compiled from individual surveys as simple Bouguer gravity maps with five-milligal contour intervals covering the entire State as well as all of New England. These maps, published by the U.S. Geological Survey, have proven to be very useful for regional structural and tectonic studies.

Simple and complete Bouguer gravity maps with 0.5 and 1.0 milligal contour intervals are available or in progress for selected areas. Maps with this level of detail are useful for local structural studies, e.g., studies of the structure of faults, domes, plutonic bodies, and large buried channels. At least three agencies have recently produced or are producing compilations of all available data as part of larger regional projects. Each compilation has unique features.

Precision gravity surveys covering limited areas for geotechnical investigations have proven to be practical and cost effective in Massachusetts. Most such surveys so far completed are for depth to bedrock for groundwater investigations. Depth to bedrock for site studies, rock structural details, voids and other small scale features are, however, also feasible targets for a properly planned, executed and interpreted precision gravity survey. The chief advantages and disadvantages of the gravity method for geotechnical applications are listed.

## INTRODUCTION

Precise measurements of anomalies in the Earth's gravity field have been used for subsurface exploration since the early part of the present century. Since those early days the techniques have undergone considerable development mostly for use in the petroleum industry. Through the years gravity measuring instruments have been developed to become increasingly accurate, drift free and portable. Numerous methods of analysis and interpretation based on mathematical and statistical models have been devised, assisted greatly in more recent times by the development of high speed computers. In this paper the progress of gravity mapping for geological applications, since its inception in Massachusetts, is briefly outlined, and an attempt is made to point out the potential use of the resulting information for geotechnical purposes.

## EARLY GRAVITY MAPS

The earliest geologically useful gravity measurements within the boundaries of Massachusetts known by the writer were made by Duerksen (1949) during 1934-1937 using a pendulum instrument. Additional data and maps were published by Woollard (1948). The maps made from the data of this period are detailed enough to show the salient features of the large regional anomalies and were interpreted geologically by Longwell (1943). The early maps are now chiefly of historical interest, having been superseded by maps with much denser coverage permitted by the development of modern gravity meter instrumentation.

## REGIONAL MAPS: FIVE-MILLIGAL CONTOUR INTERVAL

During the 1950's and 1960's new lightweight, highly accurate meters (e.g., the Worden models) were used in Massachusetts, allowing much more detailed surveys to be made than were previously possible. Data that were compiled from approximately 3700 gravity stations were used to make a simple Bouguer gravity map of Massachusetts (Bromery, 1967). The data of the Massachusetts map were soon thereafter included in a map published by the U.S. Geological Survey of all of New England (Kane et al., 1972). The contour interval of 5 milligals and station density of this map do not allow good resolution of anomalies due to local geologic structure, but regional features are well shown and the map is useful. An understanding of the nature of the sources of these regional anomalies should contribute much toward an understanding of the structure and history of the earth's crust in Massachusetts.

## MAPS WITH A CONTOUR INTERVAL OF 0.5-1.0 MILLIGAL

Since publication of the Massachusetts gravity map there have been several gravity surveys

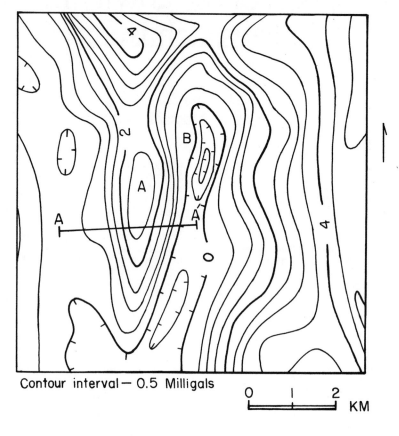

Contour interval— 0.5 Milligals

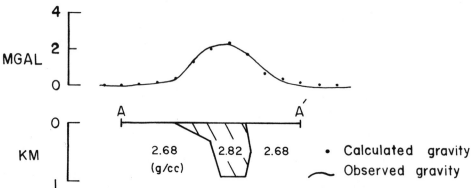

Figure 1.  Residual gravity map of a portion of north-central Massachusetts and a model cross section developed to explain the gravity profile A-A' on the map.

with greater station density and accuracy.  Several maps covering wide areas with stations spaced 1 km to 1 mile apart on the average and with contour intervals as low as 0.5 milligal are now in existence as a result of work by Hall (1973), Kick (1975), Taylor (1977), Fitzpatrick (1978) and others.  At the present time, mapping at this scale is in progress at least in the northeastern part of Massachusetts.  In the not too distant

future it may be possible to compile a second generation gravity map of the entire state at a contour interval of 0.5 to 1.0 milligal.

Surveys at this level of detail are capable of resolving local structural features such as domes, synclines, faults, plutonic bodies and sedimentary basins.  The resulting maps should be useful for geological research, seismotectonic studies, and various types of geotechnical investigations requiring information on the shape, size and depth of burial of such structures.

An example is given to suggest the kind of information on rock structure at depth that can be obtained using a sufficiently detailed gravity map. The contour map in Figure 1 is a residual gravity map prepared by a regional-residual analysis of a portion of a complete Bouguer gravity map of north-central Massachusetts by Kick (1975). Regional-residual analysis is one of several methods used to separate residual anomalies of local interest from anomalies of "regional" extent. Anomaly A on Figure 1 is associated with a synclinal mass of mafic rock (average density 2.82 g/cc) and anomaly B with an anticlinal mass of felsic rock (average density 2.68 g/cc). Information on the geology of the area is from Robinson (1963). The drawing below the residual map shows a profile of the anomaly high over the syncline along line A - A'. The geological cross section below the profile was calculated using iterative modeling techniques. A large number and variety of techniques for analysis and interpretation can be found in the geophysical journals.

A structural interpretation such as the above can have many applications including the design of a tunnel alignment or deep bedrock storage facilities.

REGIONAL COMPILATIONS

Various organizations have produced or are producing compilations of all available data. Massachusetts data have been included in a gravity map of the onshore and offshore northeast United States and southeast Canada (scale 1:1,000,000) by Hildreth (1977) for the New England Seismotectonic Study. The U.S. Geological Survey has recently published, in preliminary open file, several 1° by 2° quadrangle gravity maps for the New England region that were compiled by Bothner and others (1979) and Simpson and others (1979). The feature of interest in these maps is that the data from the contributing surveys have been recomputed and adjusted for mutual consistency. J. Doherty (Weston Geophysical) and G. Simmons (M.I.T.) are now producing a gravity compilation for New England that will include a regional-residual separation by filtering. All of the above recent compilations have unique features that could provide valuable insights for regional studies.

DETAILED GRAVITY SURVEYS

The availability of highly accurate, relatively drift-free gravity meters has made it possible to complete high precision surveys capable of resolving very local subsurface features such as sinkholes, voids, buried bedrock channels, and certain bedrock structures. The La Coste Romberg Model D meter can be read in the microgal range and is especially useful for the detection of small features. The information that can be

obtained from detailed surveys is accurate enough to be used quantitatively for many types of geotechnical investigations.

The most frequent application of detailed gravity surveys in Massachusetts to date is for determining depth to bedrock. Most of the depth to bedrock surveys have been for groundwater exploration projects, but some work has also been done in connection with various other types of subsurface investigation.

The surveys are generally carried out with stations spaced at intervals of 100 to 500 feet on traverses or at grid intersections. Stations are usually located with the use of large scale maps and surveyed for elevation to an accuracy of $\pm$ 0.1 foot. Gravity meters are read to $\pm$ 0.01 milligal. Drift corrections are made from curves constructed from a combination of tidal calculations and frequent base station readings. Terrain corrections are made where necessary in the field and on topographical maps. The resulting complete Bouguer gravity values are plotted as profiles or contoured at intervals of 0.1 to 0.2 milligal.

With careful work it is possible to calculate depths to bedrock with an accuracy in many cases comparable to that obtained by seismic refraction surveys. Quantitative results require careful field work as well as careful data reduction, analysis (removal of regional gradients) and interpretation. Calibration with geological data such as bedrock exposures, borings or seismic results is generally also necessary. A gravity survey can be especially effective when carried out in conjunction with a boring and/or seismic exploration program. The gravity survey receives calibration from the other sources of information and in turn provides a means of extending subsurface information over a larger area than would otherwise be possible.

The most detailed survey completed by the writer so far in Massachusetts was for the purpose of siting new water wells. Stations were placed at intervals of 15-30 feet on a grid layout. The gravity map that resulted from the survey (Fig. 2) has a contour interval of 0.02 milligal (20 microgals). The map shows the effect of a highly irregular bedrock surface. Presumably one would place wells in the deeper areas marked by gravity lows.

Detailed surveys can also be used to glean information from the bedrock. Changes in lithology, fault zones, tunnels, voids, etc., can often be located and delineated. The main requirement for successful application is that the target feature provide a measurable anomaly. The size of an anomaly can be roughly determined beforehand if one can provide a reasonable estimate of the approximate size and depth of the feature and its density contrast with surrounding materials. Geophysical texts such as Dobrin (1976) and Grant and West (1965) provide a variety of formulae and charts for making such estimates. In addition to having a measurable anomaly, one must also be able to screen out anomalies caused by variable

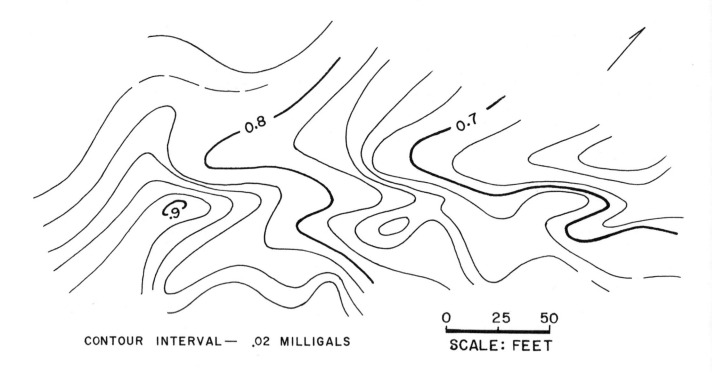

CONTOUR INTERVAL— .02 MILLIGALS

SCALE: FEET

Figure 2.  Detailed gravity map, Milford, Massachusetts.

depth to bedrock, soil density variations, and regional gradients.  Clearly, successful interpretation requires a good knowledge of local geology.

ADVANTAGES AND DISADVANTAGES OF GRAVIMETRIC METHODS FOR GEOTECHNICAL APPLICATIONS

There are several advantages of gravimetric methods for geotechnical applications.  They include:

● Field work can be carried out by one or two persons in any accessible area including highly developed urban and industrialized sites.

● The field work is silent and produces no visible disturbance to an environment other than stakes or other station markings.

● The method lends itself well to areal coverage.  Contour maps of bedrock or other features have obvious advantages over information at points or along profiles.

● Physical properties such as density or porosity of bodies can be derived in some cases to supplement other subsurface information.

● Used appropriately, it is highly cost effective either by itself or in combination with other exploration methods.

Disadvantages of gravimetric methods include:

● Instrumentation is expensive.

● Highly trained and experienced personnel are necessary for accurate, quantitative work.

● Leveling for elevations of stations is necessary.

● Calibration of some kind with geological "knowns" such as outcrops, borings, seismic profiles, etc., is necessary for quantitative work.

● Excessive topographical irregularities, access problems, and certain bedrock complexities may seriously limit the accuracy of the data.

SUMMARY

Gravity data useful for geotechnical purposes have been accumulating in Massachusetts for over 40 years.  A large number and variety of techniques are available for the analysis and interpretation of this sort of data.  The results give information about the size, shape and depth of subsurface masses varying in size from a few feet to continental proportions.

Data useful for broad crustal or tectonic investigations are present in the form of regional and statewide maps with a five-milligal contour interval.

Investigations of more local structural

features such as faults, synclines, sedimentary basins, etc., can be assisted by more detailed maps with a contour interval of 0.5 - 1.0 milligal.

Several organizations have completed or are presently compiling all available data to produce improved or more accurate regional maps.

Highly accurate and detailed gravity surveys are feasible ways of providing useful quantitative subsurface information at restricted sites for geotechnical investigations. Such detailed surveys have been most frequently used to find depth to bedrock for groundwater and engineering investigations, but any subsurface condition involving a density contrast of sufficient size is a possible target for a gravity survey.

The gravity method has limitations as does any method of exploration. The cost effectiveness of a gravity survey can only be assessed after consideration of the advantages and disadvantages of the method within the context of the goals of the exploration and the geology of the prospective site.

## REFERENCES

Bothner, W. A., Simpson, R. W., Kucks, R. P., 1979, Bouguer gravity map of the Providence 1° X 2° quadrangle, Rhode Island - Massachusetts - Connecticut - New York: U.S. Geological Survey Open-File Report 79-1084.

Bromery, R. W., 1967, Simple Bouguer gravity map of Massachusetts: U.S. Geological Survey Geophysical Investigations Map GP-612.

Dobrin, M. B., 1976, Introduction to geophysical prospecting: McGraw-Hill Book Co., Inc.

Duerksen, J. A., 1949, Pendulum gravity data in the United States: U.S. Coast and Geodetic Survey, Special Publication 244, 218 p.

Fitzpatrick, J. C., 1978, Interpretation and significance of a major positive gravity anomaly in central Massachusetts: M.S. Thesis, University of Massachusetts, Amherst, 45 p.

Grant, F. S., and West, G. F., 1965, Interpretation theory in applied geophysics: New York, McGraw-Hill Book Co., Inc.

Hall, D. J., 1973, Geology and geophysics of the Belchertown batholith, west-central Massachusetts: Ph.D. Thesis, University of Massachusetts, Amherst, 110 p.

Hildreth, C. T., 1977, Bouguer gravity map of northeastern United States and southeastern Canada: New York State Museum map and chart series 32.

Kane, M. F., Simmons, G., Diment, W. H., Fitzpatrick, M. M., Joyner, W. B., and Bromery, R. W., 1972, Bouguer gravity and generalized geologic map of New England and adjoining areas: U.S. Geological Survey, Geophysical Investigations Map-839.

Kick, J. F., 1975, Gravity study of the gneiss dome terrain of north-central Massachusetts: Ph.D. Thesis, University of Massachusetts, Amherst, 170 p.

Longwell, C. R., 1943, Geologic interpretation of gravity anomalies in the southern New England - Hudson Valley region: Geological Society of America Bulletin, v. 54, p. 555-590.

Robinson, P., 1963, Gneiss domes of the Orange area, Massachusetts and New Hampshire: Ph.D. Thesis, Harvard University, 253 p.

Simpson, R. W., Bothner, W. A., and Kucks, R. P., 1979, Bouguer gravity map of the Albany 1° X 2° quadrangle, New York - Connecticut - Massachusetts and Vermont: U.S. Geological Survey preliminary Open-File Report 79-970.

Taylor, S. R., 1977, Structure of the Clinton-Newbury and Bloody Bluff fault zones in eastern Massachusetts, in A study of New England seismicity with emphasis on Massachusetts and New Hampshire: Publication 1980 by U.S. Nuclear Regulatory Commission NUREG/CR-1186.

Woollard, G. P., 1948, Gravity and magnetic investigations in New England: American Geophysical Union Transactions, v. 29, no. 3, p. 306-317.

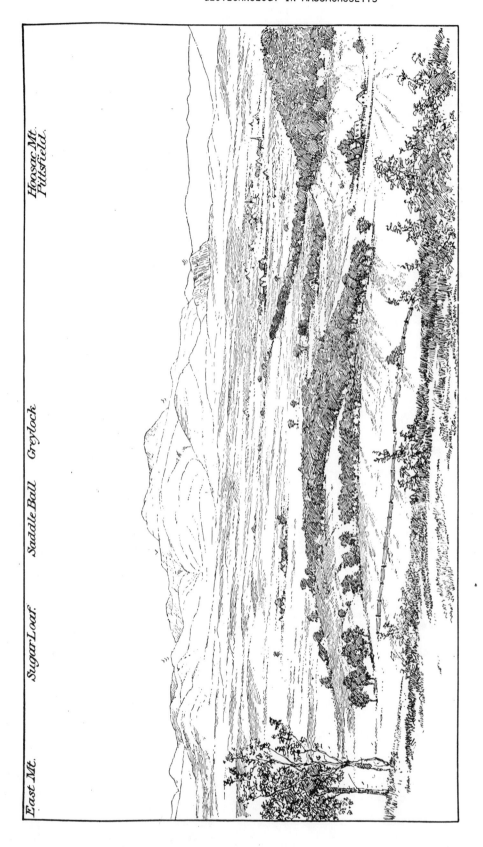

*East Mt.*  *SugarLoaf.*  *Saddle Ball*  *Greylock*  *Hoosac Mt.*
*Pittsfield.*

Hors-texte  Southern side of Mount Greylock, northwestern Massachusetts.  This is a sketch of Greylock or Saddle Mountain, south side, from the north end of Lenox Mountain, showing the saddle formed by the two summits, Greylock and Saddle Ball, due to the central syncline in the Greylock Schist.  The broad benches on either side (marked by one and two birds) are due to the Bellowspipe Limestone.  The subordinate ridges and spurs (marked by three birds) are due to minor folds in the Berkshire Schist.  The broad plain of the middle ground is underlain by Stockbridge Limestone.  Mount Greylock is the tallest peak in the state.  (From Geology of the Green Mountains in Massachusetts, by R. Pumpelly, J. E. Wolff, and T. N. Dale, U.S. Geological Survey, Monograph 23, 1894, 206 p.).

# Remote sensing applications in engineering geology

E. A. BLACKEY, JR.
New England Division
Corps of Engineers

## ABSTRACT

The value of remote sensing techniques in resolving geologic problems in the field of engineering has been well documented by the early use of aerial photography analysis. New remote sensing systems using satellite data allow for a larger field of view with less detail, but due to the continuous orbiting characteristics of the satellite they have the added potential for noting temporal changes, as well as a synoptic or "overview" capability. In general, the level of required detail defines the system to be selected, with the greater detail being obtained from the non-satellite systems. The main economic advantage of satellite imagery is the synoptic view with repetitive coverage at relatively low cost versus the higher cost of aircraft photography for smaller areas. The value of remote sensing techniques may be equally applicable to projects in the various phases of planning, design, construction, and operations.

For geologic interpretations, the geomorphic land forms, drainage patterns, erosional characteristics and color patterns delineated by photogeologic interpretation of aerial imagery are used to determine rock types and soil characteristics. Application of this knowledge to such engineering considerations as slope stability, groundwater configuration, foundation-bearing capacity, dam site selection, reservoir leakage, and availability of construction materials is an extension of previously well documented processes. Depending on the level of detail required, available imagery from aircraft or satellite can be selected. For large scale interpretation of geologic structure, satellite and NASA underflight imagery are effectively utilized in the analysis of regional tectonics, lineaments and drainage patterns, as well as mineral or lithologic signatures. This type of analysis is particularly adaptable to monitoring such conditions as sediment variations, slope stability, landslide identification and changes in water surface area, where these features are to be monitored on a continuing basis. Side-looking airborne radar is another large scale system which, by a shadowing effect, accentuates regional geologic structures. It is effective in special situations and has all-weather day or night capability.

For site specific evaluation, photo interpretation of black and white and color conventional photography at a 1:25,000 or larger scale provides a high level of detail directly relatable to project work. Estimations of material quantities and slope stability are typical studies which, when coordinated with ground truth verification, provide a reliable base for the detailed design phase of the project. Remote sensing systems such as aerial magnetometers and airborne resistivity surveys give valuable data for mineral, groundwater and in-situ rock quality studies. These are but a few of the applications which can be utilized with adequate verification by ground truth programs. Remote sensing may be applied to engineering geology in a variety of other ways by taking advantage of new systems and new techniques, utilizing previously established analysis procedures. The process is cost effective if properly scheduled and is becoming increasingly time efficient with the routine availability of remote sensing data.

## INTRODUCTION

Application of remote sensing techniques to the practical problems of engineering geology can largely be assessed by focusing on the results from either an environmental or a design aspect on a least cost basis. The collection of remote sensing data should play a key role in geologic exploration as it is the most practical method of measuring many pertinent physical properties of large, generally inaccessible, areas. The data provide a means for studying regional features, extrapolating local measurements to regional scales, and identifying critical areas for subsequent detailed studies. Ideally, analysis should begin with large regions and then progress to successively smaller key areas.

This paper discusses three recent studies initiated by the Corps of Engineers that represent a broad cross section of the cost effective applications of remote sensing techniques.

### AERIAL PHOTOGRAMMETRIC STUDY FOR LOCATION OF SURFICIAL GEOLOGY MATERIALS

This work was conducted for the Dickey-Lincoln School Lakes hydropower project located in a remote section of Maine's Aroostook County in the upper St. John River valley, adjacent to the Canadian border (McKim, Merry, and Blackey, 1978). This project will inundate an area of 138 square miles to a depth of more than 300 feet in a watershed area of 6,811 square miles. The study was initiated to apply state-of-the-art remote sensing techniques to the delineation and quantification of surficial geologic units in the vicinity of a large reservoir project. Two objectives were established.

- To locate unconsolidated deposits of sufficient quantity to provide approximately 60 million cubic yards of material for construction purposes with the physical properties required by the structural designers.

- To locate these deposits in areas which would be inundated by the reservoir and thus reduce the degree of excavation scars on the natural terrain. Further analysis of the surficial units permitted interpretation of such factors as reservoir stability and leakage conditions.

The relationship of the tones and textures evident on the photography to topographic and geomorphic position allowed 14 surficial geologic units to be delineated. The units identified were alluvial fan (AF), alluvial terrace (AT), esker (E), flood plain (FP), glacial moraine (GM), kame (K), kame terrace (KT), outwash (O), outwash terrace (OT), bed rock (R), till over bed rock (T/R), wet outwash (WO), and wet till (WT). A typical plate delineating the distribution of materials is shown as Figure 1.

The areal extent of the surficial units was quantified by using a color densitometer. The estimated thickness of each surficial unit was developed from measurements made of the field exposures, seismic refraction surveys and on-site borings.

The volume estimates obtained from the survey allowed selection of the most appropriate project design at the least possible cost. This study also reduced the material haulage distances, which could result in considerable savings in cost and a minimum of environmental disturbance outside the reservoir area.

## AIRBORNE RESISTIVITY AND MAGNETOMETER SURVEY FOR LOCATION OF ROCK CONSTRUCTION MATERIALS

This study was conducted on the Dickey-Lincoln School Lakes hydropower project for a reason similar to that of the study for the unconsolidated material, but with somewhat different parameters. Locating a massive rock type suitable for use as aggregate and slope protection in a region of thinly foliated slate required an investigative method that would reduce the area of physical exploration from a few hundred square miles to a few acres. The area of study is regionally mantled by a thin but consistent layer of glacial till with few bedrock exposures. The region also has poor access and is generally undeveloped.

This problem was approached by determining whether or not the more massive regional intrusions identified some 20 miles away might also occur closer to the site. Since haulage of

approximately one million yards of quality rock is a major expense, finding an area closer to the project could save a substantial sum of money.

A preliminary ground resistivity study was conducted to determine if resistivity contrasts of known rock types in the region were great enough to justify an extensive airborne survey using radiowave resistivity techniques at VLF (very low frequency), a frequency range well suited to a bedrock study. The preliminary study indicated that contrasts in electrical properties between intrusive rocks and other rock types in the area are large enough to permit the use of airborne resistivity to identify variations in rock types. To assist in identification, airborne resistivity and magnetometer surveys were conducted simultaneously to obtain for the rock types both electrical and magnetic property data (to detect magnetic mineralization). A normalized distribution of the ground data showing a clear distinction between the slate and the intrusive rocks is shown in Figure 2.

The study area encompassed approximately 640 square miles and included a control area of known rock types and resistivity properties. Spacing of flight lines was approximately 0.4 km or 1/4 mile. During the first week of the airborne survey, extensive ground measurements were also performed in an area of known bed rock. These special studies were made to verify the accuracy of the entire airborne survey, with respect to rock type differentiation and the effect of flight altitude upon resolution of resistivity anomalies. Airphoto mosaics and topographic maps were used as navigation aids. A flight path camera operated continuously along the flight lines. Reference points (fiducials) were placed in the flight path recovery photograph and at corresponding locations on data stored on an analogue (pentrace) recorder. Manually triggered fiducials were used to note points on the ground such as streams and lakes, as well as the start of the flight lines. Flight path recovery film was developed, and recorded data were printed each day. In cases of missing or unusable photos or other problems, the flight lines were flown again. An airborne magnetometer survey to record variations in the earth's magnetic field was conducted by the same aircraft during the resistivity survey. When resistivity values obtained during the ground control study are compared to those obtained from an airborne survey, the agreement between the ground and airborne observations becomes apparent. Slate values in Figure 2 should be compared to values for the same rock type shown as Ds values in Figure 3.

Steep topographic changes within the survey area prevented the aircraft from maintaining a constant altitude. A multi-elevation test was conducted to determine the effect on resolution of survey altitude. In general, the distribution of resistivity anomalies remains unchanged, and only the detail decreased at the higher altitude. All factors being considered, an excellent level of correlation was found between the airborne and ground reading for the test sector, ensuring the

Figure 1.  Selected portion of the surficial geology
map of the Dickey-Lincoln School Lakes project, Maine.

quality of the remaining resistivity survey.

The most noticeable features of the plotted
VLF data are the densely contoured resistivity
highs.  This pattern reflects the surficial and
bedrock geology of the area.  In areas of high
relief, the survey produced both high and low
areas of resistivity.  In general, the highest
resistivities are associated with areas of major
relief.  This could be explained on the basis
that in these locations the till is thinnest, and
the values reflect the generally more resistive
bed rock which is near the surface.  It is also
apparent from a close comparison of resistivity
contours and topographic contours that mountainous
areas where till cover is thin can likewise produce contours of relatively low resistivity.  This
indicates that the lack of a conductive overburden

is not necessarily a major influence on resistivity distinctions in these areas.  The most plausible explanations for the resistivity distinctions
in areas of high relief are either differing bedrock types or increases in the electrical field
caused by sharp topographic features, which sup-
press resistivity values.

A further correlation was made utilizing the
general distribution patterns of rock types from
a previously completed bedrock geology reconnaissance.  The bedrock units occur in broad bands in
the central part of the study area, becoming more
contorted and narrow with a greater contrast in
rock types from south to north.  When the areas
of higher resistivities, i.e., values exceeding
3,000 ohm-meters, are plotted, they coincide with
units of bed rock that were mapped as a cyclically

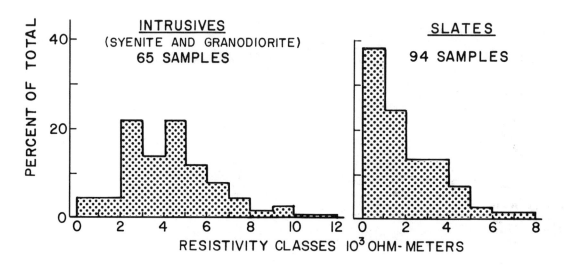

Figure 2. Normalized distribution of ground resistivity data.

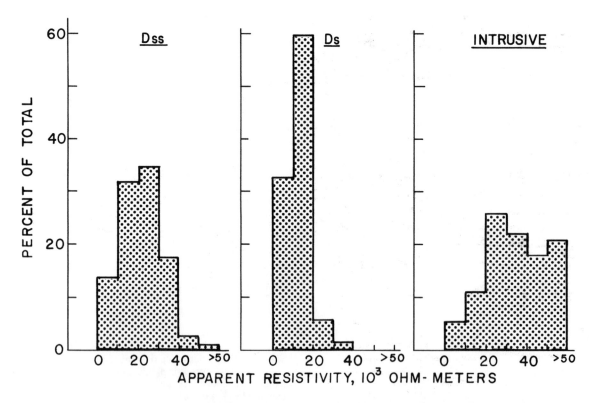

Figure 3. Airborne resistivity data for the various mapped rock types (Dss: cyclically bedded gray slate and sandstone; Ds: gray slate and minor graywacke). Values were obtained by sampling at regular intervals along the flight lines.

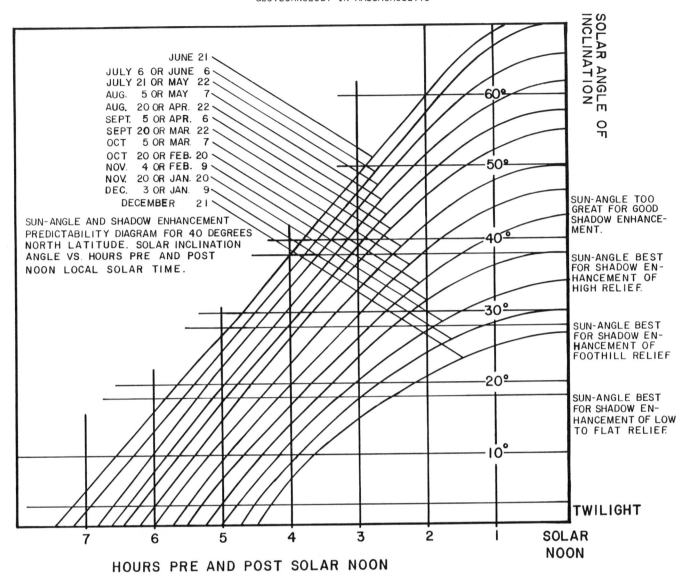

Figure 4. Shadow enhancement diagram for 40° N latitude
for predicting optimum shadow enhancement for terrain slope
angles, time of day and season. (Source: Walker and
Trexler, 1977).

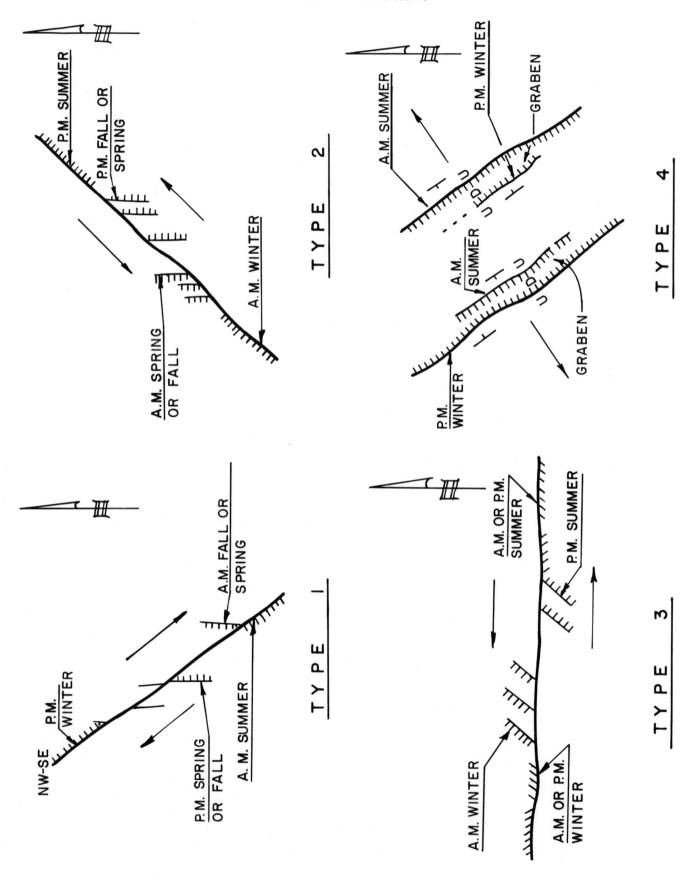

TYPE 1

TYPE 2

TYPE 3

TYPE 4

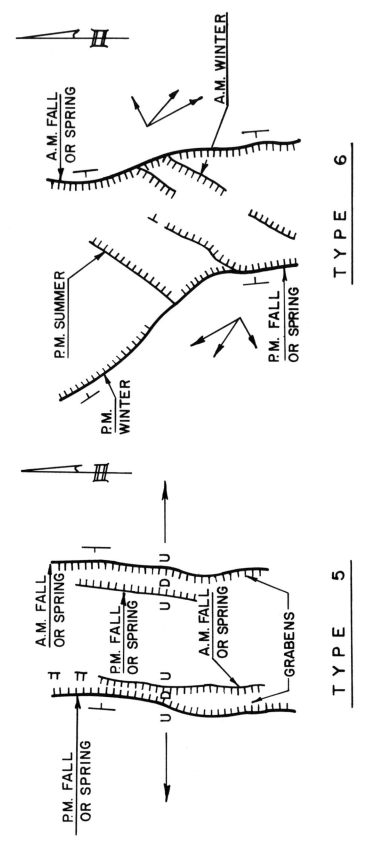

Figure 5. Application of low sun angle photography to study active faulting. (Source: Cluff and Slemmons, 1972).

bedded gray slate and sandstone. The highest resistivity values (6,000 ohm-meters) are associated with the intrusive rocks in the ground control study area.

Analysis of these results indicated that the search had been unsuccessful in locating intrusive rocks of the types present in the control area (granodiorite or syenite) any closer to the dam site than the previously known deposits. The study did, however, indicate that certain sections of the regional slate formation exhibited higher than average resistivity and could be possible sites of rock types suitable for construction (Sellman, Arcone, and Delaney, 1976). At that stage of the study, it could only be assumed that sandstone zones within the regional slate formations were the most resistive types. No magnetic anomalies were found in the area. This further verified that the granodiorite and syenite formations, which contain modal magnetite (Boone, 1962) as a common accessory mineral, were not the cause of the higher resistivity zones closer to the project structures.

Field explorations determined that these zones of higher resistivity reflected widely jointed blocky sandstone zones within the regional slate formations. Explorations conducted for a potential quarry site revealed that the sandstone zones occurred to at least 100 feet in depth and had considerable areal extent. Their locations, although generally in areas of higher relief, were not coincident with topographic highs.

Initial estimates indicate that obtaining suitable rock for concrete aggregate and select slope protection from this area would not only eliminate the use of an area which was environmentally sensitive, but would also save many millions of dollars in transporting the material to the site.

REMOTE SENSING ANALYSIS OF FAULT-RELATED STRUCTURES IN NEW ENGLAND

Another example of the use of remote sensing techniques is the comparison of satellite imagery to a series of low-sun angle oblique aerial photographs. The purpose was to find regional trends by using a remote sensing analysis to locate fault-related structures that may be related to seismic hazards in the New England area (Glass and Slemmons, 1978; Slemmons and Glass, 1978).

In the first stage of the study using Landsat imagery analysis of the area, imagery interpretation was compared with various structural, gravity, aeromagnetic, seismotectonic, seismicity and geologic maps. Remote sensing investigations in areas similar to New England in climate, topography and Pleistocene glacial processes have successfully led to the detection, delineation and determination of the character of active or capable faults. The approach involves a general search for major faults that are of sufficient length to have potential, if reactivated, for producing damage to structures. Consideration is

also given to the possibility that small earthquakes can occur because of density contrasts between major geologic units and/or proximity to adjoining faults and joint systems.

Interpretations of the imagery were made on clear mylar overlays over black and white 1:1,000,000 scale Landsat images. These were then transferred to a 1:250,000 scale map base. The lack of fine scale resolution on Landsat images and the variable quality of mapping basement faults result in most lineament maps showing many lineaments of non-fault origin and very few, if any, that are active or capable. Lineament maps of this type include zones of master joint systems as well as dead faults and other non-tectonically active or capable linear features.

The evaluation and verification program for lineaments should be conducted with priority assigned to their length and their proximity to vital structures. A guide has been established for approximate fault length versus distance from the structures using earlier guides for the surface rupture length versus magnitude (Slemmons, 1977).

To further evaluate the more critical lineaments, they are examined by the use of standard aerial photographic images of larger scale with a low-sun angle illumination. With the sun at a low angle of incidence, the structure is enhanced by either shading from back-lighting or high-lighting from frontal illumination. This system has been highly effective in other areas of the country, and is being applied to New England on a trial basis to determine its effectiveness here.

Previous experience has determined that the best conditions for illumination generally develop with illumination angles of less than 25 degrees, although this angle is slope dependent as is shown by the accompanying Figure 4. The ideal illumination is obtained at different seasons and times of day since the direction of the sun at sunrise and sunset varies greatly with the season. By planning the ideal time of day and, to a lesser extent, the ideal season, it is possible to enhance faults of varying orientation. Some examples of this are shown in Figure 5.

This work is not complete. The final stage will consist of detailed ground investigations along any selected potential fault structures.

CONCLUSIONS

These are examples of remote sensing applications which were initiated by the Corps of Engineers to solve particular problems. In most cases, these techniques have produced results much faster and at far less cost than conventional methods. In many instances, they have provided data that could be obtained only by remote sensing techniques. The value of remote sensing is its ability to narrow the area of study to one that can be investigated in a reasonable framework of time and cost. The geologic effort can then be concentrated on a smaller area with greater effectiveness.

ACKNOWLEDGMENTS

The author thanks C.J. Merry, S.A. Arcone, and D.B. Slemmons for their careful and constructive reviews of the manuscript.

REFERENCES

Boone, G., 1962, Potassic feldspar enrichment in magma--origin of syenite in Debouille district, northern Maine: Geological Society of America Bulletin, v. 73, p. 1451-1476.

Cluff, L.S., and Slemmons, D.B., 1972, Wasatch fault zone--features defined by low-sun angle photography: Utah Geological Association Publication 1, G1-G9.

Glass, C.E., and Slemmons, D.B., 1978, Imagery in earthquake analysis state-of-the-art for assessing earthquake hazards in the United States: U.S. Army Engineers Waterways Experiment Station, Miscellaneous Paper S-73-1, Report 11, 235 p.

McKim, H.L., Merry, C.J., and Blackey, Jr., E.A., 1978, Use of remote sensing to quantify construction material and to define geologic lineaments--Dickey-Lincoln School Lakes Project, Maine: Proceedings of the 12th International Symposium on Remote Sensing of Environment, p. 1027-1031.

Sellman, P.V., Arcone, S.A., and Delaney, A.J., 1976, Airborne resistivity and magnetometer survey in northern Maine for obtaining information on bedrock geology: Corps of Engineers, Cold Regions Research and Engineering Laboratory, Report 76-37.

Slemmons, D.B., 1977, Faults and earthquake magnitude: U.S. Army Engineers Waterways Experiment Station Miscellaneous Paper S-73-1, Report 6, 228 p.

Slemmons, D.B., and Glass, C.E., 1978, Remote sensing analysis of fault-related structures in New England and related seismic hazards of Corps of Engineer projects: Unpublished report, New England Division Corps of Engineers, Contract No. DACW 33-78-C-0023.

Walker, P.M., and Trexler, D.T., 1977, Low sun-angle photography: Photogrammetric Engineering and Remote Sensing, v. 43, p. 493-505.

Hors-texte

Mount Washington, New Hampshire's highest peak, viewed across the Great
Gulf. (Courtesy, New Hampshire Office of Vacation Travel; Dick Smith.)

# 5

# SITING OF CRITICAL
# AND OTHER FACILITIES

Session moderator

D. Woodhouse
Goldberg, Zoino & Associates, Inc.

# Geology of foundation excavations at Seabrook Station, Seabrook, New Hampshire

F. X. BELLINI
Yankee Atomic Electric Company

D. H. CORKUM
Morrison-Knudsen Company

A. J. STEWART
United Engineers and Constructors, Inc.

## ABSTRACT

Geologic mapping of foundation excavations at the Seabrook Station nuclear power plant was done to fulfill regulatory-licensing commitments. Mapping covered a 1000-foot by 700-foot area of exposed bedrock from which about 1,000,000 cubic yards of rock were removed. A map of the entire area was made at a scale of 1 inch = 32 feet, and maps scaled 1 inch = 4 feet were made for all floors and walls in foundation excavations for safety related, category I structures. Detailed mapping was also done in faulted areas beyond the safety-related excavations.

The site lies at the northern margin of the Newburyport pluton where the latter intrudes the older Kittery formation. Both these units and a set of cross-cutting diabase dikes occur in site excavations. The Newburyport here is a mixture of diorite and quartz diorite, and the Kittery, occurring as large xenoliths, is an impure, often foliated, quartzite. Contacts between these two are either sharp or gradational.

There are characteristic fault and joint patterns in the two formations which are clearly discernible in the excavations. Faulting in the Newburyport occurs along joints oriented N20°W, 60°E; N45°E, 60°S and 37°N; and parallel to diabase dikes at N45°E, ~ 90°. Faulting in the Kittery occurs parallel to joints, foliation and bedding at N80W, 80N. While much of the faulting occurred just prior to and just after diabase intrusion, there is clear evidence that some faulting occurred during diabase intrusion. All faulting is of a minor nature, and it is concluded that the most recent faulting is genetically related to diabase intrusion or associated late-Triassic crustal tension. None of the faults constitutes a safety hazard to the site.

## INTRODUCTION

Seabrook Station is a two-unit nuclear-powered electric generating plant. It is located along the New Hampshire coast about two miles north of the New Hampshire-Massachusetts border (Fig. 1). As of March, 1980, construction was about 30 percent complete.

This paper summarizes results of geologic mapping done in the bedrock excavations for the numerous large buildings which will contain the plant itself. A complete description of plant site, site vicinity and regional geology is pre-

sented by PSNH (1980). Mapping in site excavations was done in compliance with federal regulations which necessitate detailed geologic investigation of such exposures. Mapping was performed under a quality assurance program.

The focus of this study was on faults. Regulations essentially prevent the location of a nuclear power plant within five miles of a "capable" fault. A capable fault is defined (CFR, 1978) as: a fault which has moved once in the last 35,000 years; a fault which has moved more than once in the last 250,000 years; a fault with associated macroseismicity; or a fault of essentially unproven age. Although no capable faults have been described in New England, and earthquakes in the region do not result in surface faulting, the age of any faults found in plant site studies must nevertheless be demonstrated.

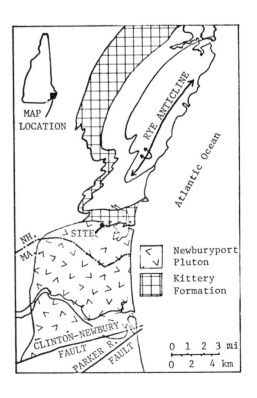

Figure 1. Site location and geologic setting.

Figure 2.

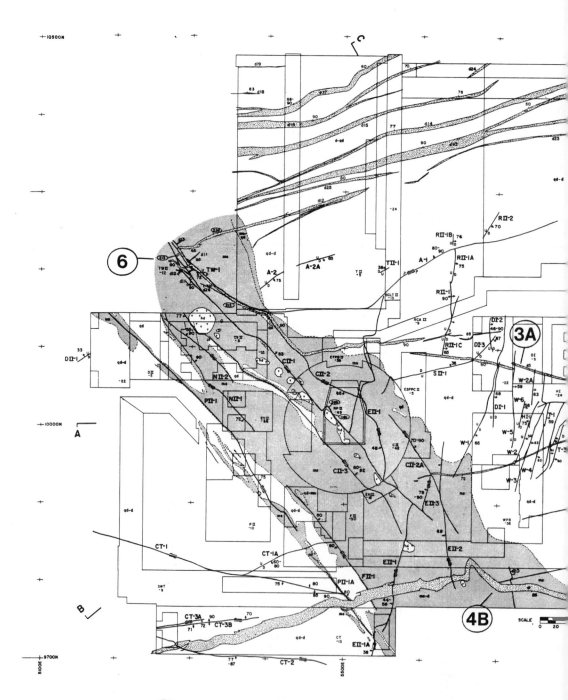

③A – Reference locations for other figures

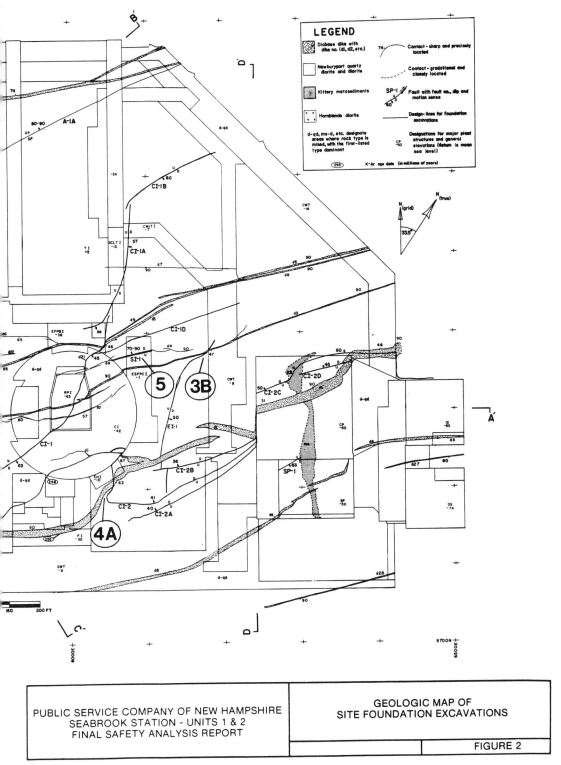

| PUBLIC SERVICE COMPANY OF NEW HAMPSHIRE SEABROOK STATION - UNITS 1 & 2 FINAL SAFETY ANALYSIS REPORT | GEOLOGIC MAP OF SITE FOUNDATION EXCAVATIONS |
|---|---|
| | FIGURE 2 |

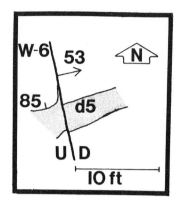

Figure 3A. Fault W-6
of set 1 displaces
diabase dike d5. Host
rock is Newburyport.

Figure 3B. Fault EI-1
of set 1 is cross-cut
by dike d5. Host rock
is Newburyport.

The area of bedrock exposed in site foundations was approximately 1100 feet by 700 feet
(Fig. 2). Mapping was carried out at a scale of
1 inch = 4 feet for floors and walls of foundations for safety related buildings. Intervening
areas were mapped at a scale of 1 inch = 32 feet.
Figure 2 is a composite of many maps produced at
those scales.

GEOLOGIC SETTING

The Seabrook site is located at the west
side of Hampton Harbor on a bedrock "peninsula"
surrounded on three sides by salt marsh. Bedrock
underlying the site consists mostly of diorite
and quartz diorite of the Newburyport pluton and
impure quartzite of the Kittery formation. A
number of diabase dikes and a minor amount of
hornblende diorite occur in the country rock.

The site is situated just a few hundred feet
south of the Newburyport pluton's northern contact
with the Kittery formation which is part of the
Merrimack Group (Fig. 1). The Newburyport is a
syntectonic (Shride, 1971) intrusive, generally
considered Devonian in age, although evidence for
a substantially older age is accumulating (Zartman, personal communication). The portion of the
pluton on land is about seven miles across. To
the south it is cut off by the Clinton-Newbury
fault which was found to have last moved in the
Permian (PSNH, 1980). The Kittery is a fine-

TABLE 1. SUMMARY OF FAULT DESCRIPTIONS

|  | Set number 1 | Set number 2 | Set number 3 | Set number 4 | Set number 5 | Set number 6 | Set number 7 |
|---|---|---|---|---|---|---|---|
| No. in set | 21 | 10 | 11 | 4 | 2 | 9 | 4 |
| Strike, dip | N2OW, 63NE | N37E, 36NW | N38E, 60SE | N40E, very steep | N70E, steep N&S | N8ON, steep N&S | N40N, 69SW |
| Length (ft) | 14- 257 | 10- 557 | 17- 390 | 44- 400 | 255+ -342+ | 89- 500+ | 33+ -378 |
| Width | 1/16-1/4in | 1/16-6in | 1/16-1/2in | 1/16-5in | 1/8-12in | 1/16in-6ft | 1/16in-12ft |
| Motion sense | NOR RL | NOR | NOR | NOR | LL NOR | LL NOR | RL NOR REV |
| Weathering | SL | MOD | MOD | SL TO MOD | SL TO SEV | SL TO SEV | SL TO MOD |
| Mineralization | QTZ, CAL | MINOR QTZ | QTZ, CAL | CAL | CAL | CHLOR, CAL, PYR | CHLOR |

NOTES: Faults are divided into seven sets based principally on orientation and motion sense. Length and
width data are ranges for each set. Lengths with a "+" represent faults which end outside the map
area.

grained, quartzitic metasediment. It has been considered Silurian in age although there are indications that the entire Merrimack Group is substantially older (Aleinikoff and Zartman, 1978). North of the site the Kittery occurs in the Rye Anticline. The nose of this structure is cut by the Newburyport pluton's northern contact.

Diabase dikes of Mesozoic age intrude the country rock throughout New England (McHone, 1978) and indeed along the length of the Appalachians. These typically trend northeasterly and are related to rifting events which originally formed the Atlantic Ocean.

## BEDROCK UNDERLYING THE SITE

The Newburyport at the site is a mixture of an older, fine-grained diorite and a younger, medium-grained quartz diorite. The quartz diorite encloses xenoliths of diorite and "streams" through the diorite, imparting a crude east-west fabric to the rock. This mixture of rock types is peculiar to the northern fringe of the Newburyport pluton and has been called an intrusion breccia by Shride (1971). The texture of this mixed rock indicates that the diorite was still somewhat plastic when the quartz diorite intruded. The minerals comprising the diorite are amphibole and plagioclase with minor quartz, plagioclase, biotite and accessories. The quartz diorite consists

of quartz, plagioclase, biotite and accessories.

The Kittery at the site is an impure, fine-grained quartzite which shows some effects of contact metamorphism. This rock consists of quartz, sericite, plagioclase, chlorite and biotite. The Kittery occurs in site excavations as two xenoliths (roof pendants?) with dimensions of tens or hundreds of feet (Fig. 2). The larger of these occurs in the unit II foundation area. The fabric in this xenolith is conformable with the fabric of the Kittery formation to the north which dips steeply south off the nose of the northeast-trending Rye Anticline, and trends about N80°-90°W. Small pods of a hornblende diorite occur along this trend in the larger xenolith. The strike of the smaller Kittery xenolith near the east end of the site is about N40°W.

The diabase in site dikes is fine grained with subophitic to ophitic texture. Minerals include plagioclase and pyroxene with some olivine, chlorite and biotite. Calcite veins and amygdales are commonly associated with this diabase. Diabase dikes generally strike N40°-45°E with steep dips to the south predominant (Fig. 2). Many include segments which deviate considerably from this average attitude and which also display considerable irregularity. Dike widths range from less than an inch to 12 feet. Twenty-eight dikes occur in site foundations, and many more have been identified in nearby borings. Seven of nine K-Ar age determinations for on-site and nearby diabase dikes ranged from 212 to 236 million years. Two other dikes yielded ages of 255 and 295 million years, respectively.

Well-developed N45°E-trending joints are present in the country rock at the site. These sets dip about 40°NW and about 60°SE. The smaller Kittery xenolith and portions of the larger xeno-

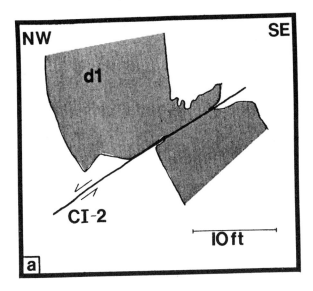

Figure 4A. Fault CI-2 cuts dike d1. Host rock is Newburyport.

Figure 4B. Fault CI-2 displaces dike d20 and ends against dike d1. Host rock is Kittery.

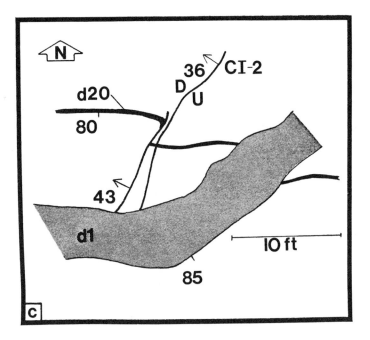

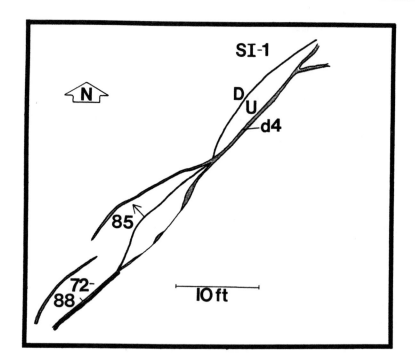

Figure 5. Fault SI-1 is cross-cut by dike d4, which also flows along the fault for a short distance. Host rock is Newburyport.

lith are devoid of these joint sets. Another strong joint set in the Newburyport is oriented N20°W, 63°NE. Weaker sets have attitudes of N45°E, 80°-90°N; N80°-90°E, 80°S-80°N; and N50°W, 50°NE.

The dominant joint set in the larger Kittery xenolith strikes N75°-90°E and dips steeply north or south. These joints are parallel to the foliation and to thin (6 inches to 3 ft) phyllitic zones. Weaker joint sets are oriented: N37°E, 60°SE; N15°W, 60°SW; N10°E, 65°W; N45°W, 70°SW.

Joints in the diabase dikes are prismatic cooling joints which typically occur at right angles to or parallel to dike contacts.

Sixty-one faults were mapped in site excavations (Fig. 2, Table 1). Displacements occurred almost exclusively along the pre-existing joints described above. The scale of this faulting indicates that it resulted from minor crustal adjustments. Cross-cutting and geometric relationships among faults and dikes indicate that the most recent faulting was contemporaneous with dike emplacement well over 200 million years ago. The faulting is thus ancient and of no consequence to site safety.

## FAULT DESCRIPTIONS

Table 1 summarizes the data collected for site faults. The faults are divided into seven sets based on orientation. A genetic relationship among faults of a given set is also evidenced by: similarity of motion sense based on offsets and slickensides, proximity in space, and cross-cutting relationships. It is also apparent that fault sets are, in turn, related to one another. This is evidenced by cross-cutting relationships, their collective presence in a limited area, and by their motion senses.

Fault sets 1 through 5, as listed in Table 1, occur in the Newburyport. Sets 6 and 7 occur exclusively in the larger Kittery xenolith. With the exception of set 5 which contains only 2 faults, fault sets consistently include both longer and shorter faults. All faults, save one, terminate with at least one end in site excavations, and it is clear from their dimensions and small offsets that these faults are minor geologic features. Widths of faults in sets 1 through 5 are narrow and fairly consistent from one set to another. Faults in sets 6 and 7 are wider. This is primarily because they have occurred along phyllitic zones in the larger Kittery xenolith, and this promoted a somewhat more diffuse shearing. Weathering along faults is only locally severe.

Mineralization for sets 1 through 5 typically consists of quartz and/or calcite. Chlorite is more typical of faults in sets 6 and 7 in the Kittery.

Fault motions are consistent with a tensional stress field, explained subsequently, which induced dike emplacement. The presence of older reverse motion components (reverse-stepping slickensides are overprinted by normal-stepping ones) on faults in sets 6 and 7 suggests that reverse motion occurred along these phyllitic zones at the time of intrusion of the Newburyport pluton.

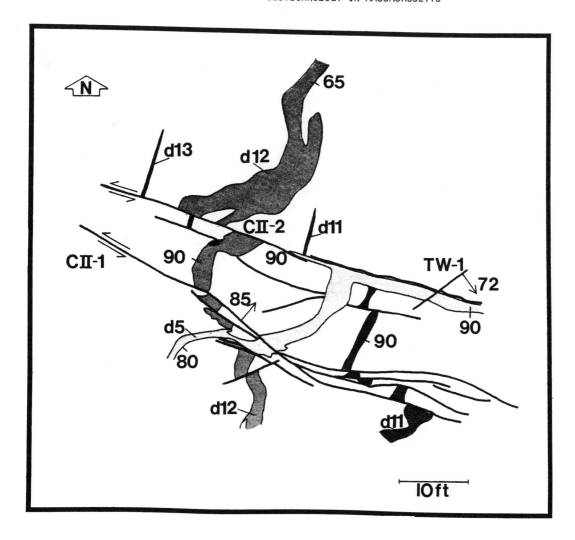

Figure 6. Faults CII-1 and CII-2 displace dikes d11, d12 and d13. Dike d5 flows along and cross-cuts fault CII-2 and is offset along only one of many shears which comprise fault CII-1. Fault TW-1 displaces both fault CII-2 and dike d5. Host rock is Kittery.

## CROSS-CUTTING RELATIONS

Five of the seven fault sets include at least two faults which are cross-cut by diabase dikes. Fault set 5, which consists of only two faults, is the only set which has no fault cross-cut by a dike. However, substantial evidence genetically relates the two faults in set 5 to the other faults on the site. This evidence includes fault orientations, geometry, locations, motion sense and mineralization.

Figures 3-6 show typical cross-cutting relations between dikes and faults in site foundation excavations. Figure 3A shows a diabase dike d5, displaced by fault W-6 from set 1. The offset, which is typical of such offsets at the site, is not clean. An aphophysis of diabase had flowed along the fault's footwall prior to or possibly during faulting. Figure 3B shows this same dike, d5, a few hundred feet northeast where it cross-cuts fault EI-1 from set 1.

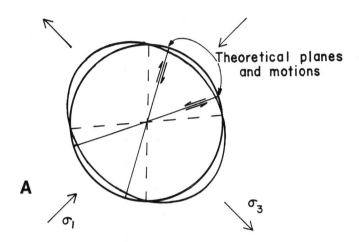

**A**

Figure 7A. Failure planes and motions as predicted by "strain theory" (Badgley, 1962) for a NW-SE tensional stress field.

Figure 7B. Site faults with observed lateral motion components indicated. Observed motions conform to those predicted in Figure 7A. Fault motions and intrusion of diabase dikes are both consistent with a NW-SE tensional stress field.

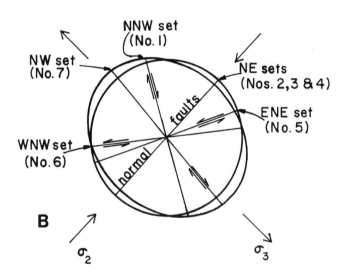

**B**

Figure 6 shows an area of original bedrock surface just beyond the plant foundation area, which was uncovered for mapping purposes. It was considered that the confluence of faults CII-1 and CII-2 with several dikes might provide an interesting exposure. The country rock here is Kittery. Dikes d11, d12 and d13 are offset by CII-1 and CII-2. Dike d5, which intrudes unbroken along fault CII-2, trends across CII-1 at this location. Dike d5 is offset less than an inch along one narrow shear in a fault zone consisting of several shears which represent CII-1 here. The displacements of presumably like-aged dikes d11, d12 and d13 along CII-1 are identical and measurably greater than the displacement of d5 as shown in Figure 6. A younger age for dike d5 is therefore implied. Indeed, K-Ar dating had indicated that the ages of dikes d5 and d12 are, respectively, 213 and 236 million years. To ascertain the age of the most recent fault motion which offset d5 at this location, another K-Ar date was determined for dike d12. Diabase was taken from the surface of d12 right along the shear which displaces d5. It was assumed that the last motion on this shear might have reset the K-Ar age for this thin plane of disturbed diabase. The date obtained was 212 million years, strongly indicating that the last motion on this fault was essentially contemporaneous with the intrusion of dike d5.

Figure 4A shows, in profile, fault CI-2 of set 2 where it cuts dike d1. No measurable displacement of dike contacts is present here, although the weathered fault surface clearly cuts the dike, and net slip elsewhere on this fault was calculated to be as much as 15 feet (the largest displacement of the site). It is obvious, however, that the intrusion path of the dike was significantly disturbed by the pre-existing surface of CI-2. About 300 feet to the southwest fault CI-2 ends against this same dike, d1, as shown in Figure 4B. This figure also shows an older dike, d20, displaced by fault CI-2.

Figure 5 shows fault SI-1 of set 4 where it is intruded by and cross-cut by dike d4. Net slip along this fault is about 6 inches.

Many other examples of dike-fault relations in site excavations make the conclusion about contemporaneous dike intrusion and faulting inescapable. This conclusion pointed to the examination of fault motions with respect to a tensional stress field as a logical next step.

## FAULT MOTIONS

Figure 7A shows theoretical fault planes and motions that result from a NW-SE tensional stress field (after Badgley, 1962) like the one which would be necessary to permit the intrusion of northeast-trending diabase dikes. Experimentally this stress field generates a NNE-trending fault plane with a right-lateral component and an ENE-trending fault plane with a left-lateral component. Figure 7B shows the lateral motion components of the faults in the various sets as they occur in the field. For most site faults the motion sense was clearly indicated by offsets or slickensides or both. In comparing Figure 7A and Figure 7B it must be noted that faulting at the site, except for set 4, parallel to the dikes, occurred along pre-existing surfaces not necessarily in strict geometric conformance with the stress field under discussion. Nevertheless, the conformance of motion direction of site faults with those in the theoretical model is very good. NE-trending faults of sets 2, 3 and 4 are normal; more northerly-trending faults of sets 1 and 7 have right-lateral components; easterly-trending faults of sets 5 and 6 have left-lateral components. The consistency of site fault motions with the theoretical motions of a NW-SE tensional stress field is judged to be further evidence of contemporaneous faulting and dike emplacement.

## CROSS-CUTTING SURFICIAL DEPOSITS

Surficial materials consisting of a crudely stratified till overlain by a marine clay-silt and outwash were deposited over much of the site prior to excavation. Mapping exposed in the unit II area showed no disturbance or offset of this unconsolidated material, even directly overlying faults in the bedrock. This condition also serves as further confirmation of the ancient age of site faults.

## CONCLUSIONS

Geologic structural evidence and radiometric dating lead to the conclusion that all faults present in foundation excavations at the Seabrook site last moved during the late Permian or early Triassic. Motion was in response to the same tensional stress field which allowed dike emplacement. These faults are thus not capable as defined in CFR (1978), and they pose no site-safety problem.

## ACKNOWLEDGMENTS

The principal owner of Seabrook Station is Public Service Company of New Hampshire. The authors appreciate cooperation of the owner in this study.

## REFERENCES

Aleinikoff, J.N., and Zartman, R.E., 1978, U-Th-Pb geochronology of the Massabesic Gneiss and the granite near Milford, New Hampshire: Geological Society of America, Abstracts with Programs, v. 10, no. 7, p. 357-358.

Badgley, P.C., 1962 , The analysis of structural patterns in bedrock: American Institute of Mining and Metallurgical Engineering, Society of Mining Engineers Transactions, v. 225, p. 381-389.

CFR (Code of Federal Regulations), 1978, Title 10, energy, part 100 [10 CFR 100], Reactor site criteria: Appendix A, Seismic and geologic siting criteria for nuclear power plants, Nuclear Regulatory Commission, Washington, D.C.

McHone, J.G., 1978, Distribution, orientation, and ages of mafic dikes in central New England: Geological Society of America Bulletin, v. 89, p. 1645-1655.

PSNH (Public Service Company of New Hampshire), 1980, Final safety analysis report, section 2.5, Geology and seismology: Docket nos. 50-443 and 50-444, in preparation.

Shride, A.F., 1971, Igneous rocks of the Seabrook, New Hampshire-Newbury, Massachusetts area: New England Intercollegiate Geological Conference, Guidebook for field trips, central New Hampshire and contiguous areas, 63rd Annual Meeting, Fall, 1971, p. 105-117.

The Fletcher quarry, Chelmsford, Massachusetts, opened in 1880. This is one of the most productive sources of dimension stone in the world. See also page 120.

Hors-texte

# Geophysical studies and measurements in eastern Massachusetts

V. J. MURPHY
Weston Geophysical Corporation

G. SIMMONS
Department of Earth and Planetary Sciences
Massachusetts Institute of Technology

R. J. HOLT
E. N. LEVINE
R. P. ALLEN
Weston Geophysical Corporation

ABSTRACT

Recently completed geophysical studies include data for both regional and site specific objectives. High resolution aeromagnetic surveys extended over eastern parts of Massachusetts and the adjacent offshore area; high resolution marine surveys consisting of both seismic and magnetic measurements provided further data on sediment thicknesses and specific anomalies.

A singularly significant finding is the detection of a previously undisclosed pluton off Cape Ann in the area of the region's highest intensity earthquakes (1727, 1755); also of importance is the trend of magnetic contours allowing the extrapolation of geologic structural features from onshore to offshore areas.

The preferred suite of offshore geophysical data, in this geologic environment, consists of both seismic reflection and refraction profiling, as well as measurements with the towed magnetometer. The "acoustic basement" determined during reflection profiling is readily identifiable by refraction profiling as either bed rock or dense glacial till if the measured refraction velocity value is either 16,000 ft/sec or 7,500 ft/sec. Measured velocity values for pluton(s) are indicative of rigidity that is 2 to 3 times that of the surrounding rock mass.

Site specific findings provided velocity/moduli data for both glacial till and softer materials such as Boston "Blue Clay"; corresponding compressional/shear wave velocity values for these overburden materials are approximately 7,000/2,500 ft/sec and 5,000/900 ft/sec, respectively.

The Fletcher quarry, showing local stress relief upon excavation. See also page 118.

Hors-texte

# Geologic assessments for real estate appraisals

A. W. HATHEWAY
J. R. HIGHT
R. V. VARNUM
Haley & Aldrich, Inc.

## ABSTRACT

Eminent domain land takings and appeals for relief of property tax valuations pose an interesting use for quantitative geologic assessments in New England. In either case, the land owner has been subject to a valuation, by others, of the worth of his holdings. Common law and legal precedence uphold the concept of highest and best use for all land, and it is on this basis that the land owner, if he disagrees with the valuation assigned to the land, must show the court that it is unjust. In cases not concerned with residential land, geologic assessments often provide the range or limits to reasonable potential use of land. In these cases, the alleged highest and best use of the land must be substantiated by geological expertise as to the effect of geological conditions on such development options as construction and extraction of resources including sand, gravel, and timber.

## DISCUSSION

Presuming that the land is zoned or can be rezoned for the intended purpose and that local and state permits can be obtained for said purpose, the geologist, owner, attorney, and real estate appraiser should discuss the objectives of legal strategy. The following steps are then implemented in the case of land takings and alleged sand and gravel resources.

- Secure an accurate plat of the holdings.

- Enlarge existing USGS topographic coverage to 1:1200 scale, or larger.

- Compile a photo interpretation of geologic and hydrologic features of the site.

- Walk the site and revise the interpretation with ground truth; record other significant features; map surficial geology.

- Meet on the site with the attorney, owner and appraiser; discuss facts and options for strategy.

- Excavate test pits at key locations in individual geologic units and along presumed contacts; take bag samples of various potentially salable sand and gravel units; note the seasonal position of ground water; install observation wells if necessary.

- Devise resource map units which reflect three-dimensional bodies of salable sand and gravel (the USCS scheme of soil symbols is ideal for this purpose): ascertain a reasonable geologic explanation for the occurrence, depth and areal distribution of each unit.

- Continue to dig test pits until the

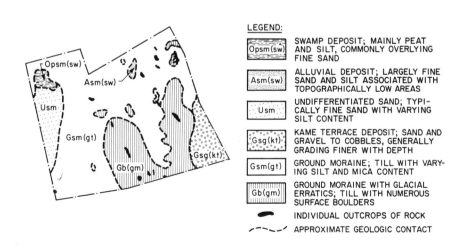

LEGEND:

| | |
|---|---|
| Opsm(sw) | SWAMP DEPOSIT; MAINLY PEAT AND SILT, COMMONLY OVERLYING FINE SAND |
| Asm(sw) | ALLUVIAL DEPOSIT; LARGELY FINE SAND AND SILT ASSOCIATED WITH TOPOGRAPHICALLY LOW AREAS |
| Usm | UNDIFFERENTIATED SAND; TYPICALLY FINE SAND WITH VARYING SILT CONTENT |
| Gsg(kt) | KAME TERRACE DEPOSIT; SAND AND GRAVEL TO COBBLES, GENERALLY GRADING FINER WITH DEPTH |
| Gsm(gt) | GROUND MORAINE; TILL WITH VARYING SILT AND MICA CONTENT |
| Gb(gm) | GROUND MORAINE WITH GLACIAL ERRATICS; TILL WITH NUMEROUS SURFACE BOULDERS |
|  | INDIVIDUAL OUTCROPS OF ROCK |
|  | APPROXIMATE GEOLOGIC CONTACT |

Figure 1. Typical sand and gravel resource unit map.

TABLE 1.  COMPUTED VOLUMES OF RECOVERABLE SAND AND GRAVEL BASED ON TEST PIT DATA
FOR A SITE IN SOUTHEASTERN MASSACHUSETTS

| Area number (Fig. 2) | Approximate area (sq. ft.) | Approximate area (acres) | A.  Depth to water entry in test pits (ft.) | Estimated average depth to water (ft.) | B.  Predominant material types (approximate average thickness) | | | C. Volume (cu.yd.) | |
|---|---|---|---|---|---|---|---|---|---|
| | | | | | Waste | Upper unit | Lower unit | Upper unit | Lower unit |
| 1 | 130,900 | 3.01 | 9.0  >  11.5 | 11.0 | 0.4' | SM 2.5' | SW&SP 10.3' | 12,120 | 49,936 |
| 2 | 39,700 | 0.91 | 7.0 to  8.0 | 7.6 | 0.6' | SW/SM 1.3' | SW&SP 5.7' | 1,911 | 8,381 |
| 3 | 189,700 | 4.36 | 9.0 to >10.5 | 9.6 | 1.5' | SW&SP 3.4 | SM&GM 4.7' | 23,888 | 33,022 |
| 4 | 262,800 | 6.03 | 7.0 | 7.0 | 2.5' | SP/SM 5.0' | SM 1.0' | 48,667 | 9,733 |
| 5 | 312,700 | 7.18 | 5.0 to  9.0 | 6.8 | 2.3' | SM 4.5 | -- -- | 52,117 | -- |
| 6 | 113,400 | 2.60 | 4.0 to  5.0 | 4.6 | 3.5' | SW&GW 2.1 | SM&GM -- | 8,820 | -- |
| 7 | 67,600 | 1.55 | >6.5 to  10.0 | 10.0 | 2.1' | SM&SP 2.8' | GW/GM 3.1' | 7,010 | 7,762 |
| 8 | 19,600 | 0.45 | >5.0 to  >7.5 | 10.5 | 2.8' | SW 2.0' | SM&SP 4.1' | 1,451 | 2,976 |
| 9 | 246,800 | 5.67 | 5.0 to  11.0 | 9.0 | 2.5' | SM 6.5' | -- -- | 59,415 | -- |
| TOTAL | 1,383,200 | 31.76 | | | | | | 215,399 | 111,809 |

Total = 327,208 cu.yd.

NOTES:

A.  In some locations, water was not encountered during test pit excavation.
Therefore, the symbol for "greater than" (>) is used to indicate the fact that
water may be significantly deeper than value shown.  Estimated average depths
are inferred from topography and test pits where water was encountered.

B.  Average thickness of material types represents recoverable units above average
depth to water in resource area.

C.  Volume of unit (cu.yd.) = Thickness of unit (ft.) X area (sq.ft.) ÷ 27.

dimensions and minimal depths of each
class of sand and gravel resource units
are assured.

- Employ seismic refraction where necessary
to define depths of resource units.

- Send the bag samples to the soil lab for
mechanical analyses; look at each sample

to determine if there are mineralogical
features which may be deleterious to
intended resource uses.

- Evaluate each of the resource units in
terms of the most commonly used materials
classified in the state (DPW specifications in Massachusetts).

- Tabulate each material type by plani-

TABLE 2.  TABULATION OF SUITABILITY AND LAND USE CLASSIFICATION DATA
IN SUPPORT OF THE TERRAIN EVALUATION SHOWN IN FIGURE 2

| Area identification | Approximate area of coverage | | Approximate developable area according to Wetlands Act | | Present land use | Development potential |
|---|---|---|---|---|---|---|
| | sq. ft. | acre | sq. ft. | acre | | |
| 10 | 63,500 | 1.46 | 14,157 | 0.33 | Undeveloped; tree covered | Restricted by wetland conditions, lies partially in wetland border strip; *C/D |
| 11 | 107,600 | 2.47 | 0 | 0.00 | West Pond | Restricted by wetland regulations; *D |
| 12 | 14,520 | 0.33 | 0 | 0.00 | Abandoned radar test facility | Good foundation conditions; *A |
| 13 | 58,100 | 1.33 | 8,228 | 0.19 | Undeveloped slope; mowed wild grass | Restricted by wetland border strip; *C/D |
| 14 | 20,600 | 0.47 | 0 | 0.00 | Wetland | Restricted by wetland regulations; *D |
| 15 | 21,780 | 0.50 | 0 | 0.00 | East Ponds | Restricted by wetland regulations; *D |
| 16 | 47,200 | 1.08 | 6,413 | 0.15 | Undeveloped slope; mowed wild grass | Restricted by wetland border strip; *C/D |
| 17 | 27,200 | 0.63 | 0 | 0.00 | Undeveloped slope; mowed wild grass | Lies within wetland border strip; *C/D |
| TOTAL AREAS | 1,171,750 | 26.90 | 750,344 | 17.25 | | |

NOTES:

1. Land classification made in course of foot traverse across site by Haley & Aldrich, Inc., engineering geologist; classifications made herein represent opinion of the reviewer and do not take into consideration particular decisions by wetland regulatory officials in the City of Watertown.

2. Areas shown are approximate, based on undated, and unscaled plat map

3. Approximate acreage shown on this table was derived from photo-interpreted square footages, which are reported herein to the nearest 100 square feet of estimated area.

4. Development potential, as discussed in Conclusions sections of this report, is identified as follows:

   *A = Developable and accessible
   *B = Mainly developable, but isolated
   *C = Usable only for current purpose
   *D = Undevelopable in terms of wetland affinity

metered area on the site geologic map, assign an average thickness of recoverable resource, considering seasonal groundwater levels, and calculate volume in cubic yards.

• Determine a minimal-cost resource development plan, to include grubbing and sale of timber, overburden removal, access road construction, drainage provisions, and site reclamation.

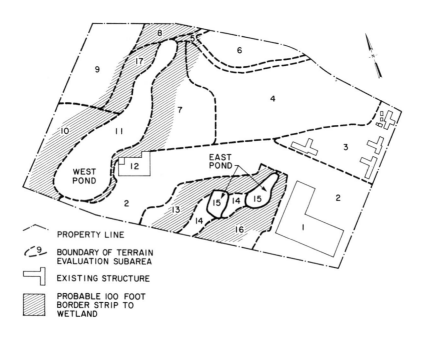

Figure 2. Appraisal map of an industrial parcel, showing probable 100 ft border strip for wetland protection.

● Present your results to the legal team members.

● Prepare your findings in graphical form and in layman's language.

A typical sand and gravel resource unit map is shown in Figure 1. Table 1 shows computed volumes of recoverable sand and gravel based on test pit data for a site in southeastern Massachusetts.

In cases in which property valuations are being challenged, it is wise to prepare an engineering/environmental geologic map of the property on a base developed from the ownership plat. It is generally not crucial to show absolute survey locations of structures; most of the data can be placed on the map by pace and compass. The key items to show are the actual or inferred geologic contacts and all indications of ground and surface water, especially those features used to delimit wetlands. The next step is to logically subdivide the property into zones of land use and geologic/hydrologic conditions. Figure 2 depicts such an appraisal map of an industrial parcel of 26.9 acres. The zones are classified by categories of possible development and those zones which will probably be denied development by virtue of existing wetland conditions. A sample of this tabulation is shown as Table 2. In making a case for

highest and best use of the property, the attorney/geologist/appraiser/owner team must keep in mind that determinations presented and exemptions allowed by the appellate tax court will probably remain with the property and may affect future sales and development plans for the property.

As in the case of resource evaluation assessments, property valuation assessments must result in graphical portrayals of the property metes and bounds, together with identification of structures, roads, and the development/wetland zones. The attorney, and the geologist expert witness, can make good use of these graphics before the judge or jury.

REFERENCES

Kiersch, G.A., 1968, The geologist and legal cases--responsibility, preparation, and the expert witness: Engineering Geology Case Histories 6-10, Geological Society of America.

Tuoni, G.M., and McDonough, T.F., 1978, Recovering land damages in eminent domain cases in Massachusetts--a summary: Massachusetts Law Review, v. 63, June.

# 6

# SOILS ENGINEERING AND ROCK MECHANICS

Session moderators

R. C. Chlanda
Soil Conservation Service
U.S. Department of Agriculture

B. K. Fowler
Pike Industries, Inc.

M. Kupferman
Northeastern University

G. E. McGill
Department of Geology and Geography
University of Massachusetts at Amherst

W. Pitt
Geotechnical Engineers, Inc.

E. T. Selig
Department of Civil Engineering
University of Massachusetts at Amherst

# Integral rock sampling—
# A technique of oriented rock core recovery

## H. A. RUSSELL
### Parsons, Brinckerhoff, Quade & Douglas, Inc.

## ABSTRACT

A technique of oriented rock core recovery is utilized for subsurface investigations for the Harvard Square Station, Cambridge, Massachusetts. The integral sampling method (ISM) (Rocha, 1971) employs common rotary core drilling machines and tools, plus some additional special equipment. The ISM involves the drilling of a 2.94 cm (1.17 in) OD pilot hole into which is placed a 2.54 cm (1.0 in) OD steel reinforcing tube, directionally oriented from the surface. The tube is also utilized as a conduit for the injection of grout through the pilot hole and into the voids and discontinuities, resulting in an integrated, cemented rock mass. A 1.52 m (5.0 ft) length of 6.99 cm (2.75 in) diameter core is drilled coaxially in the rock mass surrounding the tube, and the oriented tube and grout reinforced rock core is recovered for later true orientation analysis. Recovery is consistently approximately 100 percent. The ISM is well suited for the determination of three-dimensional rock structural elements and the nature of discontinuities and mineral fillings. It can be utilized at all depths normally of interest in engineering investigations in either vertical or angled boreholes.

## INTRODUCTION

The integral sampling method (ISM) is a system of core analysis developed by Manuel Rocha, Director, Laboratorio Nacional de Engenharia Civil, Lisbon, Portugal, in 1971. It incorporates the true orientation of joints, bedding planes, fractures and total core recovery. The method is ideally suited for severely fractured or weak rock, indicating where steel reinforcement is needed for structural flaws in the rock. Readily available rotary drilling tools are utilized, supplemented by special tools provided by Sprague & Henwood Inc., of Scranton, Pennsylvania.

In 1977 Parsons Brinckerhoff used ISM for identifying problem areas in the design of the Massachusetts Bay Transportation Authority's new Harvard Square Station in Cambridge, Massachusetts.

## PROCEDURE

The integral sampling method is applicable to either 4-inch (H size) or 3-inch (N size) boreholes. The borehole is advanced by conventional means to a depth where the ISM is to be imple-

mented. Once the borehole casing is properly seated there are four stages of the ISM, as discussed below.

## STAGE 1 - PILOT HOLE ADVANCE

A specialized stabilizing guide and an RWT size (1 5/32-inch) core barrel are lowered to the bottom of the borehole. The stabilizing guide has an outside diameter slightly smaller than the boreholes. The core barrel is centered in the stabilizing guide and is advanced by conventional rotary means to 4.8 feet below the stabilizing guide and removed (Fig. 1).

## STAGE 2 - PLACEMENT OF GROUT ORIENTATION ROD

After the romoval of the pilot hole core barrel and core, the grout orientation (GRO) tube is placed in the borehole. The GRO tube is 2 3/4 inch ID x 1.0 foot OD mild steel pipe and is joined to the orientation rod string by a union which contains a 3/32 inch diameter shear pin. The orientation rods are connected to the surface by keyways located in the flush joints of the rods. The rods are all notched on one side to identify the direction of orientation.

At the surface the orientation rods are fitted with an aiming device which is usually aligned to a known compass direction. The compass direction is chosen by field survey.

## STAGE 3 - INJECTION OF BONDING AGENT

Injection of the bonding agent may be performed by two separate processes. The simplest method is to lower the GRO tube to approximately two inches off the bottom of the pilot hole and to tremie the epoxy/bonding agent through the orientation rods. Once a predetermined quantity of grout is tremied to the sample zone the GRO tube is lowered to the bottom of the borehole. The orientation is checked with the sighting device, and a slight pressure is exerted on the rods, shearing the shear pin and thus disconnecting the GRO tube. The orientation rods and centering guide are removed and the epoxy/bonding agent is allowed to cure (Fig. 2).

A more complex system utilizes a centering guide with a self-contained chamber for containing the grout/bonding agent (Fig. 3). This centering guide is watertight, and the annulus between the

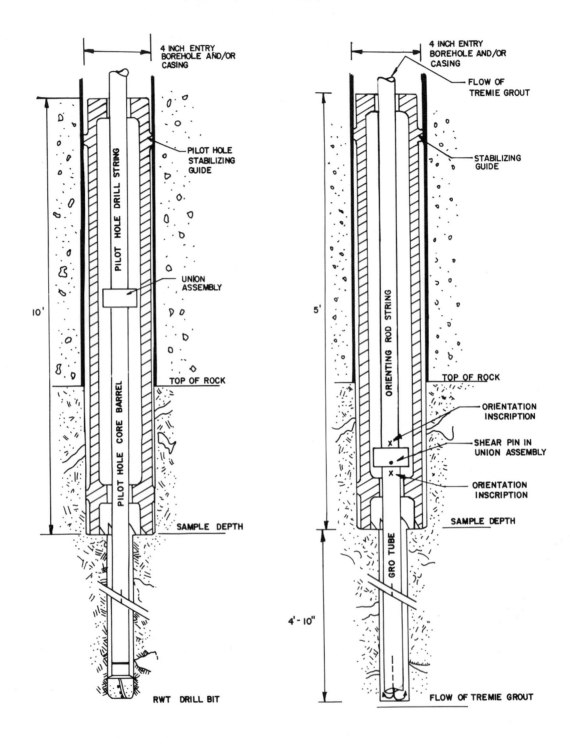

Figure 1.  Pilot hole advance.

Figure 2.  Placement of GRO tube and tremie grout.

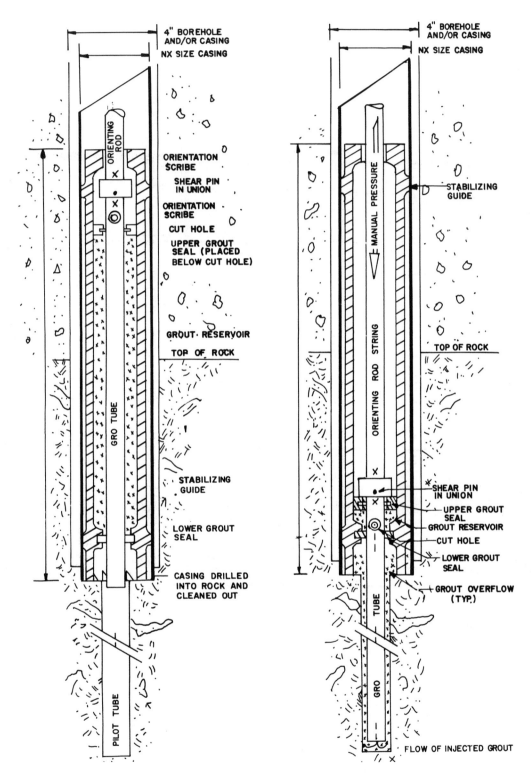

Figure 3. Grout injector
(before placement).

Figure 4. Grout injector
(during placement).

GRO tube and the inside diameter of the centering guide is filled prior to placement with the epoxy/bonding agent. The GRO tube contains a relief hole at its upper end. The unit is lowered to the bottom of the 4-inch borehole and the orientation rods connected. A slight pressure is applied to the orientation rods, and the hole in the top of the GRO tube passes into the grout reservoir. As the downward pressure lowers the GRO tube into the pilot hole the upper grout seal is also lowered and forces the grout/bonding agent into the pilot hole through the GRO tube (Fig. 4). Once a back pressure is felt the downward motion is stopped, and the connecting rods are oriented. Downward pressure is again exerted, shearing off the shear pin and disconnecting the GRO tube. The orientation rods and grout injector are removed, and the epoxy/bonding agent is allowed to cure.

## STAGE 4 - OVERCORING AND SAMPLE RECOVERY

After the epoxy/bonding agent has been allowed to cure (a time period from two to four hours), the now reinforced rock may be overcored. The overcoring is accomplished by lowering a 10-foot long NW or 2 3/4 inch x 3 7/8 inch double tube core barrel. The core barrel is fitted with a bottom discharge bit to prevent excessive washing of any soft grout/bonding agent. The overcoring is carried to approximately six inches below the bottom of the GRO tube. The rock core is sheared off and removed from the borehole (Fig. 5).

## BEDROCK GEOLOGY AT HARVARD SQUARE STATION

The bedrock at the site of the new station is approximately 30 to 50 feet below the surface and is known locally as the Cambridge Argillite. The rock ranges from a sandy argillite to an argillaceous sandstone. Although wide variations exist, the profile typically grades to slightly weathered at an average depth of 10 to 15 feet below the top of rock. The bedding ranges from less than one inch to greater than one foot. Numerous fractures are evident, probably the result of severe folding that occurred during the Triassic period.

The area contains dikes intruded into the argillite. The strike of the dikes as encountered during site exploration ranges from west to northeast, with numerous sills emanating from the parent body north and south along less resistant bedding planes. The composition of the dike is andesite or diabase. The dike is slightly to moderately weathered, with some oxidation along the joint structure.

The extreme folding and later intrusions created what appeared to be numerous shatter zones in the contact areas of the dikes and the Cambridge Argillite. In these areas recovery often dropped as low as 25 percent with some RQD values as low as 0 to 10 percent. In order to determine the extent of the poor quality rock, the ISM was utilized. Open joints were identi-

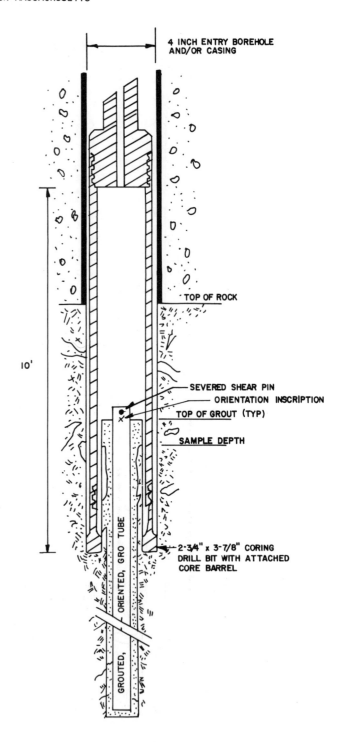

Figure 5. Overcoring the GRO tube.

TABLE 1.   ISM CORE ANALYSIS OF BORING A-1,
HARVARD SQUARE STATION

| Core run | Depth to joint ft | Strike | Dip | Remarks on joint width |
|---|---|---|---|---|
| C-1 C-2 C-3 C-4 | NOTE: For core runs C-1 to C-4, the rock was badly fractured; analysis of joints could not be made. | | | |
| C-5 | 57.2 | S80E | 22N | Tight hairline |
| | 57.25 | N70E | 27N | Open 1/2 mm |
| | 57.25 | N80E | 47S | Open 1/2 mm |
| | 57.4 | N80E | 25N | Open 1/2 mm |
| | 57.75 | N30E | 88 | Open 1 mm |
| | 57.9 | N85E | 25N | Tight hairline |
| | 58.1 | N80E | 25N | Tight hairline |
| | 58.4 | N80E | 17N | Open 3 mm |
| | 57-59.4 | N50E | 48S | Hairline |
| | 59.5 | S80E | 89 | Hairline |
| | 60.25 | S50E | 36N | Open 2 mm |
| | 59.9-60.25 | N30E | 63S | 10 cm, shatter zone |
| | 60.7 | N70E | 17N | Open 2 mm |
| | 60.9 | N90E | 23N | 15 cm. shatter zone |
| | 61.5 | N80E | 25N | Open 5 cm |
| | 61.7 | N80E | 25N | Open 5 cm |
| | 62.0 | N40E | 50S | Hairline |
| | 62.5 | N30E | 54N | Open 1 mm |
| C-6 | 62.6 | N55E | 18S | Open 3 mm |
| | 63.3 | N35E | 11N | Open 1 mm |
| | 64.4 | N90E | 49N | Hairline |
| | 64.6 | N90E | 48N | Open 1/2 mm |
| | 65.4 | N80E | 12S | Open 1 mm |
| | 65.8 | N50E | 11S | Open 1 mm |
| | 65.85 | N50E | 60N | Open 1 mm |
| | 65.9 | N40E | 54N | Open 1 mm |
| | 66.6 | N35E | 53N | Open 1/2 mm |
| | 67.0 | N40E | 70N | Open 1/2 mm |
| | 67.3 | N40E | 70N | Open 1/2 mm |

fied, and an accurate measurement of the degree
of openness of these joints was obtained.

Guild Drilling and Boring Co. of East Providence, Rhode Island, provided the rotary drilling
equipment, with special tools leased from Sprague
& Henwood.  Test borings A1 and A2 were utilized
for ISM coring.  Many types of epoxy/bonding
agents were used, the most successful being US
Gypsum's "B-11 Hydrocal," utilizing the grout

injector method (Figs. 3 and 4).  The tremie
method was also utilized, although with limited
success.

Table 1 is a tabulation of the raw data obtained from test boring A-1.  Figure 6 is a plot
of the joint sets and potential sliding rock
wedges as they would influence the tunnel walls.

CONCLUSIONS

The ISM method proved to be helpful in the
identification of shatter zones in the Cambridge
Argillite.  The method also provided valuable information on the "tightness" of the rock mass,
permitting identification of rock units that could
adversely affect the proposed open cut excavation.

ACKNOWLEDGMENTS

The author expresses his appreciation of
assistance which helped make this paper possible
by J. Holt, Clough Engineers; E. Butler, Guild
Drilling and Boring Co.; and A. Hatheway, Haley
and Aldrich, Inc.

REFERENCES

Parsons Brinckerhoff Quade & Douglas, Inc., 1978,
Harvard Square Station, geotechnical report:
Massachusetts Bay Transportation Authority,
Red Line Extension, NW, August.

Rocha, M., 1971, A method of integral sampling of
rock masses:  Rock Mechanics, v. 3, no. 1,
p. 1-12.

Rocha, M., 1972, Present possibilities of studying
foundations of concrete dams.  [Reference
incomplete]

Rocha, M., 1973, A method of obtaining integral
samples of rock masses:  Association of Engineering Geologists Bulletin, v. 10, no. 1,
p. 77-82.

Russell, H.A., & Holt, J., 1978, Integral
sampling method:  Parsons Brinckerhoff Quade
& Douglas, Inc., Boston, February, 17 p.
Unpublished technical paper.

Sprague and Henwood, Inc., ISM coring system:
descriptive marketing brochure.

**JOINTS FROM ISM CORE A-1**

**JOINT SETS**

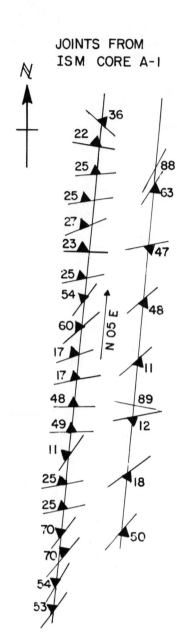

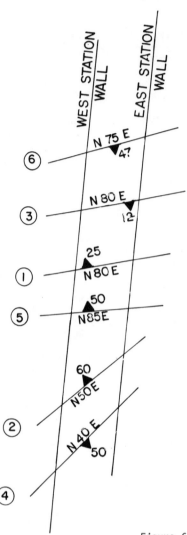

Figure 6. Core analysis by the integral sampling method (ISM), Harvard Square Station.

# POTENTIAL SLIDING
# ROCK WEDGES

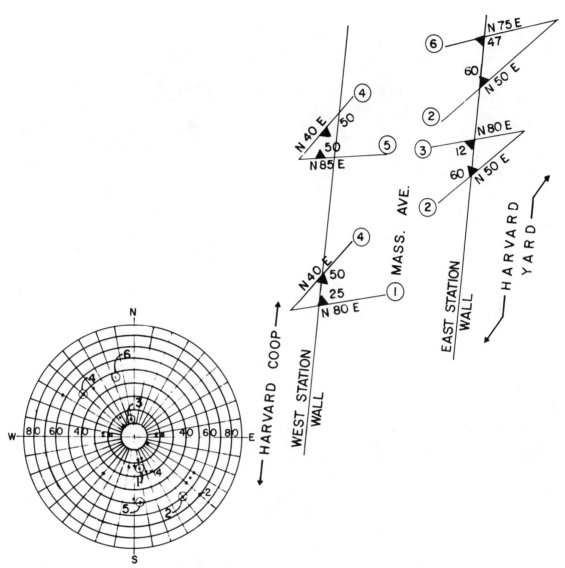

POLAR EQUAL-AREA PROJECTION
( LOWER HEMISPHERE )

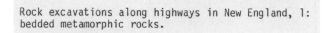

Rock excavations along highways in New England, 1: bedded metamorphic rocks.

# Rock slippage on the upper slope of a highway cut

## A. FERREIRA
Northeast Utilities, and the
Electric Power Research Institute

ABSTRACT

This paper describes the movement of rock along an interstate highway cut, suggests reasons for this movement, and outlines a field survey method for monitoring the extent of the movement.

If the rock has not stopped moving, there may be concern for the safety of persons or equipment at the base of the rock slope. Highway officials may need to determine means for removing the rock slabs before they become a hazard.

STATEMENT OF PROBLEM

A program has recently been described to investigate geologic processes affecting the stability of rock slopes along Massachusetts highways (Farquhar, 1980). This program had its background in rock falls and embankment slippages that have closed certain highways in New England for periods varying from a few days to several months. Such occurrences depend upon the rock type, the state of construction of the road, and the time of year.

The need to examine slope stability along highways in greater detail comes about for several reasons. Until the recent national and state highway programs of constructing high speed, limited access roads such as the interstates, few roads in New England ran through bedrock cuts. Also, the mechanics of landslides are now better understood, slope analysis having become a more formalized procedure. A number of new descriptive and interpretive accounts of landslides and rock slides have been reported in the geologic and engineering literature, and these can be of use in evaluating local conditions.

The program described above for rock slope stability studies has not yet been funded. However, the effort of documenting the need for these studies involved extensive reconnaissance along critical sections of the region's highways. Potential problem areas have been examined in a preliminary manner. The areas consist of cut rock slopes along interstate highways in Massachusetts and adjacent states, including Rhode Island. One section just west of Providence is the subject of this report.

Numerous signs of rock movement and actual rock falls were noticed in steep bedrock cuts in Rhode Island. Along one section rock slabs appeared to be protruding several feet from the top of the cut. Closer inspection from the base of the cut showed clearly that the rock slabs at the top are not in line with the face of the cut. Excavation drill holes are readily visible up the main rock face, and these continue along the offset face of the protruding rock sections.

FIELD VISITS AND LOCATION

In the summer of 1979, several trips were made to the site. Maps and drawings were made available for inspection at the office of the Department of Public Works, State of Rhode Island, in Providence. The site is on the west side of Interstate 295 approximately three miles west of the intersection of Routes 146 and 295, just south of the access intersection of Route 7 and Route 295. The rock cut forms a part of the Douglas Pike Interchange, Smithfield, Rhode Island, Interstate Route 295. From highway design information, the rock cut is in the vicinity of highway stations 225+00 to 227+00.

GENERAL DESCRIPTION

The slide appears to have involved the movement of a mass of rock with displacement along recognized shear surfaces as a result of stress relief. Thus, the ruptured mass has moved with a definite motion, as opposed to a more random rock fall. The direction of shearing is linear and the area of the slide is planar, i.e., the movement is parallel to the shear surface. This can be termed a slab slide in that the failure has occurred by a lateral movement. It may also be termed a mini-block glide in that the displaced bed rock maintains its integrity and geologic attitude.

The rock fall at the base appears to be the result of pieces and sections falling off the face of the cut, some being fragments left over from blasting. They have been temporarily held in place despite clearing of the rock face with steel bars. Subsequently, they have been loosened by vibration from traffic on the nearby access road and by blasting at other excavations.

These vibrations and local ground mass tremors have caused certain rock sections to disintegrate. Numerous fragments have fallen down along the top of the rock wall cut. These vary from small marble and baseball size to football size.

Another reason for the continuing spalling

Figure 1. An excavated rock roadcut set back from the edge of the traveled way on Interstate 295 S, about 200 feet south of Route 7, west of Providence, Rhode Island. The upper few feet appear to have slipped out beyond the main part of the pre-split face, as shown by the drill holes. The overhang is now over two feet. Drawn from a photograph.

of the rock fall is frost shattering, due to freezing and thawing of water in fractures opened during blasting operations.

The mechanisms causing slope failure can be divided into external and internal factors. The external factors cause an increase in the shearing stresses along the slip zones. This can result from the heightening or steepening of the slope by such processes as glacial or river erosion or simply rock removal. It can also result from increased external forces on blocks, slabs or sections of the rock, due to nearby blasting, frost action, or heavy earthmoving and excavation equipment.

There are also the internal factors. Joints bounding the blocks that slipped may be opened initially by the pressure of gases produced by blasting. The rock mass affected would be most prone to failure when lubricated by surface waters seeping into it through the shallow and porous overburden.

Figure 1 is drawn from a photograph taken looking northward along the southbound lane of I-295. The rock cut is shown on the left. The Douglas Pike bridge which carries Route 7 over I-295 is only 200 feet to the north. The vertical height of the cut where the rock has moved is estimated to be some 58 to 60 feet above the grassed shoulder section. At this location the shoulder is approximately 50 feet wide, separating the dangerous area from the traveled way. The sections of rock jutting out along the top of the cut can be seen against the skyline. The overburden above and to the left of the cut is no more than 10 feet in depth, and consists of gravel and broken rock.

Figure 2 shows a typical section through the rock cut where slippage has occurred. The original surface of the bed rock is the dotted line, this information being obtained from the holes drilled during route exploration. In this sketch the rock projection is somewhat exaggerated in scale. The dip of the rock joints indicated on this figure is about 10°-15° eastward from the face of the rock cut. The nearly vertical open joint that is visible along the edge of the rock and indicated on this figure varies from several inches to as much as six inches in width. It extends along the edge for 15-20 feet. The slope of the cut as noted on the highway plan is about 4:1, but in the field it appears to have been made steeper.

PRE-SPLITTING HOLES

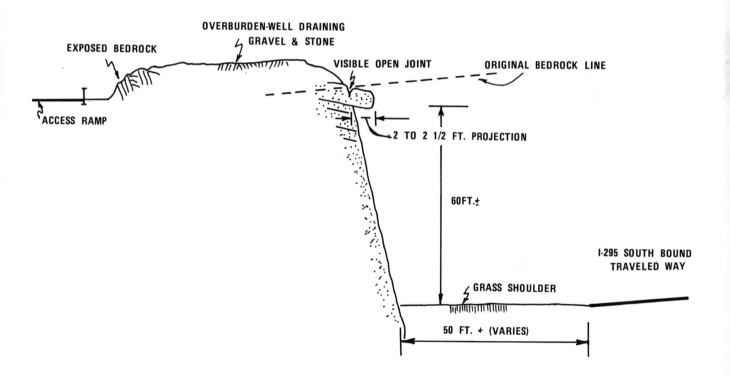

Figure 2. Typical section through rock cut showing slippage.

The contractor was required to pre-split the rock, wherever the slopes were expected to exceed ten feet in height. The pre-split plane was to follow the desired rock slope lines, extending from the top of the bedrock surface to some distance below the finished shoulder grade. The pre-splitting holes were spaced at about three feet, center-to-center, and had a diameter of less than three inches. Specifications required that all pre-split holes would lie essentially in the same plane and parallel to each other. No hole was to deviate more than one-half foot at any place from the specified slope line nor in vertical alignment.

Field inspection of the remnants of the drill holes along the rock face indicates that the above specifications were closely followed in both parallel and vertical alignment.

## USE OF MAN-LIFT FOR VISUAL INSPECTION

Sliding of rock commonly takes place near the top of slopes. In the case described herein, the movement has progressed far enough to be clearly detected from the base of the slope. In many cases movement is even more obvious due to rock sections actually falling down the slope. However, early movements may go undetected merely because they are above eye level. Close-up observation of the top sections of steep rock cuts is difficult and normally not undertaken because access is limited.

Nevertheless, rock sections can be routinely inspected by personnel having a suitable geotechnical background who are also equipped with a mechanical man-lift. There are considerable advantages in close-up inspection from a technical standpoint. Personnel safety during the inspection is also vital.

Figure 4. Man-lift for examining the tops of rock cuts. (Source: Farquhar, 1980).

Figure 3. Scissors platform to provide access to the upper part of slopes. The rocks here are shown with characteristic discontinuities. (Source: Farquhar, 1980).

Man-lifts, consisting of trucks with buckets for one or more people, are available with reaches up to 90 feet, and even higher. Use of such vehicles would enable maintenance and accompanying geotechnical people to inspect high cuts where normal access is not possible. These are the very areas where shearing joint separations and other movements are most likely to occur. Figures 3 and 4 show two types of man-lifts.

## SURVEY PROCEDURE FOR MONITORING ROCK MOVEMENT

There are numerous instruments for monitoring possible movement of rock on slopes. These have been reviewed with the object of selecting systems with least cost and minimum reliance on complex detectors. A survey procedure to provide the necessary information is described below. It requires only two surveying instrument set-ups, the measurement of certain angles, and a periodic along-the-ground measurement of the distance between the instrument stations to verify the base line.

Figure 5 illustrates the survey procedure for monitoring rock movement by triangulation.

- Survey station points A and B are established approximately 200 feet apart to provide ample sighting accuracy and reasonable sighting angles between the stations and the sighting point(s) C, to be set on the bottom of the rock sections to be monitored.

- Station points A and B should be semipermanent bounds for maintaining accuracy of measurement for several years. They

should be protected by a cover against accident or vandalism. Driving iron pins into the ground, leaving the top of the pin at ground level exposed, for marking with a steel point set, is viewed as appropriate and inexpensive. Taping between these two points should be done with a steel tape held in tension with temperature or catenary corrections applied to the measurements, first order surveying being the desired accuracy.

- Point C can be either cross hair scratches scribed on the bottom of each of the rock sections to be checked, or brass, lead, or steel pins drilled and plugged into the rock sections along the bottom near the face of the rock. Either of these procedures will have to be performed from a man-lift bucket, as previously described.

- The survey instrument to be used should be a first order theodolite with high measuring accuracy so that the angles, both horizontal and vertical, will be read to one-second accuracy. An instru-

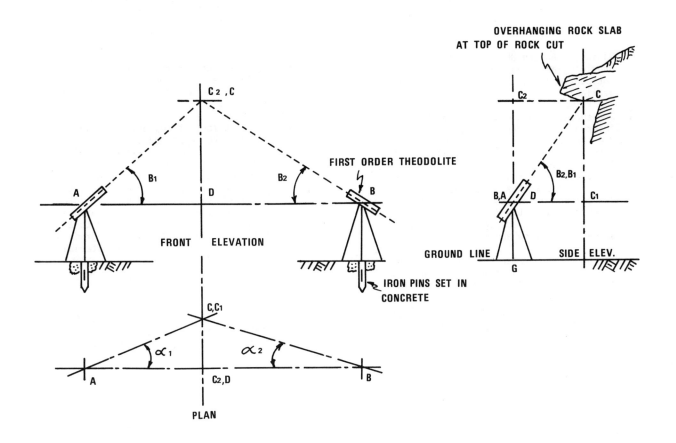

Figure 5. Survey procedure
for rock movement monitoring.

ment utilizing a diagonal eyepiece designed for steep sights would be useful for sighting up toward the survey point set or scribed into the bottom of the rock slabs.

- By setting up the survey theodolite at stations A and B, the horizontal angles and the vertical angles can be read. The standard first order survey procedure should be used, i.e., turning the angles by doubling twice and repeating this three times.

- From the plan view, the dimensions of the horizontal triangle A B C can be calculated, given the survey measurements of distance $\overline{AB}$, and the turned horizontal angles. Point C is the vertical projection of point C on the horizontal triangle A B C.

- By basic trigonometry, the distance $\overline{CD}$ can be calculated for a recorded at-date location of point C.

- By basic trigonometry, the vertical distance $\overline{CC}$ can be calculated, given the distance $\overline{AB}$ and the turned vertical angles, to which would be added the instrument height $\overline{CG}$ for a total recorded at-date height of point C.

- Distances $\overline{AD}$ and $\overline{DB}$ can be calculated providing an at-date recording of the horizontal location of point C is available.

- The survey should be made at monthly intervals for several (say, three) months and then every three months thereafter for the first year, and semi-annually for the next two years. Comparison of the calculated dimensions from these surveys in reference to the base line location can be used in assessing the amounts and rates of movement. Thus, movement of the rock slab can be adequately monitored for subsequent review and evaluation.

A plot of these movements (or non-movement, if determined) will provide important input additional to the other field inspection data. These data should aid in the determination of whether the rock should be left as is, or whether it is continuing to move and may be presenting a safety hazard to persons or vehicles parked or using the grassed highway shoulder.

CONCLUSIONS

On the basis of the field investigations and sightings, limited by inability to get close to the rock face, the following opinions are offered.

- The weathered rock slabs near the surface were further disturbed and broken by the pre-drilling as well as by the actual removal blasting.

- The down-slope dip of the upper sections contributes to the force of gravity acting on the disturbed rock slab.

- Stress relief has permitted the upper section of the rock slope to move down-dip within only a few years of excavation in the early 1970's.

- The relatively well drained gravel and broken rock overburden provides joint lubrication for any forces acting to move the rocks.

- Heavy vibration of the overburden from the grading equipment used during subsequent construction grading provided forces for moving the rock slab.

- Blasting of rock along the access ramp some 75 to 100 feet west of this rock cut contributed to the mini-seismic forces tending to move the loosened rock slabs down dip.

- The rock sections appear to be relatively stable, i.e., the center of gravity appears to be within the wall face at this time.

- A fallout zone of approximately 15 feet in width should be guard-railed off parallel to and extending along the alignment of the toe of the rock cut. The length of the guard rail should be equal to the length of the upper slipped rock section plus a substantial added safety factor, say 50 feet, at each end. The area within the fallout should be filled to a depth of 18 inches above the present grade with an energy-absorbing granular material (Ritchie, 1963).

REFERENCES

Farquhar, O.C., 1980, Geologic processes affecting the stability of rock slopes along Massachusetts highways: Engineering Geology, v. 16, p. 135-145.

Ritchie, A.M., 1963, Evaluation of rockfall and its control: Highway Research Record, v. 17, Washington, D.C.

# Preliminary stability reconnaissance, Old Man of the Mountains, New Hampshire

B. K. FOWLER
Pike Industries, Inc.

## ABSTRACT

This report contains the results of studies carried out in conjunction with the preparation of the draft environmental impact statement for Interstate 93 and its alternatives in Franconia Notch, New Hampshire, and deals with the stability of the Old Man of the Mountains profile. The results of the interpretation of the structural geologic data obtained during the work are that: (1) the dead weight load of the blocks comprising the profile and the location of the center of gravity of the rock mass are primarily responsible for the stability of the profile; (2) in view of the geological structure, the rock mass from the "nose" up is likely to be more stable than the "chin" and "upper lip" blocks below, which evidently pose the most critical stability problems on the profile; and (3) the completion of a detailed static stress analysis using accurate dimensional information must be undertaken in order that the true state of stability be determined. The report also concludes, albeit quite tentatively, that active reinforcement of the rock mass comprising the profile may be possible.

## INTRODUCTION

In August, 1976, at the request of the Federal Highway Administration, a reconnaissance was undertaken of the structural geology of the Old Man of the Mountains profile located in Franconia Notch, about 75 miles north of Concord, New Hampshire. The work was conducted in conjunction with the preparation of the draft environmental impact statement for Interstate 93 and its various alternatives between Lincoln and Franconia, New Hampshire. It was prompted by the general concern over the possible effects that the several design and construction alternatives for the highway might have on the well-known landmark, the overall stability of which has been a matter of considerable speculation and controversy. The primary purpose of the study was to measure and document for the first time the actual structural relationships among all of the blocks comprising the profile, to assess in a preliminary way the state of stability in the existing configuration, and to study ways in which dynamic stresses such as blasting might have an effect.

## PROGRESS OF THE STUDY

The work carried out included a full struc-tural geologic study of the various blocks and plates comprising the profile. In addition to the usual structural data, this included a description of the spatial relationships between the blocks and measurement of the actual dimensions of the discrete members. This information was to be utilized to complete a static stress analysis, which would assist in determining the actual state of stability in the rock mass. Much work had been completed earlier by various investigators (mostly unpublished, personal communications) such as Deere and Patton (about 1965) and the U.S. Geological Survey (about 1966 and 1968), which concentrated primarily upon the stability of the obviously unstable "forehead" block.

Nothing had been done in connection with the blocks and plates underneath, which evidently form the structural foundation on which the profile rests. Work done by Richard Schile, formerly of the Thayer School of Engineering at Dartmouth College, indicated for the first time (Schile, 1975) that the state of static stresses in the rock mass as a unit might be quite delicate and that further, detailed structural geologic information would be required before a comprehensive picture could be prepared of the overall stability of the profile. The work reported here picked up where that work left off, and was an attempt to provide dimensional and spatial information necessary to complete the stress analysis as suggested by Dr. Schile.

As work progressed in the field, it became obvious that, while the structural geologic relationships were fairly easily established, the actual dimensional data were very difficult to obtain accurately. This is because of instability on the climbing ropes and lack of adequate location control on the rock mass. Following a review of the technical problems involved, an offer of photogrammetric assistance was made by the Federal Highway Administration in an effort to insure that the most accurate dimensional information possible would be available for the stress analysis. This would also eliminate a large portion of the error inherent with the more rudimentary surveying methods in the field. A series of horizontal aerial photographs was prepared and was to be used in the construction of a detailed contour map of the features of the rock mass in a vertical plane, as viewed from the east at an altitude of approximately 3,100 feet. At this writing, however, preparation of this map has not been completed and no static stress analysis has been performed. Consequently, only preliminary and qualitative estimates of the profile's stabi-

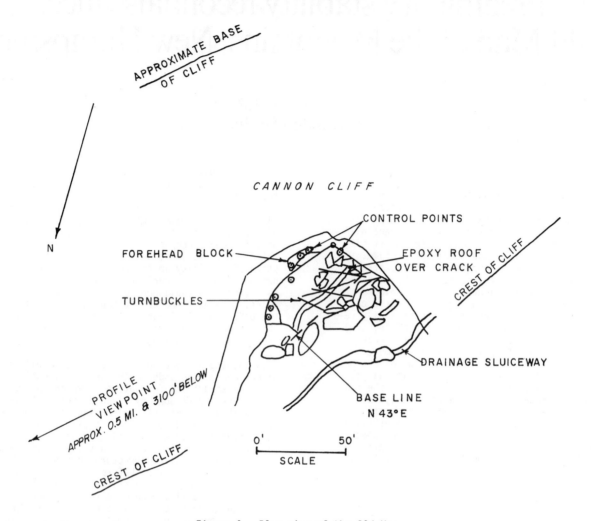

Figure 1. Plan view of the Old Man.

lity are available. Additional funding is necessary in order that this work be completed.

The sections of this report that follow deal with the geological structural information generated through these studies, and with the resulting indications of the overall stability of the profile. Unfortunately, due to limitations of space, most of the unique photographs taken during the work cannot be included. It is hoped that the diagrams and photographs that are included will suffice to provide a general overview. A highly detailed written description of the complex features of the Old Man of the Mountains is beyond the scope of these proceedings. It must be remembered that this information will be further refined following the completion of the contour map and the static stress analysis. Statements made herein are strictly preliminary and reflect only a qualitative estimate of the conditions in the vicinity of the Old Man of the Mountains.

THE FIELD WORK

All geological and dimensional measurements were referred to the baseline and control points established by Schile in 1974 (Fig. 1). Rope climbers rappelled down across the rock face from each of the control points, and all information obtained along each of these lines was related to the baseline by means of a vertical distance from the crest of the "forehead" block at the point where the control had been marked with a climbing anchorage bolt. In the case of the geological structure measurements, the climber attempted to orient himself with the surface traces of the planar features to be measured (strike) and similarly attempted to position himself so that an accurate and perpendicular measurement of the dip could be made.

All strikes were sited forward and backward whenever possible, and all dips were measured at three points along the same surface to minimize errors. All structural information was further refined in the office by correcting data to actual strikes and dips from the apparent measurements made in the field. In the case of dimensional information, taping was attempted between the vertical lines from the control points, but because of instability on the ropes (due to rope twisting, wind, and overhung positions) it was concluded that these measurements would be quite inaccurate. They could be used only as estimates of block or plate size. The measurements have been used in this report only as necessary to prepare a qualitative picture of the profile's stability.

GEOLOGIC STRUCTURE

Five discrete structural elements are involved in the rock mass comprising the profile. Figure 2 illustrates these elements on a point diagram. Set 1 includes all of the joints in a sub-horizontal plane (dip: 23NE) which cut through the rock mass and which have been selectively fractured on the easterly edge of the rock mass to form the actual profile view (Fig. 3). Set 2 includes the sub-vertical (dip: 73SE) joints along which breakage has occurred on the cliff face to the south of the Old Man (Fig. 4). Set 3 includes the joints which can be considered the "face

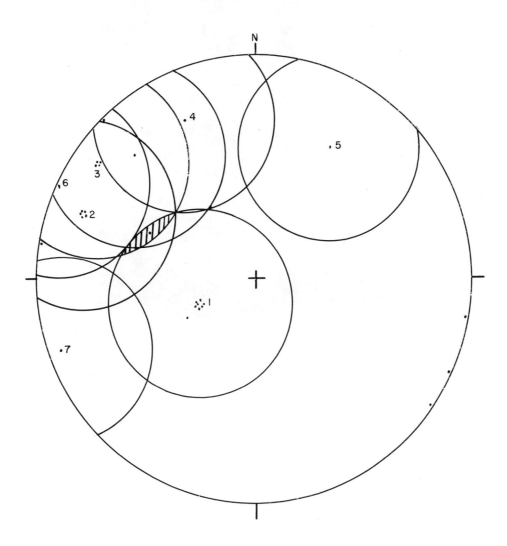

Figure 2. Pole diagram of lower hemisphere. 1. Horizontal plane through blocks. 2. Face-maker south of fault and profile. 3. Face-maker north of fault and profile. 4. Cutoff joint north of blocks 2-5. 5. South face of profile. 6. North face of profile. 7. Fault south of profile.

(Other views in the color section.)

Figure 3.  Profile of the Old Man of the Mountains, Franconia Notch, New Hampshire.

TABLE 1.  ORIENTATION OF JOINTS IN EACH SET

| Set No. | Orientation Strike | Dip |
|---------|--------------------|-----|
| 1 | N25W | 23NE |
| 2 | N20E | 75SE |
| 3 | N35E | 80SE |
| 4 | S65W | 73SE |
| 5 | N60W | 60SW |
| 6 | N25E | Vert |
| 7 | N20W | 85NE |

TABLE 2.  POSITION OF BLOCKS ON THE PROFILE

| Block number | Position on the profile |
|--------------|-------------------------|
| 1 | Forehead plate with detached crest block |
| 2 | Eyebrow |
| 3 | Nose |
| 4 | Upper lip and base of nose |
| 5 | Chin and lower lip |
| 6 | Continuation of block 5 at rear of central cavern |
| 7 | Adam's Apple, just below block 5 |

(All blocks visible in Figure 3, except No. 6)

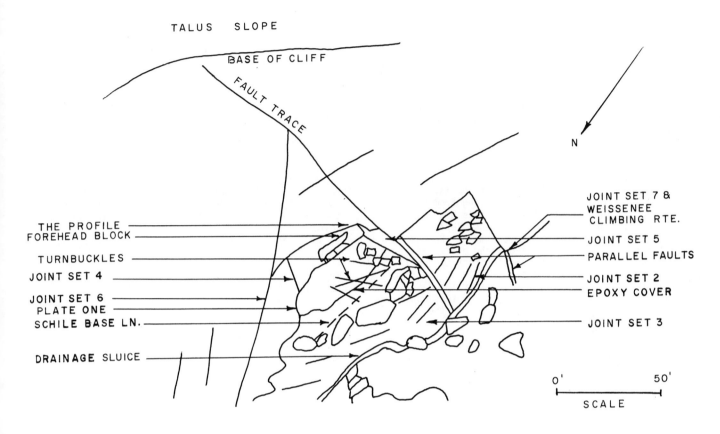

Figure 4. Geologic sketch map of the Old Man.

makers" to the north of the profile. Set 4, which includes only one joint, is located such that it represents the likely "cut-off" joint at the north end of all of the blocks making up the profile, except the actual "forehead block". Set 5, again containing only one joint, represents the south face of the profile. Set 6 represents the northerly face of the profile. And set 7, which includes two parallel faults or shear zones, represents the orientation of these faults relative to the entire structure in the vicinity of the profile. Table 1 summarizes the orientation of the joints in each set.

The structure in the vicinity of the faults of set 7 is interesting (Fig. 4). The fault at the junction of the south face of the profile and the cliff face and a similarly oriented fault 40 feet to the south at the top of the Weissner climbing route are two major features on the cliff (best observed from the floor of the notch). These two faults appear to have been formed in the Conway Granite stock at some point during its early cooling history but following the formation of the normal transverse cooling joints within the granite mass. Shearing along the more northerly fault does not appear to have been extensive. The primary changes created by this fault's

apparent displacement appears to have been a "hinging" action which, as will be noted on the point diagram (Fig. 2) and Table 1, changed the orientation of the face-making joints from N20E to N35E. This change in strike seems to have been a most fortunate development for the profile, because the dip of the joint set in the subhorizontal plane (set 1) dips slightly into the mountainside north of this fault. It would have dipped approximately parallel to the cliff face had this change not occurred. If this suggested structural situation did not exist, the dip direction of the joint set 1 might have been sufficiently parallel to the cliff face so that the Old Man would have collapsed many years ago.

This suggested structural interpretation can be further studied geometrically, using the technique of Talobre as described by Goodman (1976). In Figure 2, circles have been drawn around the main pole of each joint set. The radii of these circles are equal to the $\emptyset$ value for the Conway Granite, which is approximately 35 degrees. According to this technique, the shared area in the circles between related structural elements represents the orientation at which the greatest intact strength can be mobilized in the rock mass, in this case N23E x 45NW. In other words, because the most important joints (set 1) evidently dip slightly back and into the cliff, in the general direction of this optimum strength orientation, and because the profile has not collapsed, it is possible that the center of gravity of the profile acts just behind the junction of the lower cliff and the profile somewhere beneath the "chin" (Fig. 5). Obviously, the exact direction and magnitude of this static load is crucial if this scheme is operative, and it is the specific purpose of the more detailed analyses to more accurately assess this mechanism.

What this configuration suggests, in terms of the profile's stability, is that the natural dead weight (gravity) forces resulting from the presence of the profile's mass at this position on the cliff may actually be responsible for maintaining the stability of the rock mass. Because of the narrow difference between the estimated optimum strength direction and the rock mass orientation, the stability of the profile is apparently very delicate. Minor changes in the distribution of the stresses developed by this configuration could precipitate collapse of the structure.

These suggestions are, as stated earlier, qualitative estimates based primarily upon the orientation of the discrete structural elements in the rock mass, with many of the other, and probably influential, mechanical processes having

been overlooked due to lack of information. Obviously, more accurate dimensional and orientational information is required for any quantitative evaluation of the stability and of the potential effects of dynamic stresses from construction and other activities in the notch.

CONCLUSIONS

Several conclusions can be drawn as a result of the field work in Franconia Notch.

1. It appears from the structural information reported that the configuration of the blocks comprising the profile is perhaps responsible for the apparent stability of the rock mass at this point on the Cannon Cliff. The mechanism involved is somewhat remarkable and probably delicate. Its actual description from a quantitative point of view is critical to an accurate estimate of the profile's stability, either statically or in response to externally induced dynamic stress such as that from blasting and wind vibration.

2. A review of the structural relationships within the rock mass, and particularly the intersections of various joints lying in the sub-vertical plane, suggests that the cut-off joints for blocks 1-3 (Table 2) may be somewhat better than has previously been thought. The joints lie sufficiently to the rear and into the mountainside

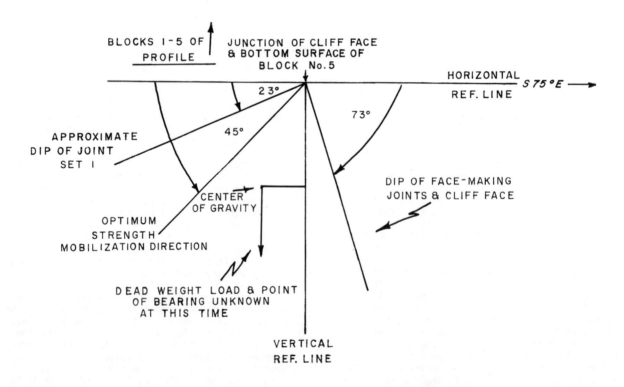

Figure 5. Cliff face, showing the center of gravity and optimum strength direction relationships.

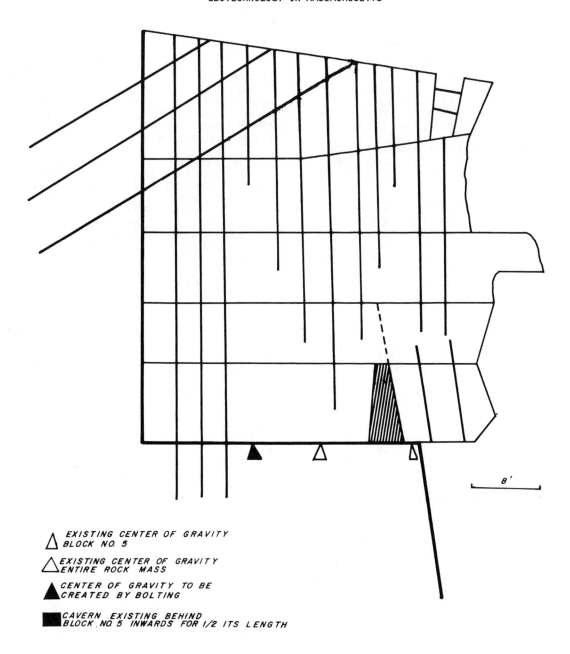

△ EXISTING CENTER OF GRAVITY
  BLOCK NO. 5

△ EXISTING CENTER OF GRAVITY
  ENTIRE ROCK MASS

▲ CENTER OF GRAVITY TO BE
  CREATED BY BOLTING

■ CAVERN EXISTING BEHIND
  BLOCK NO. 5 INWARDS FOR 1/2 ITS LENGTH

Figure 6. Possible active reinforcement
scheme, Old Man of the Mountains.

of the center of gravity that their stability is
somewhat enhanced. Here again, this suggestion
needs to be verified by the proposed mechanical
anlaysis. In any case, the structural trends
within the rock mass indicate that the cut-off
may occur as far as 50 feet behind the easterly
face of the profile at a point to the rear of the
junction of the lower cliff face and the bottom
surface of block 5, with more of the rock mass
lying behind the junction than in front.

Blocks 4 and 5, as stated in Schile's final
report (1975), continue to pose the most critical
stability problem on the profile. Unlike blocks
1-3, field measurements indicate that as much as
80 percent of their total width may be overhung,
and a large cavern has been formed behind them
(20 feet x 8 feet) on their southerly end. Based
upon Schile's estimate of the tensile strength of
the Conway Granite (1093 psi), it is likely that
the mechanism holding these blocks in place is

quite delicate. In view of this and the apparent stability of the blocks above, it seems possible that blocks 4 and 5 could fall away from the profile without the simultaneous collapse of the rest of the rock mass. Block 7, which was implicated in the delicate mechanism by Schile, is apparently not involved in the support of blocks 4 and 5. It is now physically separated from the cliff by the cracks to its rear and appears to have little structural integrity. It is clear that a more detailed study of the mechanical relationships in this portion of the profile will be necessary before an adequate assessment of the stability of block 5 will be possible.

3. It has been the aim of most previous workers to assess the stability of the rock mass and to estimate what levels of dynamic disturbance the configuration can withstand. Basic to any such determination is the quantification of the current state of stability, the magnitude, distribution and types of dynamic disturbances, and an analysis of the structure's response. Without the detailed maps and static analysis, this is impossible. From a qualitative point of view, however, it seems fair to say that the resistance of blocks 1-3 to dynamic stresses will be greater than that for blocks 4 and 5. Some of the previous work, and especially that by the U.S. Geological Survey, has shown that wind, sonic booms and distant quarry blasting are the primary sources of dynamic stress in the profile's rock mass. The existing structure is apparently able to withstand these externally induced dynamic stresses at present. But the possibility of only minor changes in the configuration occurring as a result of weathering in the granite, for example, and thus upsetting the current state of stability, must not be discounted. Until the more detailed analyses are completed and the seismic response of the various blocks on the profile quantified, estimates of allowable dynamic stress levels are tentative.

4. Based upon the results of the work reported here and pending the outcome of the additional work, it appears that active reinforcement of the profile may be possible for the purpose of prolonging its life expectancy. Active reinforcement, as opposed to passive reinforcement, entails the application of active force to the rock mass for the purpose of increasing the intrinsic strength of the existing rock structure. The obvious advantage of this type of reinforcement is that it allows for the strengthening of the rock mass through the application of active forces on the directions and magnitudes required to augment the preexisting strength characteristics. Such reinforcement eliminates the need to rely upon a passive measure, which functions only after a small failure has occurred. Tensioned rock bolts are a typical example of active reinforcement, and untensioned, grouted tendons are an example of passive reinforcement.

As suggested earlier, the natural, dead weight of the profile, acting as its center of gravity, may be responsible for the mass's stability. Further, the geometry indicates that, to augment the dead weight forces and to mobilize

additional strength within the rock mass and its elements, active reinforcement may possibly be applied at an optimum orientation of N25E x 45NW. This direction is indicated on Figure 5 for illustration. While it is impossible without additional quantitative information to prescribe specific reinforcement procedures, it is suggested that, if sufficient foundation is available to support blocks 4 and 5, satisfactory active reinforcement can perhaps be designed.

It is possible that most of this type of work could be done from the top of the profile (block 1) by progressively tying one plate to another in a yet-to-be determined, but no doubt critical and delicate, sequence. This would create a unified rock mass which would then be anchored to the mountainside as suggested by Figure 6. This sort of procedure, if it is possible, would move the center of gravity inward and downward, thus increasing the beneficial forces acting on the unified mass along the estimated optimum mobilization direction. Drilling could be accomplished without inducing potentially hazardous dynamic stresses from vibrations by using one of the many plasma or flame torch systems available in the mining industry. In any case, suggestions in connection with the profile's reinforcement must await the completion of the vertical contour map and the static stress analysis. At this point and in view of the recent settlement of the Franconia Notch controversy over I-93 these activities will require a special appropriation from the New Hampshire legislature or some other interested organization.

Much has been said, here and elsewhere, about the stability and future of the Old Man of the Mountains. It would appear from the foregoing that a careful scientific review of the nature of this important landmark would be appropriate in the interest of preserving it for future generations.

ACKNOWLEDGMENTS

The following individuals have lent valuable support and assistance to this project: Theodore Comstock, Division Administrator, Federal Highway Administration, Concord, N.H.; John Flanders, Associate Commissioner, New Hampshire Department of Public Works and Highways; George Gilman, Commissioner, New Hampshire Department of Resources and Economic Development; and George Hamilton, Director of Parks, and his staff at Franconia State Park. Roger Martin deserves special thanks for his expert rock climbing assistance without which most of this work would not have been undertaken. Roger Moody, District Construction Engineer (NHDPW&H), provided valuable assistance in the interpretation of the mechanical implications of the structural geology. Richard Hamilton provided assistance with the unique photographic problems in the field, and Douglas Leitch of Evergreen Visual Communications developed the diagrams and slides used in conjunction with the presentation and proceedings.

REFERENCES

Goodman, R. E., 1976, Analysis of a sliding block
on a plane--the friction circle concept:
Methods of Geological Engineering, West
Publishing Co., Los Angeles.  p. 237-244.

Schile, R. G., 1975, Stability studies on the Old
Man of the Mountains, Franconia Notch:
Thayer School of Engineering, Dartmouth
College.                                    □

Rock excavations along highways in New England, 2:
rocks fractured by blasting.

# Designing rock excavation programs in New England

A. W. HATHEWAY
D. E. THOMPSON
Haley & Aldrich, Inc.

## ABSTRACT

Rock excavation programs in New England are generally carried out on a production basis to obtain crushed stone, dimension stone, and riprap, or to remove rock to grade level at construction sites, or to create tunnels and other underground structures. In most instances, the relatively hard and intact nature of unweathered igneous and metamorphic bedrock dictates that blasting takes precedence over machine excavation.

Rock excavation programs can be designed with geological and geotechnical factors in mind, especially in those cases in which the owner directs or even controls the excavation crews. In other instances, it may be possible for the owner's consultant to develop enough pre-bid data to significantly influence the dollar amount of bids tendered by rock excavation contractors. Current costs for rock removal by blasting vary from about $13 to $20 per cubic metre for surface excavations and from $40 to $130 per cubic metre for underground sites. On projects involving more than about 10,000 cubic metres of excavation, there is an economic incentive to seek the lowest possible cost base for bids by performing pre-bid rock excavation tests. Additional protection from litigation costs can be afforded by specifying controls over vibration damage claims from blasting and incidences of changed-conditions claims.

Two main types of professional engineering geologic and geotechnical services are important to optimal rock excavation efforts, the first being the defining of geologic controls over the blast and rip characteristics of the rock. The second service is monitoring and modifying of blast design so as to achieve rock breakage goals with the least amount of energy expended in preparing and shooting rock masses.

## THE NATURE OF ROCK EXCAVATION

Rock is broken by mechanical or explosive energy to create an accessible volume of space or to produce a construction material. Rock excavation is normally carried out by specialist contractors who wish to expend the least force necessary to break, handle, transport and dispose of rock to create space or to produce the desired construction material.

Rock is excavated by machine or by detonation of explosives in machine-drilled blast holes. When rock is relatively soft, such as many sedimentary rock types or weathered or altered crystalline rock types, machine excavation usually proves to be the least expensive and the most time effective. However, the relative scarcity of soft sedimentary rock in New England means that machine excavation is generally limited to removal of rock in the weathered zone, and then in surface grading operations. Modern tunnel boring machines are manufactured in sizes and with fittings capable of excavating nearly all rock types.

Contractors generally favor the employment of machine excavation (ripping) because of the relatively simple nature of the one-step removal and disposal/placement of the waste. Again, in New England, generally only highway projects will be of sufficient size to give an opportunity to plan for continuous handling of muck, from ripping to placement as balanced fill. One-operation handling leads to significant cost savings, and the contractor must review the bid documents carefully to make the fundamental decision relating to what relative volumes of rock will be rippable or will require blasting. Next will be the need to determine the nature of the muck (waste) produced by excavation and the degree to which it will meet the requirements for balanced fill or other muck utilization goals of the contractor.

The data and interpretations included in the owner's bid documents usually form the basis for the decision relating to the selection of an excavation method.

### Choice of Excavation Method

Basic decisions relating to the method of excavation are the key to compilation of a sound, winning construction bid. For the purposes of this decision, rock is viewed basically as either "hard" or "soft". Soft rock includes some of the Triassic sedimentary rock of Connecticut and central Massachusetts and a wide range of weathered and altered igneous and metamorphic rock. The passage of Pleistocene glaciation did not leave appreciable amounts of weathered or altered rock in New England. The underlying rationale relates directly to the volume of rock that is specified for removal and the selection of the method that is most effective for production purposes.

Ground surface exposures of rock that is otherwise not removable by blade or scraper pan are often attacked by ripping. Most ripping is undertaken by dozers equipped with ripping teeth. These are single or double-tooth appendages located at the rear of the tractor and capable of being raised or lowered under power to gouge into soft, weathered, or fractured rock. The ability to rip is limited by the ability of the tractor to force the ripper teeth into the rock and by the tractive energy of the tractor to lift fracture-bounded blocks of rock or to shear forward through rock blocks. Ripping is generally not considered too expensive to be used routinely as a production-oriented rock excavation method. Because rippable rock lies midway between machine-excavatable softer rock and massive rock requiring blasting, ripping programs should be studied carefully before commitment on a large scale.

Blasting is an essentially expensive method of rock excavation. There are several criteria for choosing blasting either as the preferred method of excavation, or as the only practicable method (Table 1).

TYPICAL ROCK EXCAVATION CONDITIONS OF NEW ENGLAND

In a general sense, there are five main factors that lead to selection of excavation method.

- Amount of rock to be removed.

- Access space for removal.

- Degree of weathering or alteration of the rock.

- Lithology and degree of metamorphism.

- Continuity and spacing of discontinuities, such as joints, bedding and foliation.

Discounting the first two factors as being largely dependent on project layout and design, the remaining factors are strictly geologic. Pleistocene glaciation has left its imprint on New England and has affected rock excavation planning from two main standpoints: 1) glaciation has removed most of the weathered rock that existed prior to formation of the ice sheets, and 2) the majority of rock encountered for excavation will be obscured from geologic observation by glacial debris.

There are, however, some lithologically-related generalizations that should be kept in mind in developing rock excavation plans. Weathering of bedrock in New England is highly variable and generally occurs in pockets that are protected from the gouging action of the ice sheet. Detection of weathering is a very site-specific chore for the geologist and is based on indications from test pitting and core logging, and from topographic and geomorphic interpretations, along with evidence from seismic refraction traverses.

The two remaining geologic factors, lithology and discontinuities, may be deduced from knowledge of site-area bedrock or from an assessment of outcrops and road cuts in and around the site. Since discontinuities other than major faults and shear zones are non-representative of the rock mass as a whole, it is the joints, bedding planes and foliations that most influence rock excavation. Because rock is a brittle elastic material, its response to tectonic stressing and lower-grade metamorphism is a function of its lithology and petrofabric. Geologists who have worked for some time in New England bedrock terrain have come to recognize certain predictable physical property

TABLE 1. CRITERIA FOR BLASTING FOR ROCK EXCAVATION (MODIFIED FROM LUTTON, 1977)

| Blasting type | Criteria |
|---|---|
| Sensitive blasting | Undertaken in such near proximity as to have a damaging or otherwise unfavorable effect on existing structures or human activities. |
| Restricted blasting | Conducted in the vicinity of slopes or foundations which may suffer unacceptable damage, generally in the construction area. |
| Direct rock blasting | Excavation removal in the course of construction or in quarry operations, so that the fragmented rock is hauled and used directly as a construction material. |
| Crusher source blasting | Blasting used to produce feedstock for mine or quarry crushing operations without strict adherence to fragment size. |
| Rock removal blasting | As required for removal of rock for ensuing construction. Muck is to be wasted or used for a non-size-critical purpose. |
| Specialized blasting | Employment of such techniques as pre-splitting and fracture control blasting to achieve a desired break line at the edge of the blasted area. Under-water removal of rock masses which may hinder navigation is included. |

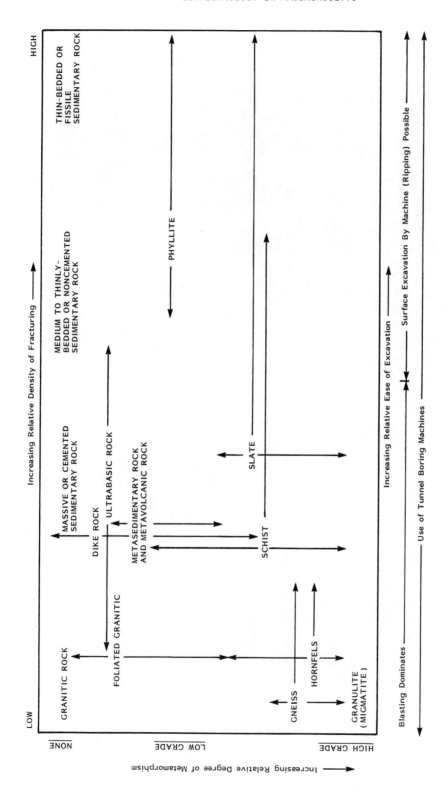

Figure 1. Diagram showing relative ease of excavation of unweathered major rock types in New England.

Figure 2. The "feather and wedge" technique of rock splitting through tensile force. This type of rock excavation is quite costly in terms of labor and is here used to bring a sewerage pump station to grade under contractor-unexpected conditions in New Hampshire.

affinities of the various bedrock formations. If one considers the bedrock formation to include the degree of metamorphism that it may have experienced, a generalization such as Figure 1 can be developed to predict approximate rock excavation character.

First-order generalizations concerning major rock types are as follows.

- Granitic rock: uniformly resistant to rock excavation, except where weathered.

- Granulitic and migmatitic metamorphic rock: usually equally resistant to rock excavation.

- Ultramafic rock: usually the most uniformly fractured in terms of spacing and orientation of discontinuities; almost always requires blasting, but tends to produce relatively small-dimensioned muck.

- Other metamorphic rock: a wide range of susceptibility to blasting and to ripping; the most difficult to predict of the hard rock types of New England.

- Sedimentary rock: about equally susceptible to ripping and blasting; depends mainly on the thickness of bedding and the power of available machinery.

## ROCK EXCAVATION AS A PROCESS

Machine excavation of rock depends largely on the application of lifting or dragging force to a mass of rock that is articulated into blocks separated by discontinuities. These include joints, bedding planes, foliation planes, and shear planes. Machine excavation is accomplished by placing separate masses of discontinuity-bounded rock into tension and then lifting (tensile force) or dragging (shear force) in the direction of motion of the equipment. If pneumatic hammers or "feather and wedge" (Fig. 2) types of hydraulically-actuated rock splitters are used, the forces are tensile. Success in rock excavation by machinery lies in the nature and frequency of rock discontinuities. When relatively large masses of rock (in comparison to the size and power of the machine) are attacked, the nature of the bounding plane nearest to horizontal is influential in the amount of force necessary to drag the rock mass in shear across that plane. Discontinuities which are rough and irregular, and/or which have been partially or wholly recemented (rehealed) by later mineralization, usually exhibit such resistance to excavation that the rock requires blasting.

Blasting, on the other hand, involves detonation of explosives in spherical columns in a pattern of shot holes. The blasting pattern is usually designed in a microsecond phasing of sequential delays so that there is always some relatively free face of broken rock surrounding the next detonation. Detonation of an explosive produces

a spherically-advancing shock wave which, in turn, develops four spherical zones of rock stressing, as shown in Figure 3. The explosion cavity, innermost and outermost zones, and the seismic zone do little to produce broken rock of a useful nature. Most rock is fragmented in the crushed zone and the blast-fractured zone. There is a crude relationship between the width of the crushed zone and the compressive strength of the host rock. According to Atchinson and Pugliese (1964), the crushed zone generally extends outward from the shot hole to only about twice the charge radius, making the blast-fractured zone the main volume of rock breakage. But this zone may be as much as six times that of the charge radius.

Aside from fragmentation of rock which was otherwise unfractured before the blast, the explosive action tends to promote fragmentation by spalling. Spalling represents increased tensile-stress splitting of incipient discontinuities such as microfractures in the rock, as well as the breaking of cohesion along bedding planes and cemented or rough joints and other discontinuities. At most of these discontinuities, the passing tail portion of the incident compressional wave is transferred into a reflected tensile wave, and the rock at each particular point of incidence is subject to elastic rebound, tending to fragment material with relatively low tensile strengths. The greater the ratio between compressive and tensile strengths, the more pronounced is rock breakage by spalling (U.S. Army, 1972). Tensile strengths of less than about $1.03 \times 10^{-7}$ N/m$^2$ (150 psi) may be considered as having a low tensile strength.

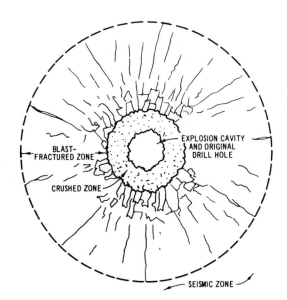

Figure 3. Geometry of an explosion as viewed perpendicular to a horizontal plane penetrated by the shothole at the center of the explosive charge. (Source: U.S. Army, 1972).

## SIGNIFICANT GEOLOGIC FACTORS

Machine excavation of rock relies on the application of force to existing rock discontinuities. Blast excavation of rock also relies on the inherent weakness of such flaws, but is heavily influenced by the relative compressive and tensile strength of the rock. Engineering geologists experienced in New England bedrock terrain will have developed basic working assessments of the general excavation response of major rock types. Aside from the New England lithologic generalities presented in Figure 1, the following geologic factors should be considered in the first reconnaissance of a project site.

### Effects of Discontinuities

Discontinuities have three basic effects on rock excavation by blasting: attenuation of blast energy, lower resistance to fragmentation of rock fractures lying essentially perpendicular to incident blast waves, and the potential for blast-related and later gravitationally-induced failure of blocks of rock along discontinuities which pitch downward and toward the open face of the excavation. The orientation of rock discontinuities is described in terms of free-face stability as favorable or unfavorable (Fig. 4). Adverse bedding is represented by discontinuities with the strike parallel or nearly parallel to the nearest free face of rock excavation and with dips inclined rather steeply into the excavated area. The various types of discontinuities affect rock excavation in the following ways.

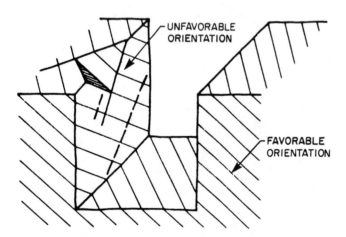

Figure 4. Rock discontinuity orientation viewed as favorable or unfavorable in terms of free-face stability in open excavations. The more prevalent discontinuities shown here are typical of sedimentary bedding planes or of metamorphic rock foliation planes. (Source: U.S. Army, 1972).

Joint discontinuities. Joints are usually the most common of discontinuities in hard rocks. Joints are the result of brittle elastic failure from previous periods of tectonic stressing. Some joints, such as those found in volcanic, igneous plutonic, and metamorphic rock were formed by thermal effects incidental to the origin and emplacement of the rock masses. Joints almost always occur in statistically-prevalent sets and can be evaluated by the use of equal-area polar plot diagrams (Fig. 5). In rock which has been subjected to recurring tectonic or other stressing throughout geologic time, the number of joint sets may increase because of changes in stress field orientation between each episode of stressing.

Joints are commonly filled by later mineralization and may be found in such a healed condition as to be essentially stronger than intact rock. Such joints should be identified separately in evaluations of the effect of jointing on blasting programs.

Shear plane, shear zone, fault, and fault zone discontinuities. Four groups of semi-parallel joints along which displacement has occurred between the opposing surfaces of rock, listed in increasing order of magnitude of width and amount of displacement, are shear planes, shear zones, faults, and fault zones. Fault zones in New England are widely believed to have been formed in pre-Cenozoic time, and later activity has probably been limited to readjustments to subsequent tectonic stresses and post-glacial isostatic rebound. Fault zones in rock requiring blasting are generally neither so sheared or brecciated or wide as to represent major bodies of machine-excavatable rock at individual sites. Faults and their related discontinuities usually represent a greater degree of rock breakage than is desired from blasting, and hence exceed the positive effect of joints in assisting rock breakage. Fault zones may also diminish the rock-breaking shock of an adjacent blast and can lead to venting, thus reducing explosion-generated gas pressure that is useful in breaking rock.

Dike and sill discontinuities. Dikes and sills are tabular bodies of intrusive rock and are important to blast programs because they are generally of a different rock type than the host rock. The dike rock usually represents a different blast medium with respect to drillability for shot holes and rock fragmentation characteristics. Such intrusives should be mapped for their general response to blasting, and for attitude, position, rock type, width, and presence or absence of alteration.

Dikes and sills were generally intruded along pre-existing discontinuities such as faults and joints and are also commonly altered differently from the host rock. Alteration may be found at considerable depths and may reduce the dike rock to weak material that cushions shock waves and is detrimental to the blasting program.

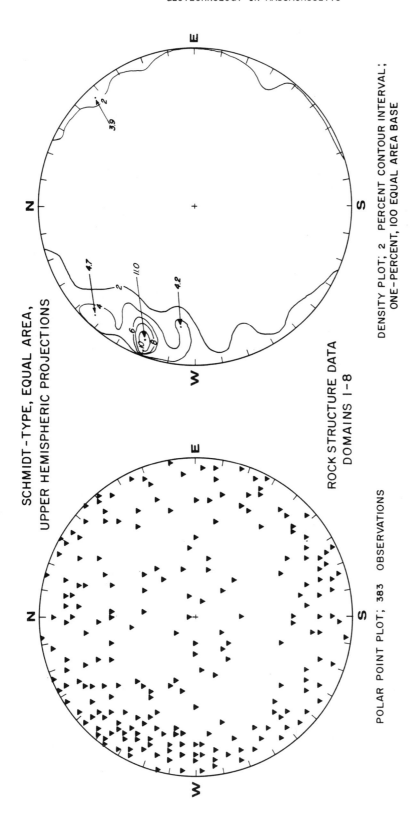

SCHMIDT-TYPE, EQUAL AREA,
UPPER HEMISPHERIC PROJECTIONS

DENSITY PLOT; 2 PERCENT CONTOUR INTERVAL;
ONE-PERCENT, 100 EQUAL AREA BASE

ROCK STRUCTURE DATA
DOMAINS 1-8

POLAR POINT PLOT; 383 OBSERVATIONS

Figure 5. A pair of equal-area polar plots of attitudes
of rock discontinuities found in outcrop and road cuts
along the alignment and in the near vicinity of an extension segment of a Federal Highway in mid-central New
Hampshire. As contoured, the density plot illustrates the
steeply-dipping nature of the pervasive NNE-trending foliation in these metavolcanic rocks.

Bedding discontinuities. Bedding represents the primary structural discontinuities of sedimentary rocks and is the repetitive, parallel occurrence of planar separations between layers of variable grain size and lithological content. Many sedimentary rocks possess bedding which is not open and in the form of discontinuities and which has no direct effect on rock breakage; however, this is not the usual case.

## Other Important Geologic Features

In addition to discontinuities, several other geologic features which will control the effect of blasting may be present. These include rock fabric and the more localized effects of zones of weathering and alteration, as well as cavities and voids.

Rock fabric. Rock fabric is the overall arrangement of the constituent minerals making up the rock and the interactive effect of many factors making up intrinsic rock strength. These factors are: the size and spatial orientation of the mineral grains; the nature of the bonds between these, other grains, and the matrix of the rock; microfractures lacing the rock; partial and total alteration of individual minerals; and evidence of locked-in tectonic or residual stress from past episodes of rock stressing. Rock fabric is best analyzed by individuals skilled in engineering petrography. In crystalline igneous rocks, such as dimension-stone-quality granitic rocks, a skilled observer can detect microscopic fabric effects that produce a "grain". This may cause clean and continuous breaking of the rock in an orthogonal and repetitive pattern.

Zones of weathering or alteration. Zones or pockets of rock weakness are difficult to detect without prior experience in a particular area and with the particular rock type. Weathering of some New England rock types appears to have progressed to an advanced state during post-glacial time. Rocks with high original percentages of iron, sulphides, biotite and ferromagnesian minerals appear to be most susceptible to Holocene weathering. Some plutonic bodies (e.g., the Winnepesaukee Quartz Diorite of New Hampshire) are particularly susceptible to differential weathering within distinct magmatic zones. Other plutonic rock bodies (e.g., the Beverly Granodiorite of Massachusetts) often contain differentially weathered pockets of rock, some harder and more excavation-resistant than others.

Alteration of bedrock is also restricted to certain rock types and in certain structural geologic settings. For example, the Cambridge Argillite of the Boston Basin, otherwise excavation-resistant, fine-grained rock, is found in the vicinity of Harvard Square and in parts of Dorchester in such a chemically altered (kaolinized) condition as to be excavatable by shovel. The kaolinization is typical of members of the Cambridge Formation that were originally tuffaceous,

rather than being the usual quartz-rich metamudstone which makes up the bulk of the argillite.

Cavities and voids. Cavities and voids, rarely in the form of sinkholes, are encountered in western Massachusetts, in the Pittsfield area for instance. Most New England carbonate rocks are calcite deficient or have been metamorphosed to an appropriate grade of rock hardness. Shot hole drillers should be able to detect the presence of cavities encountered by the drill string by greatly reduced penetration resistance or by tell-tale rod drops. The cavities and voids are negative factors in rock excavation for most purposes and, if water filled, may result in changes in explosive type and charge placement.

## ASSESSMENT OF SIGNIFICANT GEOLOGIC FACTORS

In nearly all cases, the bidding contractor will be allowed to propose a method of rock excavation, after examining the contract documents. A choice must be made between drill-and-blast methods and use of rippers for the surface, or tunnel boring machines for underground excavations. The requirements for each decision set are somewhat different, but the differences between surface excavation and underground excavation are clear. Presentation of geologic data in contract documents is always a matter of concern. Contractors justly or unjustly seeking relief from construction problems will always return to the bid documents to point out real or alleged deficiencies in the data presented for the contractor's use in determining method of construction, scheduling, and cost estimation.

Generally, there is a reasonable level of geologic information which should be presented as minimal for the decision making of the bidding contractors. Information in excess of the minimal amount required should be presented with the objective of producing a better assessment of geologic conditions and a resulting narrow spread of bids in a generally lower range of cost. Accuracy is always the critical element of information contained in contract documents. Geological and geotechnical funding will almost never be sufficient to cover all contingencies related to lithology and rock structure. However, the owner's geologic consultant should be prepared to justify the funds expended in producing the geological and geotechnical sections of contract documents.

Information in contract documents is basically of two types--raw data and interpretations. The raw data are simply those observations and measurements made during field mapping, test pitting, coring, and laboratory analysis. Interpretations extend these data in terms of bedrock surface contour maps, geotechnical profiles across the project site, and various conclusions and recommendations. It is always important to separate raw data from interpretations. The trend to do so, however, has been prevalent for only about the past five to ten years.

## Raw Data Applicable to Rock Excavation Planning

Rock is excavated by force applied to discrete, discontinuity-bounded masses of rock, and it is broken into fragments small enough to be removed as muck. These force-related activities depend mainly on rock strength and hardness parameters (for blasting and TBM excavation) and on the nature, orientation, and number of discontinuities (for blasting, TBM excavation, and machine excavation). Essential elements of this geological information are as follows.

- Description of each distinctive lithologic unit and grade of weathering or alteration encountered.

- Rock quality designation (RQD; Deere, 1964) for all rock cored in site borings.

- Percent recovery of all rock core runs attempted in site borings.

- Drill penetration rate for core borings.

- Types and orientation of discontinuities, as recorded from observations of rock core and from outcrops and as exposed by test pits and in road cuts, including spacing, classification (joints, bedding planes, foliation, shear planes, faults, etc.), tightness, planarity, and infilling.

## Interpreted Data Applicable to Rock Excavation Planning

Raw data is gathered only from outcrops and borings. Because the upper surface of the rock mass is usually not observable, key interpretations are essential to planning for rock excavation. These include:

- Estimation of the depth to competent rock, usually referred to as the "top-of-rock" line in a geotechnical profile and as a contoured surface of competent rock in site layout plans.

- Contacts and distribution of individual rock units.

- Ground water (cleft water) present in and available to feed into the rock mass upon excavation, taking into account equivalent permeability of the mass, characteristics of flow from the mass, and zonal permeability related to weathered rock, surface soil units, shear zones, or the rock mass in general.

- Continuity of sets of discontinuities.

- Orientation of sets of discontinuities.

- Subdivision of the project site into individual structural domains in which discontinuities of specific orientation (sets) are dominant. Raw data concerning the character of the discontinuities (e.g., tightness, planarity and infilling) can then be related to these domains.

## ASSESSMENT OF SIGNIFICANT GEOLOGICAL FACTORS

Significant geologic factors must be identified and assessed for each rock excavation project. Open cuts planned in rock are generally less complicated in terms of assessment than are tunnels and other underground openings. This paper does not address the aspects of temporary and long-term stability of cuts and underground openings. Its main goal is to show the need to identify the nature, spacing, and geometry of geologic units and their contacts and discontinuities, and to define their basic engineering properties. These geological inputs are essential to the planning of the rock excavation effort. Geologic mapping is the main method of investigation. Development of geologic data for subway construction in the Boston basin can be found in another paper by Hatheway in this volume.

## Geologic Mapping

Geologic mapping for rock excavation should begin with a summary reconnaissance of the area surrounding the site. Exposed types of bedrock are listed, along with weathering and alteration, and geologic discontinuities. Most urban areas

TABLE 2.  COST RANGES FOR ROCK BOREHOLE
TECHNIQUES IN NEW ENGLAND

| Technique | 1981 cost per 30 cm[1] (1 foot) |
|---|---|
| Double-tube core barrel | $25 - $40 |
| Triple-tube core barrel | $35 - $50 |
| Double-tube, split inner liner | $30 - $45 |
| Oriented core | $90 - $105 |
| Integral sampling method (ISM) | $150 - $165 |
| Borehole photography[2] | $3 - $4 |
| Sonic logging ("seisviewer" or "televiewer")[2] | $4 - $6 |

[1] Includes diamond loss charge for coring techniques

[2] The largest cost is that of mobilization, which is here prorated for a 300 lineal metre borehole recording job.

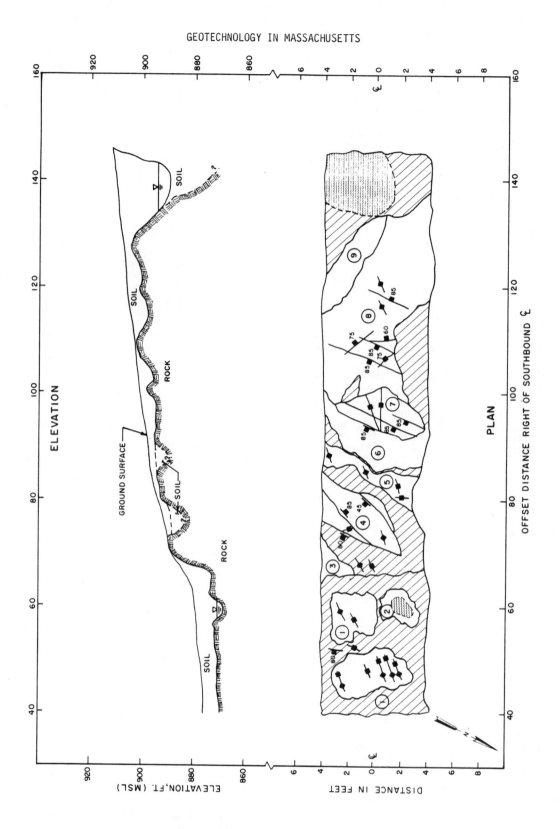

ELEVATION

PLAN

Figure 6. Structural geologic map of the exposed bottom of a backhoe trench excavated to top-of-rock. Trenches are often the only means of exposing rock for structural geologic mapping necessary to define rock excavation conditions, short of the more expensive rock borehole techniques listed in Table 2.

Visual Description of Rock Surface

Zone 1 — Polished, striated rock surface, sloping 3-6" downward to the NNE; nearly vertical foliation striking N40E; joints parallel to foliation. Some are open and filled with soil.

Zone 2 — Small depression in rock (1.3 ft. deep), filled with water, probably seeped in from overlying soil. Rock around depression is severely weathered, highly fractured, partially decomposed.

Zone 3 — Zone of decomposed rock (reduced to soil). Contact between soft material and sound rock is visible, striking generally N-S, dipping 80°W. Water is seeping into trench from this zone.

Zone 4 — Polished, striated rock surface, sloping 15-20° downward to NE; nearly vertical foliation. Some joints are open, and filled with soil material.

Zone 5 — Zone of moderately to severely weathered rock, partially reduced to soil. Rock is broken into small fragments, mainly along foliation. Many small soil inclusions.

Zone 6  
Zone 7 — Same rock surface appearance and slope as for Zone 1; joints trending typically N-S.

Zone 8 — Irregular rock surface with polished and striated areas. Foliation is following same attitude as in other zones; joints are randomly oriented.

Zone 9 — Polished surface, sloping 30-40° down toward SSW. At the foot of this zone is a depression in the rock filled with soil and water.

have few remaining outcrops, and evidence of bed-rock type may be found only in the foundation ma-sonry of individual buildings and bridges. Most New England bedrock, except for plutonic and mig-matitic types, possesses either bedding (such as the Cambridge Argillite) or at least enough evi-dence of foliation to orient the rock core, as described below. Coarse-grained sedimentary rock, such as the Roxbury Conglomerate of the Boston basin, remains without discernible bedding in in-dividual core runs. (A core run consists of the amount of core recovered intact in a single re-covery of the core barrel or split inner liner.)

Beyond actual inspection and recording of rock exposures in road cuts and construction ex-cavations, geologic mapping is carried on to pro-duce evidence of characteristic discontinuities and the orientation of bedding and foliation.

## Core Borings

For most sites, rock core borings are the prime method of obtaining information across the breadth of a surface excavation, along the align-ment of a tunnel, or across an underground open-ing. Core borings are expensive. The costs vary widely by the season and according to the tech-niques utilized. Table 2 provides some estimated cost ranges for various NX-sized (76 mm; 3-inch) coring techniques employed in New England.

Utilization of borehole data is discussed in another paper by Hatheway in this volume, dealing with hard rock mapping techniques. Boring data will usually not give information on the planar extent of discontinuities, except for major shear zones or faults. Drilled material with shear zones and faults is seldom recovered with any in-dication of spatial orientation. Shear zones and faults, however, are often distinguished by brec-ciation, slickensides, and zonal width and can of-ten be detected in three or more borings so that a strike and dip can be estimated. Where the fault or shear zone is older than other offsetting discontinuities, its surface will be displaced.

## Test Pits, Trenches, and Inspection Shafts

Access to subsurface rock exposures can also be had through excavation of test pits, trenches and inspection shafts. Figure 6 is a structural geologic map of the bottom-surface of a broom-brushed trench. The test pit and trench methods are only applicable if depth of overburden is slight (OSHA requirements call for shoring at depths of more than 1.5 m). Test pits and trenches can provide important indications of joints and other discontinuities, to the extent that the rock so exposed is not entirely weathered.

Inspection shafts, such as that excavated by churn drilling at the Porter Square subway station site in Cambridge, must be about a metre in dia-meter to allow for passage of a lift cage for the logging geologist. Costs of inspection shafts vary widely, due to their unique nature and the limited footage generally employed. A 1981 cost estimate for New England is $650 - $1000 per metre, where soil overburden is slight and casing is easily sealed with respect to limiting water inflow. All of these geologic inspections are made with maps ranging from about 1:12 to 1:60 in scale. Inspection shafts also risk intersection of non-representative rock, or rock that belongs to a single structural domain, or rock particular-ly different from that found at other locations in the project area.

## Pilot Tunnels and Test Excavations

Pilot tunnels and test excavations represent the first level of exploration activity that ac-tually results in observing representative rock excavation conditions. The unit costs for such excavations are generally higher than those that result from bidding for the entire rock excavation job. Both types of excavations (tunnels and open cuts) should be excavated within the mass of rock to be removed later, to save duplication of exca-vation and to obtain a test of the actual excava-tion behavior.

Pilot tunnels are an attractive method of gaining insight into rock excavation and ground support conditions in large underground openings, such as subway stations. In this case, the pilot tunnel can be driven at the crown of the station with the main excavation being opened up below the pilot tunnel (see Hatheway, this volume). Costs for pilot tunnel work will probably exceed those of general excavation by 200 to 400 percent, run-ning in the general range of $100 to $200 per cubic metre (1981 prices). But a preliminary ex-cavation exercise, based on direct observation of the performance of rock, will be of great value in project planning.

Contracting procedures generally result in separate contract competition for the preliminary excavation and the final construction contract. The preliminary excavation contract will permit construction bid contractors to see the excavated rock surfaces and the resulting muck and allow them to improve their bid estimates based on their blend of experience and actual observation. The preliminary excavation contract should be care-fully monitored and reported in a geological and geotechnical report available to all bidders. The availability of the preliminary rock excavation tends to save the owner money in the construction bid, often due to the fact that many contractors manage to survive in business solely on the basis of shrewd expertise. However, engineering geo-logists and geotechnical engineers are needed for evaluating the technical data of the bid docu-ments. The same preliminary rock excavation pro-gram can be used in defining ground support re-quirements.

## CONTRACT DOCUMENTS FOR ROCK EXCAVATION

Contract documents should be designed to serve four basic goals.

- To provide enough information to the bidding contractors to fairly represent the actual ground conditions, resulting in a narrow spread of bids.

- To provide the contractor with a feeling of accurate representation of ground conditions to the extent that contingency costs are kept at a minimum.

- To enable the contractor to adhere to contract schedules.

- To minimize the occurrence of changed-conditions claims.

There are no standard specifications for rock excavation. Each set must be based on the owner's functional objectives for the constructed facili-

ty, on the engineer's design requirements, and on the geological and geotechnical consultants' estimates of the data and interpretations necessary for an accurate bid. Some of the key data and interpretations for a typical project involving both surface excavation and tunneling are shown on Table 3. Blasting specifications may be developed to provide basic controls over project blasting, in terms of damage potential to abutters, the nature and quality of rock produced as muck, and the condition of free-standing rock faces after blasting is completed. Some of the key aspects of a blasting specification are shown on Table 4.

Care should be given to development of realistic "A" and "B" lines, with respect to the geologic structure of the host rock. For example, continuous, smooth and open joints spaced at 0.5 to 1.0 m may make adherence to 15-cm or 30-cm lines of tolerance impossible. The original specifications in force at the Seabrook Nuclear Station, New Hampshire, for excavation of containment

TABLE 3. CRITICAL INFORMATION FOR ROCK EXCAVATION CONTRACT DOCUMENTS

| Data | Interpretation |
|---|---|
| Definition and distribution of basic lithologic types to be expected on the project. | Estimation of volumes of rock to be excavated. |
| A representation of the nature and spacing of occurrence of the various types of discontinuities; include RQD of applicable core logs. | Geologic maps of the areas planned for excavation; the detail shown should be commensurate with the outcrop exposure and the need to collect attitudes and observations of the discontinuities. The geologic maps should portray both the areal extent of all lithologic units and representative structural geological symbols. |
| Expected zones, pockets or lenses of alteration or weathered rock; lenses of variable rock hardness (sedimentary and metamorphic strata). | Geologic sections or profiles showing the expected, generalized distribution of lithologic types with depth. |
| Presence and expected orientation of dikes, sills and other intrusions of variable hardness from surrounding rock; and veins of essentially hard minerals, such as quartz. | Generalized remarks concerning the applicability of various rock excavation techniques. |
| | Seismic refraction traverses along and across the area to be excavated. |
| | Profile representation of top-of-rock, along with a definition of the nature of that surface. |
| | A definition of the nature and expected extent of rock that is considered unsuitable for the intended construction use; such rock will be considered as waste. |
| A tabulation of averaged compressional wave velocities, from seismic refraction traverses. | |
| Such engineering property data as are necessary and which have been developed through laboratory testing of representative samples. | |

TABLE 4.  KEY ASPECTS OF BLASTING SPECIFICATION
(MODIFIED FROM LUTTON, 1977)

| Specification | Key aspects |
|---|---|
| 1. General requirements | Review of the proposed blasting plan by the owner's representative, before the start of drilling for each shot; requirement for submission of a simple sketch for the record. |
| | Use and placement of presplitting charges. |
| | Restriction of blasting within designated minimal spacing between charge centers and concrete or grout of any age. |
| | Scaling of permanent slopes or faces remaining at the conclusion of blasting. |
| 2. Acceptable and specified methods of blasting | Presplitting to achieve prescribed final cut slopes and faces. |
| | Line drilling to achieve critical tolerances at designated breaklines. |
| | Zone blasting to create a buffer of broken rock left in place as a protective barrier for minimization of damage to critical faces; the buffer to be removed in the last stages of cleanup. |
| 3. Special restrictions | Maximum acceptable depth and inclination deviation of presplit shotholes. |
| | Depths of individual shot lifts (a minimum and maximum figure constitute the acceptable range). |
| | Minimum separation distances from shot pattern to sensitive structures or rock. |
| 4. Precautions at or near final grade and final scope | Prohibition of subdrilling which may tend to weaken or break rock below final grade. |
| | Denial of use of limited shot techniques such as lifters or snake holes to achieve final break lines (the danger of overbreak is high). |
| | Reduce spacing, burden, and power factor on shot holes adjacent to presplit surfaces. |
| | Use of delay patterns especially designed to provide relief of confinement for the shot row nearest the presplit line. |
| | Provision of lines, grades and tolerances on drawings. |
| | "A" and "B" lines (maximum and minimum limits) to be shown as the basis for payment of unit rock excavation prices; no rock will remain inside the excavated area, as the minimum line of excavation for pay and rock broken beyond the "B" line will result in nonpayment, with the contractor being required to fill the void with suitable material at no extra cost to the owner. "A" and "B" lines are the tolerances for rock excavation. |

vessel no. 1, in Kittery Schist and Newburyport Quartz Diorite, called for a 15-cm tolerance on faces to be formed in a variety of geometric shapes. The contract for this and the sister excavation for containment vessel no. 2 involved over 340,000 m$^3$ of rock. The nature of jointing in the host rock was adverse to satisfactory attainment of this part of the specifications. A geologic assessment was made of what was possible and effective, and the results were presented to the parties to the project. Appropriate relief was granted to the rock excavation subcontractor.

PRODUCTION CONTROL OVER EXCAVATION EFFORT

Control measures should be exercised by the rock excavation contractor, to the degree that he is able to monitor the rate of excavation in terms of his original schedule. Early in machine excavation efforts, the degree to which the rock is rippable will soon become apparent. Farquhar (1967) made the point that a contractor in southeast Massachusetts undertook to excavate a hard, gray metasandstone member of the Rhode Island Formation by ripping, on a pre-1967 contract bid of $19.50/m$^3$. The construction contract was drawn up without benefit of seismic refraction surveying which undoubtedly would have delivered compressional wave velocities in excess of the maximum threshhold of 1600-3350 mps that is generally regarded as being the upward limit of rock that can be ripped with large dozers. Because of the hard nature of the metasandstone and the generally confined nature of the available area for excavation, the actual costs of excavation escalated to about $33/m$^3$.

While the above case illustrates a contract that was written without proper geologic input, blasting specifications are generally included for performance limits in terms of overbreak (again, paylines "A" and "B" are generally specified), condition of rock remaining in free faces, and the degree of ground vibration and air blast felt in the immediate surroundings. The design of blast rounds governs these performance requirements.

Blast Design in General

In order to take advantage of the spherical propagation of rock-breaking shock waves, most blasters use geometric shot hole patterns designed to achieve optimal breakage between individual shot holes. The basic patterns are rectangular, staggered, and single-row. Minor variations are employed wherever single obstacles or unusual breaklines are encountered. Rock-to-free-air interfaces, such as slope faces and benches, represent a relative lack of confinement in the direction of the free face. Delays are employed to produce successive free faces within a single shot pattern. Properly designed delays can achieve optimal fragmentation, reduce the throw of rock fragments, exert control over the extent of rock breakage, and limit the ground vibration associated with the blasting. The usual firing order is designed to continually remove confinement and

achieve unidirectional rock breakage by enhanced spalling, at the same time placing the broken rock slightly outward into the excavation without excessive throw. When delays are used, the ground shock wave is perceived as a momentarily longer rumble of sound and vibration, and the peak amplitude of ground motion resulting from the blast is significantly reduced.

Surface blasting programs in New England are not always planned to accommodate specific rock characteristics at the site selected. In fact, these characteristics exert considerable control over the results achieved from blasting. When the contractor is willing to accept the results of non-geologically planned blasting and these results are within the limits of contract specifications, little action by the owner is possible or desirable. When the results of blasting, do not meet specifications or if the contractor is experiencing severe difficulties, the resident engineer or geologist should at once alert his superiors. This representative must continue to maintain a careful record of the elements of the blast program, as well as of the geologic controls present in the rock, as a basis for possible negotiations or legal defense over alleged changed conditions.

Geologic notes maintained by the owner's resident should include the following.

- Typical shot hole geometry.

- Representative measurements of rock discontinuities.

- An occasional hand specimen of muck from specified shots.

- Sketch maps at the exposed face after selected blasts.

- Photographs noting the size and gradational spread of muck produced by the shot.

Design of Blast Rounds for Underground Excavation

The governing concern for blast design in underground excavation is the preservation of the quality of the rock lying outside the excavation limits. Control of overbreak is managed through orientation of the shot holes and the manner in which they are loaded, stemmed and delay-fused. Contracts usually leave the matter of round design up to the contractor, specifying only the nature of "A" and "B" lines and the quality of rock remaining at the perimeter of the excavated area. Some of the important factors of blasting procedure that should be employed by the excavation contractor are as follows.

- Line drilling: drill holes placed at 30 to 60-cm spacing and designed to provide a line of preferential rock breakage between the "A" and "B" lines of contract specifications.

- Smooth blasting: reduction of powder factor (charge size) in perimeter holes to the extent necessary to split the rock without damaging the rock outside the "A" and "B" lines.

- Cushion blasting: a variation of smooth blasting in which considerable air space or stemming surrounds charges in shot holes and serves to reduce undesirable overbreak and fracturing in the final wall surfaces.

- Presplit blasting: instantaneous detonation in a single string of shot holes drilled and loaded along the desired break line. This may induce higher levels of ground vibration than other methods due to confinement.

- Fracture control blasting: perimeter shot holes are side-notched for the entire length and subjected to equalized detonation pressure by use of cushioned charges of low explosive. Stemming is increased to prevent venting: the result is a reduction of perimeter drilling and significant overbreak in jointed rock.

Drilling Control

Drilling control should be exercised in the depth and orientation of shot holes, especially those located along the perimeter of the excavated area. Shot hole drillers frequently do not follow layout specifications to the letter, and carelessly oriented holes will often lead to overbreak. This condition will be noted by the existence of drill casts beyond the "A" or "B" lines (a cast represents the remaining portion of the shot hole lying within the surrounding wall rock).

Prediction and Control of Blasting Damage

Rock excavation by blasting is usually designed to expend the least amount of funds to create the desired volume of broken rock, whether for creation of a surface excavation or an underground opening, or to obtain construction material. The owner is concerned with the quality of rock and rock surfaces at the edge faces of the void and with the character and quality of the rock muck that is produced during the blasting program. Although the contractor is usually made to assume responsibility for damages associated with the blasting operation, it is in the best interests of the owner to help insure that the blasting program causes no damage. Most of the owner's control must be exerted through the contract specifications for blasting. The owner may also elect to monitor the strength and character of blast-generated ground and air waves in order to intercede when the blasting program is not following specifications.

Monitoring of the effects of air blast and ground shock waves is generally undertaken using a special blast vibration seismograph with an accessory piezoelectric air blast pressure gage. This is a one-man operation which may be conducted at specified or unannounced intervals, and at times when the contractor elects to change the blast program parameters. The records should be carefully annotated as to time and location of the instrument and the nature of blasting in terms of charge size, placement, delay and other key factors making up the blasting program for that shot. The seismograph should be moved from time to time in order to register effects along different bearings from the shot area in the event that localized geologic conditions are affecting the nature of shock wave transmission radially away from the shot area.

Monitoring personnel may wish to make use of existing empirical relationships for air blast propagation and levels of ground vibration as related to distance/charge magnitude and dominant frequency of vibration. The monitoring data are usually made available for contractor inspection or may form the basis for reports to the owner for appropriate enforcement of contract specifications.

CHANGED-CONDITIONS CLAIMS

It is customary to include in contracts involving earthworks, rock excavation, and other foundation-related construction some means of financial redress for contractors who encounter genuine, natural conditions not displayed in the contract documents or otherwise known. Provisions for these changed conditions are included so as not to shift the entire responsibility for risk assumption to the contractor and to thus keep the contractor bids in a reasonable and narrow breadth at the time of competition for project work. Two standard causes of changed conditions are generally cited in contract documents in North America.

- Subsurface and latent physical conditions at the site which differ materially from those indicated in the contract documents.

- Unknown physical conditions at the site which are of an unusual nature, different materially from those ordinarily encountered and generally recognized as inherent in the type of work described in the contract documents.

The frequency of construction claims has expanded in the United States by about 300 percent since 1960 (Vince, 1979). Whereas about 13 percent of construction contracts went to court in 1960, about 35 percent now end in litigation. Serious claims, those in excess of $100,000, were increasing at an annual rate of about 20 percent by 1979. When suits are filed, there is also an increasing chance that other parties to the owner's design team, his engineer and architect, and occasionally their specialist consultants, are enjoined. Advice to practicing geologists will be found in the near future in the Professional Practice Guidelines (in press, 1981) by the Association of Engineering Geologists and in the on-going publication series of the Association of Soil and Foundation Engineers, of Silver Spring, Maryland.

In the case of planning for and executing rock excavation programs, there remains the relatively high possibility that claims will be lodged during construction. This may be more frequently the case in underground construction than with surface rock excavation. There are really only two good lines of defense for the owner and his engineering and geological team: 1) production of complete and accurate contract documents, and 2) close and continuous observation of the rock excavation program, with adequate communication with the contractor.

The latter form of protection should make use of a resident geologist or geotechnical engineer, who will record the nature and progress of construction on a daily basis, compile as-constructed geologic maps of final faces in rock, make a photographic record of the construction process, observe for indications of changed conditions, and possibly serve to monitor blast-vibrations. At the slightest indication of any non-conformity, the representative should inform his superiors and, if necessary, discussions should be held with the contractor. Cases in which contractor progress is either not built up to the project schedule, or in which the schedule is suddenly not maintained, are clear warnings of impending claims. Each day that discussion of the issue is avoided, the potential claim situation worsens.

## MUCK CHARACTERISTICS

Variations in hardness and in the spacing of discontinuities in typical New England rock types (Fig. 1) will lead to a wide variety of sizes and shapes for the material produced by rock excavation. Unless disposed of as waste rock, this muck (spoil) may be utilized directly in construction. If transported for use off the site, it must meet the size gradation requirements of a third party. The form in which muck is produced governs its acceptability for cost-effective disposal.

The main factors relating to the nature of muck are concerned with the force applied to the rock and the intrinsic nature of the rock itself, that is: rock strength; rock discontinuities; nature of explosive or excavation force; and placement, orientation, and timing of the explosive.

If the method of excavation or blasting is incompatible with the geologic character of the rock mass, the muck will either vary from the desired characteristics or will require expenditure of more than optimal energy to break it to the desired size and shape. Additional handling may be necessary to move, distribute, haul, or emplace the resulting muck. Of the four main factors controlling the nature of muck, the two dealing with the type and placement of force are directly dependent upon geologic conditions.

Balanced cut and fill estimates for rock excavation depend heavily on estimation of the bulking factor (also known as earthwork factor). This is the ratio of muck volume, when placed as embankment fill, to excavation volume. A factor in excess of unity indicates that compaction or placement density will be less than that found in-situ, prior to excavation. For factors computed to be less than unity, the fill volume will exceed the volume of the original cut.

Determination of bulking factors for soils are rather straightforward and depend mainly on the state of preconsolidation of the soil and the density to which design requirements call for the embankment earthwork. For rock, however, a variety of conditions and characteristics affect the resulting density of rock fill. The California Department of Transportation (Stephens, 1978) has found that pre-excavation compressional wave velocity (determined by seismic refraction survey) offers the best basis for estimation of the bulking factor. Where rock types are uniform in muck characteristics, bulking factor curves can be developed during and after the completion of individual projects. The in-place rock volume can then be related to as-placed volume of muck incorporated as balanced fill, all in relation to the pre-excavation compressional wave velocity. Estimates can be made of the predicted bulking factors on the basis of geologic characteristics observed during the pre-design mapping and related geotechnical studies, such as: shape of rock fragments (dominantly flat fragments can tend to increase the factor), size gradation (gap-grading can tend to increase the factor), and degree of compaction (if additional fragment breakage occurs during compaction, the factor may be decreased).

## ENVIRONMENTAL ASPECTS OF ROCK EXCAVATION

Rock excavation programs in New England usually fall under the intense scrutiny of an environmental impact assessment and review. Highways and major expansion projects for subway tunneling can require long-term blasting programs and significant amounts of muck. Highway design in the semi-rugged New England terrain usually employs balanced cut and fill, and the muck is placed as fill within an economical haul distance of the excavation. Except in the vicinity of towns and cities, the rock excavation program can be designed and managed with a minimum of perceived or actual environmental impact.

Rapid transit construction generally produces muck from only its underground components, and such rock and soil waste is generally an unwanted component of construction. Urban area muck disposal poses a serious problem except in such instances as the Massachusetts Bay Transportation Authority (MBTA) muck disposal area in west Cambridge, Massachusetts, in which the waste is being contour-piled to produce a hill-like park area complete with winter sports slopes. Methods of handling and disposing of muck have been determined by Haley & Aldrich, Inc. (1977).

Costs related to the transportation of natural materials usually rise nearly exponentially with distance from source to final destination. This is naturally related to time on the road, the requirement for a fleet of trucks to provide the basic supply, and problems related to timing of hauls versus traffic patterns on the haul route. The U.S. Bureau of Mines, Twin Cities Mining Research Center, Minnesota, has conducted a program of defining the planning needs for opening new quarries near urban areas. Most of the findings are applicable to providing rock materials for transportation construction projects located in or near urban areas (Pugliese and others, 1979).

Large and long-term quarrying operations in or near New England urban areas will quite likely never be feasible, in terms of permitting. However, as the sources of suitable coarse-grained glacial outwash continue to be depleted, engineering geologists will be assigned to help develop quarry operations for production of replacement crushed stone. For that purpose, the permitting advice given by Pugliese and others (as Table 5, modified herein) will be useful.

TABLE 5. ELEMENTS OF AN ENVIRONMENTAL PLAN FOR ROCK EXCAVATION BY QUARRYING (AFTER PUGLIESE AND OTHERS, 1979)

Production objectives and probable resources in terms of project requirements.

The economics of the local aggregate market and its outlook over the project duration; includes alternate sources and associated haul costs.

Bonds and permits required.

Estimated cost of environmental assessment required for submission to regulatory agencies.

Nature of the quarry site: topographic, geologic, hydrologic, and wildlife/biologic character.

Probable plan of optimal development.

Amount of capital needed to put plans into operation.

Ability to acquire the property and mineral rights (if such apply).

Previous experience of other rock production activities in the general area.

Local zoning ordinances.

Existing alternative sources of rock, with estimated haul costs and availability during quarry-related construction.

## SUMMARY

Rock excavation efforts in New England, as in most regions of the nation, have historically been treated by civil engineering design teams primarily in terms of cut-face stability and structural ground support of underground openings. All projects, large or small, should include sequential planning for development of geological information leading to a definition of the type and occurrence of rock as an excavation medium. Excavation response characteristics should be determined and specifications written for the construction contract, detailing the alternatives in which rock excavation may be accomplished. Environmental concerns for the disposal of muck and for ground vibrations and other nuisance factors of blasting must now be met. The construction effort itself is also prone to encounter difficulties leading to changed-conditions claims and potential court litigation over rock excavation. Specialty assistance by engineering geologists and geotechnical engineers will do much to assist civil engineers, architects, and owners in securing reasonable bid costs and trouble-free construction.

## ACKNOWLEDGMENTS

The senior author is appreciative of the opportunity afforded him during his editorship of the forthcoming revision of the Manual of Subsurface Investigations of the American Association of State Highway and Transportation Officials (AASHTO), as administered by the National Cooperative Highway Research Program (NCHRP) of the Transportation Research Board, National Academy of Sciences. Much of the stimulation for writing the present paper came from the efforts to compile Chapter 11 of the manual: Planning for Rock Excavation Programs. Both authors are grateful for review of Figure 1 by Edwin Blackey (Chief Geologist, New England Division, U.S. Army Corps of Engineers), Patrick Barosh (Structural Geologist, Weston Observatory, Boston College) and Martin Ross (Petrographer, Department of Geology, Northeastern University, Boston).

## REFERENCES

Atchison, T.C., and Pugliese, J.M., 1964, Comparative studies of explosives in limestone: U.S. Bureau of Mines, Report of Investigations 6395, 25 p.

Deere, D.U., 1964, Technical description of rock cores for engineering purposes: Rock Mechanics and Engineering Geology, v. 1, no. 1, p. 17-22.

Farquhar, O.C., 1967, The Rhode Island Formation as "rock" excavation, in Farquhar, O.C., ed., Economic geology in Massachusetts: Graduate School, University of Massachusetts, p. 111-124.

Haley & Aldrich, 1977, Muck utilization in the urban transportation tunneling process: U.S. Department of Transportation, Washington, D.C., Report UMTA-MA-06-0025-77-15, 384 p.

Hatheway, A.W., 1982, Hardrock geologic mapping for underground construction in the Boston Basin, in Farquhar, O.C., ed., Geotechnology in Massachusetts: Graduate School, University of Massachusetts. This volume.

Lutton, R.J., 1977, Constraints on blasting design for construction, in Fairhurst, C., and Crouch, S.L., eds., Proceedings of the 16th Symposium on Rock Mechanics: American Society of Civil Engineers, New York, New York, p. 365-369.

McKown, A.F., and Thompson, D.E., 1981, Experiments with fracture control in tunnel blasting: Proceedings, 22nd U.S. Symposium on Rock Mechanics, Massachusetts Institute of Technology, Cambridge. Not cited.

Pugliese, J.M., Swanson, D.E., Engelmann, W.H., and Bur, T.R., 1979, Quarrying near urban areas - an aid to pre-mine planning: U.S. Bureau of Mines, Information Circular 8804, Washington D.C., 50 p.

Stephens, E., 1978, Calculating earthwork factors using seismic velocities: California Department of Transportation, Report FHWA-CA-TL-78-23, Sacramento, CA, 56 p.

U.S. Army, 1972, Systematic drilling and blasting for surface excavations: Office, Chief of Engineers, Engineer Manual EM 1110-2-3800, Washington, D.C., variously paged.

Vince, C.R., 1979, Implications of liability claims: Symposium on Reasonability in Engineering Geology, Annual Meeting, Association of Engineering Geologists, 3 October, Chicago, Illinois.                            □

Rock excavations along highways in New England, 3: rock falls and slides.

# Preventive geotechnical engineering— Placebo, paradigm, or panacea?

T. L. NEFF
Portland State University, Oregon

## ABSTRACT

The geotechnical aspects of many constructed facilities present real and unusual risks not generally found in other aspects of the project. All constructed facilities contain geotechnical elements because such facilities must rest on, in, or below the earth's surface. This paper presents the details of a proposed concept, "Preventive Geotechnical Engineering," which can and should play a key role in many projects. The need for such a philosophy remains relatively obvious when one considers the small, but increasing, number of recent failures related to geotechnical aspects of projects, especially dams. Also, the inventory of existing structures continues to grow while the average age of the elements within this inventory increases. The second law of thermodynamics clearly defines the probable end result of such situations, i.e., unless one has a formal plan to deal with changing conditions, we will experience more failures. In addition, facilities such as nuclear power plants, off-shore structures, and underground structures grow in size and complexity and demand a high level of awareness, knowledge and experience to avoid adverse performance. Other professional disciplines have addressed similar problems and have made some progress in dealing with their particular situations. This paper presents some of the key aspects of preventive efforts in medicine, dentistry, architecture, and automotive/machinery fields. The paper presents and summarizes the important elements of each of these areas.

Failures which do occur can take many forms and can occur during, just after, or long after the completion of construction. We can have partial or complete failure. The cause of failure will generally relate to both technical and non-technical causes. A good preventive engineering program must remain sensitive to both causes. The concept of synergy summarizes a key aspect of the philosophy of preventive engineering. One definition of synergy states that one cannot predict the behavior of whole systems based on the study of any subsystem. This definition demands that large complex projects must entail very creative surveillance, maintenance and/or preventive engineering efforts. Another definition of synergy states that one can have an extremely positive (or negative) result from seemingly unrelated and isolated efforts. Provided the proper incentives and other conditions exist, a positive synergistic effect remains most desirable to try to encourage high quality in the planning, design, construction and maintenance stages of constructed facilities. The paper ends by presenting the details of the proposed concept, i.e., a preventive geotechnical program. The program does not represent a panacea; it cannot solve all problems. Nor does it represent a placebo, because a casual attitude toward its use will result in a worthless (or even adverse) effect. Preventive geotechnical engineering does consist of a paradigm (or new model) for certain aspects of constructed facility projects. This paradigm remains a dynamic, ever changing, model that will only work when applied with the idea that synergy and entropy continue to act on all projects at all times. Without the formal application of such a program, the probability of experiencing adverse performance on certain projects increases with time.

## INTRODUCTION

This paper seeks to define and illustrate a concept used in other disciplines, but not yet formally applied in geotechnical engineering. The paper will show a need for preventive geotechnical engineering and suggest how it can pay dividends, reduce risks, lower the probability of failure, and have a generally positive effect when applied to certain constructed facilities. The geotechnical aspects of constructed facilities present unusual risks to planners, designers, constructors, owners and insurers. These risks demand a special approach to minimize problems throughout the total life of the project. The need for such a concept remains somewhat obvious when one considers the type and number of failures noted in recent literature. We have seen failures at all stages of a project's life, from those which occurred during construction (the Uniontown Lock and Dam on the Ohio River), to those which occurred soon after construction (the Teton Dam, Idaho) and long after construction (Bouldin Dam, Alabama).

After any failure, many individuals pose the questions: Why did it happen? Could we have prevented it from happening? I strongly believe that failures result from a combination of technical reasons (such as high pore pressures, or piping, etc.), and from non-technical reasons relating to poor inspections, poor maintenance programs, or even the "attitude" of those involved in design, construction and operation sequences of a constructed facility.

When the roof of the Hartford, Connecticut, Coliseum collapsed in 1978, the building contained no patrons (ENR, 1978). However, had the failure occurred a few hours earlier (during a basketball game) perhaps 4,000 people would have perished. Inspections immediately after the failure showed that a number of significant problems occurred during and shortly after construction. However, no one stopped the project or ordered changes. To date, no one has offered an explanation as to why authorities essentially ignored obvious signs of deterioration and very adverse conditions.

Two terms can help us appreciate the need for, but at the same time the stress limitations of, preventive engineering--synergy and entropy. One definition of synergy states that one cannot predict the behavior of whole systems by studying the behavior of subsystems. One might say that studying the pore pressures at several locations in a dam does not permit a "completely accurate" prediction of the gross behavior of the dam. The term entropy, which describes the second law of thermodynamics, defines the basic directional orientation of our world, a particular statement of the general principle of the inevitable degradation as applied to energy. Entropy remains a measure of disorder, or a loss of information, and a tendency toward a high degree of probability. Stated quite simply, these things eventually wear out, break down, and fail, unless we continually apply careful external procedures.

Can we prevent failures? I believe we can prevent many failures that now occur if we commit ourselves to a formal approach to the problem, if we can understand how things fail and why we permit conditions that result in failure.

One simple example of a basic change in operational procedure which resulted in an extremely positive effect consists of the 55 mph speed limit imposed nationally, after the oil crisis of 1973. This reduction in speed did conserve fuel. At the same time, it significantly decreased the number of auto accidents, saving millions of dollars as well as many lives. A very substantial "bonus."

As we develop in this paper the concept of preventive geotechnical engineering, I emphasize that we do not mean "early detection," a term borrowed from the medical profession. If one detects incurable cancer, even at an early stage, one generally does not feel very positive about that detection. In fact, inspectors noted a serious leak in the Teton Dam at 7:30 a.m. on the day that the dam failed. One could describe this as early detection. However, the dam failed just over four hours later. We must go beyond early detection and truly consider preventive engineering. To do this we must integrate the technical and non-tech-

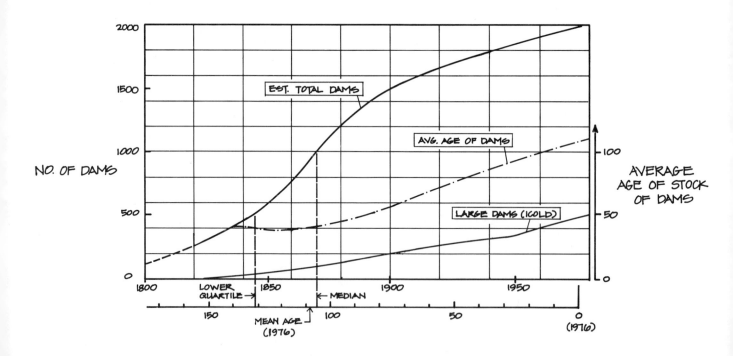

Figure 1. Cumulative stock and average age of British dams: 1800-1976. (Total dams estimated: no. refers to legislative datum of < 22.7 x 10³ m³ capacity). (Source: Moffat, 1976).

nical aspects of failure. In addition, clients and owners must furnish funds to provide a trained and experienced staff to carry out the required programs.

There is no question that the need for preventive geotechnical engineering will continue to increase with time. We have an ever-growing inventory of existing facilities, such as dams (Fig. 1), tunnels, bridges, highway embankments, etc., all of which suffer under the certainties of the second law of thermodynamics. If we do not take precautions, in time, and depending on a host of variables, we will eventually arrive at a troublesome situation. Such efforts will require money, but with proper planning, such dollars can remain cost-effective.

A second aspect of the term synergy says that it remains possible that the sum of the effects of a group of subsystems can far exceed the simple algebraic total of the effects of the subsystems. In other words, two plus two can exceed four. Again, mentioning the 55 mph speed limit, not only did it save gas and save lives, but in large urban areas caused a significant decrease in air pollution. The preventive concept has found formal application in other fields. What descriptive name can we attach to this concept? Certainly not a panacea, or cure-all, because we are too realistic to hold such false hope. At the same time, the term placebo would appear too harsh. I believe that geotechnical engineering faces serious problems, not the least of which is communicating effectively with related disciplines both the seriousness and the uncertainty of specific geotechnical situations. I offer the concept of preventive geotechnical engineering as a paradigm to begin to improve our ability to prevent problems. I look forward to assistance from those inside and outside geotechnical engineering to help flesh out this beginning model and ensure that it becomes an effective tool.

## ACTIVITIES IN OTHER FIELDS

Fields outside civil and geotechnical engineering have made attempts to initiate preventive programs as a part of their overall development. This section of the paper looks briefly at efforts in dentistry, in medicine, in architecture and in the automotive/industrial maintenance area to consider both the results of these efforts and some of their common features.

### Dentistry

The dental profession's approach to teeth care has changed significantly over the years. Early practice focused primarily on reparative dentistry. When your tooth ached, you went to the dentist, and he probably removed it. Over the years, in addition to new reparative techniques, dentists have introduced: the use of regular check-ups by a professional; better cleaning methods, i.e., with dental floss, better toothbrushes, better toothpastes; and the use of

fluoride in drinking water and in mouthwashes. The general public has an increased awareness of the importance of better dental care. Also, the use of oral surgery and orthodontics, as well as x-rays, have made the practice of dentistry more sophisticated. However, most would agree that the general condition of teeth has improved, at least for people in developed countries where sufficient numbers of dentists exist and people can afford their services. Preventive dentistry does not represent a new idea. Dentists now make very good salaries by practicing this procedure. However, the result has been better teeth and therefore healthier human beings. Dentists now perform, in my opinion, a better service to the people and to the community in which they live.

The profession has slowly adopted the idea of preventive dentistry, and people even more slowly have come to believe that prevention would pay dividends above its cost. Some dental problems do not show up for years, when it has become too late to really do anything about them (Schmid, 1977). G.B. Black spoke to a class of dental students as follows: "The day is surely coming, and perhaps within the lifetime of you young men before me, when we will be engaged in practicing preventive dentistry rather than reparative dentistry." The doctor made this statement in 1896. Today, I think we see excellent evidence that preventive dentistry does work, remains cost-effective and results in better overall general health, and fewer serious dental problems. However, we note quite clearly that it has not cured (or prevented) all dental problems. An explanation for this "short-coming" may lie in the continued high intake of processed sugar by people in developed countries. There are four key features of preventive dentistry.

- Formal examination by a professional, to monitor and control.

- Simple regular tasks that the patient performs, such as cleaning, flossing, etc.

- Record keeping of performance, such as written notes by the professional.

- Special diagnostic and reparative techniques, such as x-rays, etc.

Despite significant improvements no dentist would guarantee a cavity-free patient.

### Medicine

The medical profession has used the term preventive medicine since the 1930's. However, the essential features of this concept have existed for much longer. The earliest preventive measures employed in medicine consisted largely of non-medical items, i.e., immunization, water purification, sewage separation, adequate housing and a reasonably well-balanced diet. These measures remain quite effective, have not improved significantly with time, and also require no physician participation. In fact, the plumber, the public health inspector, the building inspector, and the civil engineer rank alongside the physician when one considers preventive medicine in its broad aspects (Neff, 1978).

In order to prevent anything, we must decide what we wish to prevent, develop a set of tests, measurements, and/or criteria that will help monitor how well we do with our preventive efforts, and then hope that we can do something about the condition should it occur anyway. In the United States, the medical profession has made relatively good progress regarding the prevention of infectious diseases, accidents, wide-scale poisoning, etc. However, in the case of more complicated diseases, such as cancer, heart disease, stroke, genetic defects and diabetes, we do essentially nothing in the way of prevention (Neff, 1977). This does not mean that we could not, but that we do not. Part of the problem of preventing these diseases lies in the fact that the tests that we use to monitor them remain relatively unpredictable. These tests lack sensitivity, and they often lack specificity. Also, accuracy and precision remain difficult to control. In addition, once the more complicated diseases develop, they remain more difficult to treat than a simple infectious disease. We can prevent some of these more complicated diseases only through changes in personal lifestyle, changes which generally come reluctantly.

A brief overview of the medical profession's attitude toward preventive medicine clearly indicates the importance of separating what one can predict from what remains unpredictable. In many areas, particularly in sports medicine, the emphasis remains on prevention rather than predicting the events (Sheehan, 1978). A change in lifestyle involves a change in attitude, and personal attitudes remain most difficult to alter, even in the face of overpowering evidence. Witness the continued high incidence of smoking among the general population, even after wide circulation of substantial evidence that it contributes to a variety of modern man's ailments.

The medical profession recognizes the need to develop incentives to cause people to carry out preventive efforts on their own. Apparently, massive data alone will not turn the tide. In view of this, the medical profession also suggests that highly effective results can occur by employing essentially non-medical efforts (McLaughlin, 1978). The importance of diet to general health has received much recent attention. In addition, the importance of the environment (in promoting general health) regarding air and water pollution has gained more acceptance.

Periodic medical check-ups alone will not prevent heart attacks, but a relatively stress-free employment, good diet, plenty of exercise, and freedom from air and water pollution will have a measurable effect on lowering the incidence of heart attacks for the general population. Some evidence suggests that personal "stress" levels can affect the incidence of cancer in individuals (Sontag, 1978). Perhaps the engineering profession should think of more effective ways to encourage "behavior" that will result in specific decreases in the number of failures noted.

Several key features of most preventive medical efforts follow.

- A "healthy" environment.

- Periodic evaluations by trained professionals.

- Records of performance data, i.e., blood pressure, pulse rate, weight, etc.

- Direct involvement of the user (patient) in the process.

- A simple method to evaluate results.

We also note the great difficulty in truly preventing very complicated diseases, i.e., the differences between cancer and a broken leg.

Architecture

E.C. Botsai, former president of the American Institute of Architecture, views the lack of competence as the most critical concern for his profession (ENR, 1977). While he admits that the bulk of architects do good work, he insists that their general level of performance remains inadequate and seeks to better this performance, i.e., to have architects become more professional. One aspect of professional development that he has suggested consists of periodic testing as a condition of recertification. Botsai favors a doubling of the national membership dues (now $100 per year per individual) to help pay for additional education and professional development activities.

Long years of studying building failures (as an architect) led him to develop a small firm that receives frequent calls as a preventive consultant in the design stage to guard against future failure. Apparently, a number of clients consider the independent opinion of an experienced architect both necessary and cost-effective in the execution of their particular projects. It also appears that long and careful study of a number of failures facilitates critical review of new projects and avoidance of future failures.

Automotive/Industrial Maintenance

Preventive maintenance has achieved wide use and recognition for almost all motors, engines, machines, and automotive type vehicles. What users did by common sense and perhaps haphazardly in the past has become a specialized and formal approach to minimizing down-time and saving money. The results of a preventive maintenance program for vehicles can represent a crucial aspect of performance, e.g., for the army during war time, for fleets of taxi cabs and trucks, and for electrical generating equipment in our major cities. Simple tasks such as lubrication, changing air filters, etc., can mean the difference between a piece of equipment that operates and one that does not operate when required.

The lack of preventive maintenance can result in excessive costs (Wheaton, 1978). New York, Boston, Philadelphia, and Chicago represent large U.S. cities with existing subway systems. Boston's system, however, still utilizes 20- to 30-year-old equipment that frequently malfunctions, and the system has never carried out a thorough program of preventive maintenance. For this reason, maintenance costs remain relatively high, the cost of operating and riding the system remains relatively high, and the dependability of the service remains low. Train failures and even accidents occur with remarkable regularity.

In other areas such as home building or general construction, one should consider the preventive aspects of engineering. For example, the lack of controls to restrict swelling and shrinking of certain soils (present throughout the United States) results in great damage to structures and high costs of remedial repairs. A recent study (American Society of Civil Engineers, 1978) stated that each year $2.25 billion of damage occurs to buildings as a result of swelling and shrinking soils. We could prevent a large portion of this damage by controlling the moisture content of the soil at the structure location and thus preventing adverse volume changes. In this case, a system of preventive maintenance that achieved the goal of no moisture change could result in savings of a billion dollars.

The importance of preventive maintenance has increased with time, and now university level courses seek to achieve a more formal approach to the subject (Simpson, 1978). A course taught at Clemson University stresses that the key to such programs lies in coordination with other related activities, such as production, surveillance, etc. The success of such programs hinges on many factors. However, some appear more important than others. For example, any such system must remain flexible in order to absorb changes. The people that carry out the system must receive adequate training. It remains necessary to record and measure the performance improvement brought on by the maintenance program and also to determine costs and potential savings. The users must update the program as they gain experience, and insure that all individuals associated with the program remain fully aware of the importance of the program and the potential positive benefits to the total operation.

## ANATOMY OF FAILURES

### Definition

When discussing the subject of failure, we must avoid ambiguity and stay within acceptable definitions. Failure consists of any nonconformity with design expectations (Feld, 1968). Failures need not result in collapse or total destruction of a system or facility. With the above definition, it becomes apparent that we can experience rather complex failures, and the aspects of failures (or of adverse performance) must receive careful study in order to reduce the real risk of occurrence.

The general public, and even some engineers, have a rather ambivalent feeling toward the subject of failure. It should not require great effort to extract public funds for the maintenance of public facilities to protect public safety. The average motorist, for example, does not complain too heavily as he drives a vehicle that wears out and requires replacement in all too few years. Why should a collection of these same citizens then not understand that the bridges they cross year after year also wear out and need rebuilding or replacement? As long as vehicles can cross a bridge, we consider that the bridge conforms to design expectations. Vehicles cross one day; yet, a "good" bridge can collapse the next. We should and, in most cases, do prevent bridge collapses (Smith, 1977).

### Types of Failures

Because the definitions of failure can vary, the study of failure can present many contrasts. The theme of failure has become so dominant in our time that staff and students at MIT have organized a course to explore its causes and effects, and to ponder ways to cope with it (Reinhold, 1973). The developers of the course used as a definition, "the inability of a mechanism of man to fulfill the function for which it was designed." They talk about failures-bad which carry negative overtones, i.e., the failure to achieve a goal, and also of failure-learn, wherein the failure (such as a scientific experiment) may steer one toward a better theory. The class further distinguishes between failures of a personal nature and failures of an institutional nature. Does the collapse of a publicly-owned bridge or dam result from a failure of the bureaucratic system which designs, builds and maintains these structures, or the personal failure of an engineer involved in the structure?

In Great Britain, certain legislative acts have attempted to mitigate the problem of having a large bureaucracy deal with narrow technical subjects by creating the position of panel engineer, where individual engineers retain absolute authority and responsibility over individual dams (Moffat, 1976) (Fig. 1). Safety records under such a system have shown relative promise.

Some in the profession speak of technical failure versus non-technical failure, and I believe such talk is a simple restatement of personal versus institutional failure. If a dam fails because of high pore pressures in the downstream slope, we may find a neat, tidy explanation of the failure. However, in looking at reasons why the pore pressures increased, we may find evidence of a bureaucratic failure.

Causes of Failure

Depending on what kind of structure is studied, one could develop a rather lengthy list of causes and failures. In describing geotechnical projects, we may start with the following list.

● Incompetent engineering and design.

● Complex problem, not well understood.

● Conditions changing after design, or after construction, or both.

● Poor method(s) of analysis (too simple for the real field situation).

● Inaccurate material properties (not representative of field conditions).

● Poor construction practices.

● Poor maintenance practices.

All too often, owners stop thinking about their structures from the standpoint of potential failures after completion of construction, and concentrate on maximizing profits from the associated business interests. Engineers and contractors generally also stop worrying about the completed structure, because they don't get paid to worry beyond that point. However, in some cases the risk may remain high. If the consequences of failure also remain very high, such as for a large dam, we must develop and carry out preventive engineering programs.

In the mineral extraction industry, operations remain fluid and flexible. The profits in such an industry depend on the extraction costs. Therefore, the owner seeks to minimize such costs while maintaining safety and continued production. Over-conservatism wastes dollars.

The true risks associated with geotechnical problems do not generally lend themselves to complete understanding. In the case of the Teton Dam we have evidence that even an "expert" design carries significant risk. Although we have few such failures, they "cost" a lot in terms of time, money and lives. The geotechnical profession has developed good analytical tools, but these tools require good data to use properly and effectively. Any site may have subtle geologic anomalies which no instrument can completely uncover. We still search for the perfectly undisturbed sample and that "perfect" laboratory test which will permit us to know accurately the strength values, independent of sample size. One must conclude, however, that the performance of actual structures must be studied in the field, both to monitor and evaluate this performance, because field conditions change with time. Lambe has used prediction-performance evaluation programs to help advance our state-of-knowledge regarding geotechnical engineering (Lambe, 1973). Only through such continued efforts will we develop better predictive methods and hopefully have better control against failure. We must continue to emphasize, however, that prevention, not prediction, remains our goal. Many experts "predicted" a long healthy life for the Teton Dam.

Smith's study of bridge failures (1977) has shed light on the subject of general failures. Table 1 lists the cause of failure for some 143

TABLE 1. BRIDGE FAILURE CATEGORIES (AFTER SMITH, 1977).

| Cause of failure | Total number of failures | Remarks[1] |
|---|---|---|
| Flood and foundation movement | 70 | Two earth slip One floating debris 66 scour One foundation movement |
| Unsuitable or defective permanent material | 22 | 19 by brittle fracture of plates or anchor bars |
| Overload or accident | 14 | 10 ship or barge impact |
| Inadequate or unsuitable temporary works or erection procedure | 12 | Inadequacy in permanent design, a supplementary cause in one instance |
| Earthquake | 11 | |
| Inadequate design in permanent material | 5 | |
| Wind | 4 | |
| Fatigue | 4 | Three cast iron One hastened by corrosion |
| Corrosion | 1 | |
| Total number of failures | 143 | |

[1]Except in the remarks column, secondary causes are omitted from this table. Each failure is listed only once.

bridge failures that he studied. These failures occurred throughout the world during the period 1847 through 1975. It remains interesting to note that floods and foundation movements caused nearly half of these bridge failures, i.e., geotechnical related aspects of the structures. Few, if any, of the failures listed followed from the inexactness of available methods of computing stresses and strains. We achieve sound design by the appropriate matching of safety factor to analytical technique and, above all, by proper use of wisdom and judgment as the designer "applies" his results. Behind every engineering mistake lies an engineer who makes it, either alone or as part of a bureaucracy. A good engineer/client relationship, along with a good contractor, formally "involved" and sharing responsibilities, will go a long way toward producing cost-effective, efficient, and "failure-proof" constructed facilities.

## ROLE OF SYNERGY

### Definition

A general definition of the term synergy states that one cannot predict the behavior of complete systems using as a basis the known behavior of one or more subsystems. We can come close often, for a variety of reasons, but a degree of uncertainty exists regarding all predictions. Another definition of synergy states that the sum of the combined effects of groups of subsystems can greatly exceed, or greatly fall short of, the simple algebraic total of the separate effects.

The concept of synergy remains an ever present and very real aspect of life. Some suggest that synergy, or the concept represented by the term synergy, constitutes one of the natural laws of the universe. These two definitions suggest that we cannot make totally accurate predictions, even when experts try (Garlanger and Lambe, 1973); and that the combined effects of groups of subsystems can produce "unusual" results. We only have to ponder briefly these two definitions and look about us for a mountain of evidence that virtually proves the validity of this natural law. Consider such areas as weather prediction, economic forecasting (Partee, 1976), the musings of stockbrokers and Jimmy the Greek, and the rather haphazard careers of such public figures as Richard Nixon, Mohamed Ali, Howard Hughes, and Adolph Hitler. With such background thought, we should then consider that the rational, prudent and logical approach to dealing with the geotechnical aspects of constructed facilities should be cautious and carefully-studied.

When we deal with geotechnical aspects of constructed facilities, we must face uncertainty. The size of samples tested in the laboratory and the "disturbance" of those samples render it difficult to produce truly accurate parameters. The three key parameters that we deal with, i.e., strength, compressibility, and permeability all change with time and with variations of effective stress.

Another problem in this regard stems from the second law of thermodynamics, i.e., the entropy law. Others have discussed in great detail the role of the "entropy law" in economics (Georgescu-Roegen, 1971) and in the current battle of preserving certain environmental standards (Commoner, 1976). The entropy law remains involved in every aspect of our behavior. Since the introduction of the term entropy by a German physicist, Rudolph Clausius (in the 1860's), many different interpretations and definitions have emerged.

The physical concept of entropy appears quite intricate and its technical details perhaps overwhelming. A "simple" definition states that the entropy of the universe, or of an "isolated" structure, increases constantly, and this increase remains continuous and irrevocable. The modern interpretation of this degradation of energy consists of a continuous turning of order into disorder. This law suggests that one of our weaknesses consists of our reluctance to recognize and then deal realistically with our limitations in relation to space, time, matter, and energy. Some interest in entropy and soil behavior has been shown (Morgenstern, 1963; and Jowitt and Munro, 1978). However, the result of this work has not found application in practical engineering problems.

In some areas of geotechnical engineering, we now see attempts to blend mechanical laws with an uncertainty specific to the notion of probability. Some consider that the entropy law does not express a natural law, but instead reflects the difficulty of the human mind in describing a state that involves a large number of details. Certainly, this law has a unique place in science in that it marks the recognition by that most trusted of all the sciences, i.e., physics, that qualitative change exists in the universe. The entropy law does not determine when the entropy of a closed system will reach a certain level, nor exactly what will happen at that point. However, it does determine the general direction of the entropic process of any isolated system. The concept of synergy remains linked in a fundamental fashion to the concept of entropy because of another principle, the emergence of novelty by combination.

Most of the properties of water do not logically follow from universal principles applied to the elemental properties of its components of oxygen and hydrogen. Again, if we look around us, we see many physical examples of the entropy law. Things do generally wear out, systems tend toward a condition of high probability, i.e., failure, if we don't apply external energy. Our automobiles require periodic tune-ups and other maintenance, our houses require painting, etc., and our bodies require food, rest, recreation and fresh air. To study a constructed facility, especially one with the special properties that geotechnical aspects often present, demands that we apply the same philosophy.

Synergy says, even if you try very hard, you

may be unsuccessful, or you may suffer adverse surprises. Entropy says if you don't try, eventually you lose, i.e., failure in some form will occur. Our attitude toward risk remains a choice, and the risks simply remain. A whole new science of risk analysis using probability theory has grown to great sophistication in recent years (Barbateu, 1972), to help managers and owners decide how to spend money to reduce risk, and how much to spend to achieve a certain level of risk (Fig. 2).

In a particular situation, if one truly understands the fundamentals involved, and if one can identify several key parameters that control performance (with a high degree of correlation, not perfect, but very good), then one can greatly reduce risk with the expenditure of a relatively small amount of money. This happy thought remains one goal of preventive geotechnical engineering; we want to maximize risk reduction with a minimum expenditure of time and money.

I believe that we cannot ignore either aspect

of synergy, i.e., the lack of predicted preciseness, or the relative indeterminacy of any situation where a number of fundamental elements combine. We also must not ignore the second law of thermodynamics, i.e., the entropy law, as nature works against us, constantly and often irrevocably. We must accept the potential consequences of these facts, all generally bad, and we must take formal steps to reduce these consequences by specific actions on specific projects.

The following paragraphs describe an all too frequent scene. The managers of a large high-rise apartment complex in New York City got into a great deal of trouble because of the lack of understanding of fundamentals and the lack of long-range planning. Co-op City in New York, consisting of thirty-five 24- to 33-story buildings, was built in the late 1960's on 290 acres of tidal marsh, and constitutes a massive residential complex. The builders of this complex sought to take advantage of otherwise useless land. The Bronx location seemed ideal. The designers placed the building foundations on piles to rock. However,

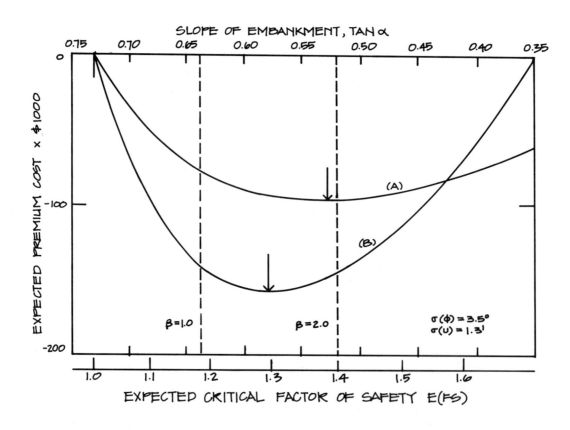

Figure 2. Typical shape of the variation of the expected premium cost versus type of design. (Source: Baker, 1976).

utilities and sidewalks not placed on piles have undergone large settlements and have caused much difficulty throughout the project. Some of these problems include the dangerous situation of ruptured gas mains. Some feel these problems resulted from poor design, compounded by inadequate maintenance that did not consider the long-term effects of surcharges in the area, and other factors which resulted in continuing settling of surrounding ground. Some feel that this sad result did not have to happen. One approach, peer review, consists of the requirement that a qualified engineer check all designs before construction, in order to avoid some of these kinds of problems (Gnaedinger, 1978).

## KEY ELEMENTS IN A PREVENTIVE ENGINEERING PROGRAM

### General

Even a casual review of the literature would suggest that we continue to experience a number of geotechnical related failures in civil engineering. A prudent approach to fulfilling our professional responsibilities would encourage us to reduce these adverse events to a lower number at some reasonable cost (Wahler, 1976). Other fields such as dentistry and medicine have used a variety of preventive concepts with promising results. In many cases, under close examination, these success stories reflect a more than acceptable degree of cost-effectiveness.

The concepts of synergy and entropy can help to form a basis for a preventive engineering program. These concepts, when viewed logically, provide incentives to follow through with programs once they take shape. These concepts force us to give emphasis to (a) the emergence of novelty by combination, and (b) the steady and often irrevocable tendency of systems to recede toward disorder, loss of information and a high order of probability (failure).

In formulating ideas for a preliminary outline of a preventive geotechnical engineering program, we wish to emphasize approaches that have worked in other fields, and discard approaches that have not served well, especially taking note to understand (when and where possible) the reason(s) for the failure. Above all, we should focus our attention, and raise our level of awareness, to the task of avoiding problems, while remaining ready to solve them if they occur. In addition to the need for effective incentives (that promote awareness and encourage prompt action), we must also strive for a program that has clear lines of responsibility and accountability for all important tasks, and one that contains a mechanism to force decisions that will ensure favorable "control" of events, not merely produce a good "record" of a system failure. Early detection constitutes an acceptable "event" only when the time of detection permits decisions and actions that avoid a previously identified "unacceptable" situation (Thomas et al., 1975).

Table 2 presents a preliminary view of a

TABLE 2. ELEMENTS OF A PREVENTIVE GEOTECHNICAL ENGINEERING PROGRAM.

A. Clear statement of desired performance (owner/operator/designer)
   -during construction
   -shortly after construction
   -long after construction

B. Identify a single person in responsible charge of each concerned group
   -owner
   -designer(s)
   -contractor(s)
   -operator(s)
   -maintenance

C. Review and evaluate precedence with previous similar projects
   -risks
   -failures
   -remedial tasks
   -costs

D. Review for owner by independent designer
   -value engineering
   -safety engineering

E. Review for owner by independent contractor
   -construction methods
   -construction sequence
   -cost estimate

F. Formal written document by designer and reviewers
   -major uncertainties in design
   -key assumptions in design
   -key parameters that control performance
   -critical values of key parameters at each stage of construction, including post-construction
   -possible consequences of adverse performance and operation
   -method(s) to obtain values of key parameters

G. Identify method(s) to provide incentive and increase awareness of all team members
   -awareness of key aspects of desired performance
   -incentives to cost-effectively achieve desired performance

H. Form geotechnical task force
   -includes staff from owner, designer, contractor (after chosen), consultants and contracts group

I. Develop and implement a construction monitoring/control system
   -input from owner, designer, contractor, and consultants

J. Develop and implement continuing evaluation plan for expected life of project
   -cost
   -responsibility
   -accountability

comprehensive preventive geotechnical engineering program. As more experience and field data appear, this table will change to reflect reality and circumstance. The author does not consider the outline all-inclusive for very complex projects, nor that every project will require all of the items listed in this outline. The author encourages comments from readers to help modify this table and add to its usefulness and effectiveness.

The geotechnical task force (Table 2, H) must have the power (from the owner) to make decisions and take action and thus seek to avoid costly delays and litigation. The group must quickly respond to changing field conditions (all too common an occurrence with geotechnical aspects of many projects). This group must have access to accurate, up-to-date field data regarding the technical aspects of the project, but, in arriving at decisions, they must also review appropriate non-technical factors such as geographic location, environmental factors, and economics. They seek to reach or exceed the stated performance criteria agreed upon by the owner, but at a reasonable cost.

The construction monitoring/control system group (Table 2, I) must obtain, reduce and analyze field data in the most efficient method possible. The key function of this group consists in securing accurate data and, after appropriate reduction, plotting and evaluation, in comparing the actual performance of the structure with the predetermined expected performance. All data and plots, especially those data which show variations from expected performance, must reach the geotechnical task force (or similar review group) for decisions and/or actions regarding remedial work and alterations in designs or construction procedures.

## SUMMARY

Few would argue that one possible desirable goal of the civil engineering profession consists of continuing efforts to reduce the number of adverse events associated with the geotechnical aspects of constructed facilities. The unusual nature of risk associated with geotechnical factors presents a special challenge. We have geotechnical failures, and often they result from a breakdown in human organization rather than the shortcomings of a purely technical point, such as an improper analytical technique, inaccurate parameter, or unsuitable design method. Another aspect of these failures relates to the inability of all concerned parties to agree on failure criteria and the means to enforce the criteria. Our profession does not stand alone in its lack of effective incentives toward the prevention of problems, although we do well in solving problems once they have occurred (but often at great expense). The attitude of some engineers and of a large percentage of contractors, owners and the general public toward risk reduction after construction remains one of benign neglect.

Other professions, i.e., dentistry, medicine, architecture, and the automotive industry have made fairly substantial efforts in the development of programs to prevent problems. We have seen relatively cost-effective progress in some areas. In all cases, these programs emphasize the need to develop and implement incentives toward actually achieving desired goals of acceptable long-term performance.

This paper has briefly reviewed two fundamental factors that make it difficult to prevent adverse performance, first, the concept of synergy which tells us that we simply cannot make accurate predictions of the behavior of whole systems, and, second, the entropy law which (as a natural law) reminds us that all systems continually move toward a non-ordered (failure) state without the application of external energy. These two factors remain linked by the principle of emergence by novelty, which states that combining subsystems (even those about which much is known) can result in a "novel" (unexpected) occurrence.

I do not suggest that we remove or lessen the emphasis on the purely technical aspects of these types of problems. Such an attitude remains unthinkable. We must continue to seek a better understanding of the fundamentals that control performance of constructed facilities. But after choosing, with good engineering judgment, the most appropriate material parameters, analytical and design methods, and construction practices, we must recommend and take part in a critical review of the total system that exists to achieve the level of performance agreed on by all interested parties. We must give particular attention to both short-term and long-term situations for the planned or expected life of the facility. Such an attitude will surely require a continuing, though in many cases modest and inexpensive, effort to achieve these ends.

The author fully acknowledges the preliminary and somewhat elementary nature of the remarks put forward in this paper. A great deal of work must occur before such preventive geotechnical programs can find effective application in a wide variety of projects. A critical review of these ideas and concepts should promote further discussion on their merit. The author welcomes criticism and further suggestions to improve the role of our profession as a people-serving one by actually reducing the number of adverse events associated with the geotechnical aspects of existing or future constructed facilities.

## REFERENCES

American Society of Civil Engineers, 1978, General notes: Conference on Shrinking and Swelling Soils, Denver, April.

Baker, W.J., 1976, Reliability analysis and optimization of earth slopes: M.I.T. Special Summer Program on Risk and Decision in Geotechnical Engineering, July, Cambridge,

Massachusetts.

Barbateu, G., 1972, Reliability of earth slopes, M.S. Thesis, Civil Engineering, M.I.T., Cambridge.

Commoner, B., 1976, The poverty of power; A.A. Knopf, Inc., 297 p.

Engineering News-Record, 1977, New AIA chief Botsai urges competence: December 8.

Engineering News-Record, 1978, Someone should have sounded the alarm: April 6.

Feld, J., 1968, Construction failures: John Wiley, New York.

Garlanger, J.E., and Lambe, T.W., 1973, Proceedings of a Symposium on downdrag of piles: M.I.T., November, 103 p.

Georgescu-Roegen, N., 1971, The entropy law and the economic process: Harvard University Press, Cambridge, 457 p.

Gnaedinger, J.P., 1978, Peer review--old concept in new situations: Civil Engineering, February, p. 45.

Jowitt, P.W., and Munro, J., 1978, The influence of void distribution and entropy on the engineering properties of granular media: Report from Imperial College, London.

Lambe, T.W., 1973, Predictions in soil engineering: 13th Rankin Lecture, Geotechnique, v. 23, no. 2, June.

McLaughlin, L., 1978, Another health care system that works: Boston Globe, April 23, D10.

Moffat, A.I.B., 1976, British reservoir legislation and the Reservoir Act, 1975: Proceedings of Engineering Foundation Conference on Dam Safety, Pacific Grove, California, November, p. 39-56.

Morgenstern, N.R., 1963, Maximum entropy of granular material: Nature, v. 200, p. 559-560.

Neff, MD, J.C., 1977, Personal communication, November.

Neff, MD, J.C., 1978, Personal communication, March.

Partee, J.C., 1976, Economic forecasting: Business Horizons, Indiana University Graduate School of Business, v. 19, no. 5, October.

Reinhold, R., 1973, Special report, New York Times, December 1.

Schmid, DDS, D.A., 1977, Personal communication, December.

Sheehan, G.A., 1978, Dr. Sheehan on running: World Publications, Mountain View, California, p. 117-118.

Simpson, C.S., Jr., 1978, Course outline, maintenance workshop: Clemson University, Clemson, South Carolina.

Smith, D.W., 1977, Why bridges fail: Civil Engineering, November, p. 58-62.

Sontag, S., 1978, Illness as metaphor: Farrar, Straus and Giroux.

Thomas, H.E., Miller, E.J., and Speaker, J.J., 1975, Difficult dam problems--cofferdam failure: Civil Engineering, August, p. 69.

Wahler, W.A., 1976, Dam safety guidelines--responsibility and liability: Proceedings of Engineering Foundation Conference on Dam Safety, Pacific Grove, California, November, American Society of Civil Engineers, p. 479-499.

Wheaton, W.C., 1978, Letter to editor: Boston Globe, April.

Rock excavations along highways in New England, 4: shear planes.

# Engineering behavior of the Taunton River clays

W. S. ZOINO
N. A. CAMPAGNA, JR.
Goldberg, Zoino & Associates, Inc.

## ABSTRACT

The paper discusses the engineering behavior of
the Taunton River clays. The results of laboratory
tests and the field performance of two instrumented
large scale building site preloadings within the
Taunton River varved clays are presented. The geologic origin of the clay, occurrence of the clay, and
its engineering properties are described. The case
histories include descriptions of the projects and
performance of the instrumented preloads. There are
typical loading, settlement and pore pressure plots
versus time for each site. A comparison of the field
results with settlements predicted using laboratory
data is also included. The paper shows that preloading Taunton River clays is an effective means of
reducing post-construction settlement. Conditions
are favorable for preloading because the clay is
heavily overconsolidated, has a relatively high rate
of consolidation, and is not excessively thick.

## INTRODUCTION

The Taunton River is the main drainage system
for the Narragansett basin located in southeastern
Massachusetts and extending into Rhode Island. The
present course of the river meanders through clay and
varved clay deposits which were deposited in two
major glacial lakes. While considerable construction
activity has occurred within these former glacial
lakes along the Taunton River over the past 350
years, published data have been lacking on the
engineering properties of these clays, particularly
data based on actual field performance of the clays
under loading.

The purpose of this paper is to present some
engineering data on the Taunton River clays accumulated by the writers during their professional practice in foundation engineering. Data from five sites
are presented. Included in these data are results of
laboratory tests performed on samples of varved clay
within the Taunton River watershed and the results
of instrumented large scale building site preloading
performed at two of the five locations within the
Taunton River varved clays. A comparison of the
field results at these two sites with settlement
predictions made utilizing laboratory data is
included. The paper also contains a brief discussion
of the geology of the Taunton River clays and the
occurrence of these clays within the Narragansett
basin.

## GEOLOGY

The Taunton River is formed by the confluence of
the Town River with the Matfield River near the
intersection of the towns of East Bridgewater and
Bridgewater, Massachusetts. The river flows
initially east by southeast toward Middleboro and
then southwest until it enters the waters of
Narragansett Bay. The river lies entirely within
the Narragansett basin, which is a geologic/structur-
al basin and topographic lowland. During the
Pleistocene epoch a glacial ice sheet advanced
through this area leaving a very dense non-strati-
fied unsorted deposit known as glacial till
directly over the bed rock. During a later period
of glacial activity, a second, somewhat less compact
upper glacial till was deposited.

During the retreat of the ice sheet two glacial
lakes of considerable size were formed in the areas
adjacent to the present course of the Taunton River.
The northern lake extended across Bridgewater for
several miles and existed as far north as the Brockton quadrangle in Massachusetts. The southern, somewhat smaller, lake existed mostly northward of Weir
Village near Taunton, Massachusetts. However, the
exact extent of the lake to the south is unknown.

The presence of the glacial lakes may be easily
identified by kame deltas and varved clay deposits.
The clay deposits commonly ranged in thickness from a
few feet to about 50 feet, but a few test holes have
penetrated as much as one hundred (100) feet of fine-
grained, stratified materials which are believed to
be lake bottom sediments. The materials identified
as lake bottom deposits include stratified silty
clays, clayey silts, silts, and/or sandy silts. The
grain size of these sediments ranges from coarse sand
to clay. However, the predominant materials are clay,
silt, and fine sand. Silt and clay layers occurring
as pairs are useful indicators of the origin of these
deposits. This layering system within these deposits
is referred to as varves. The sand and silt varves
normally occurred in summer, whereas the clay varves
settled in quiet water during the following winter.
The clay varves generally are much thinner than the
silt varves. The varves show that the lake may have
lasted for more than two hundred years.

Varved clays and laminated silts from the Taunton River basin have been used in the brick industry
since colonial times. One of the largest clay pits
exists near Weir Village in Taunton and another
large clay pit exists along the Taunton, and another
east of the Massachusetts Correctional Institute in
southern Bridgewater.

The large glacial lakes were in time drained
toward the sea through successive stages of lower
elevation outlets. Rivers and streams were re-
established in new channels, and the sediments along

these streams were reworked, and redeposited as alluvium consisting of gravel, sand and clay in areas occasionally flooded by modern streams.

## OCCURRENCE OF THE CLAYS

The occurrence of the Taunton River clay (Fig. 1) has been mapped in the Taunton, Bridgewater, Brockton, and Whitman quadrangles by Hartshorn (1967, 1960), Chute (1950) and Petersen and Shaw (1967) respectively. They occur along the Taunton, Town, and Matfield Rivers where two large glacial lakes

once existed. As can be seen in Figure 1, there are localized areas where no clay exists. These areas are hills or drumlins which rose above the glacial lakes. The large clay pits referred to previously in Taunton and southern Bridgewater are shown in Figure 1. The exact extent of the clays south of Weir Village in Taunton is not known. However, most of the clays are believed to be north of this area.

## ENGINEERING PROPERTIES

Laboratory soil test data from five sites (see Fig. 1) underlain by Taunton River clays have been

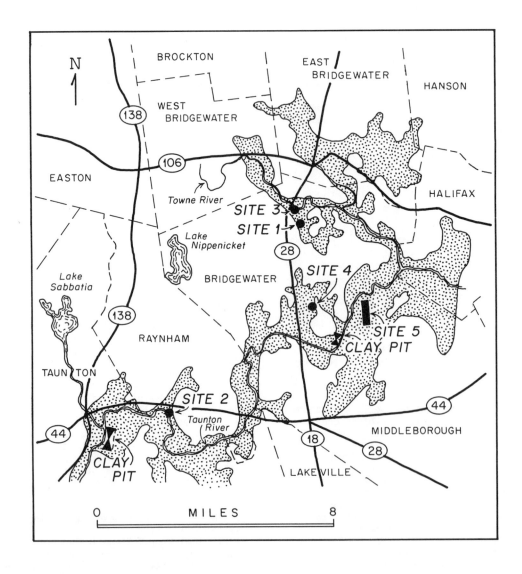

Figure 1. Occurrence of Taunton River clays.

TABLE 1. SUMMARY OF LABORATORY DATA

NOTE: Numbers are average values for all clay samples tested at the site. The numbers in parentheses ( ) are the range of values.

| Site | Natural water content (percent) | Liquid limit (percent) | Plastic limit (percent) | Total unit weight (pcf) | Coefficent of consolidation (ft² day) | Max past pressure (tsf) | Recompression ratio | Undrained shear strength (tsf) |
|---|---|---|---|---|---|---|---|---|
| Site 1 Bridgewater | 42 (29-52) | 47 (31-61) | 25 (23-28) | 110 (106-115) | 1.5 (0.4-2.9) | 4 (3.5-4.3) | 0.03 (.022-.036) | 0.64 (.25-.90) |
| Site 2 Raynham | 36 (27-45) | 42 (32-68) | 23 (21-28) | 115 (110-120) | 1.5 (0.3-2.4) | 3.5 (3-4) | .025 | 0.49 (0.1-0.8) |
| Site 3 Bridgewater | 30 (19-38) | 40 (28-59) | 24 (21-27) | ---- | ---- | ---- | ---- | ---- |
| Site 4 Bridgewater | ---- | 24 (18-34) | 17 (15-22) | ---- | ---- | ---- | ---- | ---- |
| Site 5 Middleboro | 35 (22-48) | 38 (25-72) | 25 (22-31) | 115 (113-117) | ---- | ---- | ---- | ---- |

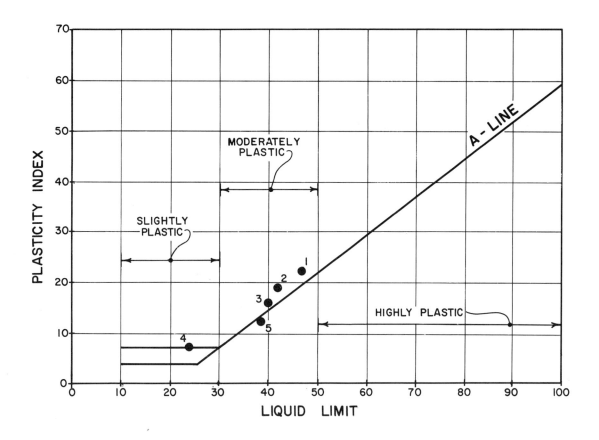

Figure 2. Average Atterberg limits at five sites within Taunton River varved clays.

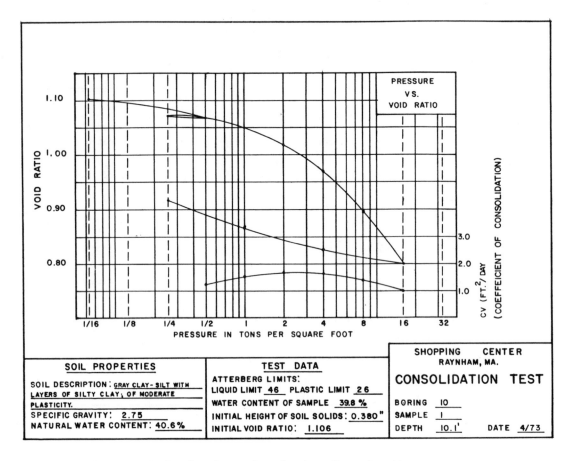

Figure 3. Consolidation test at the shopping center, Raynham, Massachusetts.

Figure 4. Site 1, plan.

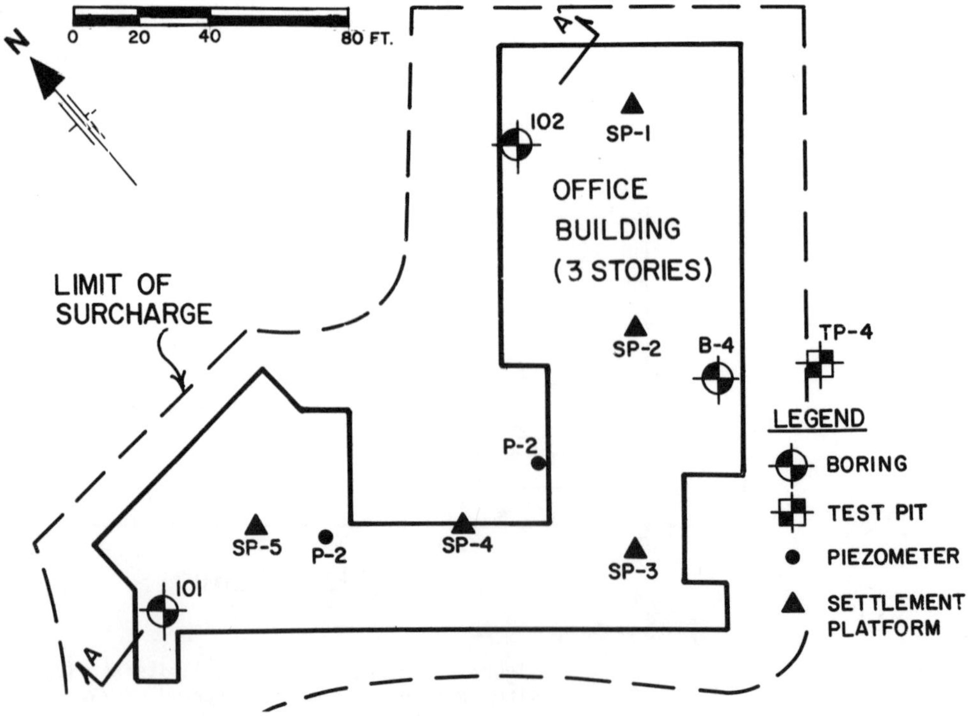

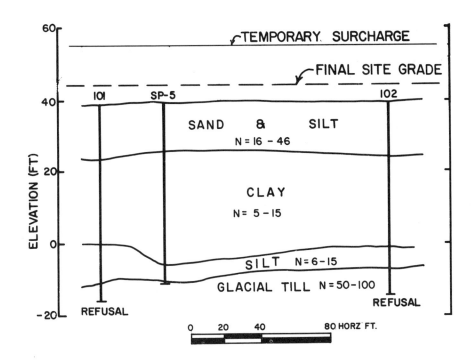

Figure 5. Site 1, subsurface profile A-A.

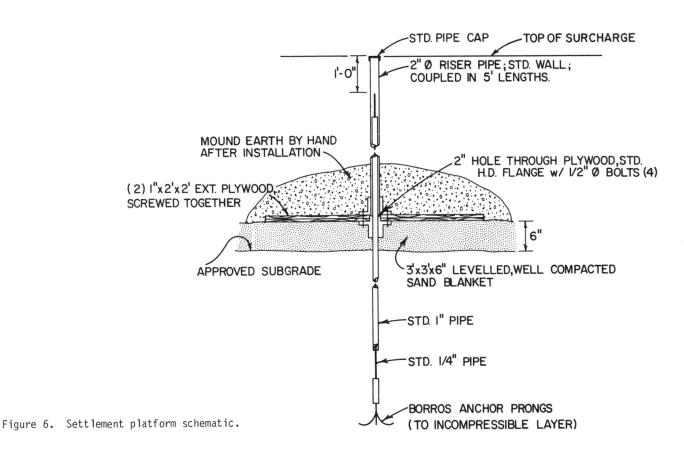

Figure 6. Settlement platform schematic.

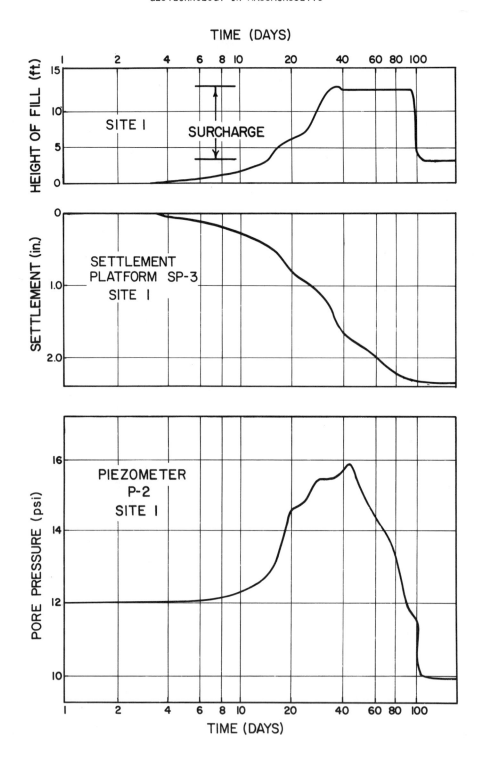

Figure 7. Site 1, loading - settlement - pore pressure versus time.

collected by the authors. A summary is shown in Table 1.

Atterberg limits were determined on samples of the clay from all five sites. Most of the data plots at or slightly above the A-line on the standard plasticity chart in the moderately plastic zone (liquid limit 30 to 50). At site 4, which is close to the edge of the old glacial lake, the samples were only slightly plastic. At site 5, the limits were generally slightly below the A-line in the moderately plastic range. At site 1, 36 percent of the samples were in the highly plastic range (liquid limit greater than 50). A plasticity chart plot of the average Atterberg limits from each site is shown in Figure 2.

Natural water contents of samples from four of the sites tended to be 3 to 10 percent below the liquid limit.

At sites 1 and 2, four one-dimensional consolidation tests from each site were run on three-inch diameter "undisturbed" Shelby tube samples of the clay. At both sites the clay is heavily overconsolidated. At site 1 the overconsolidation ratio (OCR) is in the range of 4 to 7, and at site 2 the OCR is in the range of 7 to 10. The coefficient of consolidation calculated from laboratory tests in the overconsolidated range at both sites was approximately 1.5 square feet per day. The average recompression ratio computed in the overconsolidated range was .03 at site 1 and .025 at site 2. The clay at site 2 also had a slightly higher average total unit weight (115 versus 110 pcf). A typical consolidation test result from site 2 is shown in Figure 3.

CASE HISTORIES

At two of the sites (Nos. 1 and 2) the clay was preloaded to reduce post-construction settlement of buildings which were subsequently constructed. These preloads were instrumented to determine when to remove the preloads and to compare engineering predictions with field results. These two cases are discussed in more detail in the following sections.

Bridgewater Training School-(site 1)

Site 1 is the Bridgewater Training School Facility at Bridgewater State College, Bridgewater, Massachusetts. Part of this training facility is a three-story office building which is founded on shallow foundation overlying 18 to 32 feet of varved Taunton River clay. The building and boring locations are shown in Figure 4. In addition to the load of the building, the site grade was raised approximately three feet. It was estimated that the ultimate settlement under these loads would be 1 to 2 inches. A typical soil profile through the building area is shown in Figure 5. It consists typically of the following.

| Depth in feet | Soil description |
|---|---|
| 0 - 1.5 | Topsoil |
| 1.5 - 14 | Dense to medium dense, fine sand and silt |
| 14 - 40 | Varved clay and silty clay with thin lenses of find sand and silt erratically interspersed |
| 40 - 48 | Inorganic silt |
| Below 48 | Very dense, glacial till, consisting of sand and gravel with a little silt |

In order to reduce the amount of post-construction settlement, the area of the three-story building was preloaded by placing a surcharge of 10 feet of granular fill above the finish floor elevation. This allowed most of the settlement to occur prior to construction of the building.

Five settlement platforms and two pneumatic piezometers were installed prior to placement of fill in order to monitor the settlement and pore pressure dissipation and to determine when the surcharge could be removed. Their locations are shown in Figure 4. The settlement platforms were installed first. During the installation of the settlement platforms, standard split spoon soil samples were taken at five feet intervals down to the top of the glacial till. At each settlement platform location borros anchors were installed in the till as a stable bench mark to which to refer any settlements. At the stripped ground surface a settlement platform, as shown in Figure 6, was installed prior to placement of any fill. Also, two pneumatic piezometers were installed and sealed at the mid-depth of the clay layer. The location of the mid-depth of the clay layer was estimated based on the settlement platform borings (SP-1 through SP-5).

All of the instruments were read approximately twice a week during placement of fill and weekly after the surcharge fill was at full height. The rate of loading and typical settlement and pore pressure readings are shown in Figure 7. It is believed that the pore pressure dropped to less than the initial pore pressure because static groundwater levels went down in the period of preload (April to July 1978). It took approximately 35 days to place the fill to full surcharge height. Based on this gradual loading rate and the rate of settlement, the field coefficient of consolidation was calculated to be approximately 3 square feet per day. This is twice the value computed from laboratory tests. Also, measured settlements were slightly less than the computer settlements based on laboratory tests. This was probably due to running consolidation tests on the more highly plastic samples and to some sample disturbance. The average liquid limit and plasticity index for the consolidation tests were 50 and 24 respectively as compared to an average for all clay samples of 47 and 22.

Raynham Shopping Center-(site 2)

Site 2 is the Raynham Shopping Center located near the intersection of Route 24 and Route 44 in Raynham, Massachusetts. Most of the site was flat. However, in the area covered by the building there was a sharp drop off in the southeast corner requiring as much as 11 feet of fill.

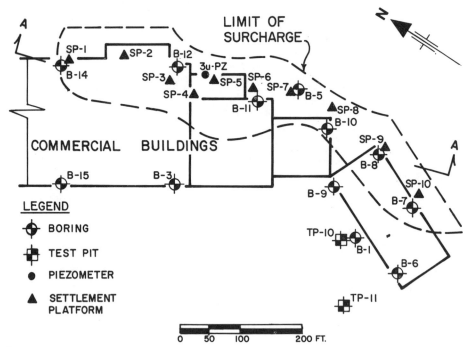

Figure 8.  Site 2, partial site plan.

Figure 9.

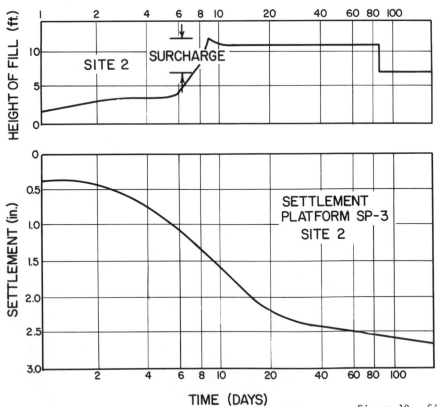

Figure 10.  Site 2, loading - settlement versus time.

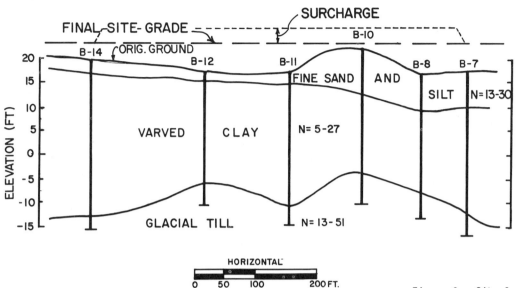

Figure 9. Site 2, subsurface profile A-A.

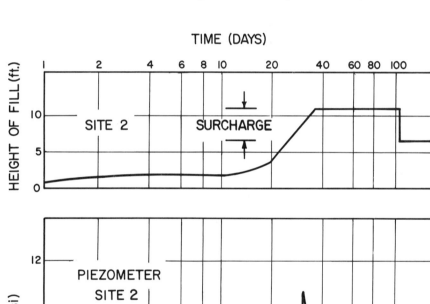

Figure 10.

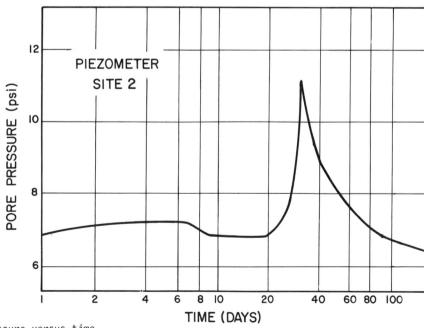

Figure 11. Site 2, loading - pore pressure versus time.

The subsurface conditions at the site consist of fine sand and silt extending to depths of 2 to 8 feet below existing ground surface. The fine sand and silt strata are in turn underlain by varved clay, which extends to depths of 24 to 33 feet below ground surface. The clay is generally medium to stiff in consistency within the top 3 to 5 feet (N = 11-27) but changes to soft to medium consistency with depth (N=5). The maximum thickness of clay with soft consistency was about 20 feet in the vicinity of the southeast corner of the site. The clay stratum is in turn underlain by a dense silty fine sand and gravel at depths of 24 to 35 feet below ground surface. This stratum is a glacial till. A general location plan and a subsurface profile are shown in Figures 8 and 9.

Laboratory tests were performed on undisturbed samples of the clay. Tests included natural water content, unit weight, Atterberg limits, laboratory vane shear (Torvane) and one dimensional consolidation. A typical consolidation test result is shown in Figure 3. Strength data were used to assess bearing capacity of the clay as well as edge stability of the deeper fill areas. Settlement analyses were performed for the selected building lines having the most critical combinations of loading and compressible clay deposits, in an attempt to bracket the potentially most severe cases of settlement. Estimated gross settlements ranged from a maximum of four inches to a minimum of one inch, while estimated differential settlements of the order of three inches were expected. Since these settlements were judged to be intolerable, it was decided to preload the site by placement of earth fill to cause settlement prior to construction of the buildings and to carefully monitor the preloading so that the post-construction settlement could be minimized. Since the clay was thickest in the southeast corner of the site and the amount of fill required was greatest in this area, it was decided to surcharge only this area, as shown in Figure 8.

The average amount of fill to achieve the desired raise in grade was approximately six feet and the height of surcharge was approximately five feet. The program of preloading was monitored by ten settlement platforms and one piezometer at the mid-point of the clay stratum. Typical plots of settlement versus time and piezometric pressures at the mid-point of the clay stratum with time are shown in Figures 10 and 11. Also, included on these figures are the results of the loading versus time in terms of the height of fill at the particular location. As may be noted, the maximum settlement under settlement platform #7 was about 2-1/2 inches under the surcharge load over a period of 60 days.

The recorded settlements were somewhat smaller than those predicted based on laboratory test results and the loading condition. Post-construction settlements have generally been less than 1 inch in the 5 year period since removal of the surcharge and construction of the building.

SUMMARY

Where settlements of structures founded on or above the Taunton River clays are a concern, preloading is an effective means of reducing post-construction settlement. The Taunton River clays are overconsolidated, have a relatively high coefficient of consolidation, and are not excessively thick. All of these factors help make preloading effective. Based on the results of two instrumented full-scale preloads, the field behavior agrees fairly well with the laboratory test results except that the field rate of consolidation is nearly twice as fast as that predicted from laboratory tests.

Tabulated below is a comparison of compressibility characteristics of the Taunton River clays with the familiar Boston blue clay, for clays with an overconsolidation ratio of 4 to 10.

|  | Virgin Compression Ratio $C_c/1+e$ | Recompression Ratio $C_r/1+e$ | Coefficient of Consolidation (ft$^2$/day) |
|---|---|---|---|
| Taunton River clay | .15-.25 | .025-.035 | 1.5-3 |
| Boston blue clay | .1 -.3 | .02 -.04 | .2- .6 |

The virgin compression and recompression ratios for both clays are similar, but the coefficient of consolidation is much larger for the Taunton River clay.

REFERENCES

Chute, N.E., 1959, Surficial geology of the Brockton quadrangle, Massachusetts, United States Geological Survey, Geological Quadrangle Map GQ-6.

Fessenden, F.W., Ayres, J.E., and Dean, S.L., 1975, A summary of the geology of eastern Massachusetts: Corps of Engineers, Planning Division, New England Division, Sheet EM S-2.

Hartshorn, J.H., 1960, Geology of the Bridgewater quadrangle, Massachusetts: United States Geological Survey, Geological Quadrangle Map GQ-127.

Hartshorn, J.H., 1967, Geology of the Taunton quadrangle, Bristol and Plymouth Counties, Massachusetts: United States Geological Survey Bulletin 1163-D, 67 p.

Petersen, R.G., and Shaw, C.E., Jr., 1967, Surficial geologic map of the Whitman Quadrangle, Plymouth County, Massachusetts: United States Geological Survey, Geological Quadrangle Map GQ-632.

# Significance of glacial till terminology in engineered construction

A. W. HATHEWAY
Haley & Aldrich, Inc.

## ABSTRACT

Tills and their associated glacial debris blanket significant portions of New England. These surficial geologic units have been mapped historically by a number of techniques and have been variously labeled, including the non-generic terms till and drift. These soils are best characterized by their extreme heterogeneity and generally well-graded nature, presenting the geotechnical engineer with material gradations spanning the entire range from clay to the sometimes gigantic erratics found in the New England countryside. Because till is so common, experienced geotechnical engineers in New England can generally draw on a vast background source of strength and performance data, once they are presented with an accurate geological description of the material, SPT blow count values, and size-gradation curves. The engineering geologist must provide accurate descriptions of till, by genesis and character, along with good definitions of its depth and areal extent at a give project site.

## DISCUSSION

The key to accurate determinations by engineering geologists is the recognition and correct labeling of the varieties of till. Over the years, to most earthwork and foundation contractors in New England, the term "till" has come to mean what we now commonly call "lodgement till," the relatively most dense variety of till, with the most favorable suite of engineering properties for many geotechnical purposes. However, modern surficial geologic mapping in New England, beginning with the efforts of R.H. Jahns in the Ayer, Massachusetts quadrangle (1940), began to differentiate the most important characteristics of New England till. It is our belief that use of the term "till" should be abandoned by engineering geologists and geotechnical engineers and that all parties associated with construction in New England should be provided with correctly identified glacial-debris terminology.

Basically, granular-type glacial debris should be defined, for geotechnical purposes, on the basis of four categories: Lodgement Till, Ablation Till, Flow Till, and Outwash. The several established sub-terms for Outwash will not be discussed further herein. Definitions for the various types of glacial debris are contained in Table 1. Through the use of this classification, which is already established in the modern works and literature of Quaternary mapping, engineering geologists and geotechnical engineers will be able to impart a range of performance-related materials assessments to other uses, and they will have a better option for portraying the areal distribution of such units on their site geologic maps. In reviewing the classification for site use, the engineering geologist should discuss the intended use of the site with the project engineer and determine which of the key engineering characteristics will most affect design and construction. We realize that these materials were often produced by a blend of glacial mechanisms and that individual units of glacial debris may contain lenses or pockets of mixed origin. It is a matter of individual professional preference to select the detail to which the exploration and mapping effort is carried, but glacial debris should be classified into the single, dominant category representing the bulk of each deposit. Table 2 contains a broad estimate of the relative ranges of important physical characteristics and engineering properties of the three types of till and their associated melt debris. The values should be used in a relative sense, for comparison only; deviations are to be expected.

Engineering geologists can detect classification differences in glacial debris by careful observation of boring samples and auger cuttings, along with test pit samples. The key items of observation are listed below.

- Unified Soil Classification System (USCS) visual description.

- Angularity of particles.

- Density (SPT or excavation effort).

- Color (including mottles).

- Nature of parent rock, to include soft and weathered fragments and deleterious minerals.

- Clay-sized fraction.

- Percentage and size range for boulders encountered in the test pit excavation.

TABLE 1.  GLOSSARY OF TERMS USED TO CLASSIFY
GRANULAR GLACIAL DEBRIS

(Source: <u>Glossary of Geology</u>, published in 1972 by
the American Geological Institute, Falls Church,
Virginia.)

<u>ablation till</u>  Loosely consolidated rock debris,
formerly contained by a glacier, that accumulated
in place as the surface ice was removed by ablation.

<u>basal till</u>  A firm clay-rich till containing many
abraded stones dragged along beneath a moving
glacier and deposited upon bedrock or other glacial
deposits.  Cf: <u>lodgment till</u>.

<u>drift [glac geol]</u>  A general term applied to all
rock material (clay, sand, gravel, boulders)
transported by a glacier and deposited directly by
or from the ice, or by running water emanating from
a glacier.  Drift includes unstratified material
(till) that forms moraines, and stratified deposits
that form outwash plains, eskers, kames, varves,
glaciofluvial sediments, etc.  The term is generally
applied to Pleistocene glacial deposits in areas
(as large parts of North America and Europe) that
no longer contain glaciers.  The term "drift" was
introduced by Murchison (1839, v. 1, p. 509) for
material, then called diluvium, that he regarded
as having drifted in marine currents and accumulated
under the sea in comparatively recent times; this
material is now known to be a product of glacial
activity.  Partial syn:  glacial drift;
fluvioglacial drift.

<u>flowtill</u>  A superglacial till that is modified and
transported by plastic mass flow (Hartshorn, 1958,
p. 481).

<u>ice-contact deposit</u>  Stratified drift deposited in
contact with melting glacier ice, such as an esker,
kame, kame terrace, or a feature marked by numerous
kettles.

<u>lodgment till</u>  A basal till commonly characterized
by compact fissile structure and containing stones
oriented with their long axes generally parallel
to the direction of ice movement.

<u>outwash [glac geol]</u>  (a) Stratified detritus
(chiefly sand and gravel) removed or "washed out"
from a glacier by meltwater streams and deposited
in front of or beyond the terminal moraine or the
margin of an active glacier.  The coarser material
is deposited nearer to the ice.  Syn: glacial
outwash; overwash; outwash drift.  (b) The meltwater
from a glacier.

<u>stratified drift</u>  Fluvioglacial drift consisting of
sorted and layered material deposited by a meltwater
stream or settled from suspension in a body of quiet
water adjoining the glacier.  Cf: <u>till</u>.  Obsolete
syn:  washed drift; modified drift.

Upper, A spoil pile of ablation till, as excavated during site exploration test pitting
in Wilmington, Massachusetts.  Note the granular and cohesionless nature of the material as
it sloughs naturally to the angle of repose,
below the backhoe bucket.  The white card on
the front-facing slope is 18 cm (7 in) across.

Lower, Typically dense and cohesive lodgement
till as exposed by pneumatic hammer action in
a sewage pump station at Lake Winnepesaukee,
New Hampshire.  Lodgement till often defeats
the excavating ability of small to medium-sized
backhoes.

TABLE 2. AVERAGE ENGINEERING CHARACTERISTICS OF GRANULAR GLACIAL DEBRIS IN NEW ENGLAND

Average values shown are intended to represent realistic, relative ranges encountered in typical deposits. Values encountered in individual cases will be primarily dependent on the accuracy of classification and should be expected to vary with the primary nature of each deposit encountered.

| Characteristic | Lodgement (Basal) Till | Ablation Till | Flow Till | Outwash |
|---|---|---|---|---|
| Particle Size Gradation | Well-graded; very heterogeneous | Moderately well-graded heterogeneous | | Gap-graded/poorly sorted semi-homogeneous |
| Presence of Boulders | Many, including erratics | Fewer, including erratics | | Few to nil |
| Percent (-)200 Sieve | 20-60 | 0-15 | | 0-10 |
| Percent (-) 0.02 mm | 5-30 | 0-10 | | 0-5 |
| Effect of Fines | Governs engineering properties | Negligible | Flow till may have characteristics of either lodgement or ablation till, depending on which of these two types was the parent. It does tend to be less dense, somewhat more underconsolidated than lodgement till. | Nil |
| Relative Density | Stiff - hard | Loose - moderately compact | | Loose - moderately compact |
| Dry Unit Weight (Kg/M$^3$) | 1.8-2.1 | 1.7-1.9 | | 1.6-1.9 |
| Particle Shape | Angular-subangular | Subangular-subrounded | | Subangular-rounded |
| Liquid Limit | 15-30 | Non-plastic | | Non-plastic |
| Plasticity Index | 0-20 | Non-plastic | | Non-plastic |
| SPT Range (N values) | 20-200+ | 10-50+ | | 0-20+ |
| Cohesion (KN/m$^2$) | 0-25 | $\approx 0$ | | $\simeq 0$ |
| Friction Angle ($^0$) | 15-33 | 30-40 | | 25-45 |
| Consolidation Ratio | Overconsolidated | Normal to underconsolidated | | Normal to underconsolidated |
| Permeability (in-situ) (cm/sec) | $10^{-5}$ to $10^{-9}$ | $10^{-3}$ to $10^{-5}$ | | $10^{-2}$ to $10^{-5}$ |

CONCLUSION

Avoidance of non-specific terms such as "drift" and "till" will promote accuracy in portrayal of geological conditions in the field and will enhance their correct identification and optimal usage in engineered construction.  □

Rock excavations along highways in New England, 5: foliation and jointing.

# Tunneling through the Cambridge Argillite

T. R. CULLEN
L. W. YOUNG, JR.
Bechtel Incorporated

F. M. KEVILLE
Massachusetts Bay Transportation Authority

## ABSTRACT

The 3.1 mile Northwest Extension of the MBTA Red Line consists of two deep tunnel sections and a cut-and-cover section. The first section, which is 4,400 ft (1342 m) long, connects the proposed Harvard Square Station (a cut-and-cover structure) to the proposed Porter Square Station (a deep rock structure). Porter Square Station is, in turn, linked to the proposed Davis Square Station (a cut-and-cover structure) by the second deep tunnel section, which is 2,900 feet (884 m) long. Beyond the Davis Square Station, the Northwest Extension continues as cut-and-cover along a railroad right-of-way to Alewife Brook Station in Cambridge, Massachusetts. This paper discusses the two deep tunnel sections which have been under construction since late 1978 or early 1979. The paper will discuss the site geology, excavation techniques, and ground support methods utilized in the shafts and tunnel sections, and the instrumentation methods employed to measure ground deformation in response to the excavation activity. A description of the current geologic mapping programs in the tunnels and shafts is included.

The deep tunnels are twin-bore (excavated) and 22 feet in diameter, with construction access shafts which will later serve as ventilation and emergency egress shafts at intervals along the alignment. A variety of excavation and support techniques is being utilized during the construction and support of the shafts and tunnels. The support methods employed in shaft construction differ according to the geometry of each structure. Although most of the deep tunnel section lies in bed rock, there are portions of the tunnel where mixed-face conditions are anticipated, or the entire face is in soft ground.

The bed rock along the alignment is the Cambridge Argillite, a highly indurated siltstone with common igneous intrusive bodies. The soft ground sections will be within the overburden deposits of till, marine clay, outwash sand and gravel and fill in ascending order from the bedrock surface. Mixed-face conditions are, of course, in the transition zones from a rock tunnel to soft ground tunnel sections.

## INTRODUCTION

Construction of the Massachusetts Bay Transportation Authority's (MBTA) Red Line Extension-Northwest is currently in progress. The project encompasses a 3.1 miles (5.0 km) addition to a network of 120 miles (192 km) of rapid transit lines serving the Boston metropolitan area (Fig. 1). The project involves construction of large diameter tunnels and other underground construction that, with regard to size and scope, are firsts in both rapid transit construction in the Boston area and for construction in the Cambridge Argillite bed rock. Construction started early in 1978 with preparatory utility relocation work, and work now in progress includes two major tunneling contracts with five ventilation and/or construction access shafts, and two cut-and-cover station construction contracts, both making significant use of cast-in-place concrete diaphragm walls for excavation support and building protection, and a station construction contract involving the excavation of an underground rock cavity to form the station platform area. Work on all contracts, which were competitively bid, is spread between several nationally known underground constructors.

The pre-construction geotechnical exploratory programs and design work associated with selection of a tunnel alignment to minimize community impact and to provide for improved tunneling conditions were the subject of a previous paper (Keville, and others, 1979). This paper describes the current programs of geologic mapping of tunnels and shafts that are providing verification of subsurface conditions. As a point of reference for the description of the tunneling conditions, the basic design features of the tunnels are reviewed in combination with a description of the construction methodology being employed by the contractors. In addition, the geotechnical instrumentation program that was developed to monitor the interaction between the subsurface conditions and the contractor's excavation methods, using devices to measure ground deformation and stress, is discussed.

## DESCRIPTION OF PROJECT

The MBTA Red Line Extension-Northwest extends from the reconstructed Harvard Square Station in Cambridge, Massachusetts, through tunnels and cut-and-cover construction to the currently planned terminus at the Alewife Brook Station in north Cambridge, Massachusetts. The alignment of the Harvard to Davis Square tunnels is shown in Fig. 2. The portion of the subway between Harvard and Porter Squares generally follows below Massachusetts Avenue for its entire length of approximately 4,400 feet (1342 m). Massachusetts Avenue is lined with academic, commercial, religious, and residential buildings up to six stories high. In addition, numerous utility systems including two electrical distribution systems, two water systems, sewers--some of them of old brick construction--telephone ducts, and gas mains are located beneath Massachusetts Avenue. The portion of the subway between Porter Square and Davis Square follows a diagonal alignment passing directly beneath a shopping center at Porter Square and numerous two- and three-story wood frame houses elsewhere. The length of the Porter to Davis Square alignment is approximately 2,900 feet (884 m). Both tunnels drive at maximum gradient from Davis and Harvard toward the deep Porter Square Station to give maximum rock cover. Most of the deep tunnel is below sea level.

The Harvard Square to Davis Square section of the subway has twin, single-track tunnels with an inside diameter of 19.2 feet (5.8 m). This diameter provides adequate clearance for all of the cars used on the MBTA lines including new vehicles that may be considered for the Red Line. The tunnel configurations are conventional ones for soft ground and rock, as shown in Figure 3. For sections driven through rock, pre-construction exploration borings were used to predict what types of support would be needed. The following data were utilized: the thickness

of rock cover over the crown of the tunnel, the quality of rock over the crown of the tunnel, and certain layout and design considerations such as the location of cross-passages and shaft portals. Based on the above considerations, minimum rock support requirements were specified for certain areas, consisting of steel sets or rock bolts. For other areas, the method of rock support was left up to the contractor dependent on conditions disclosed by tunneling. It was anticipated that the support would consist of rock bolts with straps or wire mesh.

Based on the expected subsurface conditions, the minimum support requirements specified for the tunnels are as follows:

- Length of tunnel with circular steel ribs and wood lagging for soft ground and mixed-face conditions.    4,850 T.F.*

- Length of rock tunnels with steel sets specified.    3,560 T.F.

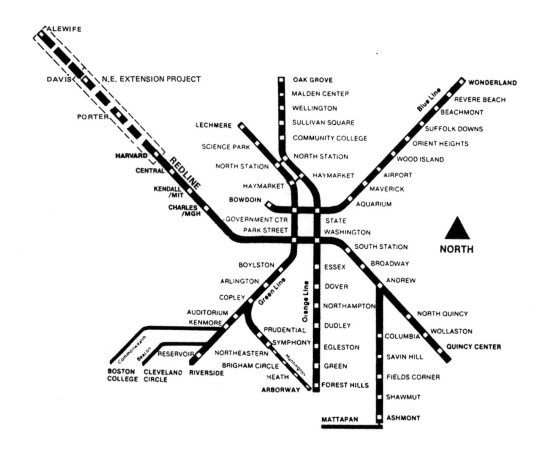

Figure 1. MBTA rapid transit lines. No scale.

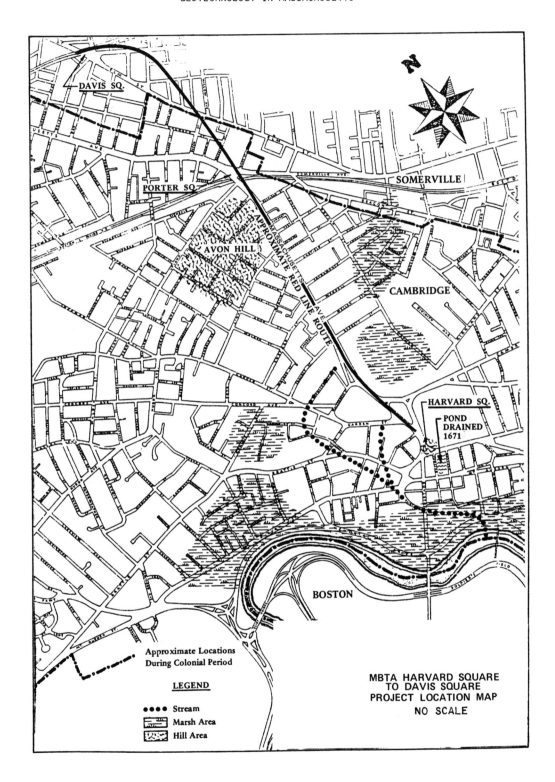

Figure 2.  MBTA Harvard Square to Davis Square, project
location map.  No scale.

● Length of rock tunnels      6,120 T.F.
with rock bolt support
or support at contractor's
option.

\* T.F. - Tunnel Feet (Note: 1 ft. = 0.305 m.)

## REGIONAL GEOLOGY

The Red Line Extension alignment lies within the Boston Basin (Fig. 4) which is a structural and topographic basin with fault boundaries on the north-northwest-west side (Northern Boundary Fault) and on the southeast-south side (Ponkapoag Fault and Blue Hills Thrust). The southwest margin is complicated by tight folds that plunge to the eastward, while the eastern limit of the basin is submerged beneath the waters of Boston Bay.

The Boston Basin is a depression filled with late Paleozoic rocks younger than the rocks that surround it (Fig. 4). The basin is floored by the Precambrian basement complex above which, in ascending order, rest: Mississippian; Mattapan and Lynn Volcanic Complexes; Pennsylvanian; and Boston Bay Group (Roxbury Conglomerate and Cambridge Argillite) (Billings, 1976).

This paper is concerned with only a portion of the Boston Bay Group, i.e., the Cambridge Argillite. However, a brief description of the general geology is in order.

The Precambrian basement lies unconformably beneath the basin in the northwest and southeast (Cameron and Naylor, 1976). In the southwest it is exposed in the cores of northeasterly-plunging anticlines.

The Mattapan and Lynn Volcanic Complexes are felsites and melaphyres that underlie the Boston Bay Group. Tentative age assignment of these rocks is Mississippian (Pollard, 1965). They are considered older than the Boston Bay Group because clasts of similar lithology are found in the Roxbury Conglomerate.

The Lynn Volcanic Complex lies north of the Boston Basin, outside the Northern Boundary Fault. The two volcanic complexes are similar lithologically and both cross-cut the Precambrian Basement (Fig. 4).

Traditionally, the Boston Bay Group is separated into two formations, the lower Roxbury Conglomerate and the upper Cambridge Argillite. Emerson (1917) and LaForge (1932) recognized that the Roxbury Conglomerate was comprised of three members, the Squantum, Dorchester, and Brookline members. Billings (1976) has further defined the stratigraphy of these members by combining tunnel data and surface outcrop information. The lower sequence lies in the southern side of the basin. The argillite is sparingly reported to the south with most surface exposures north of the Charles River Syncline axis (Fig. 4). The Red Line Extension lies wholly in the Cambridge Argillite.

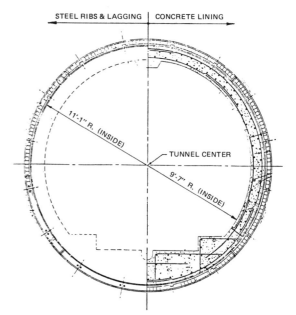

**SOFT GROUND TUNNEL**
**CONCRETE LINING WITH STEEL RIBS AND LAGGING**

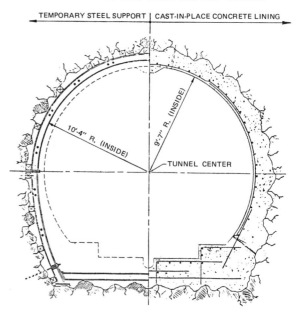

**ROCK TUNNEL**
**CONCRETE LINING WITH STEEL RIBS**

Figure 3. Typical tunnel sections.

In general terms, the Cambridge Argillite is a sequence of highly indurated siltstone. Bed thickness ranges from 1 mm to 8 cm (.04-3 inches). There are color differences in the sequence that can be attributed to either grain size variation, or a compositional variation, or both. The darker gray beds are clay- or silt-rich layers while the lighter colored beds are comprised of very fine to fine sand with occasional lenses of medium sand mixed with clay and/or silt.

The argillite is typically varved or rhythmically layered as exposed along the tunnel alignment. Bed structures observed along the alignment include graded beds, ripple marks, and cross-bedding. Locally, indications of penecontemporaneous deformation have been observed, such as slump structures and intraformational conglomerates.

## STRUCTURAL GEOLOGY

The structure of the Boston Basin is comprised of a series of broad folds with wavelengths on the order of 5 km (3 miles) (Billings, 1976) that plunge gently east-northeast.

The Red Line Extension is located in the north flank of the Charles River Syncline (Fig. 4). The regional dip of bedding in the argillite is generally to the south. Local variations occur which are associated with small drag folds or flexures usually associated with shear zones.

The major structural features trend east-northeast. Folds observed along the alignment have wavelengths ranging from 1 m to 5 m (3.3 to 16.3 feet). They plunge gently (5°-15°) to the east-northeast. Longer wavelength folds are indicated by changes in bedding attitude but are less discernible due to their subtle expression.

Fault and shear zones mapped in the Boston Basin generally trend east-northeast. The tunnel exposures show all scales of faulting and shears. Many of the dikes observed along the alignment have one or both contacts sheared. The question arises as to which came first, the faults or the intrusions. A detailed study of these contact relationships, beyond the scope of this paper, may shed light on the question.

## TUNNEL MAPPING

The purpose of the geologic mapping is to provide the client (MBTA) with a detailed record of ground conditions that exist along the Red Line Extension alignment.

Geologic mapping in the running tunnels and shaft excavations is being accomplished by constructing scaled plan view sketches and face sketches of the headings and sidewalls. Field mapping in the shafts is done at 1 in = 20 ft scale, and in the running tunnels at a 1 in = 10 ft scale. The final copy geologic map is being drawn at springline from these field sketches and notes at a 1 in = 20 ft scale.

In addition to being the client's document of record of the geotechnical conditions, the tunnel mapping of the Cambridge Argillite provides a unique opportunity to contribute to the geologic and geotechnical knowledge of the Boston Basin.

## GEOTECHNICAL FEATURES AFFECTING CONSTRUCTION

On the site-specific scale, the engineering geologist must be aware of a variety of geotechnical features and their possible impact on the structure in engineering terms. These features must be considered during the design, as well as the construction phases of a project.

Classically, the frequency, orientation and characteristics of discontinuity surfaces (bedding planes, joints, etc.), the effect of faults or shear zones, and groundwater inflow have been the pertinent parameters by which the competence of a rock mass in a tunnel is judged.

During excavation of the twin bore tunnels from Davis Square in Somerville to Harvard Square in Cambridge, these and other more specific features are being observed and evaluated as an ongoing process. The condition of the bedrock surface, rock type, bedding attitudes and characteristics, joints, intrusive rocks, faults and shear zones, weathering, ground water, and the thickness and stratigraphy of overburden soils contribute to the evaluation of the rock mass as excavation progresses.

### Bedrock Surface

The top of the rock along the Red Line Extension alignment reflects past glacial events (preglacial, glacial and post glacial). It is not a uniform surface (Weston Geophysical Engineers, Inc., 1977), but has ridges and valleys resulting from the combined effects of glacial scouring and mass-wasting and erosion by paleodrainage systems. Glacial effects have resulted in blocks of argillite tens of meters in dimension being transported varying distances laterally or lifted vertically by ice jacking. Kaye (1976) and others working in the area have documented these effects so that a well executed drilling and logging program is a necessity to enable designers and contractors alike to predict any unexpected conditions at or near the bedrock interface with the overlying sediments.

### Rock Type

The primary rock type along the tunnel alignment is the Cambridge Argillite with lesser amounts of intrusive rocks that penetrate the country rock. The argillite, though non-uniform in appearance, does not show any significant variations from a geotechnical standpoint except where faulted or sheared. The obvious varieties in appearance such as color, banding or sedimentary structures appear to be the result of depositional control. The physical properties of the

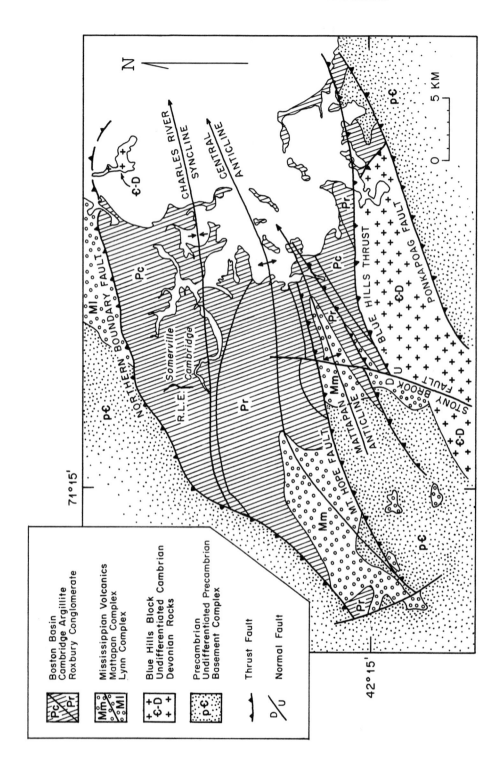

Figure 4. Generalized geologic map showing major structural features and the project location (R.L.E. - Red Line extension) in the Boston basin. (Source: Billings, 1976).

argillite are affected mechanically and chemically when associated with fault zones or shear zones, especially where ground water has been introduced.

Bedding Attitudes

The tunnel alignment is located in the northern limb of the Charles River Syncline (Fig. 4). Generally speaking, the bedding dips gently to moderately (20°-45°) to the south.

Bedding characteristics in the argillite along the Red Line Extension show extreme varia-

bility. The bed rock varies from a massive dark- to medium-gray, fine-grained type, to argillite exhibiting rhythmic bands (varves?) of light gray layers alternating with medium- to dark-gray layers. The coarser grained layers (generally lighter colored) have well developed bedding structures. These structures include graded sequences, cross bedding and ripple marks. Bedding plane joints are usually spaced 30 cm - 50 cm (12-20 inches) apart. The presence or absence of these bedding features does not normally affect the stability of the tunnel opening. The exception exists when nearby faulting or proximity to the top of the rock results in extreme jointing

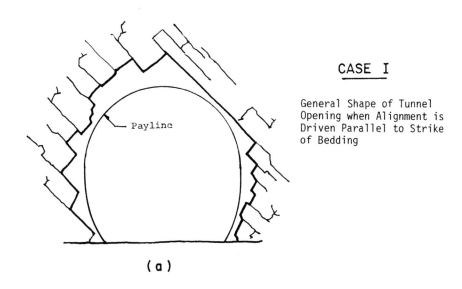

## CASE I

General Shape of Tunnel Opening when Alignment is Driven Parallel to Strike of Bedding

(a)

## CASE II

General Shape of Tunnel Opening when Alignment is Driven Normal to the Strike of Bedding

0'    10'

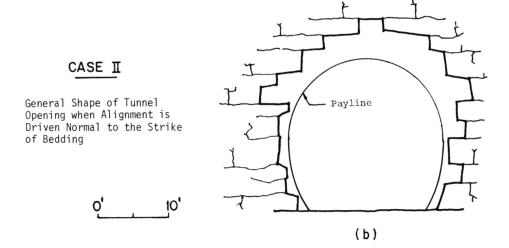

(b)

Figure 5. Tunnel geometry (schematic representation only) influenced by bedding and joint orientation.

developed parallel to the bedding surfaces. The joint spacing in these cases is usually 10 cm - 25 cm (4-10 inches).

The orientation of the alignment is obliquely down-dip or up-dip (depending upon the direction the heading is being driven) in the tangent sections. On the curved section from Porter Square Station to Davis Square Station, the alignment swings around almost parallel to the strike of the beds.

This gradual change results in a varying response by the bed rock to the tunneling activity which translates into a differently shaped tunnel opening. The extreme situations are shown diagrammatically (Figs. 5a and 5b). Case I demonstrates the conditions where the tunnel is driven parallel to the strike of the regional fabric (in this case, bedding).

Case II shows the geometric relationships that exist when a tunnel is driven across (or nearly so) the strike of the regional fabric in the argillite.

The limit of overbreak involved with advancing a tunnel is affected by the relative orientation of the alignment to major geologic features. This effect can be favorable or unfavorable. Overbreak also depends upon several other factors, of which the following are the most critical:

- spacing between the joints;

- shattering effect of blasting on the rock beyond the payline;

- distance between the working face and the roof support; and

- length of time which elapses between removal of rock support of the roof by blasting and the installation of temporary support (rockbolts or steel ribs).

With a properly designed and executed blasting program, an adequate and timely temporary support system can be economically achieved if these geotechnical conditions are sufficiently considered.

## Jointing

The number of joint sets present along the alignment are far too numerous to document here. Like the bedding plane discontinuities, these surfaces play a major factor in the stability of the tunnel opening. Some are more influential than others, depending upon repetition, tightness, coatings, spacing and attitude relative to the tunnel alignment.

The major joint sets along the alignment (other than bedding plane joints) generally strike north-northeast, with nearly vertical dips. Jointing parallel to bedding is commonly developed striking nearly east-west with gentle to moderate dips, either north or south. A strong set of

joints is developed nearly parallel to shear zones, which are usually oriented more east-northeast. These joints tend to die out with increasing distance from the shear zone. These shear zone joint sets have not contributed to major support problems because most have been oriented nearly normal to the tunnel alignment. Occasionally, local overbreak is experienced in the sidewalls when a shear zone is oriented parallel to the alignment.

## Intrusive Rocks

The occurrence of igneous intrusive bodies along the alignment is not uncommon; the characteristics of each occurrence are unique. They vary in composition, texture, orientation and contact relationships with the country rock.

Compositionally the intrusive rocks range from mafic to felsic. These terms are necessarily general, and, due to the aphanitic texture of the groundmass of most of the intrusives and without the aid of petrographic studies at this time, this is the classification scheme used. The majority of the rocks are of the felsic variety. Others have either porphyritic or amygdalitic textures. The mafic varieties tend to be porphyritic while any amygdales found are within the more felsic rocks. More can be said about these rocks after a systematic petrographic study is undertaken. They are usually oriented north-northeast, varying from 15°-45° east of north. Dips range from 60° to 90°. A felsic sill has been mapped for a short distance in the tunnels between Davis Square and Porter Square. Some dikes have been mapped with both contacts intact; others have been found with one or both margins sheared. Where the igneous contacts are preserved, an aureole is formed with scales ranging from several inches to several feet. The thickness of the baked zone seems to be directly proportional to the width of the intrusion. Development of sulphide mineral phases accompanies the contact reactions; pyrite is the most common with lesser amounts of chalcopyrite observed. From a construction standpoint, these rocks have not created a potential for problems unless they are in extremely sheared zones and ground water is present. They tend to weather more readily than the argillite when exposed to ground water. When accompanied by shearing, the development of clay gouge at the contact increases the potential instability of the rock mass in these areas.

## Fault Zones and Shear Zones

Fault zones are defined as areas where relative movement has been inferred either by observed offsets or by mapping the drag sense of other features into these zones. Shears are those zones where movement may have occurred but no relative direction can be inferred. Slickensides, gouge or breccia are some of the indications used to identify these zones. Either faults or shears may be expressed as a discrete plane or a zone several inches to tens of feet in width.

Shear or fault zones without associated clay gouge have not had much effect on the construction aspect of the tunnel other than the variable fracturing effect on the rock. Where gouge is present, however, the stability is affected because of reduction of the frictional forces binding blocks of rock together around the opening. The integrity of the tunnel opening is further affected when these zones are nearly parallel to the alignment.

Movement along these zones has altered the original bed rock by mechanical processes. The grinding or milling effects of movements have produced a fault gouge (clay) or a fault breccia (fragments). The clay coating these surfaces may act as a lubricant when disturbed by blasting or the readjustment of the rock after blasting. Added to this are the effects of groundwater infiltration, which further reduces the coefficient of friction along the coated surface by its presence and also causes chemical alteration of the rock along these surfaces.

Ground Water

The pre-construction boring investigations yielded data regarding the nature and occurrence of ground water along the alignment. Subsequent construction has verified the early projections. There are two principal water-bearing horizons—the outwash sand and gravel and the bedrock/till interface zone.

These two zones do not appear to be in hydraulic communication because of the clay below the pervious sand and gravel and the till above the bedrock surface effectively isolating the two zones. Only in those areas where the clay and till are absent does the potential exist for communication between the two (Bechtel Geotechnical Report, 1978).

The upper groundwater zone is under unconfined (water table) conditions, lying 8 to 18 feet below grade with a measured fluctuation of about 3 feet. The lower pervious zone is likely to be under confined (artesian) conditions (Bechtel Geotechnical Report, 1978).

The primary source of groundwater infiltration into the tunnel is from the lower zone via open joints where the tunnel alignment is near the top of the rock or where it intersects shear zones that act as conduits for the ground water. Although the clay gouge associated with shear zones may act as a barrier to ground infiltration, the shattered and broken rock that is usually present provides pathways for the water to enter the tunnel opening. When ground water does find its way into the excavation by whatever means, it has several effects, none of which are advantageous during excavation. The ground water very likely may cause instability along joints that have been loosened by blasting. The presence of ground water has a long term deteriorating effect on the rock caused by chemical weathering. The most severe effects occur on the joint surfaces

along which the ground water is introduced. The mineralogy of the rock mass and the chemistry of the groundwater solutions determine the rate at which the reactions proceed. The depth at which these reactions take place is negligible, and the geologic environment of the Boston Basin (i.e., the lack of near-surface geothermal activity) limits the rate of reaction.

Overburden Soils

The Boston Basin has been subjected to numerous major glaciations, each having left its unique mark upon the stratigraphic picture. From the earliest reported glaciation, 2 million years before present (B. P.), through the most recent, 12,000 years B. P. (Kaye, 1976), glaciations have both eroded and scoured the bedrock surface while others deposited thick blankets of till, clay and gravels. The transposition of earlier masses of glacially derived sediments in an intact form above younger glacial sediments has further complicated the picture (Kaye, 1979).

The Quaternary stratigraphy along the Red Line Extension alignment in ascending order from the bedrock surface is a till zone (0-70 feet thick), marine clay (0-60 feet thick), outwash sand and gravel (0-50 feet thick), and miscellaneous fill (0-15 feet thick). Table 1 summarizes the engineering properties of each stratum (Bechtel Geotechnical Report, 1978).

CONSTRUCTION TECHNIQUES:  SHAFTS

There are five shafts located along the alignment, in addition to the Porter Square Station. They will function as either ventilation or construction shafts during construction; when the tunnels are completed and the system is operational, they will serve as ventilation and emergency access shafts. The shafts are variously designed and supported, with three circular structures, and three box structures.

Shaft excavation on the Red Line Extension involves removal of material classified as rock (defined as material which requires drilling and blasting or some other hard rock mining method for removal) and soft ground (all other materials) (UMTA, 1978, MBTA Contracts, 105, 106).

Circular Shafts

Of the three circular shafts on the project, the Jarvis Street Outbound shaft (Sta. 195+68) is entirely soft ground. It is 86.5+ feet deep. The Jarvis Street Inbound shaft (Sta. 196+50) is 100 feet deep with several feet (2 feet-6 feet) of rock in the invert. Both Jarvis Street Shafts have pre-augured soldier piles (HP 14 x 13) installed prior to excavation. The soldier piles are 64 feet long (OB) and 68 feet long for the IB-structure respectively, spaced 5 feet on center.

TABLE 1.  SUMMARY OF ENGINEERING PROPERTIES OF MATERIALS (BECHTEL GEOTECHNICAL REPORT, 1978)

| Stratum | Consolidation condition | Effective friction angle | Total unit weight PCF | Allowable bearing pressure TSF |
|---|---|---|---|---|
| Fill<br>Sands distributed along entire project | Loose to medium dense | 28°-33° | 110-120 | 1.0 |
| Sands & Gravels<br>Glacial outwash deposits; sands, gravelly sands, silty sands | Medium dense to very dense | 32°-36° | 110-125 | 1.0-2.5 |
| Marine Clay<br>Silty clay | Over-consolidated | 24° | 110-120 | 2.0-4.0 |
| Till<br>Glacially deposited mixture of sand, gravel, cobbles, boulders, silt, clay | Dense to very dense | 36° | 125-140 | 3.0-5.0 |
| Cambridge<br>Argillite<br>Bedrock (slightly indurated) | Medium hard to hard with locally weathered and broken layers | 45° | 165-170 | 10-20 |

Excavation inside the soldier piles to a point 10 feet above the pile tips was supported by timber lagging installed behind the inside flange of the soldier piles. Below this point the side of the excavation was supported by steel liner plates. In both timber lagged sections and steel liner plated sections, steel rings (W12x 79) were installed to provide lateral support.

Excavation of the Summer Street shaft (Sta. 247+62) required removal of both soft ground and rock. The total depth is 100 feet soldier piles (HP 14 x 132) which were pre-augured on six-foot centers to the top of the rock. Excavation of the soft ground was achieved using an in-hole mucker and clam-shell. The sides were supported with timber lagging between the soldier piles. Lateral support was provided by the installation of steel rings (W12 x 73).

Rock excavation was conventional drill, blast and muck. The sidewalls were supported by fully encapsulated, point anchored and torqued rock bolts (1 inch Ø x 10 feet long). Wire mesh was installed along the sides of the shaft to minimize hazards of rock falls.

Rectangular Shafts

In the box structures, internal support is achieved by wale and strut systems working in concert with either soldier pile and timber lagging (Garfield Street) or slurry wall systems (Porter Square) or sheet pile (Grove Street) in the unconsolidated sedimentary sections. As in the circular shafts, the rock support on the sides is maintained using rock bolts and wire mesh.

Soft ground excavation is achieved by using a small mucker within the shaft confines to loosen the material for a larger bucket and crane to remove. It is then hauled away in trucks.

Rock excavation in all shafts is achieved using the drill and blast method. Smooth wall blasting techniques are being practiced. Overbreak, except locally, has been minimal.

CONSTRUCTION TECHNIQUES:  TUNNELS

There are three types of tunneling modes to be considered along the Red Line Extension alignment:

● rock tunneling;

- soft ground: confined to a portion of Harvard Square-Porter Square Tunnel section (Sta. 184+94± to Sta. 203+00±); and

- mixed face.

At this writing no soft ground tunneling has been undertaken.

Figure 3 shows the tunnel configuration with temporary and final support for each tunneling mode.

## Rock Tunneling

The tunneling activity to date includes four headings out of the Grove Street shaft, two headings south of the Porter Square shaft and two out of the Garfield Street shaft. All headings were started as a top-heading and bench operation initially for reasons of maintaining rock stability around the portal, as much as because of equipment capabilities imposed by space limitations.

Areas of potentially high rock loads were designated during the design phase to require steel rib sets for temporary support. The criteria for selection of these sites were dependent upon one or more conditions being valid:

- the intersection of a cross-passage or shaft with the tunnel alignment;

- less than 1.5 Ø thickness of sound rock cover above the crown of the tunnel; and

- low RQD values determined from the subsurface exploratory boring program.

Steel rib sets (W8 x 35) on four-foot centers were installed in the four headings out of the Grove Street shaft as temporary rock support. After the first one hundred feet the two headings toward Porter Square were supported with rock bolts. The rock bolt system as designed requires full encapsulation and torquing for optimal rock support. Where required, 10-foot long rock bolts are to be installed on 5-foot spacing each way from tunnel centerline to springline. The rock bolts are point anchored by a fast-setting cartridge of epoxy at the bottom of the hole, and the remaining annular space is filled by slower setting epoxy. The bolts are torqued to 32 KIPS after the anchor resin has set.

## Grove Street Headings

The two west headings out of Grove Street toward Davis Square have steel rib sets installed on four-foot centers the entire length. They are being advanced in 5-foot rounds, with steel rib sets erected after each round. Because of the limited rock cover above the tunnel crown and the shallow depth of the tunnel, a cautious mining approach is utilized in an effort to minimize any adverse effects from blasting that may be felt at the surface and to restrict the fracturing of the poorer quality rock generally found at the top of the rock interface with the till. The two headings towards Porter Square from Grove Street are being advanced using 10- to 12-foot rounds. The depth of the tunnel at this point along the alignment and the adequate rock cover are the reasons for the different approach employed in these headings.

## Mixed-Face Tunneling

The Outbound west tunnel heading is presently being advanced toward Davis Square Station from the Grove Street shaft in mixed-face conditions under an operating railroad. The tunnel heading has emerged from sound fresh rock into till above moderately weathered and jointed rock.

The pre-tunneling ground treatment involved a combination of cement grouting of the fractured rock and chemical grouting of the till zone at the top of the rock. A backup compaction grouting system was designed to stabilize the ground, if settlement at the surface should exceed a specified limit (3/8 inch). This involves grout pipe emplacement 10-15 feet above the tunnel crown on 10-foot centers. At this writing, the compaction grouting system has not been used.

The excavation sequence at the face involves a system of sliding crown bars that are advanced through the soft ground after manual excavation of a void. After the crown bars are advanced 5-6 feet beyond the last complete rib, blocking is inserted above, then the rock face is drilled, shot and mucked out. The steel ribs (circular in the mixed face and soft ground sections) are installed on four-foot centers. The cycle is then repeated. The dry condition at the face so far is evidence of the success of the pre-tunneling ground treatment combined with the draining effect of the Grove Street shaft.

## Porter Square Tunnel Headings

The tunnel headings began as a heading and bench operation until enough room was gained to utilize a larger drill jumbo and muck removal machinery. Temporary support of these tunnels is accomplished by rock bolts installed in a 5-foot x 5-foot grid from springline to springline. The Inbound (IB) heading is slightly ahead of the Outbound (OB) and it is situated so that the IB invert is approximately level with the OB springline. Because of the slabby nature of the IB sidewalls that are controlled by a high angle joint set striking 5°-15° off the alignment, additional rock bolts have been installed on the pillar wall to within 5 feet of the invert.

## Garfield Street Tunnel Headings

There are two tunnel headings out of this shaft structure at this time; both are in the

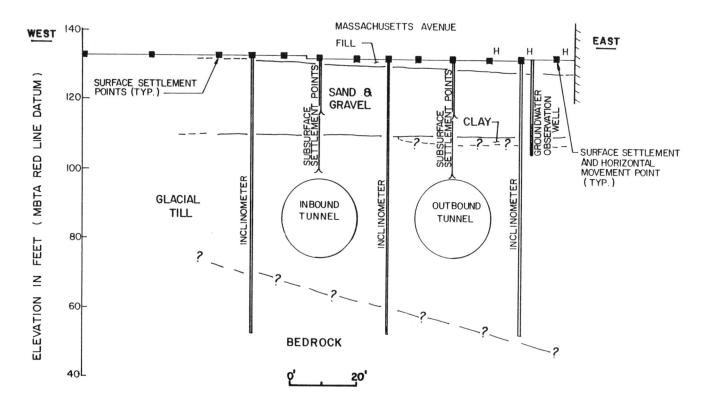

Figure 6. Typical high-intensity instrumentation profile.

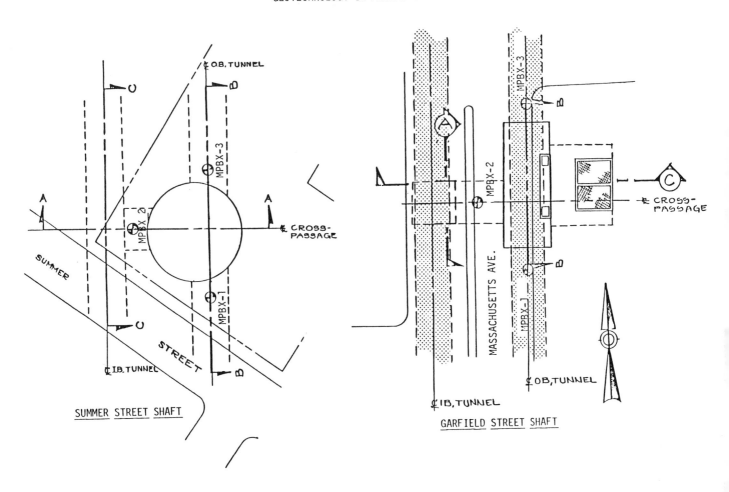

Figure 7. Location plan of shaft instruments.

Outbound side, one north toward Porter Square and the other south toward Harvard Square. Rockbolts are employed as temporary support in these two headings. The Inbound headings will commence upon completion of the cross-passage at this location.

## GEOTECHNICAL CONSTRUCTION MONITORING

The monitoring of geotechnical aspects of construction through programs of instrumentation and observation (such as tunnel mapping) is an integral part of the design and construction of a rapid transit tunnel in an urban environment. It provides not only the basis with which to verify the criteria used in design but also the information to help confirm compliance of the contractor to the construction specifications. The design and construction documents have provided for the implementation of a comprehensive program of instrumentation and monitoring of soil and rock performance during construction. The following sections describe the purpose, implementation, and results of the monitoring to date.

### Instrumentation

The needs and benefits of instrumentation as applied to rapid transit tunneling have been thoroughly discussed in the literature. The instrumentation installed on the Red Line Extension tunnels has the primary purpose of monitoring ground deformation due to tunneling, in order to minimize potentially unnecessary costs associated with underpinning of structures or utility relocations.

The monitoring program was based on first defining the relationship between tunneling equipment (i.e., shield details, etc.), tunneling methods (i.e., amount of breasting, excavation methods, etc.) and the response of the soil and ground water. This is achieved through the use of several high intensity instrumentation stations at the beginning of soft ground tunneling. The selection of instrumentation hardware was based on subsurface conditions and specific monitoring objectives.

These high intensity stations consist of inclinometers to measure lateral soil deformation, surface and subsurface settlement points to measure vertical soil deformation, and observation wells and piezometers to measure changes in groundwater level due to construction. The results of monitoring this instrumentation will help verify the response of the ground to tunnel driving and then judge the adequacy of predictions made for ground deformation. A cross section of a typical "high intensity" instrumentation profile is shown in Figure 6. In addition to the high intensity stations, measurement of settlement of the ground surface is being obtained using surface settlement points spaced along the alignment over the crown of the tunnel. Periodically, lines of settlement points normal to the tunnel alignment are also

positioned along the alignment in soft ground sections to monitor settlement close to the crown of the tunnel.

Instrumentation has been installed to monitor the performance of structures due to adjacent excavation. In particular, instrumentation consisting of surface settlement points and inclinometers, as well as lateral and vertical structural points, were used to monitor both the deformation of the Porter Square access shaft excavation support system and the adjacent (as close as 15 feet) Commonwealth Lock Building. This instrumentation was used to demonstrate the effectiveness of the excavation support system to limit ground deformation and settlement of the adjacent structure. The readings that were being obtained during construction verified that the diaphragm wall and its internal bracing system were adequately supporting the structure.

The majority of the instrumentation is installed in the soft ground sections of the tunnel. Construction to date in soft ground areas has been limited to access shaft construction. Instrumentation that has been installed in rock tunnel areas includes multiple point borehole extensometers for measuring rock movement and strain gauges installed on steel sets to identify the rock load on the steel sets.

### Multiple Position Borehole Extensometers (MPBX)

There are two locations where preliminary geotechnical studies indicated a need for rock instrumentation to monitor possible rock deformations during tunneling activity. Summer Street vent shaft and Garfield Street shaft (Fig. 7) have an array of three, four-anchor instruments, one being located above the outbound tunnel crown 10 feet upstation and another 10 feet downstation from the portals to the shaft. The third instrument is located above the crown of the cross-passage that connects the inbound tunnel to the shaft structure. The anchors are located approximately 3, 5, 9, and 20 feet outside the limit of the tunnel excavation ("A"-line).

The data collected over the 8-month life of the Summer Street shaft instruments indicate no anchor movement into the tunnel opening in excess of 0.05 inch at the deepest anchor. (MPBX data are uncorrected for head settlement.) This movement at MPBX-3 (Sta. 249+90+) occurred when the tunnel heading holed-through into the Summer Street shaft. There was no response to tunneling indicated from readings taken from Instrument No. 1 or No. 2.

The Garfield Street shaft instruments, installed nearly 7 months prior to this writing, have not been read because there has been no tunneling activity beneath them.

### Strain Gages

Several locations were selected during the design phase of the project for installation of instrumented steel ribs. The steel ribs were located on the contract drawings to coincide with areas where calculated rock loads indicated the necessity for this type of support. The instrumented ribs were to be installed to verify the rock loads in these areas and, whenever possible, in locations below MPBX instruments, so that the data could be correlated as much as possible.

The MBTA assumes the responsibility of monitoring the instrumented ribs. No data have been made available for study yet by the authority.

CONCLUSIONS

The construction of the Red Line Extension from Harvard Square to Davis Square (discussed in this paper) to Alewife Station will benefit many interests in the Boston-Cambridge area.

Boston Basin geology will be served by this project in that it will help to define some of the less well-documented geologic problems associated with the Cambridge Argillite, through which the tunnel is driven.

The geotechnology of the Cambridge Argillite will be better understood. Although many foundation studies in the Boston area have been involved with the Cambridge Argillite, this is probably the largest project of its kind in this lithology. The instrumentation programs monitoring the excavations will provide a unique opportunity to observe the behavior of the rock and soil mass along the alignment as work proceeds. The geologic mapping program will tie these two fields of interest together--the geologic structure and its influence on the geotechnical properties of the rock and soil along the Red Line Extension alignment.

Finally, but not least in importance, the general public will benefit directly by the increased efficiency of the MBTA system by the Red Line Extension completion. Less evident to the public, but just as important to them, is the fact that future projects in the area will utilize lessons learned and techniques employed during the design and construction of the Red Line Extension.

ACKNOWLEDGMENTS

The authors would like to acknowledge the assistance provided through his review and suggestions by Harry Sutcliffe, Project Manager for Bechtel Incorporated on the design and construction support services on the Red Line tunnels. Also appreciated was the assistance and cooperation provided by William Beebe, Project Manager for Morrison-Knudsen, White, Mergentine on the Harvard to Porter tunnels and by Roger Borggaard, Project Manager for Perini Corporation on the Porter to Davis tunnels during the tunnel mapping. The continued interest and assistance provided by Clifford Kaye, Geologist, U.S. Geological Survey,

during his visits to the job sites, with stimulating discussions of the stratigraphy and the geotechnological aspects of the Boston Basin, are recognized and appreciated as well.

REFERENCES

Bechtel Geotechnical Report, 1978, Subsurface investigation for tunnels, Phase 1, 1a, 1b, Red Line extension-northwest, Harvard Square to Davis Square, Cambridge-Somerville, Massachusetts: MBTA contract no. 065-001.

Billings, M. P., 1976, Bedrock geology of the Boston Basin: New England Intercollegiate Geological Conference, 68th Annual Meeting.

Cameron, B., and Naylor, R. S., 1976, General geology of southeastern New England: New England Intercollegiate Geological Conference, 68th Annual Meeting.

Emerson, B. K., 1917, Geology of Massachusetts and Rhode Island: U.S. Geological Survey, Bulletin 597.

Kaye, C. A., 1976, Outline of the Pleistocene geology of the Boston Basin: New England Intercollegiate Geological Conference, 68th Annual Meeting.

Kaye, C. A., 1979, Engineering geologic framework of the Boston Basin: American Society of Civil Engineers National Convention, Boston.

Keville, F. M., Stangenberg, J. K., Thompson, D. E., and Young, L. W., 1979, MBTA Red Line extension-northwest--impact of geotechnical programs: American Society of Civil Engineers National Convention, Boston. Not cited.

LaForge, L., 1932, Geology of the Boston area, Massachusetts: U.S. Geological Survey, Bulletin 839.

Pollard, M., 1965, Age, origin and structure of the post-Cambrian Boston strata, Massachusetts: Geological Society of America Bulletin, v. 76, p. 1065-1068.

UMTA project no. MA-23-9008, 1978, Red Line extension, Harvard Square to Arlington Heights: Specifications for MBTA contract no. 091-105, Porter Square to Harvard Square tunnels and shafts, Cambridge City dump and material hauling, Cambridge, Massachusetts.

UMTA project no. MA-23-9008, 1978, Red Line extension, Harvard Square to Arlington Heights: Specifications for MBTA contract no. 091-106, Davis Square to Porter Square tunnels and shafts, Somerville/Cambridge, Massachusetts.

Weston Geophysical Engineers, Inc., 1977, Seismic survey, MBTA Red Line extension - Harvard to Davis Squares, for Bechtel Inc.          □

Rock excavations along highways in New England, 6: cuts through schist.

# Geologic factors affecting failure of the Dorchester Tunnel, Boston

## D. D. ASHENDEN
### Metropolitan District Commission, Boston

ABSTRACT

The Dorchester Tunnel is a high pressure (200 psi) water supply tunnel designed to serve the southern Greater Boston area. Constructed between 1968 and 1974, it is 6-1/2 miles long, has a 10 ft concrete-lined internal diameter, and is in bedrock 150-250 ft below the surface. The tunnel is mostly in rocks of the Boston Bay Group (Roxbury Conglomerate and Cambridge Argillite). Water seepage into a few cellars near the tunnel line, commencing almost immediately with initial pressurization in November of 1974, suggested leakage. Subsequent inspection revealed longitudinal cracks (hairline to a maximum of 1/4 in.) in the concrete liner for a distance of about 2500 ft through a section of the tunnel in Cambridge Argillite. This rock is thinly bedded to submassive siltstone to fine-grained sandstone striking N70-80°E and dipping 70°SE. The writer believes failure of the concrete liner is due to a combination of discontinuities in the rock and the internal water pressure in the tunnel. There is considerable evidence for an abundance of subhorizontal joints in the rock throughout the failed section: these fractures are not known to occur beyond the limits of the failure. The internal water pressure caused a vertical compression and movement of the rock above and possibly below the tunnel by the closure of the voids between the sub-horizontal joints. Vertical extension occurred along the sub-horizontal joint or joints nearest the mid-section (springline) of the tunnel causing the concrete liner to tear in tension, producing longitudinal fissures. A total compression and separation of only a small fraction of an inch would have been sufficient.

## TUNNEL DESCRIPTION

The Dorchester Tunnel is a high pressure (200 psi) water supply tunnel constructed and operated by the Metropolitan District Commission (MDC) for water delivery to the southern Greater Boston area. The tunnel is the most recent MDC water supply tunnel, having been constructed between 1968 and 1974. City Tunnel from the west and City Tunnel Extension to the northeast were constructed in the 1950's. The Dorchester Tunnel extends southeastward for about 6-1/2 miles from shaft 7B (sta. 286+81) in the Chestnut Hill Reservoir area to shaft 7D at Dorchester Lower Mills on the Neponset estuary (Fig. 1). Shaft 7C (sta. 506+92) was the construction shaft and now serves as an intermediate access point used primarily for water distribution to surface mains. The tunnel is circular in cross section, and is lined with one foot or more of concrete to provide a 10 ft finish internal diameter. Invert (floor) elevations range from approximately 100 ft below sea level at shaft 7B to 200 ft below sea level at shaft 7C and 210 ft below sea level at shaft 7D. The tunnel was excavated entirely in bedrock. Excavation was by traditional drill-blast methods except in the section from near shaft 7C to about sta. 548+85, a distance of nearly 4000 ft, where an Alkirk hard-rock tunneller (more commonly known as a mole) was used.

## GEOLOGIC SETTING

The tunnel is mostly in rocks of the Boston Bay Group of the Boston basin consisting of Roxbury Conglomerate, Squantum Tillite, and Cambridge Argillite (Billings, 1976a, b). The Boston basin, approximately coinciding with the Greater Boston area, is bounded on the north by the northern border fault, a thrust with a north over south displacement (Billings, 1976a, b). In addition to the rocks of the Boston Bay Group, the tunnel also passes through rocks of the Mattapan Volcanics, principally in the core of the Mattapan anticline and also immediately southeast of the Mount Hope fault. Richardson (1977) indicates that the tunnel passes through the following structures, all identified in Figure 1.

```
Central anticline shaft 7B (286+81) to 501+40
   includes Stony Brook fault zone 403+50 to 450+00
                                   and 480+00 to 484+55
Roslindale syncline            501+40 to 547+52
Mount Hope fault               547+52
unnamed syncline               547+52 to 562+30
Mattapan anticline             562+30 to 586+18
unnamed syncline               586+18 to 615+40
Lower Falls anticline          615+40 to 622+00
                                        (shaft 7D)
```

Figure 1 is a generalized map of the bedrock geology of the Boston basin and has been adapted from that of Billings (1976a, b). The reader is referred to those papers for descriptions of the rock units and structures. Structure of the rock units south of the Mount Hope fault is complex. The relationship of the Neponset fault to these units and whether or not it cuts them is unclear (Billings, 1976b; Richardson, 1977). The failed section of the tunnel, however, is restricted to the Cambridge Argillite in the Roslindale syncline north of the Mount Hope fault and, therefore, with the exception of that rock unit, further description of the rocks and their structural relations is beyond the scope of this paper.

Shaft 7C (sta. 506+92) is in the Cambridge Argillite of the Roslindale syncline, and the use of

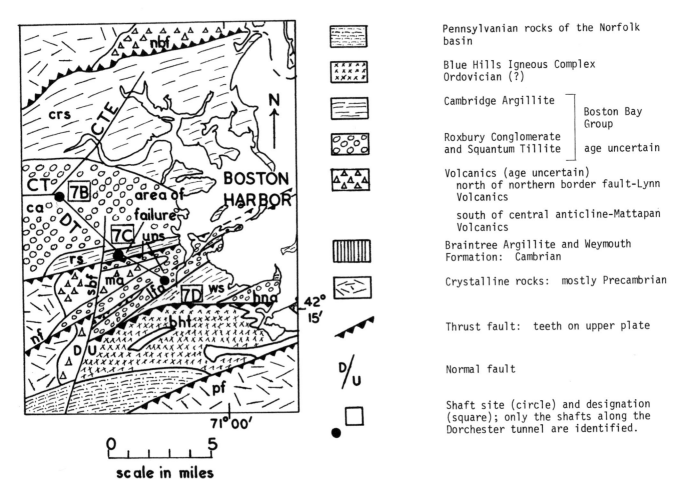

Figure 1. Generalized bedrock geologic map of Boston area (adapted from Billings, 1976 a, b). Water supply tunnels indicated: CT-City Tunnel; CTE-City Tunnel Extension; DT-Dorchester Tunnel (shafts 7B, 7C, and 7D). Thrust faults: nbf-northern border fault; mhf-Mount Hope fault; nf-Neponset fault; bht-Blue Hills thrust; pf-Ponkapoag fault. Normal fault: sbf-Stony Brook fault. Folds: crs-Charles River syncline; ca-central anticline; rs-Roslindale syncline; uns-unnamed syncline; ma-Mattapan anticline; lfa-Lower Falls anticline; ws-Wollaston syncline; hna-Houghs Neck anticline.

the mole was started in this unit at about 300 ft southeast of shaft 7C. Excavation with the mole was toward shaft 7D but, upon its reaching the Mount Hope fault and passing into the Mattapan Volcanics, it was determined that the mole was incapable of excavating those rocks satisfactorily, and it was removed from the tunnel. Traditional drill-blast excavation was substituted to complete the tunnel to shaft 7D. These relationships are indicated in Figure 2.

## FAILURE

The finished tunnel was put under full pressure in November of 1974. Almost immediately, within a few days at the most, water inflow occurred in the cellars of a few houses located near the tunnel line and about 2000 ft southeast of shaft 7C. The basements of these few houses had been excavated to or even a short distance into the Cambridge Argillite on a small localized bedrock high covered by only a few feet of overburden in an area where overburden otherwise runs 40-50 ft thick. The water,

subsequently shown to be leaking from the tunnel into the fracture system of the rock, presumably in most cases was dispersed at the bedrock-overburden contact and simply added to the ground water in the overburden. In such areas the water did not show on the ground surface. Those cellars excavated to or into the bedrock, however, were either in direct contact with the joints and or faults transmitting the water from below or very close to them. The pressure in the tunnel was more than adequate to raise the water to the surface, and the elevation of the local groundwater high has been shown to fluctuate directly with application of pressure to the water in the tunnel. Had it not been for this localized bedrock high with several cellars approaching it or even cut into it, the tunnel leakage would probably not have been suspected and the damage not known to this day.

The tunnel was drained and inspected because of the suspected failure. Inspection revealed extensive cracking in the concrete liner from about sta. 510+00

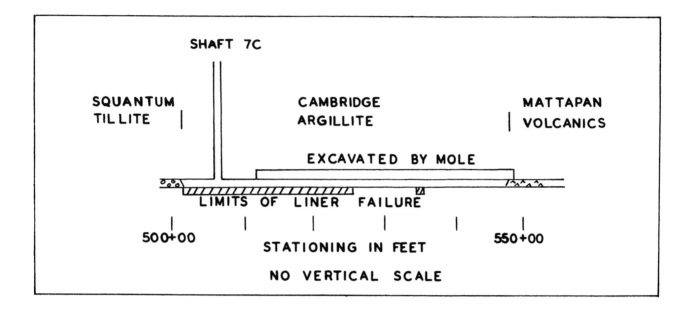

Figure 2. Diagram showing comparative extent of liner failure and use of the "mole" in the Roslindale syncline section of the Dorchester Tunnel.

(308 ft southeast of shaft 7C) to about sta. 525+00. Limited damage also existed near sta. 535+00 and from sta. 510+00 to the northwest through the section of the tunnel directly below shaft 7C and on as far as about sta. 500+00 (or about 150 ft northwest of the contact between the Cambridge Argillite and the Squantum Tillite) (Fig. 2). The cracks were almost entirely longitudinal or parallel to the tunnel axis. As far as could be determined they are flat or nearly so but actual measurement of their dips proved to be impossible. The cracks occurred principally along the springline (midsection) or by separation of the construction joint (described below) between the arch and the invert sections which had been poured separately. The cracks ranged from hairline up to 1/8 in. but locally were as great as 1/4 in. in width. Some extended for tens of feet before dying out only to be replaced by another crack slightly higher or lower on the tunnel wall in an en echelon manner. There was no doubt that the cracks were sufficient to pass significant quantities of water under high pressure from the tunnel into the fracture system of the rock. Figure 3 consists of two sketches traced from photographs showing typical cracking along the springline. There were also areas where the cracks were more complex, multiple, or branching.

Figure 4 is a diagrammatic cross section through the tunnel indicating a typical failed section of the concrete. In this example there is a fracture in the southwest wall near the springline. On the northeast wall the tunnel is broken at the construction joint. Generally the tunnel liner was cracked at two locations around its circumference, one on either wall. The great bulk of the fracturing occurred either at the springline or at the construction joint, but at some stations fractures occurred at other points around the liner. Cracks were rare in the

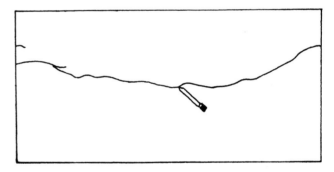

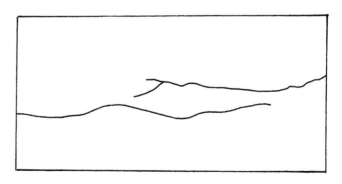

Figure 3. Sketches from photographs showing typical fractures along the springline of the tunnel. Pencil stuck in crack gives scale. Cracks range from about 1/16 in. to 1/4 in. Lower figure shows an echelon style of fracturing commonly observed.

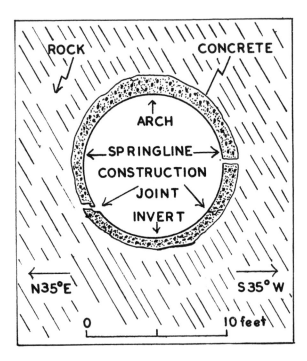

Figure 4. Cross section of Dorchester Tunnel looking downtunnel (toward shaft 7D) showing cracks in concrete liner. Size of cracks is exaggerated. Lines in rock represent trace of apparent strike of bedding in a N35E-S35W vertical section.

invert or top of the arch.

To understand the separation of the construction joint (also known as the cold joint), a digression into the method of concrete liner emplacement is necessary. The concrete was poured in two stages. First, the invert (lower section) was poured from shaft 7C to shaft 7D up to the level of the construction joint (Fig. 4). Note that there is a keyway on the top of the sides of the invert section. The arch was then poured from shaft 7D back toward shaft 7C, using forms that rolled along the keyway of the invert section. Where the fresh concrete of the arch met the older, long-set concrete of the invert, the construction joint formed. This contact is less well bonded than the main mass of concrete and is a zone of weakness in the liner.

The initial inspection of the tunnel gave the impression that the liner had failed extensionally and that the arch had been driven upward, separating along the construction joint or fracturing the concrete of the arch in tension near the spring line. The driving force for such an extension along a vertical axis would have been the internal water pressure. For the concrete to move in this manner, even a fraction of an inch, meant that the rock behind the concrete liner also presumably gave way and moved. An unreinforced concrete liner for a high pressure conduit is like an eggshell, and its tensile strength is inadequate to withstand such a force. The rock is expected to serve as a rigid backing to the liner, to hold it in place, and to contain the

pressure. In this case it did not. The problem is why? The facts to be noted are these.

- Damage to the liner was confined to the Cambridge Argillite of the Roslindale syncline (with very minor damage extending 150 ft into the Squantum Tillite).

- Damage occurred in both the moled and drill-blast excavated sections although it was far more extensive in the moled section.

- About 1700 ft of moled section in the Cambridge Argillite was unaffected.

- Shaft 7C located within the damaged area was itself completely unaffected except that cracks in the tunnel do occur directly under the junction of the shaft and the tunnel.

Thus, it is seen that, although the failure is restricted to the Cambridge Argillite of the Roslindale syncline and occurs primarily in the moled section, much of the moled section in the Cambridge Argillite is unaffected. But the drill-blast section in that rock is affected. It would seem, therefore, that it is inaccurate to summarily conclude that the Cambridge Argillite as such is poor rock or that the mole was to blame, or some combination of the two. Other factors must be examined and considered.

GEOLOGY OF THE FAILED SECTION

Petrographic description of the rock is based upon the writer's examination and study of diamond drill cores made for original planning and 12 thin sections made from them. The Cambridge Argillite is not exposed in outcrops in the immediate vicinity. Direct examination of the rock during the inspection of the tunnel failure was limited to three small (about 1 ft x 2 ft) inspection ports cut through the concrete liner. Structural description is based upon unpublished data from Billings (1968), who mapped the tunnel 300 ft from either side of shaft 7C and from Richardson's original field notes on the mapping of the tunnel through the Roslindale syncline.

The Cambridge Argillite of the Roslindale syncline is thinly bedded to sub-massive siltstone to fine-grained sandstone. It can be subdivided into two members with a contact at approximately sta. 519+10. These are summarized in Table 1 below. Member A occurs northwest of sta. 519+10 and is a dark gray siltstone with layers formed of prominent couplets. The basal light-gray, coarser-grained, silt-sized layer is composed predominantly of poorly-sorted, angular, quartz grains grading upward into a darker gray to black, very fine-grained layer. Composition of this darker, fine-grained layer of the couplet cannot be determined in thin section and is not known to the author. Graded bedding between the coarser and finer-grained members of the couplet was observed in one thin section and has been reported in outcrop (Billings, 1976a, b). Cores of the argillite display numerous breaks (bedding-plane partings) between the upper finer-grained layers and the next silt layer. The surface along the partings is usually smooth, shiny, and slippery. Thickness of the couplet is variable but 1/8 in. to 1/4 in. is typical. Member B occurs southeast of sta. 519+10 and is lighter gray, coarser-grained siltstone to fine-grained sandstone with only minor darker, finer-grained layers. Bedding plane partings along these darker, finer-grained layers are comparatively rare in member B, which as a whole is more sandy and massive than member A. Characteristics of the two members are summarized in Table 1. Minor mafic intrusives, primarily parallel to the bedding, are present in both members. The mafic rocks are now greatly altered.

TABLE 1. COMPARISON OF THE TWO MEMBERS OF THE CAMBRIDGE ARGILLITE

| Member A | Member B |
|---|---|
| northwest of sta. 519+10. | southeast of sta. 519+10. |
| finer-grained; silt maximum particle size. | coarser-grained; up to fine sand-sized particles - less very fine-grained material; in general more sandy. |
| rock thinly layered in couplets. | rock more massive. |
| bedding-plane partings common. | bedding-plane partings much less abundant. |
| joint frequency greater. | joint frequency less. |

Bedding throughout the failed section of the tunnel consistently strikes N70-80°C and dips 70° to the southeast. The strike makes an angle of 45-55° with the trend of the tunnel. The rock has both high-angle fractures (joints and faults) and also low angle fractures. The frequency of fractures is somewhat greater in member A than in member B. The fault zones are now mostly healed with veins of quartz, calcite, and sulfide. Secondary calcite and sulfide are abundant both in veins and also as general accumulations throughout the rock.

FACTORS AFFECTING FAILURE

MDC engineers and also those of the MDC's consultant, Haley & Aldrich, Inc., of Cambridge, Massachusetts, are generally agreed that the internal water pressure in the tunnel was transmitted through the liner and caused compression of the rock. There is, however, no general agreement among those who have considered this problem as to the precise mechanism for the rock compression and why it occurred only where it did. The observations and suggestions rendered below are the personal conclusions of the writer and are not to be construed as an official MDC explanation for the failure of the tunnel liner.

Considerable sub-horizontal jointing was reported both by Billings and Richardson in the Cambridge Argillite of the Roslindale syncline between stas. 501+85 and 523+50. No other such jointing was reported except locally at about sta. 535+00. These positions correspond very closely with the failed sections of the tunnel and are probably more than coincidental. Two of the flat fractures reported by Richardson correspond with some of the most prominent

cracks in the tunnel liner. There are probably more sub-horizontal joints than were reported, only the most prominent having been recorded. Photographs taken during construction through this section of the tunnel also reveal many subhorizontal joints. In three locations small sections of concrete liner (about 1 ft x 2 ft) were removed across a crack in the liner for inspection purposes. In all three cases the cracks in the liner were extensions of sub-horizontal joints in the rock (Fig. 5). One of the joints illustrated in Figure 5 was open about 1/16 in. and partially filled with rhombs of calcite and cubes of pyrite. This is obviously a very old joint in which there has been void space for a very long time. If numerous sub-horizontal joints occur in the rock at tunnel level, they are also assumed to occur both above and below the tunnel. The writer is of the opinion that the presence of abundant sub-horizontal fractures in the rock is the primary cause of the failure. Other factors such as the presence of additional high-angle joints and the bedding-plane parting probably compounded the problem by reducing the overall coherence of the rock mass. No tectonic explanation for the presence of the sub-horizontal fractures will be attempted here, but it is of interest to note that they are mainly restricted to that section of the Roslindale syncline 1800 ft ± southeast of the Squantum Tillite (measured perpendicular to strike, not along the tunnel axis). Also, they occur in both members A and B described above, but are not present (as far as is known) in the Squantum Tillite or Roxbury Conglomerate of the central anticline.

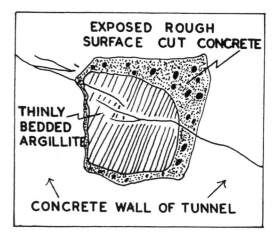

Figure 5. Diagrammatic view inspection port 1 at Sta. 513+05, southwest wall. Shows continuity of fracture in concrete wall of tunnel and old joint in rock. Joint has voids partially filled with calcite and pyrite.

Under full head (200 psi) the internal water pressure acted equally in all directions through the liner. The rock, however, was compressible vertically by the squeezing together of relatively closely spaced sub-horizontal joints (Fig. 6). It may even be that there had been some sagging in the arch between the time of excavation and emplacement of the concrete liner (2 years) but this is not known for a fact. In effect, the tunnel had insufficient solid rock cover (despite its being 200 ft below the top of ledge), so that the vertical component of the water pressure pushed the arch upward and/or even perhaps the invert downward. The rock would have had to yield by only a small fraction of an inch to cause the concrete liner to tear in tension. The sub-horizontal joint or joints closest to springline could have served as a plane of separation, the rock above and below being compressed vertically by the pushing together and closure of the voids along the sub-horizontal joints. The concrete tore in tension along that plane of separation, so that the cracks in the tunnel liner are essentially extensions of the fractures in the rock. A compressive movement of a fraction of an inch would have been sufficient to cause failure. Where there were no sub-horizontal joints to serve as planes of separation near the springline, the arch section was simply lifted off and separated from the invert section along the construction joint, a point of weakness in the tunnel liner by the nature of its construction outlined above.

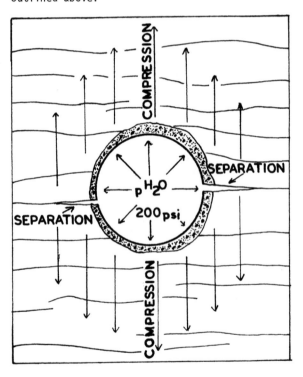

Figure 6. Diagrammatic cross-sectional view of tunnel and sub-horizontal fractures in surrounding rock. Internal water pressure (pH2O) causes vertical compression by squeezing together joints above and possibly below tunnel, causing separation along joint nearest springline and fracturing concrete liner. Size of fractures in liner is exaggerated.

CAUTION FOR FUTURE TUNNELS

In the past, engineering practice has been to plan the depth of high-pressure water-supply tunnels sufficiently deep in bedrock such that the litho-static load exceeds that of the hydraulic head.

Under such conditions the rock has been assumed to be immovable and has been relied upon to serve as a rigid backing for the concrete liner and hold it in place. Support or reinforcement has been restricted to serve primarily as a means of keeping the tunnel open during excavation and to protect the workers in areas of spalling rock or squeezing ground. No further consideration has been given to the opposite condition, the pushing out of the rock by high pressures in the finished tunnel, beyond the initial theoretical considerations of placing the tunnel sufficiently deep for the rock to hold the pressure. Experience in the Dorchester Tunnel has indicated that, in addition, a full assessment of the rock is needed during excavation with regard to how water pressure may affect it. Suspect areas could then be provided with a reinforced liner or some other precaution could be taken to insure that failure is less likely.

CONCLUSIONS

Data collected by Billings and by Richardson in mapping the exposed Cambridge Argillite during construction of the Dorchester tunnel indicate the presence of sub-horizontal joints through the section which subsequently failed. Such low-angle fractures are not reported from the rock of the other sections of the tunnel which did not fail. Close correspondence of the failed section of the tunnel with rock from which the low-angle fractures were reported is taken to be more than coincidental. The force of the internal water pressure contained within the concrete liner of the tunnel was transmitted through the liner to the rock and compressed the rock vertically by squeezing together and partially closing the voids between the sub-horizontal joints. Such compression of the rock, probably by only a small fraction of an inch, caused separation and opening along the sub-horizontal fracture nearest the springline of the tunnel. This separation tore the concrete of the liner in tension producing the longitudinal cracks along the springline of the tunnel. Thus, it is concluded that the concrete liner of the tunnel failed by vertical extension caused by the force of the internal water pressure on the rock, which has voids and discontinuities along closely spaced sub-horizontal joints.

ACKNOWLEDGMENTS

M. P. Billings reviewed a preliminary draft. Professor Billings served as geological consultant during construction of most of the MDC tunnels in the Boston area including the Dorchester tunnel. Although now retired, he has followed the problem of the failure with some interest and has assisted the writer with several discussions. John Shea, resident MDC engineer in charge of repairs to the tunnel, also reviewed the manuscript for accuracy of the engineering data and details.

REFERENCES

Billings, M.P., 1976a, Geology of the Boston basin: Geological Society of America, Memoir 146, p. 5-30.

Billings, M.P., 1976b, Bedrock geology of the Boston basin, in Cameron, B., ed., Geology of southeastern New England:  Guidebook for the 68th annual meeting, New England Inter-collegiate Geologic Conference, p. 28-45.

Richardson, S.M., 1977, Geology of the Dorchester tunnel:  Journal of the Boston Society of Civil Engineers, v. 63, no. 4, p. 247-270.  □

Rock excavations along highways in New England, 7: mainly pre-split.

# Pressure grouting to repair
# the Dorchester Water Tunnel, Boston

## J. P. DUGAN, JR.
## Haley & Aldrich, Inc.

ABSTRACT

The paper describes the results of pressure grouting, instrumentation, testing and final inspection in connection with repairs of a deep pressure tunnel in rock. The 10 ft diameter Dorchester water tunnel, constructed in Boston from 1969 through 1974, is lined with unreinforced concrete. It runs in bed rock 250 feet below ground surface and over 200 feet beneath rock surface. Inspection in 1976 disclosed a pattern of longitudinally-oriented, structural cracks in the concrete lining over a tunnel length of approximately 1500 feet. Following investigations, plans and specifications were prepared for pressure grouting to repair the cracked lining. Pressure grouting was done from within the tunnel. A neat, type III Portland cement grout was used, with a maximum injection pressure of 400 psi. Following grouting of the primary stage holes, secondary stage grouting was undertaken at split spacing. Results of water pressure tests, grout take and core borings were used to evaluate the effectiveness of the grouting. After the grouting was completed, a test section of the tunnel lining was instrumented to measure the behavior of the tunnel and adjacent rock during pressure testing. Instrumentation included diametric convergence meters, strain guages, extensometers and piezometers. Over a period of 1 1/2 months, the tunnel was water tested under service pressures. In addition to the instrumentation readings, observation well measurements were made to observe the effect of water flow from the tunnel on groundwater levels in the area. Finally, the tunnel was drained and its condition inspected.

INTRODUCTION

The Dorchester tunnel, constructed between 1969 and 1974, extends 6.3 miles from shaft 7B in Chestnut Hill to shaft 7D in Dorchester Lower Mills. The tunnel measures 10 feet in inside diameter and is lined with unreinforced concrete, designed to be 8 in. minimum and 13 in. average thickness. In the section through which the grouting work was done (sta. 510 through sta. 536), the tunnel invert ranges from about elevation -200 to -202. The tunnel in this area normally carries water under an operating pressure of about 205 psi, which corresponds to a piezometric head of elevation 274, measured in reference to Boston base datum.

Shortly after the tunnel was placed in service in November 1974, the basements of certain homes in the Johnson Road area became flooded. Tests made by the owners, the Metropolitan District Commission (MDC), subsequently confirmed that the flooding was the result of water flow under pressure from the Dorchester tunnel. Inspection of the tunnel indicated that the lining was significantly cracked, with major water flow occurring between sta. 510 and sta. 523. Following a detailed geological and geotechnical investigation, a decision was made to grout the fractured section of the tunnel. The grouting was planned in order to reduce water flow from the tunnel into the rock and to consolidate and strengthen the jointed rock mass.

In addition to the grouting repairs, an instrumentation program was planned and implemented to monitor performance of a test section of the tunnel.

GROUTING

Materials and Equipment

Grout used in the tunnel consisted of a neat mixture of type III Portland cement and water. The grout was mixed in the tunnel at the work area. Major components of the grout plant consisted of:

- mixer      Acker "Colgrouter" high-speed, colloidal mixer;

- holding tank      150 gallon capacity holding tank with agitator;

- grout pump      Moyno, progressive helical-type pump, model 6M4 type CDQ.

1-1/2 in. diameter (EX size) diamond-tipped rotary drills were used for drilling grout holes. Connections for grouting consisted of mechanical packers.

Water pressure test equipment consisted of a model 6M4 type CDQ pump, and a type 5 high-pressure water meter, manufactured by Neptune Meters Company.

Procedures

All grouting work was done from inside the tunnel. Grout holes were drilled in a ring pattern, with four 20 ft long holes per ring and primary rings spaced 13 ft center to center. Holes were angled at 45 degrees to the lining to optimize interception of bedding plane fractures. Primary grouting was undertaken over a total length of 1800 feet of tunnel.

Secondary stage grouting, done at split spacing, followed primary grouting. In light of the good results of the primary grouting, secondary grouting was limited to a combined total of 400 linear feet, over five selected critical areas.

Following drilling, each hole was pressure washed with a jet of air and water and pressure tested to evaluate the groutability of the rock.

Grout mixtures ranged from 1:1 to 4:1 water: cement ratios (by volume) (7.5 to 30 gals/bag). Holes were started with thin mixtures and thickened depending on rate of take. All holes were grouted to a refusal condition, defined as flow less than two gallons in a 10-minute period at 400 psi pressure.

The work proceeded around-the-clock, five days per week. Grouting was monitored with two technicians in the tunnel on each shift, controlling mixes and pressures, observing refusal conditions, drilling, and pressure testing.

NX core borings were used throughout to check the effectiveness of the grouting. Cores were observed for visual evidence of grout travel, and were water tested and grouted to check the rock permeability.

## SUMMARY AND EVALUATION OF GROUTING DATA

### Primary Stage Grouting Data

Water Pressure Tests. The water pressure tests on primary grout holes confirmed that the permeability of the rock mass is highly variable, as would be anticipated based on the discontinuous nature of the rock. Water test flow rates in primary holes ranged from 0 to over 100 gpm per 100 psi test pressure. Based on pressure tests and other data and observations, five sections of relatively high permeability were identified. Water pressure test data on primary holes for these sections are summarized in Table 1.

The following factors led to uncertainty in evaluation of water pressure test results:

- Piezometric head in the rock mass surrounding the tunnel was unknown.

- Some of the water pumped into the drill hole may have short circuited back into the tunnel through lining fractures.

Cement Take. Cement take in primary holes was also highly variable. In general, high cement take occurred in areas of relatively high water test flows. Cement take for 588 drill holes totaled 4641 bags. A histogram of the cement take along the tunnel in terms of the number of bags of cement injected per ring of four grout

TABLE 1.  SUMMARY OF WATER PRESSURE TEST FLOW BEFORE AND AFTER GROUTING

| Section | Number of secondary holes | Average and (range) of water test flow in gpm per 100 psi | | Ratio of test flow after to before primary grouting |
|---------|---------------------------|-----------------------------|------------------------------|-----------------------------------------------------|
| | | Before primary grouting | After primary grouting | |
| 513+96 to 515+00 | 36 | 13.6 (0.3 to 29.1) | 4.0 (0 to 9.5) | 0.29 |
| 516+30 to 516+95 | 24 | 15.8 (0.4 to 97.0) | 3.0 (0 to 8.8) | 0.19 |
| 519+55 to 520+07 | 20 | 7.8 (0 to 55.0 | 3.0 (0 to 4.3) | 0.38 |
| 522+02 to 523+19 | 40 | 10.2 (0.4 to 25.0 | 3.0 (0 to 8.6) | 0.29 |
| 524+36 to 524+75 | 16 | insufficient data | 2.5 (0 to 5.6) | --- |
| | | | Weighted average for four sections | 0.29 |

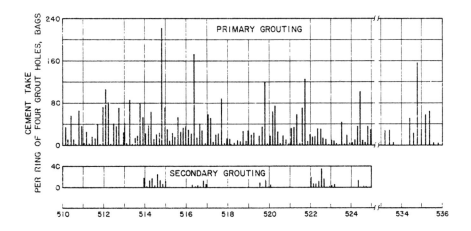

Figure 1. Summary of cement take per ring of grout holes.

holes is shown in Figure 1.

Core Holes. Rock cores were generally drilled in areas where the effectiveness of primary stage grouting was considered uncertain or questionable. The rock cores obtained during the primary stage grouting were examined for the presence of cement grout. Of the 174 joints observed in the cores, a coating or filling of cement was observed on 59 joints, or 34 percent of the total. For the most part, the water pressure test flow and grout take data on the completed core holes confirmed that the rock had been satisfactorily grouted.

Secondary Stage Grouting Data

Secondary stage grouting was undertaken in areas where one or more of the following criteria were applicable.

1. High primary water test flow rate.

2. High primary grout take.

3. High water inflow through cracks prior to grouting.

4. Water flow observed through rock during tunnel construction.

5. High grout take during tunnel construction.

6. Relatively high grout take in core holes.

Comments on results of secondary stage water testing and grouting follow:

Water Inflow and Pressure Test Flow. Substantially less water was observed to be draining into the tunnel during secondary grouting than during primary grouting. Generally, no significant inflow of ground water occurred through secondary drill holes. Holes which were not dry typically dripped water at a slight to moderate rate. At the 100 psi test pressure, 91 of 136 holes (67 percent) did not take water. In most of these holes, water flow was initiated at the 300 psi test pressure. The average water flow per section grouted ranged from 2.5 to 4.0 gpm per 100 psi, with a maximum test flow in one hole of 9.5 gpm per 100 psi. Secondary stage water test data are summarized in Table 1.

Cement Take. Consistent with results of the core hole grouting, relatively low cement take occurred in the secondary holes. Cement take for the 136 holes for secondary grouting totaled 314 bags. A histogram of the secondary stage cement take along the tunnel is included in Figure 1.

Engineering Evaluation

Water Pressure Test Data. (relative permeability of rock). A commonly accepted parameter, particularly in European grouting practice, for judging the permeability of a rock mass based on borehole pressure tests, is the lugeon. One lugeon is equal to a water take of 1 liter/meter/min at an injection pressure of 10 bars (or 150 psi). Converting to the English units used on the project, and considering the approximately 20 ft penetration of the grout holes into the rock,

1 lugeon = 1.2 gpm per 100 psi pressure.

In a paper written on the subject of grouting for dams, Houlsby (1977) indicates that current practice, in cases where the value of water loss is most precious, is to grout to a maximum permeability criterion of one lugeon. This is gener-

TABLE 2. COMPARISON OF CEMENT TAKE DATA FOR PRIMARY AND SECONDARY GROUTING

| Section | Number of secondary holes | Average and (range) of cement take per hole in bags | | Ratio of cement take secondary to primary grouting |
| | | Primary grouting | Secondary grouting | |
|---|---|---|---|---|
| 513+96 to 515+00 | 36 | 15.1 (0 to 166) | 3.1 (0 to 26) | 0.20 |
| 516+30 to 516+95 | 24 | 13.0 (0 to 146) | 1.4 (0 to 7) | 0.11 |
| 519+55 to 520+07 | 20 | 9.4 (0 to 103) | 1.6 (0 to 12) | 0.17 |
| 522+02 to 523+19 | 40 | 6.8 (0 to 50) | 2.9 (0 to 35) | 0.43 |
| 524+36 to 524+75 | 16 | 9.3 (0 to 99) | 1.4 (0 to 13) | 0.15 |
| | | | Weighted Average | 0.24 |

ally considered to be the practical limit for injection of cement grout, and it is not considered necessary to grout rock which has a permeability of less than one lugeon.

For projects in which water loss is considered worth the cost of intensive grouting, a relative permeability value of three lugeons is a commonly used grouting criterion (see Houlsby [1977] and Littlejohn [1975]). Accordingly, with reference to the water test flow data on the project, it appears that 4 gpm per 100 psi pressure is a suitable criterion for assessing the grouting with respect to water leakage from the tunnel.

As noted above, secondary grouting was done primarily in the more permeable sections of the tunnel, and also in sections where the primary grouting may not have been fully effective. The primary stage grouting successfully reduced the rock permeability to acceptable values in the range of 2.5 to 4.0 gpm per 100 psi. The ratios of average water test flows after compared to before primary grouting ranged from 0.19 to 0.38, for an overall average of 0.29 (see Table 1). That is, a 71 percent reduction in average permeability is indicated. Also, the secondary grouting further reduced the rock permeability in the areas considered critical. The effect of the secondary grouting could not be quantified since tertiary stage grouting was not undertaken.

Cement (Grout) Take Data. Table 2 presents a comparison of cement take data for primary and secondary grouting. As indicated, cement take

during secondary grouting was significantly less than during primary grouting. The ratio of average secondary to primary cement takes ranged from 0.11 to 0.43, with an overall average of 0.24. These ratios are consistent with comparison ratios based on the average water test flow data.

Summary. The results of the water test flow and cement take data were evaluated during and immediately upon completion of the secondary grouting work. It was concluded, at that time, that no further grouting was required on the project.

PRESSURE TESTING OF THE TUNNEL

Tunnel Test

After grouting of the tunnel was completed, waste grout and materials were removed, and instrumentation was installed. The tunnel was filled with water and pressurized immediately following the instrumentation installation. Pressure testing activities extended from the beginning of filling on 13 August 1979 through 13 October 1979, when the tunnel was unwatered to permit inspection.

During the final period of the test, flow measurements were made by the MDC Water Division to determine the rate at which water must be pumped into the tunnel to maintain constant pressure. Results of the flow tests are summarized as follows:

| Elevation of piezometric head in tunnel (ft) | Rate of water pumped into tunnel (gpm) |
|---|---|
| 261 | 269 |
| 277 | 309 |

These piezometric head values correspond to approximate minimum and maximum operating head levels in the tunnel.

Basement Conditions During Tunnel Test

Flooding of basements of certain homes on Johnson Road was the first observed effect of the cracked pressure tunnel. In particular, the house at 31 Johnson Road experienced nearly continuous flow of water into the basement during the time the tunnel was in service from November 1974 to October 1976. This basement, as well as those at other locations of previous flooding, was observed by MDC personnel at times during the tunnel test period, and there was no observed or reported condition of basement water seepage.

INSTRUMENTATION

General

A test section at sta. 513+00 was instrumented in order to measure the behavior of the tunnel and adjacent rock at that location during the pressure testing. Station 513+00 was selected for the following reasons.

●  It is the most highly cracked section of the tunnel.

●  Detailed information on the rock was available from core borings made during earlier studies.

●  It was relatively close to the utility shaft. Thus, lengths of readout cables were within workable limits.

Use of instrumentation to measure movements and water pressures for a deep pressure tunnel is essentially unprecedented, and the work represents state-of-the-art design of instrumentation systems. The following sections provide general descriptions of the instrumentation types and installation methods and summarize the data obtained.

Instrumentation Systems

Tunnel Diameter Deflections. Redundant measurements were obtained from two types of systems, as described below.

Sonic probe convergence meters. Two sonic probe convergence meters were used to measure vertical and horizontal dimater deflection of the tunnel. The sonic probe device, manufactured by IRAD Gage, Inc., of Lebanon, New Hampshire, uses magneto-strictive properties of special components to permit measurement of movement between two points. The meters were installed by bolting to the tunnel lining.

Induction coil convergence meters. Two induction coil convergence meters were also used to measure vertical and horizontal deflection of the tunnel lining. These instruments were designed and fabricated by Haley & Aldrich, Inc., utilizing one-inch diameter induction coils manufactured by Bison Instrument Company. At one installation, one coil was mounted near the face of the lining and a second coil was mounted approximately one inch apart and attached to a 2 in. diameter PVC pipe bolted to the diametrically opposite point on the tunnel lining. Change in distance between the two coils, which is the diametrical deflection of the tunnel, is correlated to the intensity of current induced in one coil due to current passed through the other coil.

Crack and Joint Deformations. Lining deformations at existing cracks and at the construction joints between the arch and invert sections were measured primarily with induction coil strain gauges and also with a limited number of mechanical strain gauges.

Induction coil strain gauges. A total of 14 induction coil strain gauges were employed to measure crack and joint movements. Each gauge consisted of a pair of Bison-manufactured, one-inch diameter coil units, with the coils mounted on opposite sides of a crack or joint. Crack or joint movement was correlated to signal output induced in one coil by the other, as described above for the convergence meters.

Mechanical strain gauges. Five scratch-type mechanical strain gauges were also mounted on opposite sides of lining cracks and joints. The gauge, manufactured by Prewitt Associates, operates by scribing marks on a brass disk as movement occurs between the anchored end points of the gauge. When the tunnel was drained following testing, the brass disks were removed and read with the aid of a special magnifying instrument.

Bedrock Deformations Adjacent to the Lining. Both single and multiple point extensometers were utilized to measure deformation behavior in the rock outside the lining.

Multiple-point sonic probe extensometers. Five-point sonic probe extensometers were installed at orientations of 0, 90, 180, and 270 degrees at the test section. The units were grouted into 2 1/2 in. diameter drill holes, with points at distances of 5, 10, 15, 20 and 30 ft beyond the inside face of the tunnel lining. The boreholes were grouted after the extensometer rods were installed. Each extensometer provides a direct reading of the distances between a sensing head mounted on the lining and each of the five points grouted into the rock.

### Single-point induction coil extensometers.

Four single-point extensometers were installed at orientations of 45, 135, 225 and 315 degrees, at the test section. The units were installed and grouted into 1 1/2 in. diameter drill holes, and utilized one point at a depth of 10 ft beyond the lining and a reference point mounted on the lining. The units were designed and fabricated by Haley & Aldrich, Inc., using 1 in. diameter Bison induction coils. Movement was measured between a coil mounted on the lining and a second coil about one inch away, which was mounted on a 1/4 in. diameter aluminum rod anchored by grout into the rock at a 10 ft distance from the lining. PVC sleeves were placed over the extensometer rods to isolate them from the grout between the anchor point and lining.

### Water Pressure in the Rock and Tunnel.

Four piezometers were installed in the rock at a distance of 20 ft from the lining, to measure piezometric head in the rock during tunnel testing. A fifth piezometer was mounted on the inside of the tunnel in order to determine the piezometric head in the tunnel at the test section.

The piezometers were model PW-500 vibrating wire piezometers, manufactured by IRAD Gage, Inc. Installation in the rock began with drilling of a 3 in. diameter hole to depths of 15 to 30 ft. The piezometer was then enclosed in a sand bag and placed to a depth of 10 ft into the hole, leaving the remainder of each hole open. A bentonite seal was then formed adjacent to the sand bag and the remainder of the hole was sealed with cement grout.

### Temperature.

Thermistors were mounted within each of the five piezometers. These permitted monitoring of the temperature of the water in the tunnel and also within the rock.

### Cabling and Readout Equipment.

With the exception of the mechanical strain gauges, all instruments were read remotely, utilizing electrical cables. The cables extended over a distance of about 770 ft, from the test section of sta. 513 in the tunnel to the readout equipment near the top of the utility shaft. Induction coil readout utilized four sheilded, twelve-conductor cables, while the other instruments each utilized a separate, shielded multi-conductor cable.

## Data

A set of readings was routinely obtained once every three hours, every day, for the duration of the testing. Additional readings were made at times to better document the effects of certain test operations.

It is emphasized that the instrumentation measured the tunnel behavior at the location of the test section only, and the results should not be considered to be typical or representative of the overall tunnel performance. To the contrary, the test section was located where the tunnel had displayed the most intensive fracturing and movement. Therefore, tunnel deformations measured by the instrumentation could be considered to be greater than those at most other locations.

### Tunnel Diameter Deflections.

Results from the two independent types of instruments agreed well. The data indicated that, at the test section, the tunnel diameter increased up to 0.19 in. vertically and contracted up to 0.07 in. horizontally. The movement was relatively elastic, with net changes in diameter ranging from only 0.01 to 0.04 in.

### Crack and Joint Deformations.

The 16 induction coil gauges indicated variable response of cracks and joints in the lining to the pressure test. At eight locations, or one half the total number of gauge pairs, significant opening of existing cracks and joints was measured. At these locations, the total movement during the test ranged from 0.05 in. to 0.40 in. At the remaining instrumented locations, either no movement or a closing of the crack width was noted.

Net movement after completion of the test was generally significantly less than the peak value during the test. At two locations net opening of cracks equal to 0.17 in. and 0.20 in. was indicated by the data. These were not consistent with the visual inspection made after the tunnel test, which showed that net crack openings of this magnitude did not occur.

Of the five Prewitt scratch gauges, only one gauge showed movement, with the crack opening of 0.09 in. measured.

### Bedrock Deformations Adjacent to the Lining.

Interpretation of the extensometer data raises questions regarding the validity of some of this information. The movements are interpreted by assuming that the deepest anchor point is fixed and does not move during the test.

The extensometer data show that, at the test location, the tunnel diameter increased a maximum of about 0.03 in. vertically and contracted about 0.05 in. horizontally. The vertical movements do not agree well with a maximum vertical diameter increase of 0.19 in. based on convergence meter data. However, the horizontal movements show good agreement with convergence meter results, which indicate 0.05 in. and 0.07 in. maximum decrease in diameter.

The vertically-oriented extensometers indicate an inconsistent trend of movement with depth in the rock. The horizontally-oriented extensometers indicate that about one-half of the total movement occurred within a 5 ft depth behind the lining.

At the sonic probe extensometers, net movement at all positions after the tunnel test ranged from 0.00 to 0.01 in.

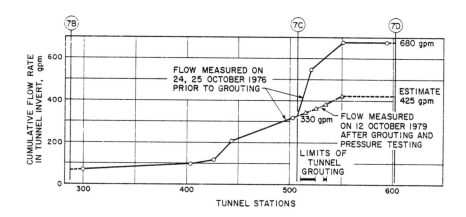

Figure 2.  Measured water inflow before and after grouting.

Water Pressure.  The piezometers showed an essentially instantaneous increase in water pressure in the rock as water is applied to the tunnel.  Similarly, the pressure readings dropped as the pressure was removed and the tunnel was drained.  Prior to the start of the test, two of the three functional piezometers showed piezometric heads of elevation 30 to 35, corresponding to levels about 10 ft below the normal range of ground water in the area.  At these piezometers, the piezometric head stabilized during the test at elevations of 190 and 225.  These levels were about 30 ft and 65 ft less than the piezometric head in the tunnel.

One piezometer showed piezometric head levels very close to those existing within the tunnel at all stages of the test.  It is possible that the grout seal at this piezometer was faulty, or that the piezometer intercepted a joint which communicates directly to an open crack or joint in the lining.

Temperatures.  Data from the thermistors in the piezometers was quite consistent, indicating temperatures in the tunnel and in the rock in the range of 52 to 55 degrees Fahrenheit during the test period.

TUNNEL INSPECTION AFTER TESTING

Tunnel Condition

In summary, there appeared to be no significant change in the tunnel condition after pressure testing, as compared to the condition after the grouting was completed and prior to testing.  The lining was observed to be essentially tight with no specific locations of concentrated leakage.  Some cracks were seeking water very slowly, as they had prior to the tunnel test.  It was con-

sidered impractical and unnecessary to attempt to totally seal off all water penetration through the tunnel cracks and joints.  Existing cracks and the construction joints were observed to be essentially closed tight.  Also, no new cracks were observed due to the testing.  The conditions of cracks which were monitored for movement in the test section at sta. 513+00 were observed closely.  None of the cracks were open.  For the most part, gauge locations at which hairline cracks were observed corresponded with those gauges which had indicated some opening of the crack or joint during the tunnel test.

Water Inflow

Water flow measurements were made at approximately 500 to 1000 feet intervals during the inspection on 12 October 1979, after the tunnel was tested.  The data and subsequent calculations indicate that, with the tunnel drained, water inflow occurs between sta. 502 and sta. 550, at a uniform rate of 1.9 gpm per 1000 feet of tunnel.

Figure 2 presents plots of measured water inflow both before and after grouting.  As indicated, inflow rate after grouting and testing represents a substantial reduction, compared to flow rates calculated during the October 1976 inspection, made prior to grouting.  Also, Figure 2 indicates that the inflow rate in the repaired section of tunnel is comparable to the inflow rate in the tunnel section between shafts 7B and 7C, which did not require repair.

SUMMARY

A cement grouting program was undertaken to repair an 1800 ft long section of the Dorchester Tunnel, a deep pressure tunnel in rock.  The purpose of the grouting was to seal the rock surrounding the tunnel to reduce leakage and to strengthen and consolidate the rock mass.

The grouting was carried on from within the tunnel. Primary stage drilling and pressure testing confirmed the highly permeable nature of portions of the jointed rock. Significant cement take was measured throughout primary stage grouting, and varied up to a maximum of 166 bags injected through a 20 ft deep drill hole.

Secondary stage grouting, with drill holes at split-spacing, was done in selected sections. The water pressure test and cement take data confirmed the effectiveness of the primary stage grouting in reducing the rock mass permeability. Additional grout injected during the secondary stage further reduced permeabilities and strengthened the rock in critical areas.

After grouting was completed, instrumentation was installed at a test section to measure behavior of the tunnel under pressure. The tunnel was then filled and tested, under in-service pressure conditions. Although measurements indicated that some water flowed from the tunnel when pressurized, basements of homes above the tunnel alignment, which had flooded before the grouting repair, remained dry.

Overall, the unique instrumentation system installed at the test section performed well. The data indicated that the tunnel, at that location, expanded up to 0.19 in. on the vertical diameter, and cracks opened as much as 0.40 in. under pressure. Measured movements at the test section are likely to be greater than those at most other sections of the tunnel.

The grouting substantially sealed cracks and joints in the lining against water inflow with the tunnel drained. Based on observations made by experienced MDC personnel, the condition of the grouted section of tunnel is equivalent to or better than typical conditions of other tunnels in the system. With the exception of the grouted cracks, the lining remains in sound condition after testing. Inflow through the repaired section is generally consistent with inflow levels through sections of tunnel that did not require repair.

## ACKNOWLEDGMENTS

The grouting work was included in a contract prepared and monitored by the Metropolitan District Commission for repairs to the Dorchester Water Tunnel. Key MDC personnel involved in the project included Francis Bergin, Chief Construction Engineer, Engineering Division; John Shea, Resident Engineer; and David Ashenden, Engineering Geologist. Haley & Aldrich, Inc., Cambridge, Massachusetts, provided geotechnical engineering services in connection with design, specifications and monitoring of the grouting. The grouting and related repair work was done by the Perini Corporation of Framingham, Massachusetts.

## REFERENCES

Houlsby, A.C., 1977, Engineering of grout curtains to standards: Journal of the Geotechnical Engineering Division, American Society of Civil Engineers, v. 103, no. GT9, September.

Littlejohn, G.S., 1975, Acceptable water flows for rock anchor grouting: Ground Engineering, March.

# Failure of the concrete lining in the Dorchester Tunnel (discussion)

## M. P. BILLINGS
### Department of Geological Sciences
### Harvard University

I should like to congratulate Messrs. Ashenden and Dugan on their excellent papers. I agree with Ashenden on the cause of the failure of the concrete lining of the Dorchester Tunnel. When water under a high hydrostatic pressure was introduced into the tunnel the rock did not offer sufficient resistance, so that the concrete lining stretched and failed under tension. As Ashenden points out, the principal culprits were probably subhorizontal joints that opened up during driving of the tunnel but closed up under the hydrostatic pressure.

Mr. Dugan has given a very clear account of the methods taken to correct the deficiency. Haley and Aldrich are to be congratulated on their analysis of the problem and the methods used to seal off the leakage of water.

What methods should be taken henceforth to prevent similar failures? Should there be changes in design or in methods of inspection during construction?

Before getting into specifics, it is desirable to repeat a few well-known generalizations. Firstly, the quality of rock in underground excavations may differ greatly from place to place and even within short distances. Secondly, because these differences may take place within short distances, their recognition must be on a day-to-day basis, even after each shift.

Should the tunnel support be designed for the worst possible conditions or should a sufficiently flexible design be used to meet varying rock quality? Who then decides which design to use and on what basis to make the decision? I think all would agree that a flexible design should be used. In the past in these MDC tunnels, decisions on the amount of support to use during construction have been made by the contractor and the MDC engineer. Experience has been the sole factor, and sophisticated instruments to measure strain have not been used. Someone would have to decide where to make such measurements and evaluate their significance. Incorrect analysis could lead to a sense of false security. Obviously, these investigations cannot be made for every foot of the tunnel. Moreover, the culprits in this case, the subhorizontal joints, were visible during driving of the tunnel.

Failure of the type experienced in the Dorchester Tunnel could have been prevented in one of two ways: (1) using reinforced concrete for the lining throughout the tunnel, or (2) using more structural steel where necessary. I once discussed the first proposal with the former chief engineer, the late Fred Gow; he pointed out that it would greatly increase the expense, and experience showed it was unnecessary. I did not disagree, as I felt adequate use of structural steel would suffice.

I think the use of the "mole" gave a false sense of security. In the past, the criteria for judging the need for structural steel were based on the appearance of the walls after blasting. Moreover, because of the jaggedness of the walls the concrete lining would have been thicker.

In summary, the criteria for visually judging the rock quality are not the same in tunnels driven by the "mole" as in those driven by conventional methods. The judicious use of structural steel where necessary is less expensive than reinforcing the concrete lining throughout the tunnel to prevent failure under hydrostatic pressure. □

Rock excavations along highways in New England, 8:
fallen blocks. The eight plates in this portfolio
from the editor show examples of modern highway
engineering. Throughout the country the interstate system alone now extends for almost 42,300
miles, major portions going through rock cuts like
these. New exposures in many areas have greatly
expanded knowledge of rock formations and regional
structure, as well as rock behavior and geotechnical design. Geology now more than ever, in all
of its intricacy and wonderment and in its useful
applications, is at the window of every traveler.

# Method for determining rock loads for moderately sized, shallow-depth rock tunnels

## W. C. PARIS, JR.
### Bechtel Associates Professional Corporation

## ABSTRACT

Since 1946, geotechnical engineers and engineering geologists have been designing temporary support systems for tunnels in rock using the Terzaghi method of calculating rock loads. Other methods have been developed over the years relating rock span and stand-up time to tunnel support. The disadvantage of using these methods is that they are qualitative and largely dependent on judgment and personal experience. Recently there have been attempts to develop a standardized engineering classification of rock masses and better analytical methods of calculating rock loads for the design of temporary and final tunnel support systems. These methods are based on the geological information obtained from the visual inspection of rock outcrops or, more often, from the detailed logging of rock core borings. The procedures range from the numerical rating of physically measured parameters in the rock core to a more simplified analysis based only on the Rock Quality Designation (RQD), method of excavation, and size of tunnel.

The purpose of this paper is to combine some earlier concepts by Terzaghi; Deere et al.; Wickham, Tiedemann and Skinner; and Barton, Lien and Lunde into a new method of determining rock loads for a project consisting of moderately-sized (less than 30 feet in diameter), shallow-depth (less than 65 feet of rock cover) rock tunnels in non-squeezing, non-swelling ground.

## INTRODUCTION

The following concept was developed for a specific project consisting of moderately-sized (less than 30 feet in diameter), shallow-depth (less than 65 feet of rock cover) rock tunnels in non-squeezing, non-swelling ground. Bed rock consisted primarily of bedded and jointed metasedimentary rock. The vertical alignment of the tunnels had been determined by the planning and design of connecting facilities. Therefore, the invert elevation could not be lowered any farther. Because of the nearness of the tunnel crown to the top of the rock, it was feared that the quality of the rock would necessitate heavy support. It was assumed that conventional tunneling methods would be implemented. Therefore, rock disturbance due to drilling and blasting would be likely.

The state-of-the-art methods for calculating rock loads determine the most suitable method of support. The most widely known of these is the Terzaghi method (1946), which has been used for over 30 years. This method is based mainly on Terzaghi's observations of the failure of wooden blocking in conventionally mined tunnels in Europe, as well as his studies of the arching effects of sand grains as related to blocks of rock. His method is considered by many to be too conservative and not applicable to modern tunneling because of recent advancements in tunneling techniques, development of new support methods, and better understanding of rock behavior. Furthermore, we determined that the Terzaghi method was too general to permit an objective evaluation of the rock quality. However, we did decide that his method could be used as a basis for the development of an alternative method of determining rock loads.

Other methods evaluated included those by Deere et al.; Wickham, Tiedemann and Skinner; and Barton, Lien and Lunde. The Deere et al. (1969) approach is based on a relationship between RQD and tunneling for 20 to 40 feet diameter tunnels. Although RDQ can be an important indicator of rock quality, geologically it is not the most important parameter for determining rock loads. The method developed by Wickham, Tiedemann and Skinner (1974) provides a rating of the overall rock quality based on three major parameters. These are: general geology and structure, joint spacing and orientation with respect to direction of tunnel drive, and ground water and joint condition. For our project, these parameters were not sensitive enough to provide an adequate determination of changes in rock mass quality.

The estimation of rock quality developed by Barton, Lien and Lunde (1975) is based on their analysis of over 200 case histories of tunneling projects in Scandinavia and was developed primarily to determine amount and type of underground support. This method provides a classification of rock mass based on a number of parameters each having numerical importance. The result is a five parameter description of rock mass, each having 5 to 16 sub-categories of rock condition. This concept includes the whole spectrum of rock mass quality, resulting in over 300,000 combinations. For rock load determinations the most sensitive parameter is the joint roughness number. This parameter is based on the weakest significant joint set in the given zone, unless the joint set is favorably oriented. This is a judgment decision which can significantly affect the resulting rock load depending on interpretation of the conditions. Furthermore, the system emphasizes the characteristics of discontinuities as measured in

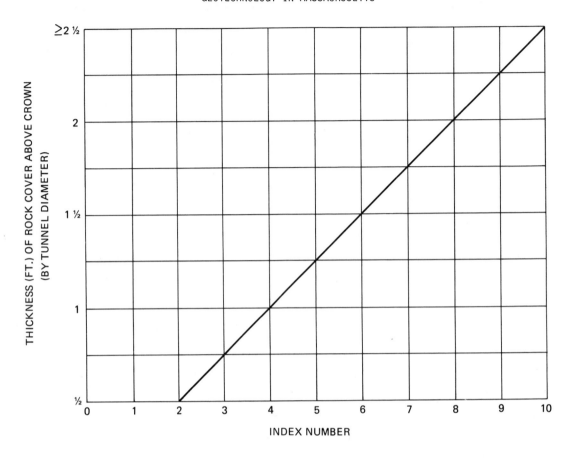

NOTE:

For less than ½ diameter of rock cover
the corresponding index number is 0.

Figure 1. Parameter A - thickness of rock
cover above crown.

outcrops. Therefore, some of the critical rock conditions may not be adequately determined when logging rock core in urban areas, where outcrops are not common.

For our project we developed a simple rock mass classification system based on the quantitative evaluation of the physical discontinuities within the zone of expected deformation (equal to one tunnel diameter). From the rock mass classification an empirical method of determining the appropriate rock loads was developed for the design and selection of the underground support system. This method has subsequently been simplified and refined to permit greater sensitivity.

THE METHOD

Five parameters (Table 1) were selected to determine the rock mass quality:

A. Thickness of Rock Cover Above Crown

The thickness of rock cover as related to arching becomes significantly more important as it decreases.

B. Weathering One Diameter Above Crown

The degree of weathering has a direct relationship to the condition of the discontinuities. In a shallow depth rock tunnel the effects of chemical or mechanical weathering are more significant than in a tunnel deeply embedded in rock. This is a subjective classification and there are many individual interpretations of weathering. In implementing this method the following definitions were used.

Fresh. The rock exhibits no weathering although there may be slight staining along discon-

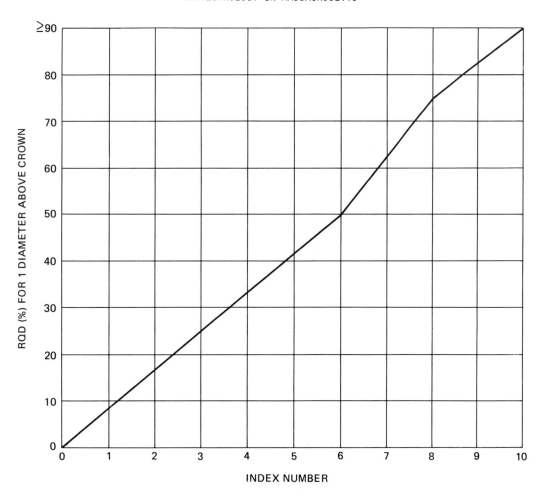

Figure 2.  Parameter C - RQD (%) one diameter
above crown.

tinuities.  The discontinuities are very clean
and tight.

Slight.  Slight discoloration up to one inch
into core from the discontinuity.  Discontinuities
may be open slightly, but free from infilling.

Moderate.  Significant portion of rock core
discolored or stained.  Discontinuities are open
slightly and contain thin mineral coating.

Severe.  Rock core deeply discolored or
stained throughout, severe loss of strength,
discontinuities are open and contain clay
infilling.

C. RQD (percent) One Diameter Above Crown

The rock quality designation (RQD) (Deere

and Miller, 1966) has been successfully correlated
with other engineering properties of rock and is
accepted as a reliable index of rock quality.

D. Average Length of Core (feet) from Crown to 1/2
Diameter Above Crown

Although RQD has been correlated with fracture frequency and joint spacing (Hall, Newark,
and Hendron, 1974), it nevertheless can be mis-
leading especially in non-massive rocks exhibiting
schistosity, foliation, cleavage, fissility, weathering, or bedding.  Rather than establish a
site-specific fracture frequency-RQD correlation,
it was decided to measure the average length of
core for every RQD measurement.  The rating of
this parameter was made more severe than parameter
E, because this zone is immediately affected by
the relaxation of the rock due to the excavation.

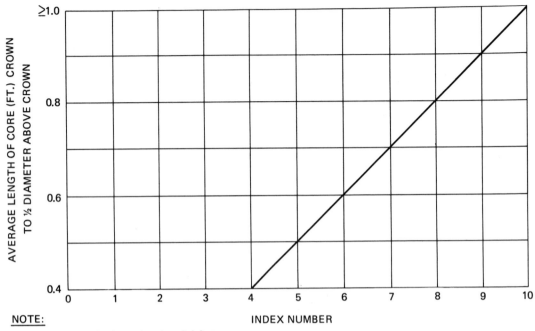

NOTE:

For average length of core less than 0.4 feet
the corresponding index number is 0.

Figure 3.  Parameter D - average length of
core from crown to 1/2 diameter above crown.

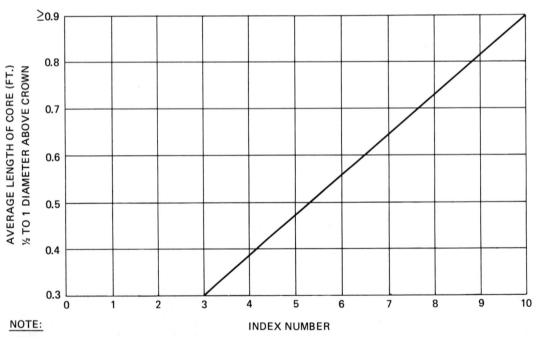

NOTE:

For average length of core less than 0.3 feet
the corresponding index number is 0.

Figure 4.  Parameter E, average length of core
1/2 to one diameter above crown.

E. Average Length of Core (feet) 1/2 to One
   Diameter Above Crown

This parameter is also used to modify the
RQD. However, the rating is slightly less severe
than parameter D, because of the greater distance
of the rock from the crown. This interval is
still within the zone of expected deformation.

These measurements are made directly from
the rock core with only the weathering parameter
being subjective. The parameters are further
subdivided by the assignment of an index number
indicative of the numerical rating of the particular condition. The index numbers range for 0 to

### TABLE 1. ROCK LOAD INDEX NUMBERS FOR FIVE PARAMETERS (A-E)

| A. Thickness of rock cover above crown | Index number[1] |
|---|---|
| ≥ 2 1/2 tunnel diameters | 10 |
| 2 tunnel diameters | 8 |
| 1 1/2 tunnel diameters | 6 |
| 1 tunnel diameter | 4 |
| 1/2 tunnel diameter | 2 |
| < 1/2 tunnel diameter | 0 |

| B. Weathering one diameter above crown | Index number[1] |
|---|---|
| fresh | 10 |
| slight | 7 |
| moderate | 5 |
| severe | 0 |

| C. RQD (percent) for one diameter above crown | Index number[1] |
|---|---|
| ≥ 90 | 10 |
| 75 | 8 |
| 50 | 6 |
| 25 | 3 |
| 0 | 0 |

| D. Average length of core (feet) from crown to 1/2 diameter above crown | Index number[1] |
|---|---|
| ≥ 1.0 | 10 |
| 0.8 | 8 |
| 0.6 | 6 |
| 0.4 | 4 |
| < 0.4 | 0 |

| E. Average length of core (feet) for 1/2 to 1 diameter above crown | Index number[1] |
|---|---|
| ≥ 0.9 | 10 |
| 0.6 | 6.5 |
| 0.3 | 3 |
| < 0.3 | 0 |

For interpolation between index numbers, except
parameter B, see Figures 1 through 4.

10 (Table 1). The interpolation of index numbers
for a given parameter, except weathering, is shown
graphically on Figures 1 through 4. A summation
of the index numbers results in a rock quality
factor which was made to correspond to rock load
conditions modified after Terzaghi (1946) (Table
2). It should be noted that a rock quality factor
of 36 to 40 can be considered as either hard,
stratified or schistose, or moderately blocky and
seamy. Therefore, the selection of the corresponding Terzaghi rock load for a rock quality
factor of 36 to 40 is dependent on the interpretation of the geologic conditions. The rock
quality factors range from a minimum of 20 to a
maximum of 50. The better the rock quality the
higher the rock quality factor and consequently
the lower the rock load. The actual rock load is
calculated by multiplying the corresponding
Terzaghi rock load by the unit weight of the rock.
This method accommodates rock disturbance due to
conventional tunneling techniques. Studies by
Deere et al. (1969) indicate that rock loads may
be reduced an additional 25 percent if machine
driven tunneling is implemented.

Because this concept had never been used
before, we reviewed records of previously designed
and constructed tunnels having similar characteristics, but found the data insufficient to proper-

### TABLE 2. ROCK QUALITY FACTORS

| Rock quality factor (1) | Hp | Rock condition |
|---|---|---|
| 46-50 | 0 | hard and intact |
| 46-50 | 0 | hard stratified or schistose |
| 41-45 | 0.25B | |
| 36-40 | 0.5B | |
| 46-50 | 0 | massive, moderately jointed |
| 41-45 | 0.25B | |
| 41-45 | 0.25B | moderately blocky and seamy |
| 36-40 | $0.20(B+H_t)$ | |
| 31-35 | $0.35(B+H_t)$ | |
| 31-35 | $0.35(B+H_t)$ | very blocky and seamy |
| 26-30 | $0.50(B+H_t)$ | |
| 20-25 | $0.70(B+H_t)$ | |
| <20 | $1.10(B+H_t)$ | |

(1)  Rock quality factor is summation of index
     numbers. Does not include swelling of
     squeezing ground.

$H_p$ = Feet of rock on roof based on conventional
       tunneling. (The rock load is computed by
       multiplying Hp times the unit weight of the
       rock.)

B   = Width of tunnel (ft)

$H_t$ = Height of tunnel (ft)

ly evaluate this new method. We then decided to compare this method of determining rock loads to other methods used.

Many cases of rock quality were selected for a horseshoe-shaped rock tunnel having a height and width equal to 23 feet, located at a depth of less than 65 feet below the top of the rock. Conventional tunneling techniques were assumed. A unit weight of 170 pcf was used in computing the actual rock loads for each case. The comparative methods selected were:

> Terzaghi (1946)
> Deere et al. (1969)
> Wickham, Tiedemann and Skinner (1974)
> Barton, Lien and Lunde (1975)

The results indicated that the Terzaghi method typically is the most conservative, whereas the Deere et al. method generally results in lower rock loads. The Wickham, Tiedemann and Skinner and the Barton, Lien and Lunde methods were similar to the results obtained by the new method for the better quality rock conditions. However, where the thickness of rock cover was less than about 1-1/2 diameters, the new method was found to be more sensitive to changes in rock quality. In these cases, the new method provided a more conservative rock load than the other methods. This was considered appropriate because of the potential for roof failure in the areas where the thickness of rock cover was less than 1-1/2 diameters.

## CONCLUSIONS

This concept will be evaluated more thoroughly after the tunnels have been constructed to confirm the effectiveness of the method. It will also be possible to determine which parameters were the most sensitive to the actual conditions and whether any other parameters should be considered in the future. At that time the details of the geologic conditions as actually encountered will be described.

The advantages of this system are:

● Simple to use.

● Quantitative.

● Minimizes subjectivity in the rock logging process.

● Provides a calculation that can be duplicated by others.

● Provides analysis of only the rock in the zone of expected deformation.

● The rock load does not increase proportionately to an increase in the size of the excavation.

● Provides a method of determining rock loads that may be expanded to accommodate

geologic conditions other than those encountered on this project.

## SUMMARY

In summary, it should be realized that the various methods available for determining rock loads should not be considered in a "cookbook," manner. Experience and judgment are still required for proper evaluation of rock conditions. Most methods have been expanded to encompass all types of rock quality. However, they were probably developed to accommodate specific geologic conditions, construction practices or economics, and they may not be applicable in all cases. Therefore, current methods should be evaluated for each case, so that the most applicable method can be selected. Use of these methods should stimulate thought, so that further improvements can be made in the evaluation of rock conditions for the design of underground support systems.

The single most important aspect of determining rock quality is the geologist's logging of the outcrops and rock core. To reduce personal interpretations, the same understanding of terms should be used by all geologists describing the rock conditions. The exploration should consist of NX double or triple tube core barrels or ISM (Holt and Russell, 1978) rock drilling equipment, to minimize breakage during drilling and handling. The log should include all details required by current state-of-the-art methods so that the various techniques can be evaluated. It is also important that all of the drilling methods used be reported and all of the descriptive terminology be defined and provided with the logs.

Discontinuity should include any natural zone of weakness in the rock mass that may affect the design or construction of the tunnel, including but not limited to joints, bedding, cleavage, schistosity, faulting and foliation.

We need more instrumentation and field evaluation of as-built conditions to properly evaluate the various design methods and support systems. Often a "good" job means only that the design was too conservative.

Regardless of the accuracy of the rock quality evaluation or rock load determination, the actual effectiveness of the rock support system is directly proportional to the method and care used in excavation and the rapidity with which the support is placed.

## REFERENCES

Barton, N., Lien, R., and Lunde, J., 1976, Estimation of support requirements for underground excavations, in Fairhurst, C., and Crouch, S.L., editors, Design methods in rock mechanics: 16th Symposium on Rock Mechanics, American Society of Rock Mechanics, p. 163-177.

Deere, D.U., and Miller, R.P., 1966, Engineering classification and index properties for intact rock: Technical Report No. AFWL-TR-65-116, Air Force Weapons Laboratory, Kirtland AFB, New Mexico.

Deere, D.U., et al., 1969, Design of tunnel liners and support systems: University of Illinois, for Office of High Speed Ground Transportation, U.S. Department of Transportation, Washington, D.C.

Hall, W.J., Newmark, N.M., and Hendron, A.J., Jr., 1974, Classification, engineering properties and field exploration of soils, intact rock and in-situ rock masses: Contract No. AT (49-5)-2667, U.S. Atomic Energy Commission, Washington, D.C.

Holt, J.R., and Russell, H.A., Jr., 1978, Integral rock core sampling: a technique of oriented core recovery: Geological Society of America Northeastern Section Meeting, Abstracts with Programs, v. 10, no. 2.

Terzaghi, K., in Proctor, R.V., and White, T.L., editors, 1946, Rock tunneling with steel supports: Commercial Shearing, Inc., Youngstown, Ohio, revised 1968.

Wickham, G.E., Tiedemann, H.R., and Skinner, E.H., 1974, Ground support prediction model RSR concept: 2nd North American Rapid Excavation and Tunneling Conference, San Francisco, Volume 1, American Institute of Mining, Metallurgical and Petroleum Engineers, New York.

# Hardrock geologic mapping for underground construction in the Boston Basin

A. W. HATHEWAY
Haley & Aldrich, Inc.

## ABSTRACT

Completion of the Dorchester Bay sewer tunnel nearly 100 years ago heralded the appearance of underground space utilization in Boston. Six major water transport and sewer tunnels followed over the years (Table 1; Fig. 1), culminating with completion of the Dorchester water supply tunnel in 1974. These six tunnels were driven in rock and were construction-mapped by Professor Marland P. Billings and colleagues of Harvard University. Boston's subway system, initiated in the 1890s, is now undergoing a major westward expansion toward the suburbs. The Red Line Extension, Harvard Square to Alewife Station, features some major segments of hard rock tunneling and an underground rock station at Porter Square. It is possible that other uses of underground space in Boston will develop in the future, and engineering geologists must be prepared to provide cost-effective and accurate interpretations of rock conditions to be encountered.

The requirements for funneling large numbers of people into the Boston subway system, along with the severe space restrictions for access and construction, have dictated the use of unusual geometries between station main galleries and access ways. Relatively high levels of ground stress tend to concentrate at arches, corners and junctions in the stations. Adverse geologic structure, usually factored into layout orientations, becomes a condition to accommodate rather than to avoid.

## BEDROCK GEOLOGY OF URBAN BOSTON

The general lack of bedrock outcrops in the Boston basin necessitates careful incorporation of geologic data from a number of surface and subsurface techniques into a hardrock geologic mapping assessment of individual sites. LaForge (1903) continued W. O. Crosby's early (1880-1900) geologic studies in the basin, with his outcrop map of the Somerville area, made before urbanization had removed or obscured the few rock outcrops not mantled by the extensive lodgement till and its overlying Boston blue clay. Numerous publications by Billings, since 1929, and LaForge's summary paper on the basin (1932) have constructed what is basically a framework of the gross structural and stratigraphic features of the basin. Beginning in about 1959, Clifford A. Kaye, Jr., of the U.S. Geological Survey, undertook a long-term recording of the most minute details of local geology wherever exposed by construction activity

in the basin. Kaye's long-awaited urban geologic quadrangles (1:12,000; surficial and bedrock) of the basin are currently in the manuscript stage. Over the years the complexity of Boston basin structure and stratigraphy has increased proportionally with the amount of geologic detail that has been exposed and mapped by Kaye.

This paper does not have as its purpose the discussion of basin structure and stratigraphy. Rather, it leaves that to Kaye and attempts to place the nature and level of detail of available geologic knowledge in a proper perspective for engineering geologists faced with developing design and construction recommendations for future underground construction in basin bedrock.

## PURPOSE OF HARD ROCK GEOLOGIC MAPPING

With the vast percentage of the greater Boston urban area being covered by pavement and structures, the few outcrops remaining north of the Charles River (for example) number perhaps fewer than ten. As one progresses eastward into the City of Boston, occupying the narrow neck of land of the original Boston peninsula, bedrock is totally obscured by the lodgement till of the Beacon Hill drumlin and the extensive glaciomarine blue clay and marginal fill that has been placed in ever-increasing amounts since Colonial days. Whenever an underground structure or tunnel is planned, including deep foundation excavations into bedrock (such as at the Boston Company Building; Johnson, 1972), geologists should consult Kaye's developing bedrock geologic map of Boston. The information of interest is the basic stratigraphy (argillite versus tuffaceous sandstone, sandy tuff or Roxbury Conglomerate) that may be expected in the excavation and the near-regional strike and dip of the bedding that is usually discernible in the argillite.

Argillite bedding (Fig. 2) becomes the key to deciphering the geologic details recoverable from rock cores, in the absence of outcrops or more expensive oriented-coring techniques. Double-tube rock core currently (1981) costs in the range of $80-$130 per metre and represents the least expensive, yet sophisticated, method of obtaining meaningful, quantitative subsurface geologic data in the Boston basin. Using the technique detailed later in this paper, the attitude of discontinuities observed in rock core can be oriented in space according to the attitude of bedding planes in the metasedimentary argillite, as observed by Kaye and other workers in the area

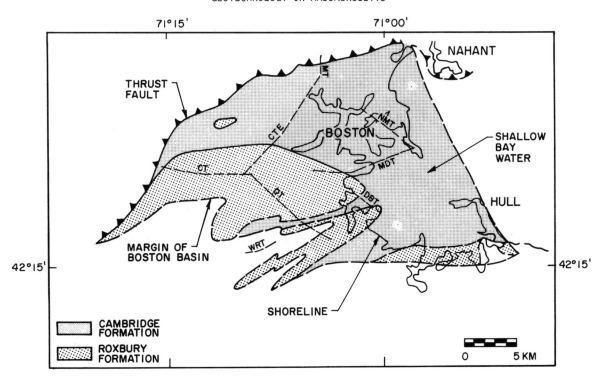

Figure 1. Generalized geologic map of the Boston Basin. The tunnels listed in Table 1 are: CT (City Tunnel), CTE (City Tunnel Extension), DT (Dorchester Tunnel), DBT (Dorchester Bay Tunnel), MT (Malden Tunnel), NMT (North Metropolitan Relief Tunnel), WRT (West Roxbury Tunnel). (Source: Billings, 1976b).

TABLE 1. PREVIOUS ROCK TUNNELS IN THE BOSTON BASIN

| Tunnel and purpose | Dates of construction | Length (km) | Diameter lined (m) | Scale of geologic face mapping | Reference |
|---|---|---|---|---|---|
| DORCHESTER BAY (Sewer) | 1880's | ----- | ----- | none | Clark, 1888 |
| CITY TUNNEL (Water Supply) | 1947-1951 | 7.70 | 3.7 | 1:240 | Tierney, Billings, and Cassidy, 1968 |
| CITY TUNNEL EXTENSION (Water Supply) | 1951-1956 | 11.43 | 3.1 | 1:240 | Billings and Tierney, 1964 |
| NORTH METROPOLITAN RELIEF TUNNEL (Sewer) | early 1950's to 1956 | 6.33 | 3.1 | 1:240 | Billings, 1975 |
| MAIN DRAINAGE (Sewer) | 1954-1959 | 11.46 | 3.1-3.5 | 1:240 | Rahm, 1962 |
| MALDEN TUNNEL (Water Supply) | 1957-1958 | 1.60 | 3.8 | 1:240 | Billings and Rahm, 1966 |
| DORCHESTER TUNNEL (Water Supply) | 1969-1974 | 10.20 | 3.1 | 1:240 1:12/1:120 | Richardson, 1977 Haley & Aldrich, Inc., 1977 Aldrich and Dugan, 1979 |

Figure 2. Bedding features typical of the Cambridge
Argillite, as exhibited in NX-size rock core. From left
to right: very faintly laminar; faintly laminar; laminar;
and laminar in contact with felsic dike rock.

Figure 3. Planar features typical of the Cambridge
Argillite, as exhibited in NX-size rock core. From left
to right: two bedding-plane foliations in a tuffaceous
siltstone variety; calcite-surfaced joint; and healed
slump structure originated when the parent material was
soft sediment.

of the site. Hatheway and Paris (1979) have detailed the various key geologic features in the Cambridge Formation.

- Top-of-rock
- Lithologic type
- Dikes and sills
- Bedding attitude
- Bedding plane foliations (cleavage)
- Joints (Fig. 3)
- Faults and shear zones
- Weathering
- Alteration

Hardrock geologic mapping for underground structure design has several purposes, depending on the particular phase of the project.

- Prediction of general ground support requirements and excavation character before construction.

- Monitoring of results of rock excavation and the ensuing ground support requirements.

- Protection of the owner against unreasonable contractor claims.

- Provision of a basis for remedial treatments in the case of later failure or extensions or modifications to the structure.

## DEVELOPING STRUCTURAL ASSESSMENTS FROM UNORIENTED CORE

When the strike and dip of argillite bedding is known to within five to ten degrees (strike and dip), significant cost savings can be effected by referring discontinuities observed in unoriented rock core to the known strike and dip of bedding. Without such reference, oriented rock core (Fig. 4) or the Integrated Sampling Method (ISM; Fig. 5; Holt and Russell, 1978) will be required to determine the site-related argillite bedding. Production-basis cost estimates (per metre) for 1981 lie in the range of $300-$350 for oriented core and $500-$550 for ISM. This is compared to the $80-$130 range cited above for double-tube rock coring. If argillite attitude is unknown or the reference attitude is suspect, an alternative would be to employ a limited amount of oriented coring or ISM recovery in order to establish bedding attitude for later reference to unoriented coring. The 1981 estimated costs for both these sophisticated recovery techniques are then probably too low to absorb mobilization/demobilization costs and the development of site-specific techniques. Limited use of oriented core or ISM will probably result in costs that exceed those cited above by about 20 percent.

When bedding or foliation lies between about 15 and 75 degrees, orientation permits measurement of strike and dip of individual discontinuities recovered in rock core. The reorientation can be accomplished through the use of a large-scale

goniometer (Fig. 4) in which the core is repositioned with its bedding or foliation lying in its site-area spatial orientation. One good method is to use the bedding oriented with strike placed artificially perpendicular to the long axis of the core box and with the dip pointing down toward one end of the core box. This measured departure of discontinuity (in terms of strike and dip) from site-area bedding is then plotted on a meridional stereonet along with the known or estimated strike and dip of bedding or foliation. The known foliation is then rotated in space, on the stereonet, from its horizontal position (as placed in the core box) to its true (estimated or measured) position in the site area. When the bedding or foliation attitude is rotated, the observed discontinuity attitude is also rotated into its true position in space. The measurement is recorded on the boring log and summary and on an equal-area plot for analysis.

## HARDROCK MAPPING SEQUENCE

Hardrock mapping is the best method of developing phased geologic input for underground geotechnical design recommendations in the Boston basin. The following steps, with proper modifications to meet individual site design objectives, should be considered.

- Drilling of at least two rock core borings at the extreme ends of the site. If site-area strike and dip of the Cambridge Formation is not known, then one of the borings, at a minimum, should be of the oriented or ISM variety. These borings will identify the major rock type present, define the general state of rock discontinuities present, such as joints, bedding plane foliation, faults, etc., and provide a site-dependent strike and dip of metasedimentary bedding. Indicators of rock character and engineering properties are found in Hatheway and Paris (1979).

- Comparison of the strike and dip of argillite bedding between the borings, and with depth. This requires oriented borings, and it is helpful to know the attitude of bedding as recorded in nearby projects. If all agree within reasonable limits, it may be possible to assume that deviant folds or other major displacements are not present.

- Optional continuation of the rock coring program with unoriented borings. This is undertaken to measure and describe all observed planar discontinuities in the core, and to relate these to the observed bedding. One method of conversion is to use a goniometer rigged to accept rock core, so that bedding can be aligned with the known, site-specific attitude. An optional technique is to use a meridional stereonet to resolve questions of rock core bedding and the

Figure 4. Oriented NX-size rock core placed in the
Christensen goniometer for the purpose of reorientation
and measurement of strike and dip of structural features.

Figure 5. Integral Sampling Method (ISM) core retrieved
from Harvard Square, Cambridge, Massachusetts. Pencils
point to two grout-filled joints in sandy, tuffaceous
rocks of the Cambridge Formation. Without the use of ISM,
the geological structure would be obliterated as in the
ungrouted core run lying in the core box trough at the
bottom of the view. Carpenter's rule is in English units;
photograph by J.R. Holt, December 1977.

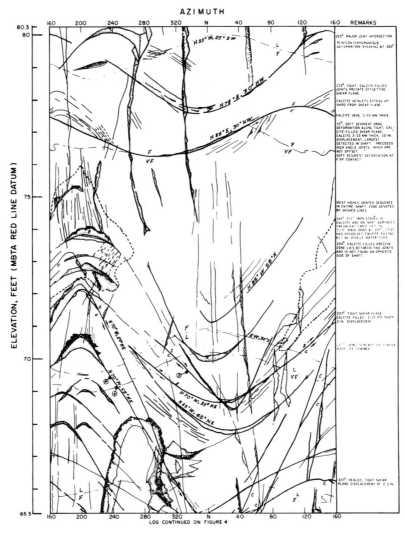

Figure 6.  A full-peripheral geologic map of a 4.5-m
(15-foot), vertical segment of the Porter Square Station
(Cambridge, MA) exploration shaft.  This segment is in
Cambridge Argillite.  Mapped at 1:12-scale by A.W.
Hatheway, in 1978.  Courtesy of the Massachusetts Bay
Transportation Authority.

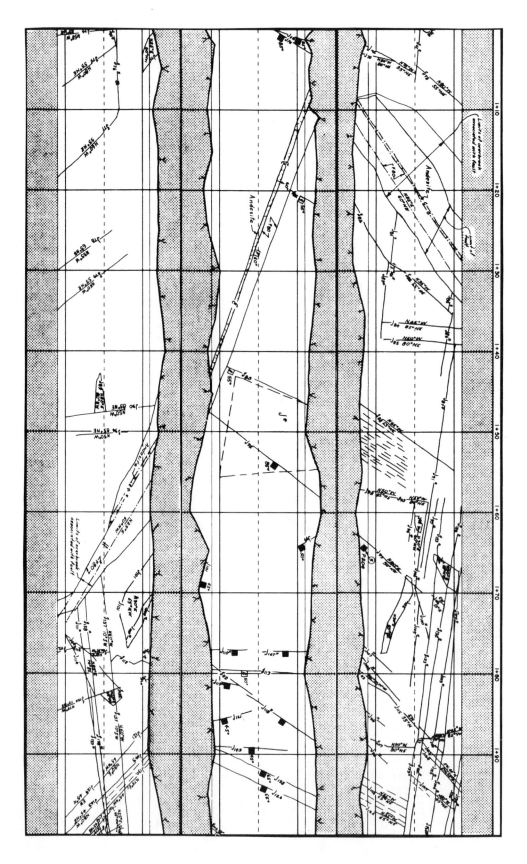

subject discontinuity by returning them to their proper position.

• Conversion of the data from each boring to actual site strike and dip. Analyze these measurements so that each successive boring is placed to intersect features of interest or to cover critical points in the engineered structure.

• Construction and geologic mapping of an exploration shaft (at about 1:12 scale; Fig. 6). This is done to gather information about the true nature of discontinuities, including planarity, roughness, the degree of openness of their planes, and tendencies to produce an inflow of water.

• Plotting of points to poles (equal area net). This is done for each boring or for clusters of borings to test similarities and differences in the statistical grouping of discontinuities between borings. If warranted, designate different structural domains across the site of the proposed structure and analyze the effect of dominant attitudes on faces and surfaces to be exposed in the engineered structure.

• Drilling of one or two inclined borings. These should be advanced to test the presence and nature of major discontinuities observed in other borings which may influence rock structural support requirements.

• Construction of pilot shafts and tunnels for the purpose of verifying ground support and rock excavation conditions. The full peripheral method (Fig. 7; U.S. Army Corps of Engineers, 1970) is recommended for as-constructed geologic mapping as it depicts all features in their natural position, without distortion.

As with other types of detailed geologic mapping, hardrock mapping for underground construction is at first plagued with little available detail and many data gaps. As the ground is opened up to exploration shafts and pilot tunnels, the data available are almost endless and can be de-

feating to the mapping geologist. Pattern recognition and decision-making abilities are essential if time is to be spent effectively in the mapping. One soon learns that the generally planar quality of natural rock discontinuities is rare and that the average joint surface, over only a square metre of surface area, is slightly warped in potato-chip fashion. Some of the "warp" is apparently due to minute offsets of individual surfaces along intersecting joints.

The full-peripheral method of face mapping was developed by the U.S. Army Corps of Engineers (1970). This method has the advantage that a discontinuity (say a joint) detected on one wall of a tunnel may be projected across the crown and onto the map of the opposite wall and hence presents a true check on measured attitudes as the trace is plotted. Strike and dip are read directly from the sine-curve type of trace of a plane on the interior surface of a circular tunnel (Fig. 6) or as strike on the crown of a square-set tunnel and corrected for apparent dip on either wall (Fig. 7).

Construction mapping is often the more harried form of geologic recording due to the fact that progress must be kept with open rock faces before shotcrete or other lining materials are installed.

Detailed hardrock mapping serves the dual purpose of recording attitudes of important rock discontinuities and contacts and affords the eye an instant appreciation of the interrelationships of rock structure and project design features.

## REFERENCES

Aldrich, H.P., and Dugan, J.P., 1979, Investigation of a cracked pressure tunnel lining in rock: Transportation Research Board, 58th Annual Meeting, Washington, D.C., Abstract.

Billings, M.P., 1929, Structural geology of the eastern part of the Boston Basin: American Journal of Science, 5th Series, v. 18, p. 97-137.

Billings, M.P., 1975, Geology of the North Metropolitan Relief Tunnel, Greater Boston, Massachusetts: Journal of the Boston Society of Civil Engineers, v. 62, no. 3, p. 115-235.

Figure 7. A full-peripheral geologic map of a nominal 3.2-m (10-foot) square pilot tunnel for a larger underground station. The map was compiled at a scale of 1:60 and depicts all significant discontinuities, all geologic contacts, and the line of overbreak in the tunnel crown. The map may be printed on transparent plastic stock and assembled for a three-dimensional model. The tunnel axis is nearly north-south. The planar representation of the crown is the center view, the west wall lies at the top of the view, and the east wall is at the bottom. Porter Square Subway Station, Cambridge, Massachusetts, 1979. Courtesy of the Massachusetts Bay Transportation Authority.

Billings, M.P., 1976a, Geology of the Boston Basin: Geological Society of America, Memoir 146, p. 5-135.

Billings, M.P., 1976b, Bedrock geology of the Boston Basin: Geology of southeastern New England, New England Intercollegiate Geological Conference Guidebook.

Billings, M.P., and Rahm, D.A., 1966, Geology of the Malden Tunnel, Massachusetts: Journal of the Boston Society of Civil Engineers, v. 53, p. 116-141.

Billings, M.P., and Tierney, F.L., 1964, Geology of the City Tunnel Extension, Greater Boston, Massachusetts: Journal of the Boston Society of Civil Engineers, v. 51, p. 111-154.

Clark, E.C., 1888, Main drainage works of the City of Boston: Boston, 217 p., 3rd edition.

Crosby, W.O., 1880, Contributions to the geology of eastern Massachusetts: Boston Society of Natural History, Occasional Paper 3, 286 p.

Crosby, W.O., 1893, Geology of Boston Basin; Nantasket and Cohasset: Boston Society of Natural History, Occasional Paper 4, v. 1, pt. 1, p. 1-177.

Crosby, W.O., 1894, Geology of Boston Basin; Hingham: Boston Society of Natural History, Occasional Paper 4, v. 1, pt. 2, p. 179-288.

Crosby, W.O., 1900, Geology of Boston Basin; The Blue Hills Complex: Boston Society of Natural History, Occasional Paper 4, v. 1, pt. 3, p. 289-503.

Haley & Aldrich, Inc., 1977, Report on geological and geotechnical investigations, MDC, Dorchester Water Tunnel, Boston, Massachusetts: Metropolitan District Commission, Boston, variously paged.

Hatheway, A.W., and Paris, W.C., Jr., 1979, Geologic conditions and considerations for underground construction in rock, Boston,

Massachusetts: American Society of Civil Engineers, Boston Convention Preprint 3602, 20 p., bound with four other papers, New York, N.Y.

Holt, J.R., and Russell, H.A., Jr., 1978, Integral rock core sampling: A technique of oriented core recovery: Geological Society of America, Abstracts with Programs, v. 10, no. 2, p. 48. Abstract.

Johnson, E.G., 1972, Unique foundation features, the Boston Company Building, Boston, Massachusetts: Journal of the Boston Society of Civil Engineers, v. 59, no. 4, p. 170-193.

Kaye, C.A., 1979, Engineering geologic framework of the Boston Basin: American Society of Civil Engineers, Boston Convention Preprint 3602, 18 p.

LaForge, L., 1903, The geology of Somerville (Massachusetts): unpublished doctoral dissertation, Harvard University, Cambridge, Massachusetts, 94 p., one outcrop map and one structure map, 1:6000.

LaForge, L., 1932, Geology of the Boston area, Massachusetts: U.S. Geological Survey, Bulletin 839, 105 p.

Rahm, D.A., 1962, Geology of the Main Drainage Tunnel, Boston, Massachusetts: Journal of the Boston Society of Civil Engineers, v. 49, p. 310-368.

Richardson, S.M., 1977, Geology of the Dorchester Tunnel, Greater Boston, Massachusetts: Journal of the Boston Society of Civil Engineers, v. 63, p. 247-269.

Tierney, F.L., Billings, M.P., and Cassidy, M.M., 1968, Geology of the City Tunnel, Greater Boston, Massachusetts: Journal of the Boston Society of Civil Engineers, v. 55, p. 60-96.

U.S. Army, 1970, Geologic mapping of tunnels and shafts by the full periphery method: Department of the Army, Office of Chief of Engineers, ETL 1110-1-37, Washington, D.C., 16 p.

# 7

# USE OF UNDERGROUND SPACE

Session moderators

H. H. Einstein
Department of Civil Engineering
Massachusetts Institute of Technology

V. J. Murphy
Weston Geophysical Corporation

O. L. White
Ontario Geological Survey

# Preliminary studies of underground energy storage for the Boston Edison Company

S. N. THOMPSON
M. R. VANDERBURGH
Acres American Incorporated

ABSTRACT

The site selection process has become increasingly important to utilities over the last five to six years. Utilities are continuously being questioned by public and licensing agencies as to whether they have picked the "best" or "most acceptable" site based on economic, technical, and environmental considerations. Acres American has been involved in a variety of siting studies for underground energy storage over the last six to seven years. The extent of the study areas has ranged from small geographic areas to regions as large as the State of California.

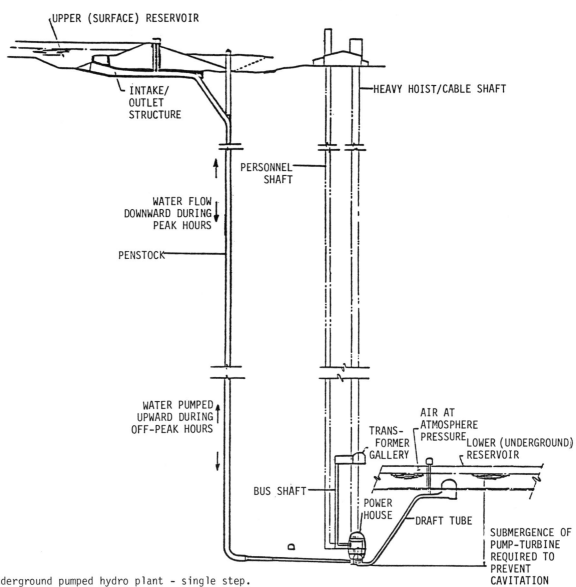

Figure 1. Underground pumped hydro plant - single step.

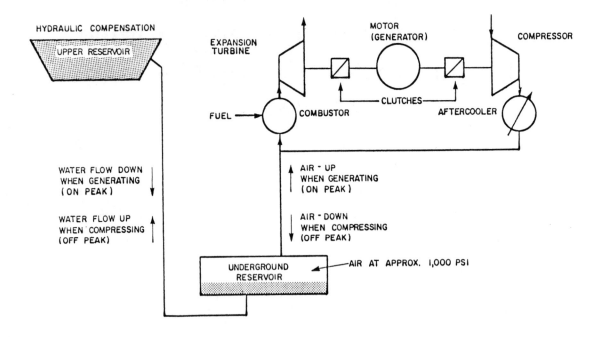

Figure 2.  Compressed air energy storage system.

## UNDERGROUND PUMPED HYDRO AND COMPRESSED AIR ENERGY STORAGE

Many types of underground energy storage exist.  The two concepts that are addressed in this paper and form the basis for this study are underground pumped hydro (UPH) and compressed air energy storage (CAES) systems.  Figures 1 and 2 are diagrammatic sections showing these two systems.  The UPH scheme works on the same principle as a conventional pumped storage facility with the exception that the lower reservoir and power house are located in excavated caverns at considerable depth.  Off peak or surplus power is used to pump the water from the lower reservoir to the surface.

The CAES scheme works on the same general principle as the UPH concept; however, in this case, air is compressed into underground caverns up to pressures of 1000 psi.  Although there are several varied design concepts for CAES, two fundamental CAES schemes exist for excavated caverns --the compensated and uncompensated scheme.

The compensated scheme as shown in Figure 2 uses a water column to displace the air in the caverns.  This maintains a constant pressure to the surface generating equipment.  The uncompensated CAES works on the big balloon principle.  Such a plant is currently in operation in solution-mined salt caverns in Huntorf, West Germany.  The advantage of the compensated scheme as compared to the uncompensated scheme is that it requires less underground excavation for a given generating capacity.

TABLE 1.  SITING CRITERIA

| | |
|---|---|
| 1. Geologic criteria | A.  Geologic column<br>B.  Rock structure<br>C.  Rock strength & in-situ stresses<br>D.  Rock mass permeability<br>E.  Shafts |
| 2. Topographic criteria | A.  Upper reservoir<br>B.  Capacity<br>C.  Reservoir fluctuations<br>D.  Watertightness<br>E.  Filling water<br>F.  Intermediate power facilities<br>G.  Seismicity |
| 3. Location criteria | A.  Effect of sea water<br>B.  Transmission<br>C.  Site access<br>D.  Rock disposal<br>E.  Property acquisition |
| 4. Environmental criteria | A.  Aesthetics<br>B.  Noise<br>C.  Socio-economic<br>D.  Ecological |

The depth of the CAES caverns is dependent on optimum generating requirements but usually ranges between 2000 and 2500 feet, whereas the UPH caverns may be as deep as 5000 feet.

As can be seen, these two schemes require suitable geotechnical conditions for excavating and sustaining large underground openings at depth.

Acres has developed siting criteria that utilize both qualitative and quantitative para-

## TABLE 2. DETAILS OF SITING CRITERIA

### 1. GEOLOGIC CRITERIA

A. Geologic column — Defining adequate rock thickness at lower reservoir level.

B. Rock structure — Defining the need for cavern support.

"ideal" — 50 ft x 75 ft tunnels supported by 1-inch Ø, 15 ft long bolts, 7 ft pattern, wire mesh arch.

"worst" — 1 3/8 inch Ø by 20 ft long bolts, 5 ft pattern, 7 ft pattern 2/3 ft S wall and wire meshed.

C. Rock strength & in-situ stresses

"ideal" — No additional support.

"worst" — As "B" above.

D. Rock mass permeability

"ideal" — Mass permeability of $10^{-15}$ cm/sec.

"worst" — Major feature encountered every 1000 ft costing $100,000 each.

E. Shafts

"ideal" — Good quality igneous or metamorphic rock for full shaft length.

"worst" — Collaring shaft through 150 ft poor overburden and sinking shaft through shale-sandstone sequence with major aquifer say 200 ft thick at 500 ft.

### 2. TOPOGRAPHIC CRITERIA

A. Upper reservoir — Penalty for construction of surface reservoir.

"ideal" — No surface reservoir.

"worst" — Reservoir constructed on reasonably flat impermeable surface with no special treatment required. Daily fluctuations of 5 ft.

B. Capacity

no — No expansion possible.

yes — Expansion possible.

C. Reservoir fluctuations

"ideal" — 5 ft daily fluctuations.

"worst" — 50 ft daily fluctuations.

D. Watertightness

"ideal" — Reservoir constructed on impervious foundation, compacted rockfill dikes with either impervious water-retaining zone of clay or till and shallow grout curtain and gravel or crushed rock filler zone.

"worst" — Reservoir requiring impervious lining of asphaltic concrete.

E. Filling water — Cost of $200,000-$300,000 per mile from nearest likely source.

F. Intermediate power facilities

"ideal" — As "B"

"worst" — As "B"

G. Seismicity — Additional cost for seismic design and construction.

### 3. LOCATION CRITERIA

A. Effect of sea water — Additional cost for equipment design & protection against sea water damage.

B. Transmission      - Cost determined
                       separately.

C. Site access

   "ideal"           - Site next to public
                       highway with rail
                       access in immediate
                       vicinity.

   "worst"           - 5 miles of new road.

D. Rock disposal

   "ideal"           - Use of all rock for
                       construction and sale.

   "worst"           - Haulage of rock up to
                       5 miles.

E. Property acquisition

                     - Cost determined
                       separately.

4. ENVIRONMENTAL CRITERIA

   "A"               - Minor environmental
                       constraints.

   "C"               - Major environmental
                       constraints.

---

meters in screening sites for acceptability for
UPH and CAES. One study completed for Boston
Edison involved the assessment of sites for both
2000 and 500 MW UPH and CAES plants in proximity
to Boston.

## SITE SELECTION METHODOLOGY

The site selection methodology utilized by
Acres considered four principal siting criteria:
1) geologic, 2) topographic, 3) location, and 4)
environmental. A detailed breakdown of those
factors considered important for site selection
under each of these criteria is shown in Table 1.

A hypothetical "ideal" and "worst" condition
was defined for each of the siting criteria. The
"ideal" condition was the cost that would be expended for site construction under assumed best
site conditions, while the "worst" would be the
costs associated with the most adverse site conditions. From these values, a cost penalty index

was determined by:

$$\text{cost penalty} = \frac{\text{WORST (\$) } - \text{ IDEAL (\$)}}{\text{INSTALLED PLANT CAPACITY}}$$

The factors considered for this study in defining the "ideal" and "worst" conditions are
shown in Table 2. Upon determination of the cost
penalty values, a range for each criterion was
defined from "0" for the "ideal" condition to the
"worst" cost penalty. The values utilized in this
study are shown in Table 3.

Numerical penalty values were assigned to all
the criteria categories with the exception of environmental, which was given a relative rating
from A to C for overall environmental impacts.
Those environmental factors outlined in Table 1
form the basis for impact assessment.

Each site was then individually evaluated for
each of the siting criteria categories, and an appropriate penalty value assigned. Because many
of the sites may have very little or no available
subsurface data for assigning an appropriate penalty value, it became necessary to assess these
sites on a more generic basis. For example, certain rock types are known to be better suited than
others for construction of large underground facilities. Granites and certain high-grade metamorphic rocks are better quality rocks than are
shales and certain low-grade metamorphic rocks
such as schists and phyllites. Therefore, the
geologist must carefully assess the geologic setting and tectonic history so that he can provide
a judgmental evaluation for each individual site.
Care was exercised to avoid either penalizing or
rewarding sites which had more or less information
than others.

Once the sites had been evaluated, the penalty values for each were summed and the sites
ranked from the lowest (most favorable) to the
highest (least favorable). The results of the
study were then finalized and provided in a final
report.

## CONCLUSION

The site selection procedures utilized for
this study are adaptable for any geographic region
of the country and provide a rapid and inexpensive method for defining the overall suitability
of sites for the construction and operation of UPH
and/or CAES facilities. Depending on the objectives of the project, a more detailed site selection of favorably ranked sites can then be carried
out.

TABLE 3.  INDEX VALUES FOR PRELIMINARY SITE RANKING

| Criterion | UPH 2000 MW | UPH 500 MW | CAES 2000 MW | CAES 500 MW |
|---|---|---|---|---|
| 1. Geologic column | descriptive only | | | |
| 2. Rock properties at lower reservoir | | | | |
| - structure | 0 to 30 | 0 to 50 | 0 to 6(24)* | 0 to 6(24)* |
| - rock strength | 0 to 4 | 0 to 7 | 0 to 1(3)* | 0 to 1(3)* |
| - permeability | 0 to 3 | 0 to 6 | 0 to 3 | 0 to 3.5 |
| 3. Rock properties at intermediate levels | | | | |
| - shafts | 0 to 6 | 0 to 11 | 0 to 2 | 0 to 5 |
| - intermediate reservoir | 0 to 2 | -- | -- | -- |
| 4. Seismicity | 0 to 1 | 0 to 3 | 0 to 2 | 0 to 3 |
| 5. Surface reservoir | | | | |
| - requirement | 0 to 4 | 0 to 10 | 0 to 1.5 | 0 to 2.5 |
| - extension | descriptive, N - not feasible, Y - feasible | | | |
| - surface reservoir fluctuation | 0 to 6 | 0 to 18 | 0 to 3 | 0 to 6 |
| - watertightness | 0 to 7 | 0 to 14 | 0 to 2 | 0 to 2 |
| - filling water | 0.15 per mile (2000 MW schemes) 0.5 per mile (500 MW schemes) | | | |
| 6. Effect of sea water | 0 to 5 | 0 to 8 | 0 to 2 | 0 to 3 |
| 7. Transmission | | | | |
| - surface | 0.25 per mile (2000 MW schemes) 0.50 per mile (500 MW schemes) | | | |
| - underground | 2.25 per mile (2000 MW schemes) 2.50 per mile (500 MW schemes) | | | |
| 8. Access to site | | | | |
| - access roads | 0 to 1 | 0 to 3.5 | 0 to 1 | 0 to 3 |
| - fuel supply (5 miles) | -- | -- | 0 to 0.5 | 0 to 2 |
| 9. Spoil disposal | | | | |
| - up to 5 miles | 0 to 4.5 | 0 to 7.5 | 0 to 1(3)* | 0(1.5)* |
| 10. Land acquisition | $ per KW based on estimated land cost | | | |
| 11. Environmental restraints | A - minor restraints B - moderate restraints C - major restraints | | | |

*Boston Basin sites only.                                                    □

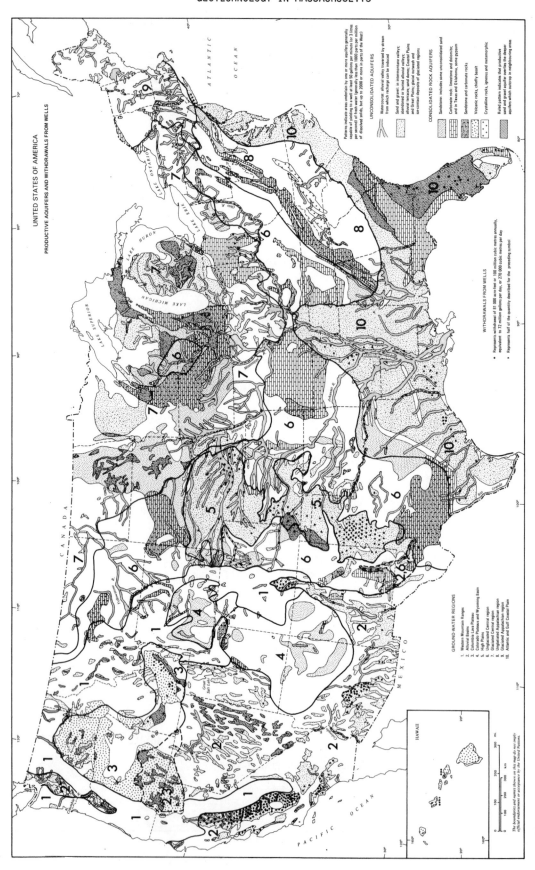

Hors-texte

Aquifers of the United States, based on the map prepared under the direction of H.E. Thomas for the National Atlas. Some of the deeper aquifers may be suitable for storage of compressed air energy. (Courtesy, United Nations.)

# Swedish experience from construction and use of energy-related underground facilities

L. E. SÖDERBERG
C. G. BJORK
Skanska (USA), Inc.

## ABSTRACT

In Sweden underground space is being utilized to a much greater extent than in many other countries. The reason for this is primarily the good Swedish bedrock. Weathered and decomposed rock was removed during the ice age, and because of that it is easy to reach the good hard rock from the surface without major excavations through overburden.

## DISCUSSION

Mining traditions going back to the 14th and 15th centuries made it possible for Sweden to become a great power in Europe. Mines included the copper mine in Falun and the silver mine in Sala. Through this mining tradition several industries that are now well-known throughout the world were created, including Nitro Nobel, Sandvik Steel and Atlas-Copco. Consultants and constructors are now carrying on these traditions in various parts of the world.

Mining techniques were adopted at an early stage by Swedish contractors, especially in the energy sector. The first underground hydro power station was constructed in 1910. The blasting technique was steadily improved during the following decades due to the extensive construction of hydro power projects where some form of blasting was almost always necessary.

This development has not been unique for Sweden; what was unique was the close cooperation between manufacturers of drilling machines, drill steel, and explosives and constructors. Because of this a rapid development into better and less expensive methods for underground excavation was achieved. The methods that were developed during this hydro power era have been extremely useful in the pursuit of another use of the underground within the energy sector, the underground storage of oil.

Today we have more than 30 years experience of oil storage in unlined rock caverns. This method has proven to be inexpensive and safe, with little or no impact on the environment. It is now widely accepted by authorities and the public.

The principles for storing oil underground are simple. A cavern is excavated so that its roof lies under the water table. The ground water that leaks into the cavern is continuously pumped out so that a cone of depression is shaped around the cavern. The oil will then float on top of the water, because oil is lighter than water and insoluble.

With basically the same system, gas in liquid form can be stored under pressure in rock caverns. But, as this system does not allow a cone of depression, a horizontal tunnel is constructed over the cavern. Holes are drilled around the perimeter and the tunnel is filled with water and pressurized. This is done in order to maintain the original water table. The pressure in the rock fissures from the ground water at the cavern roof is greater than the gas pressure inside the cavern.

Skanska has executed more than 80 underground oil storage facilities. Most of these facilities were constructed on a turn-key contract; we have been responsible for design as well as construction. As shown in the table, facilities have been built for a variety of products, and the number of rock caverns is now over 265 with a combined volume in excess of 85 mbbl.

The excavation of these huge underground caverns has further improved the technique and the following experience represents the state-of-the-art in Sweden.

In order to keep the excavation costs at a relatively low level, it has been necessary to use modern heavy equipment. First, we construct an access tunnel with a cross sectional area of 200-600 sq ft with a maximum grade of 1 to 7. The cross sectional area of the rock cavern is selected in such a way that a minimum cost for excavation and support is achieved. In good rock the cross section can be 65 x 100 ft and in rock of lesser quality it can be 50 x 65 ft. The drilling is done with hydraulic drill jumbos which have been shown to be superior to the earlier pneumatic drilling equipment.

The penetration rate in hard granite with 1 7/8 in rock bits is around five feet per minute. The drill factor varies with the cross section as shown in the graph. The same equipment is used for drilling the top heading and the benches, normally two or more. The drill factor for the bench drilling is normally around 1.4 feet per cubic yard.

The loading of the explosives is done with pneumatic equipment, and the powder factors are between 2.4 and 2.7 pounds per cubic yard for top headings and 0.8 and 1.10 pound per cubic yard

(Figure 1 in the color section.)

Figure 2. Mining and smelting in Sweden in the Middle Ages.

LKAB

FAGERSTA

LINDEN-ALIMAK

NITRO NOBEL

HÄGGLUND & SÖNER

CONTRACTORS

ATLAS COPCO-SANDVIK

Figure 3. Tunneling and mining, providing a base for important Swedish industries.

Figure 4.  Underground hydro power station in Sweden.

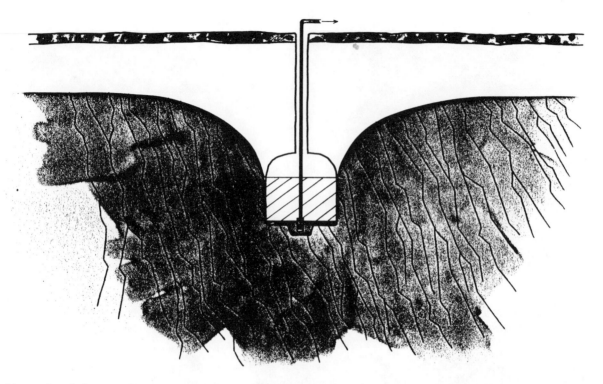

Figure 5. Underground storage of oil at atmospheric pressure.

Figure 6. Storage at over-pressure.

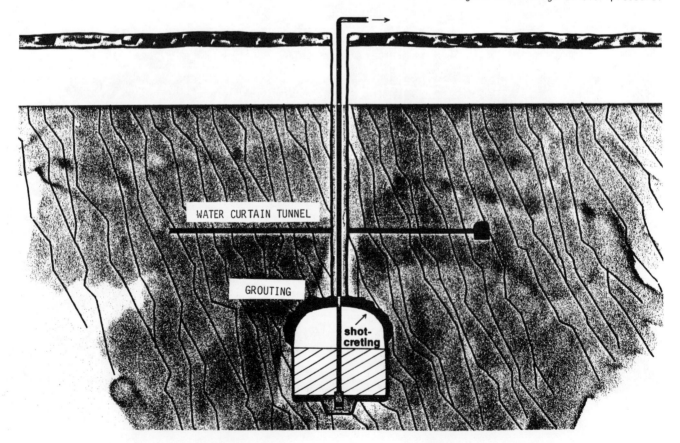

## Underground Storage Caverns Constructed for Petroleum Products

SKANSKA SENTAB

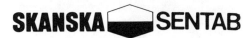

| Products | Number of plants |
|---|---|
| GAS (LPG) | 5 |
| LIGHT VIRGIN NAPHTA, JET FUEL | 4 |
| GASOLINE | 8 |
| DIESEL FUEL OIL | 18 |
| GASOLINE DIESEL FUEL OIL (MIXED PLANT) | 12 |
| HEAVY FUEL OIL | 30 |
| CRUDE OIL | 3 |
| | Total 80 |

**Total Storage Volume, 85 million bbl**
**Total Number of Caverns, 265**

Figure 7. Underground storage caverns constructed for petroleum products.

Figure 8. Access tunnel to underground storage.

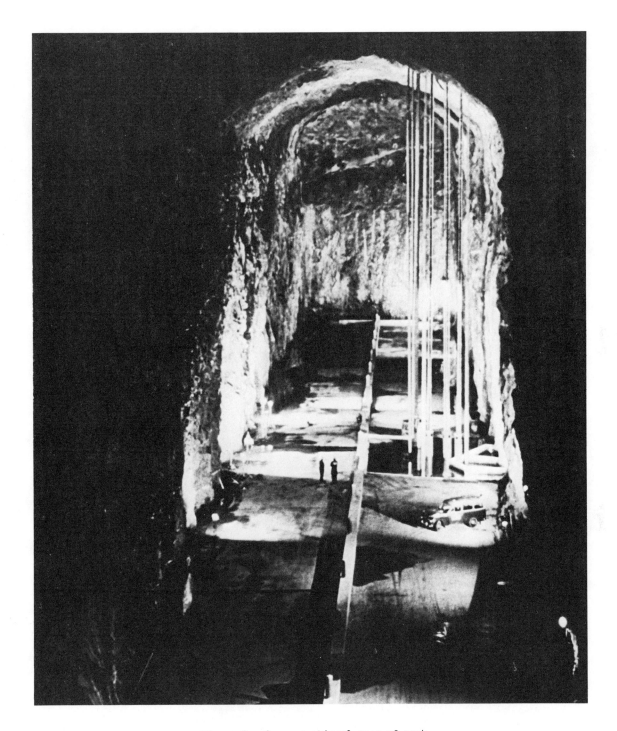

Figure 9.  Cross sectional area of rock
caverns:

```
good quality rock
     width              65 ft
     height            100 ft

poor quality rock
     width              50 ft
     height             65 ft
```

Figure 10. Hydraulic drill jumbos.

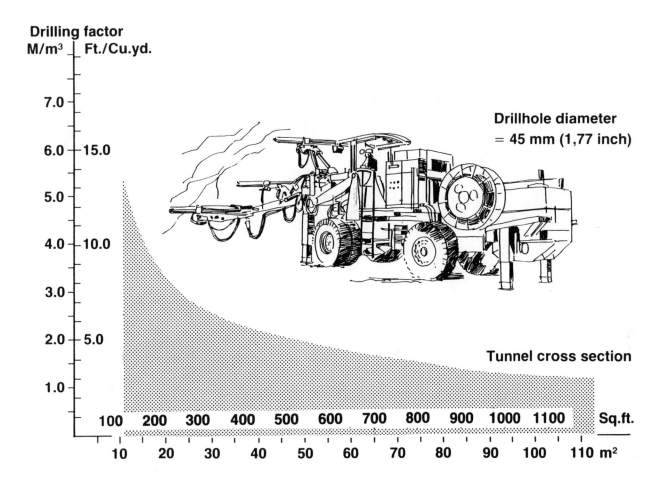

Figure 11.  Drilling factor related to tunnel cross section.

for benches.

The mucking of the rock is normally done with front loaders with bucket capacities of 4 1/2 to 6 1/2 cubic yards.  The mucking capacity is between 100 and 150 cubic yards per hour.  The rock reinforcement is normally done on a continuous basis using rockbolts and shotcrete.  For the shotcrete we have developed special equipment such as the remote controlled robot nozzle and the trixer for the mixing of the material.

By using the preceding methods, high progress rates can be achieved, and the time for construction can be estimated for various size caverns.

The good results that have been reached in Sweden might prove to be a solution for oil storage problems in other countries of the world and not only for Norway, Finland and Sweden.  The technique should be of special interest in the New England area because of the resemblances of its geology to that of Sweden.

We were able to carry out a very interesting project with our associated companies here in the United States.  This was a project for the Strategic Petroleum Storage for the Department of Energy.  We undertook this project by designing a 30 mbbl facility located in Portland, Maine, the work running from November 1978 to August 1979 when the program was cancelled by the U.S. government.

Underground pumped hydro facilities with a lower reservoir in a deep underground cavern, as well as compressed air storage in rock connected to gas turbines are other uses of the underground that have been discussed in Sweden.  However, for various reasons these projects have not progressed beyond the planning stage and, therefore, will not be discussed in this paper.

Within the nuclear field there are several uses for the now well developed rock cavern technology.

Figure 12. Loading explosives.

Figure 13. Mucking with front loaders.

Figure 14.  Special equipment for
mixing and applying concrete.

Temporary access tunnel                    400-500 ft./month
Top galleries                  400,000-700,000 cu.ft./month
Benches                      1,000,000-1,600,000 cu.ft./month

Figure 15.  Excavation capacity per month.

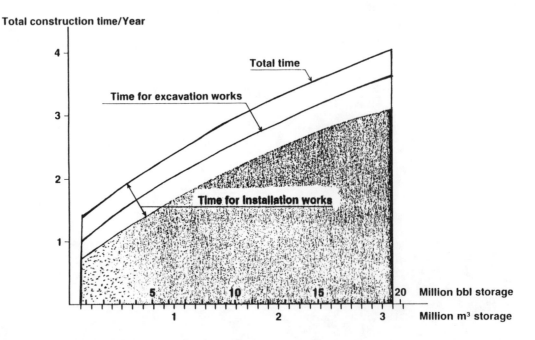

Figure 16.  Construction time related to storage volume.

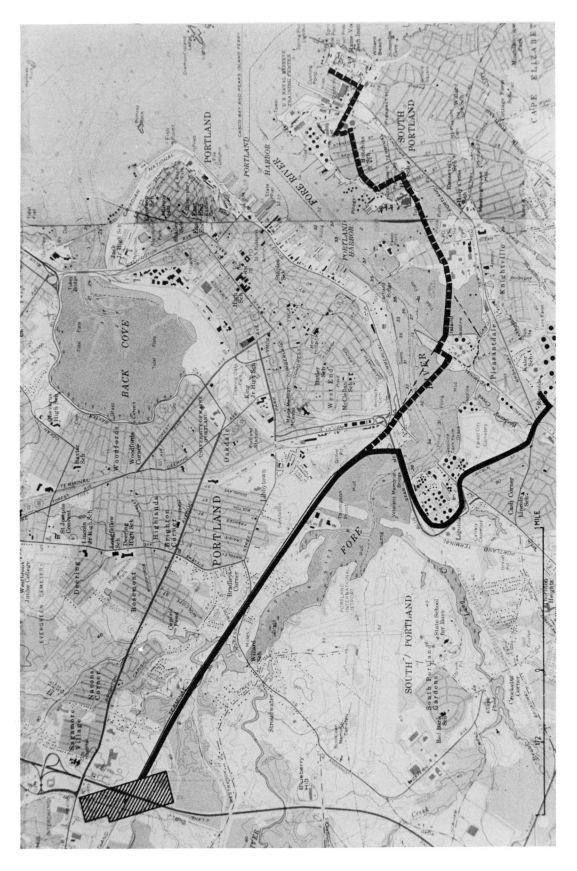

Figure 17.  Pipelines and underground storage facility planned for oil storage, Portland, Maine.

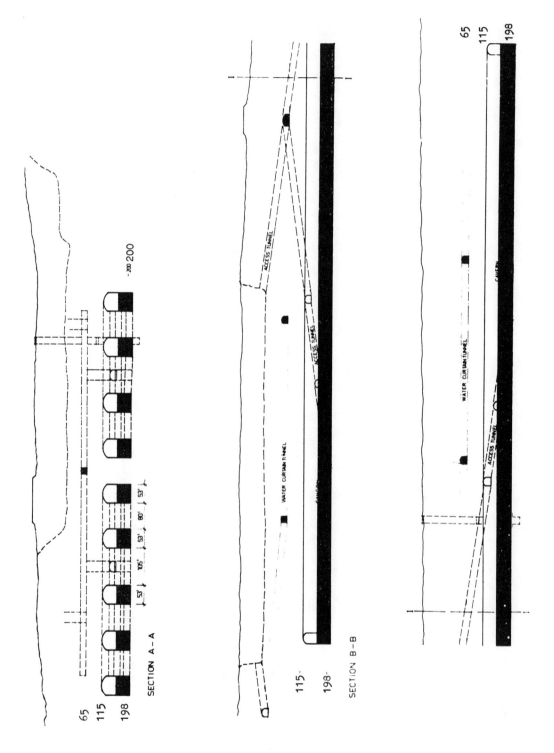

Figure 18. Sections through the facility planned for Portland.

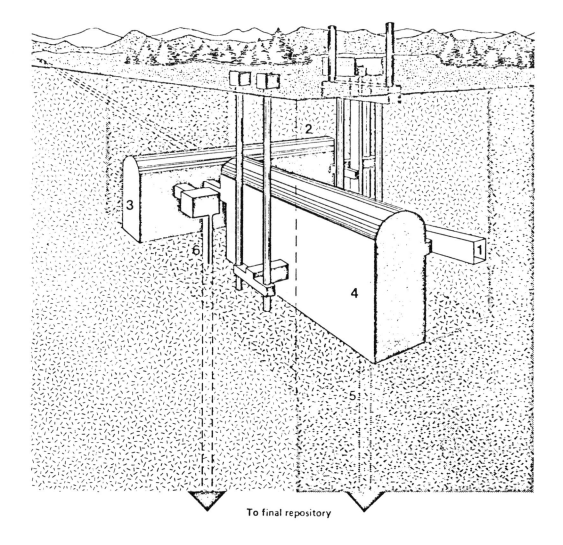

To final repository

Figure 19.  Perspective drawing of a plant for intermediate
storage and encapsulation to be located underground with a
rock cover approximately 30 m thick.  The plant can be
located above the final repository.

1.  Access tunnel
2.  Receiving station
3.  Encapsulation station
4.  Intermediate storage
5.  Main shaft
6.  Hoist shaft for waste canisters

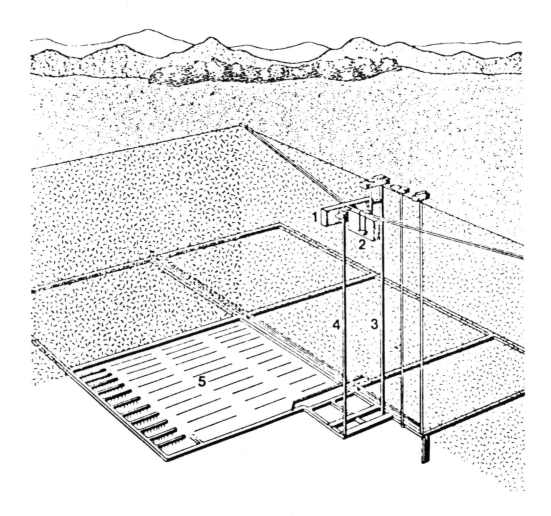

Figure 20. Perspective drawing of final repository with plant for intermediate storage and encapsulation. The final repository consists of a system of parallel storage tunnels situated 500 m below the surface. Construction is planned for a site near the Swedish city of Oskarshamn.

1. Receiving and encapsulation station
2. Intermediate storage facility
3. Main shaft
4. Hoist shaft for waste canisters
5. Final repository

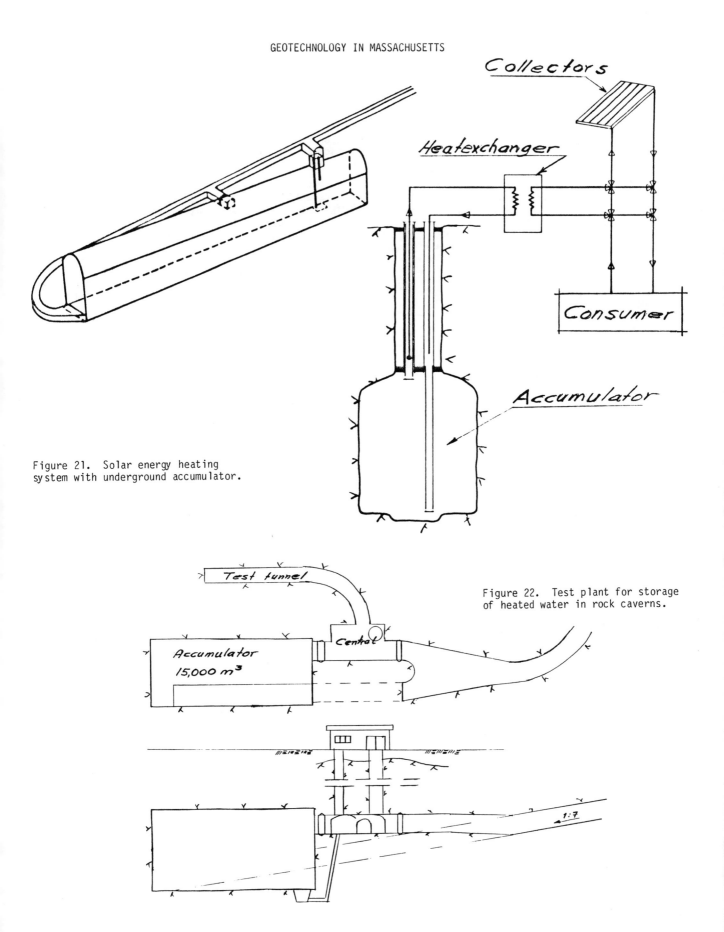

Figure 21. Solar energy heating system with underground accumulator.

Figure 22. Test plant for storage of heated water in rock caverns.

- Reactor situated in an underground rock cavern.

- Intermediate storage for spent nuclear fuel.

- Final repository for nuclear waste.

To site the reactor underground requires large spans which sometimes are difficult to achieve even in our good Swedish rock without extraordinary methods of support. This alternative is therefore very costly and can be contemplated only as a means to increase the safety for the nuclear reactor. At the present time there are no plans in Sweden to locate nuclear reactors underground.

An intermediate storage for nuclear waste situated in an underground rock cavern will, on the other hand, be constructed within the near future close to the Swedish city of Oskarshamn where two nuclear reactors are located. This facility will serve all nuclear power plants that now exist in Sweden as well as the ones that are planned for the future. From a rock mechanics point of view, the facility will be constructed with conventional rock cavern technology and situated at a depth of 90 feet (30 meters). The spent fuel will be stored in large water-basins while awaiting reprocessing in another country, or be transported to the final repository without treatment.

The facility for final storage can be located in connection with the intermediate storage by a system of tunnels situated approximately 1500 feet below the surface (500 meters). The waste will be stored in special canisters placed in holes drilled in the bottom of the tunnels. Then the holes will be filled with bentonite. The canister itself, the bentonite and the surrounding rock are the barriers that will prevent the radioactive material from spreading to live organisms for thousands of years. A great deal of research and development is underway within this field.

The world's future supply of energy is probably the most important political concern today. The debate in Sweden is concentrated around three main questions.

- How do we secure our future supply of oil and how do we reduce our dependence on oil?

- Can we use nuclear power safely and can existing safety measures be further improved?

- How can alternate or recyclable sources of energy help the balance of energy?

We have already shown how improved rock cavern technology can contribute to solutions for the supply of oil and safety for nuclear power. For alternate energy sources the storage of energy is an important concern. A great deal of work has been accomplished in the research and development of energy storage in rock. A pilot project was started in spring 1980 with underground hot water storage connected to a garbage incinerator station. The storage volume was 15,000 $m^3$.

A system for solar heating can be developed as illustrated here. The water is heated in solar panels located on roof tops and/or on the ground. The heated water can be distributed directly for immediate use or the excess, via a heat exchanger, can be stored for later use in heating accumulators in the form of unlined uninsulated rock caverns. The loss of heat is estimated to be within acceptable tolerances if the storage temperature is limited to approximately 90°C (195°F). No rock mechanical difficulties are expected even though the temperatures are high. This has been proven in laboratory and field trials as well as experience from oil that required heating in order to be pumped or transported.

A full scale pilot project in combination with solar energy is now being designed for a new residential area north of the city of Uppsala. Five hundred apartments will be heated with a solar system as described earlier. For this project the size of the rock cavern was estimated to be 100,000 $m^3$. The cost for this storage, including pumps, heat exchangers and other necessary equipment has been estimated to be $3,000,000 or $6,000 per apartment. The total investment, including solar panels and distribution system, will be approximately $20,000 per apartment. As a comparison one can mention that the heating cost per apartment from an oil fired power plant in Sweden is approximately $625 per year. Considering the ever increasing oil prices and dwindling supplies, it is obvious that this system can be extremely attractive.

The solution with a heat accumulator in the form of a water-filled underground rock cavern is especially interesting due to the fact that there are good possibilities of fitting these caverns into urban areas, where a conventional surface tank of the same size would require too much space. In the event that the planned research facilities are successful, prospects for the use of new unconventional sources of energy will be good.

CONCLUSION

As representatives for Sweden's rock cavern constructors, we are confident about the future. Our rock cavern construction experience is important regardless of the direction of the energy supply for Sweden in the future. Finally, it is our hope that this presentation may give an impulse to an increased use of the underground here in the United States as well.

# DOE/EPRI underground energy storage study

S. N. THOMPSON
D. C. WILLETT
Acres American Incorporated

## ABSTRACT

In 1977, Acres American was awarded a contract from the Department of Energy (DOE) and the Electric Power Research Institute (EPRI) under subcontract to the Potomac Electric Power Company (PEPCO) to perform an energy storage study for underground pumped hydro (UPH) and compressed air energy storage (CAES). The objectives of the study, which extended over a period of nearly three years, were:

Site selection and confirmation.

Establishment of optimum installed capacity and storage.

Development of detailed plant layouts.

Identification of aspects for developmental work.

Preparation of detailed construction and operating costs.

Preparation of engineering and construction schedules.

Preparation of preliminary equipment specifications.

Identification of key environmental and safety concerns.

Development of modular designs.

Comparison of UPH and CAES costs and performance.

Identification of future R and D.

Assessment of applicability to electric utility industry.

## UPH AND CAES SCHEMES

Before proceeding, a brief summary of the CAES and UPH schemes may be helpful. The UPH scheme works on the same principle as does a conventional pumped storage scheme with the exception that the lower reservoir is placed at depth in excavated caverns. The UPH scheme affords the advantage of locating pumped storage facilities in areas of flat or low relief and frequently in close proximity to urban centers, thereby minimizing the cost for transmission.

Two UPH schemes were investigated for this study: the MSRPT (Multiple Stage Reversible Pumped Turbine) (Fig. 1) and the SSRPT-2 (Single Stage Reversible Pumped Turbine) which features two power houses and a lower and an intermediate reservoir (Fig. 2). The difference between these two schemes is principally the pumping limitation of the equipment. The scheme assessed for this study involved the development of a 2000 MW generating capacity, with 10 hours of storage. Depths to the lower power house and reservoir were in excess of 5000 ft. This capacity requires the excavation of more than 10 million cubic yards of rock.

The CAES scheme is shown in Figure 3. The CAES plan utilizes surplus power to compress air into underground chambers up to pressures in excess of 1000 psi. There are many types of CAES designs that can be used in many types of geologic media; however, discussion of these various concepts is beyond the scope of this paper. This study was directed to the design of a water-compensated system which uses a column of water to maintain a constant pressure for the surface equipment. This system minimizes the amount of cavern space required for total generating capacity. The scheme was designed for 1000 MW, 10 hours of storage. Cavern depths for CAES are at approximately 2500 feet.

## OVERALL STUDY

The study was performed in five major tasks.

Task 1 - Establish design criteria and analyze effect on power system

Task 2 - Select site and establish site characterization

Task 3 - Develop optimum arrangement of facilities

Task 4 - Review safety and environmental aspects

Task 5 - Prepare layouts, drawings, preliminary specifications, cost estimates.

## TASK 2

Since this presentation does not allow sufficient time to adequately address each of these

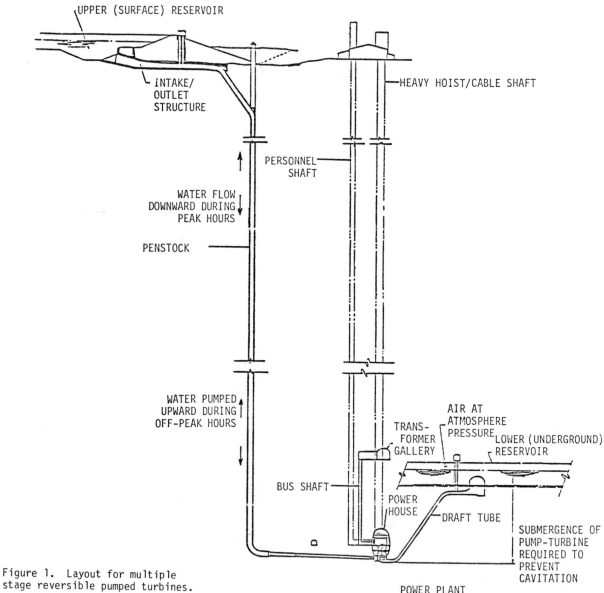

UPPER (SURFACE) RESERVOIR

INTAKE/
OUTLET
STRUCTURE

HEAVY HOIST/CABLE SHAFT

PERSONNEL
SHAFT

WATER FLOW
DOWNWARD DURING
PEAK HOURS

PENSTOCK

WATER PUMPED
UPWARD DURING
OFF-PEAK HOURS

TRANS-
FORMER
GALLERY

AIR AT
ATMOSPHERE
PRESSURE
LOWER (UNDERGROUND)
RESERVOIR

BUS SHAFT

POWER
HOUSE

DRAFT TUBE

SUBMERGENCE OF
PUMP-TURBINE
REQUIRED TO
PREVENT
CAVITATION

POWER PLANT

Figure 1. Layout for multiple
stage reversible pumped turbines.

tasks individually, the remainder of the presentation concerns the activities of Task 2, the purpose of which was to:

(a)  identify siting criteria for UPH and
CAES facilities,

(b)  select the optimum site for a UPH and/
or CAES facility within the boundaries
of the PEPCO or contiguous service
area,

(c)  perform a shallow drilling program to
define site subsurface conditions, and

(d)  drill one deep hole and perform in-hole
testing to confirm suitability of the
host rock body for sustaining a large
underground opening.

(a)  Site selection

A six-step selection process was developed
for the study (Fig. 4).  The region of study was
bounded by the Pennsylvania/Maryland border on
the north and Maryland/Virginia border on the
south.  The east border was defined by the eastern
edge of the Maryland Piedmont and the west border
by South Mountain.

UPPER (SURFACE) RESERVOIR

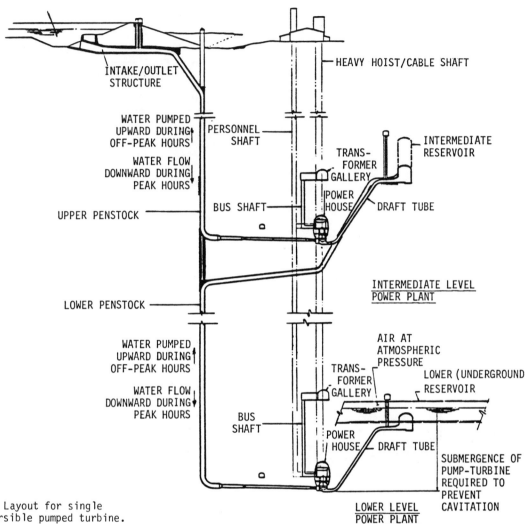

Figure 2. Layout for single
stage reversible pumped turbine.

The most suitable rock formations were identified within this area, and those portions of the
rock bodies that were found to be totally unacceptable due to environmental and/or socioeconomic reasons were eliminated. The remaining
areas were subdivided and subsequently evaluated
by a Technical Index Matrix system. A series of
ranking systems was developed which resulted in
the delineation of seven sites which were found
to be both technically and environmentally acceptable as UPH/CAES sites.

(b) Exploration and (c) Shallow drilling

Of these sites, one in the vicinity of the
Triadelphia Reservoir was selected for exploration
(Fig. 5). The exploration consisted of geologic

mapping, shallow soil and rock drilling, deep
drilling, and in-hole testing and laboratory testing. Figure 6 shows the location of the drill
holes for this study. Holes BH-101 thru BH-110
were part of the initial shallow drilling program.
The MB holes had been drilled previously and BH-
301B was the deep hole.

In summary, the site is underlain by the
Sykesville Boulder Gneiss, a heterogeneous group
of pebble and boulder-bearing arenaceous to peli-
tic foliated metamorphic rocks. The bed rock is
overlain by 20-75 feet of alluvial and residual
soils.

(d) Deep drilling

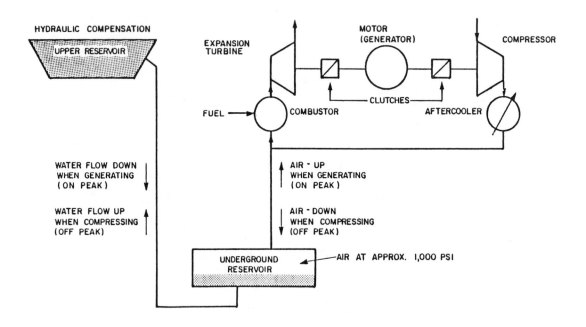

Figure 3.  Compressed air energy storage system.

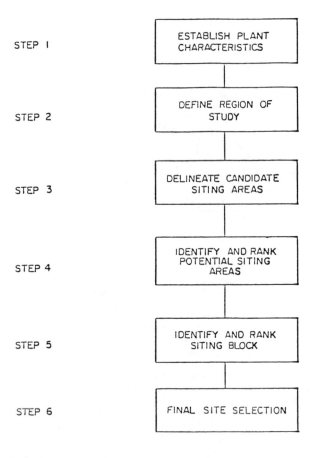

Figure 4.  Six step site selection methodology.

The deep drilling program consisted of continuous rock coring and sampling to a vertical depth of approximately 2500 feet.  Upon completion, in-hole testing to include geophysical logging, permeability measurements, and in situ stress measurements was performed.  Laboratory testing of rock samples was undertaken to determine the rock's physical and mechanical properties.

GEOPHYSICAL SURVEY AND ROCK TESTING

The Sykesville Formation was found to be continuous throughout the total length of the drilled hole and was of excellent quality.  The geophysical survey program consisted of these measurements.

- Natural gamma

- Relative density

- Temperature

- Caliper, and

- 3-D sonic velocity

Tests showed the rock matrix permeability to be on the order of $10^{-15}$ cm$^2$ or less, and the average permeability of the more highly fractured zones to be on the order of $10^{-12}$ cm$^2$.

In situ stresses showed that below 1300 feet the maximum horizontal stress was oriented in a NW-SE direction.

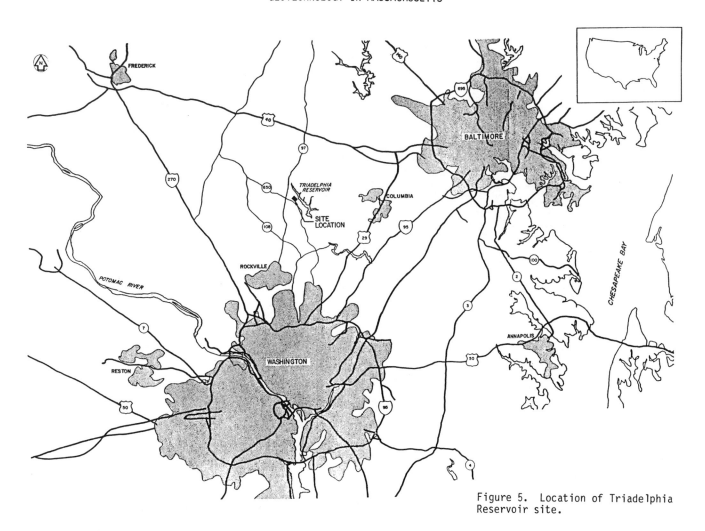

Figure 5. Location of Triadelphia Reservoir site.

Rock testing showed the rock strength to have a high degree of strength anistropy with the lowest strength chiefly along foliation planes.

CONCLUSION

The geotechnical task was successful in identifying suitable sites within the PEPCO service area for the construction and operation of a UPH/CAES facility. The exploration program, although limited in extent, determined the overall technical suitability of one of the sites for excavating a large underground opening at great depth.

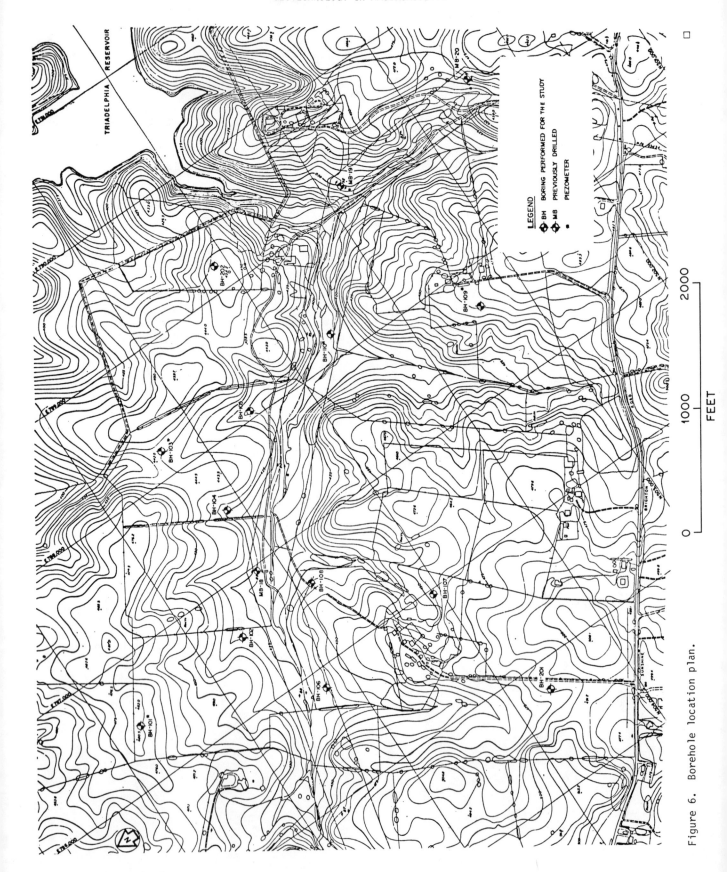

Figure 6. Borehole location plan.

# Underground energy storage plant siting in carbonate rock

S. BAHADUR
M. J. HOBSON
Acres American Incorporated

## ABSTRACT

Both underground pumped hydropower and compressed air energy storage facilities can meet system peak power and regulation needs of a utility company. However, further development is required before the concept can be widely commercialized. The demands placed by both facilities require the subsurface rock body to be suitably competent in order to host the underground storage system economically. This paper reviews technical criteria for siting such facilities in a carbonate rock, examines geotechnical characteristics of limestone and dolomite, and enumerates potential benefits if a storage system is located in a carbonate rock. The information is partially drawn from a study performed by Acres American Incorporated for the Tennessee Valley Authority.

## BACKGROUND

The electric utility industry is experiencing problems in matching its electric generation mix to changing load demand characteristics. Peak daytime loads have historically been met by cycling older and smaller coal and oil-fired units and more recently by oil or natural gas-fired turbines. These conditions typically result in increased operating cost per unit of power generated. In addition, the recent rapid rise in oil cost has raised the cost of fuels for gas turbines and mid-range and base load oil-fired units, further increasing system operation costs.

Both underground pumped hydropower (UPH) and compressed air energy storage (CAES) systems show promise of alleviating some of these problems by eliminating the peaking plants and providing a night time load for base load units. The reduction of energy costs is illustrated for UPH and CAES systems in Figures 1 and 2 respectively. However, these systems do require further development before commercialization can be expected.

To date, no UPH facility has been constructed. However, the present technological state of pumped hydropower in general is represented by over 250 conventional (surface) facilities with heads to 5800 feet and storage capacities to 50,000 MWh. At present, pumped hydropower storage is the only method of energy storage, other than the storage of conventional fuels, practiced by U.S. electric utilities, and has gained acceptance as a viable means of meeting peak and intermediate load demands.

The present technological state of CAES is represented by a natural gas-fired plant located in Huntorf, West Germany. A similar plant constructed in the U.S. would probably be oil-fired. The fuel consumption of this plant is less than 50 percent of a gas turbine for similar power output. However, due to the present adverse trade balance caused by oil imports, a coal-fueled CAES plant using coal either directly or as a feedstock for synthetic liquid or gaseous fuel would be more acceptable to both the electric utilities and the U.S. economic system. If heat dissipated during the compression phase of a CAES cycle could be stored and used for heating during the generation phase, no fuel would be required (adiabatic CAES). This concept would also be more acceptable than oil-fired CAES.

This paper is based on information developed during a study performed by Acres American Incorporated for the Tennessee Valley Authority to determine the feasibility of siting large scale energy storage facilities in the TVA service area.

## BENEFITS OF ENERGY STORAGE

A basic problem facing most electric utilities is a marked daily, weekly and seasonal variation in the demand for electric power. UPH/CAES systems are intended to receive electrical energy generated during periods of low demand, to store this energy underground, and to release the stored energy during periods of high demand.

UPH/CAES systems operating in this mode could have the following beneficial effects:

- The reduction in overall system production costs by the replacement of higher cost peak energy by retimed energy from off-peak generation, leading to the conservation of petroleum fuels by utilization of coal and nuclear fuel.

- Improved generation system stability and operating flexibility by providing spinning reserve, system frequency regulation, and synchronous condenser operation for a rapid response to load swings.

- The provision of standby reserve capacity and facilities capable of prompt return to generation at times of major system outage.

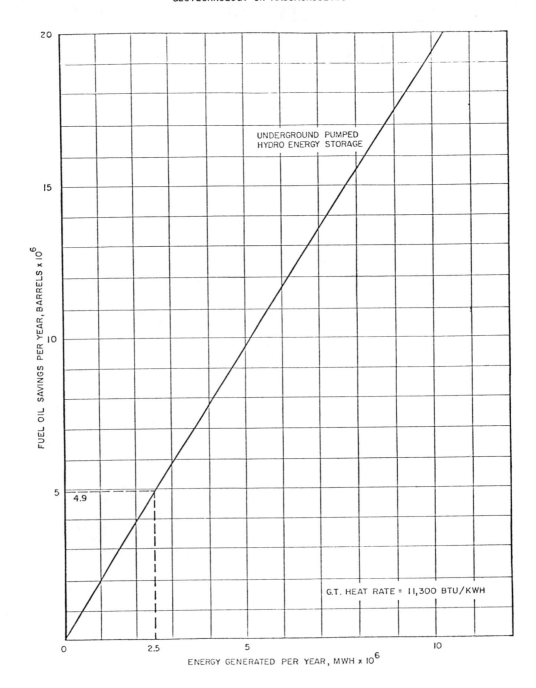

Figure 1. Fuel oil savings versus energy generated for substitution of gas turbines with
underground pumped hydro (UPH).

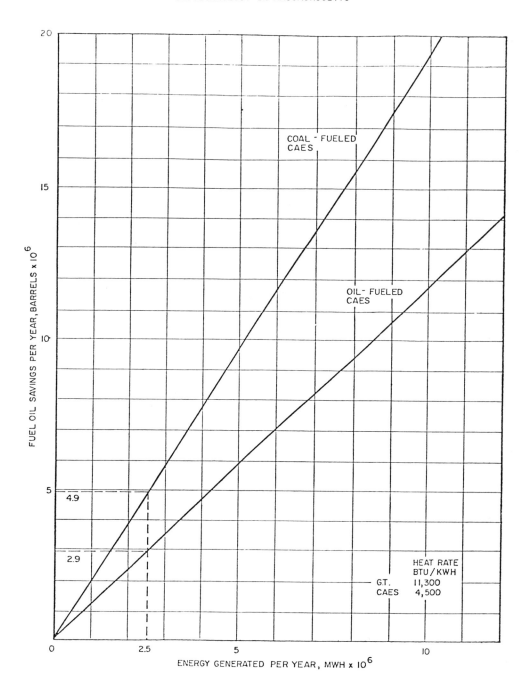

Figure 2. Fuel oil savings versus energy generated for substitution of gas turbines with compressed air energy storage (CAES).

- Improvement of the mode of operation, and hence overall efficiency, of base load and intermediate thermal cycling generating units by keeping these units more fully loaded during periods of low demand.

- The provision of significant pumping/compressing load during periods of particularly low system demand (e.g., weekends/holidays) to system generation at a level from which returning demand may be met.

- Increased transmission and distribution capability by reducing the load levels experienced in networks upstream of the storage system.

- Reduced environmental impact of utility expansions as compared with primary generating equipment. Energy storage is a relatively benign form of generation and can be designed as very close to a self-contained plant.

- Provision of a necessary complement to energy technologies such as solar, wind, and wave which have discontinuous outputs. Storage capability will greatly enhance the contributions made by these sources in the future.

In addition, depending on the particular characteristics of the energy storage system, UPH/CAES storage may provide these benefits.

- Deferred or reduced transmission and distribution costs.

- Improved load-following characteristics.

- Improved system voltage stability.

- Reduced thermal plant maintenance.

- Additional regulating capacity.

## THE UPH CONCEPT

An underground UPH system differs from conventional pumped hydro storage in that the head is developed between a surface reservoir and a reservoir located in a cavern, either existing or excavated at some depth below the surface, rather than between two reservoirs at the surface separated in elevation by some topographical feature. During the charging mode, the motor-generator drives the pump-turbine while drawing off-peak power from a local utility system. This pumps water from the lower reservoir to the surface reservoir. During the generating mode, the pump-turbine drives the motor-generator while the water flows from the surface to the lower reservoir.

Maximum head in a one-step multiple-stage reversible unit can be developed up to 4100 feet (Fig. 3). Alternatively, single-stage turbines can be used in a two-step arrangement with an intermediate level reservoir and powerhouse at 2500

feet, and a lower level reservoir and powerhouse at 5000 feet below the surface (Fig. 4).

Both UPH schemes require a surface reservoir to develop the head between the underground cavity and the surface. This reservoir must be at least the volume of the underground cavity so that complete cycle pumping can be achieved. The surface reservoir may utilize either existing natural reservoirs or artificial dike structures which use excess rock from the cavern excavation as fill. However, due to inherent problems with fluctuating water levels, water quality and safety requirements, it is doubtful that a naturally occurring reservoir would be a viable alternative.

In addition to the upper reservoir and the underground reservoir, the primary features of UPH facilities are the intake works, the penstocks which convey the water to and from the underground reservoir, and the underground powerhouse with its associated access shafts for personnel, ventilation, cables, etc.

## THE CAES CONCEPT

A compressed air energy storage (CAES) system consists of an electric motor driven air compressor for supplying an underground storage cavern and a gas turbine generator designed to withdraw the air from storage for electric generation during peak power periods. Simple CAES cycles utilize a motor/generator with clutches to both the compressor and the turbine. During the charging mode, the motor/generator drives the compressor while drawing off-peak power from the local utility system. During the generating mode, the stored air is withdrawn from storage, heated in the combustor with distillate oil or natural gas, and expanded through the turbine. The shaft power drives the motor/generator through the turbine clutch.

Air may be stored underground in two modes, either the dry non-compensated variable pressure mode, or the water-compensated constant pressure mode. The impact of the dry cavern storage configuration on the surface plant design is relatively high due to inherently large pressure variation. Also, the storage volume requirements are considerably larger. In contrast, the compensated cavern imposes few constraints on surface machinery design due to negligible pressure variation. The volume for storage requirements is also minimized.

Most commercially available open-cycle gas turbines operate at air pressures in the 10 to 16 atmosphere range. Previous studies have shown that it is generally uneconomic to store air at such low pressures due to the large volumes required. Based on the incremental capital cost of CAES machinery and the storage system, air storage pressures in the range of 40 to 70 atmospheres appear to be the most attractive. Therefore, the underground cavern should be located between 1400 and 2400 feet below the surface. Figure 5 shows a basic CAES system design for 70 atmospheres

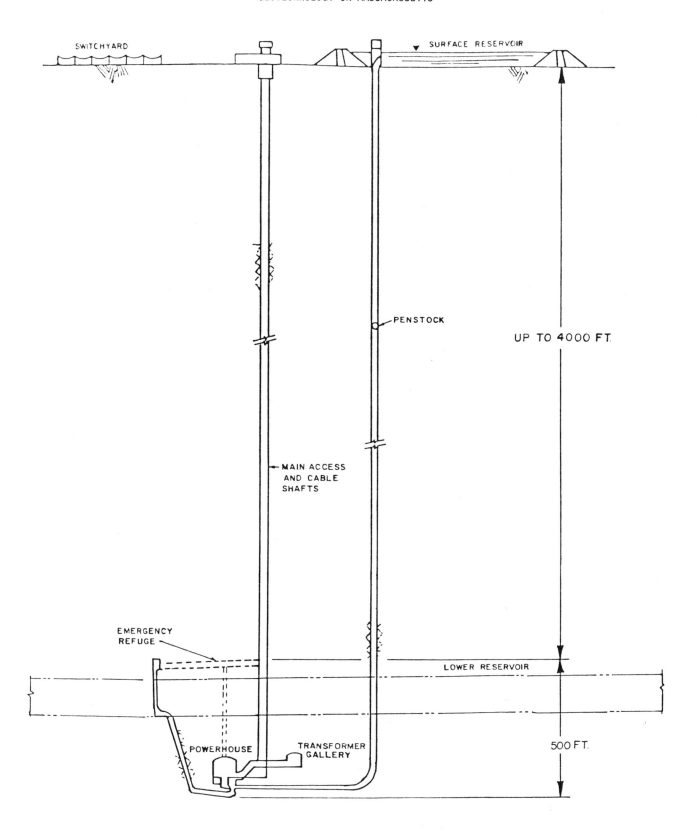

Figure 3. Single-step UPH configuration.

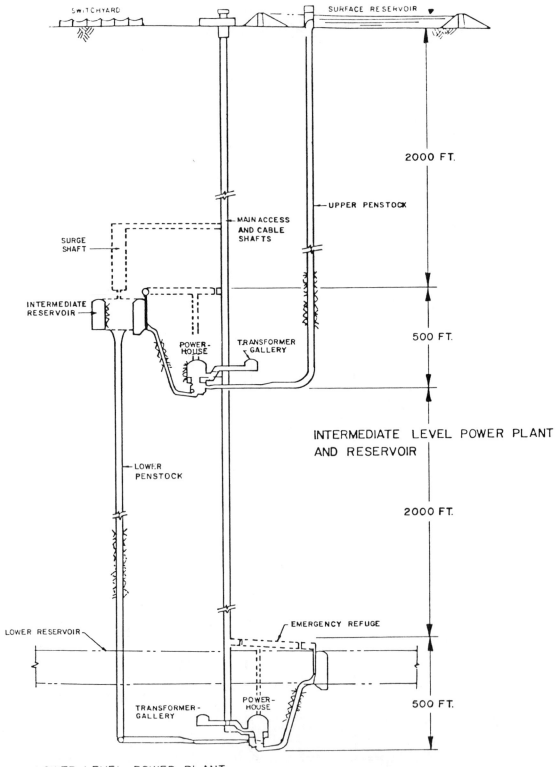

Figure 4. Two-step UPH configuration.

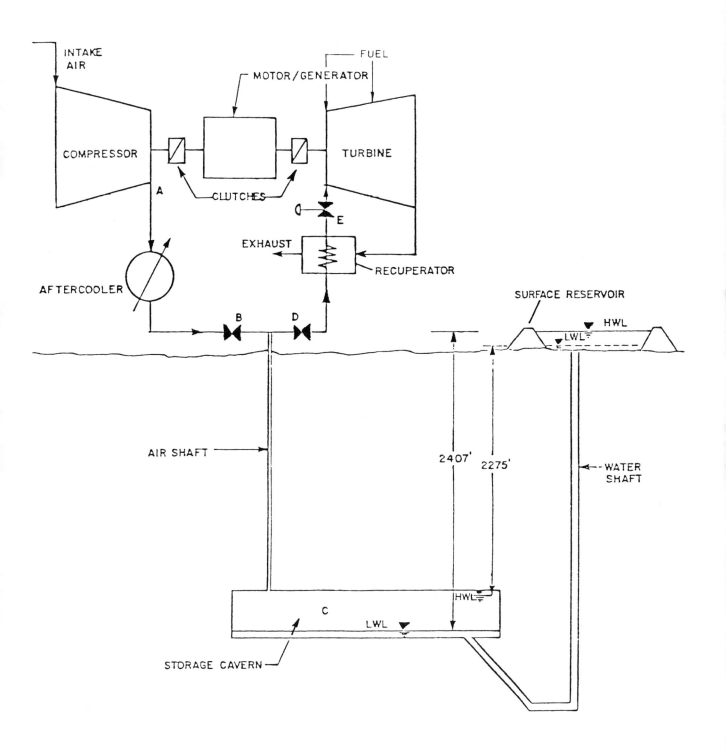

Figure 5. Typical CAES configuration.

storage pressure utilizing water compensation, and incorporating two-stage heating of air in the turbine train with heat recovery from the turbine exhaust.

The primary features of CAES facilities, in addition to the underground storage cavern, are the surface compensating reservoir and intake structure, air and water shafts, and powerhouse.

The development of "advanced" CAES concepts, each leading to reduction or elimination of dependence upon high quality oil fuels by using coal or renewable resources, is proceeding in several directions at Acres with DOE funding. These advanced concepts include the adiabatic concept (Fig. 6), the atmospheric fluid bed (AFB) and the pressurized fluid bed (PFB) combustors in conjunction with air storage (Figs. 7 and 8), and the coal gasifier air storage concept (Fig. 9).

CRITERIA FOR SITING

Preliminary cost estimates prepared for a 1000 MW 10 hour storage CAES plant and a 2000 MW 10 hour storage UPH plant, shown in Table 1, are from a joint study of the Department of Energy, the Electric Power Research Institute, and the Potomac Electric Power Company.

As evident, the cost of the storage system is a significant proportion (45 percent in UPH and 15 percent in CAES) of the total project in both facilities. Because the storage system demands a considerable volume of underground excavated space, unfavorable conditions presented by poor rock quality may result in prohibitive construction costs. Thus, it becomes a primary factor in siting a UPH/CAES facility to select a rock

body which can host large underground excavated spaces utilizing its natural strength characteristics to a maximum benefit.

Requirements such as water availability, transmission lines, and environmental/socioeconomic considerations may confine the search for a suitable site to some predetermined area. However, an examination of the geology of the study area is necessary in order to identify rock bodies that will satisfy the following criteria for the economic construction of underground facilities.

- Sufficient lateral and vertical dimensions of a competent rock body to provide enough space for the underground structure.

- Adequate rock depth to provide the most economic head in UPH and storage pressure for CAES.

- Rock properties which will assure short-term stability during construction and long-term integrity of the excavated chambers with minimal support.

- Rock composition which will not be degraded by contact with air/water and temperature fluctuations.

- Generally low permeability and absence of discontinuities to prevent air loss (CAES only).

SYSTEM DEMANDS ON ROCK

Both facilities require rock excavation in substantial volumes ranging up to one million cubic yards for a 1000-MW CAES plant and ten million cubic yards for a 2000-MW UPH plant. For

TABLE 1. PRELIMINARY COST ESTIMATES PREPARED FOR A 1000 MW 10 HOUR STORAGE CAES PLANT AND A 2000 MW 10 HOUR STORAGE UPH PLANT

| | * Capital costs in 1979 dollars/kW | |
| | CAES | UPH |
|---|---|---|
| Surface facilities | 31 | 9 |
| Underground powerhouse | - | 43 |
| Storage system | 58 | 222 |
| Major mechanical system | 173 | 63 |
| Mechanical BOP | 31 | 7 |
| Switchyard | 38 | 15 |
| Electrical system | 15 | 20 |
| Construction, engineering, and management costs | 104 | 114 |
| Total estimated cost | 450 | 493 |

NOTE: *These estimates do not include the escalation, IDC, and contingency costs.

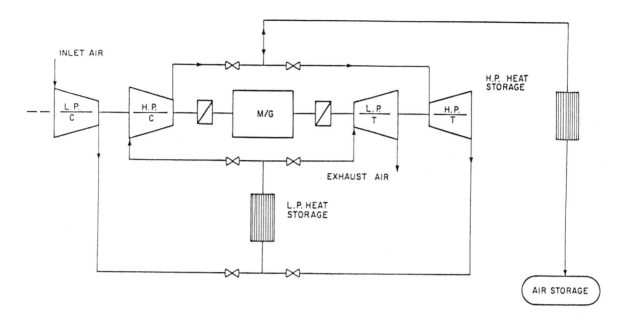

Figure 6. Adiabatic (no fuel) CAES configuration.

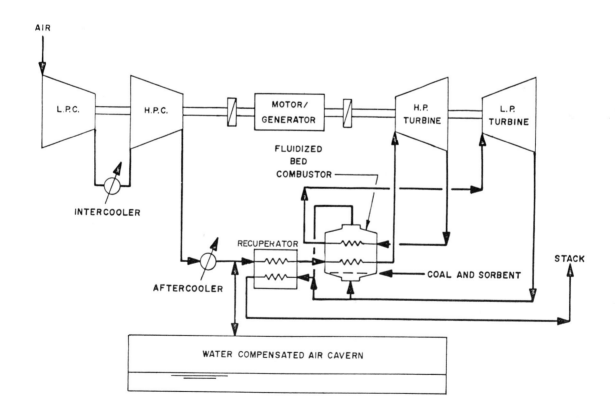

Figure 7. Coal-fired atmospheric fluidized bed
(AFB) CAES configuration.

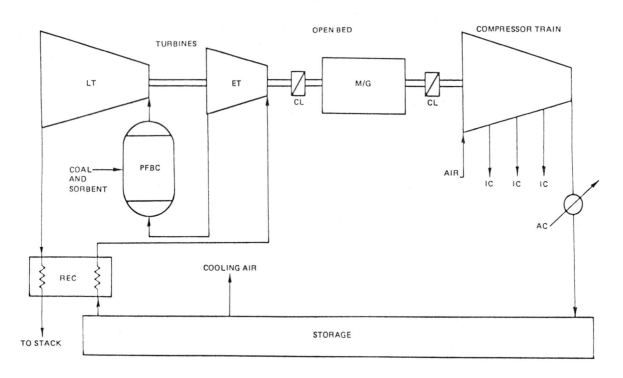

Figure 8.  Coal-fired pressurized fluid bed
(PFB) CAES configuration.

Figure 9.  Coal gasifier CAES configuration.

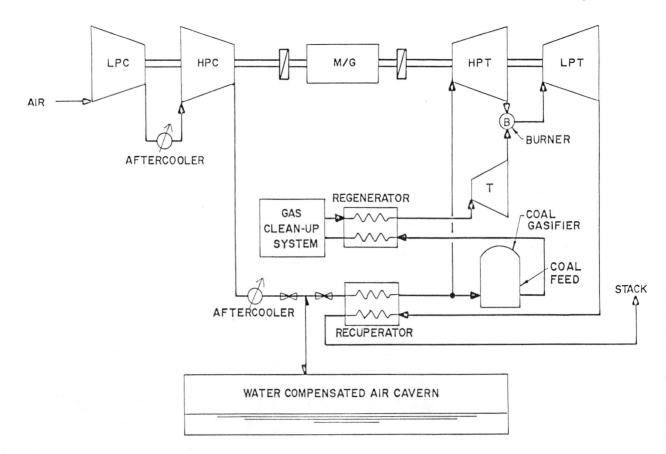

UPH the excavation may include such dimensions as 200 x 100 x 150 feet powerhouse chamber, 500-feet long 40 x 50 feet transformer galleries, 40-feet diameter pressurized penstocks, and other shafts for access, air, water, and cables, and a series of storage caverns with a typical length of 700 feet, cross section of 60 x 85 feet, and an over-all arrangement that has to be dictated by con-struction and geotechnical considerations.

Typical stresses around the underground open-ing as determined by a finite element analysis are shown in Figure 10 for the following parameters:

Modulus of elasticity = $8.0 \times 10^6$ psi
Poisson's ratio = 0.25
Vertical stress = Overburden
Horizontal stress = 1.8 x vertical stress

In a CAES facility, the rock will be additionally influenced by the thermal stresses caused by fluc-tuation of the compressed air/water interface.

Geological factors such as anisotropic rock mass properties, presence and extent of disconti-nuities, and state of in situ stress field require detailed examination, as these will have a signi-ficant influence on the overall cavern arrange-ment.

While the depth and the dimensions of a rock body will depend upon the specific data based on plant characteristics, the following physical and mechanical properties can be generalized for a suitable rock material based on considerations of rock mechanics, underground space design, and construction method.

| | |
|---|---|
| Compressive strength | 16 to 32 kips per square inch |
| *Modulus ratio | 400-500 |
| **Rock quality | Good to excellent (75 to 100 percent RQD) |
| Joint spacing | Greater than 3 feet |
| In situ stresses | Very low to low |
| Permeability | Low ($10^{-6}$ centimeters per second) |

---

*Modulus ratio is defined as the ratio between the tangent modulus at 50 percent ultimate strength and uniaxial compressive strength.

**Rock quality designation (RQD) is defined as the sum of the lengths of recovered core pieces, 4 inches in length or more, divided by the total length of rock core drilled.

*

These properties are anticipated to provide optimum geomechanical characteristics in the con-

struction of shafts, caverns, and connecting tunnels.

CARBONATE ROCK

Limestone and dolomite are two relatively common sedimentary rocks that are composed domi-nantly of carbonate minerals, principally carbon-ates of calcium (calcite) and magnesium (dolo-mite). The term limestone is used for those rocks in which the carbonate is calcite. The group in-cludes rocks of a wide variety of origins and textures, and the use of the term limestone tends to obscure any genetic interpretation. Dolomite is a rock in which at least one-half of the car-bonate is in the form of the mineral dolomite. Most commonly the mineral dolomite composes more than 90 percent of the rock. Dolomite rocks may be associated with limestone, either interbedded, or in a laterally gradational contact. Many dolo-mites have replaced limestones through the intro-duction of magnesia. Some dolomites show evidence of reorganization of an original magnesian lime-stone deposit.

The origin of the carbonate rock can be attributed to the following three processes.

● Organic or chemical processes. Includes tufa, and reef-core rocks.

● Mechanical fragmentation, transportation and redeposition as solid particles. Includes oolitic limestone.

● Recrystallization and introduction of magnesia. Includes dolomite and dolo-mitic limestone.

The carbonate rock ranges from a thinly laminated limestone to a massively bedded dolomite rock. Limestones tend to split along certain bedding planes and not on others. Frequently, the parting surfaces show evidence of having been avenues for groundwater migration and solution movement. In some limestone rocks the parting surfaces are clearly clay seams.

Within massive dolomite units, bedding shows up in a variety of ways: thin laminations of slightly different color or texture; parallelism of large inequidimensional grains; lining up of flattened fossils and clay interclasts; change in the character and proportions of constituents; etc. However, these bedding planes are mostly genetic, and do not necessarily signify a struc-tural discontinuity or a plane of weakness.

Dolomite produced by recrystallization and reorganization of limestone is a uniform-grained crystalline rock in which original textures are completely obliterated or are largely obscured. The resulting rock is homogeneous, isotropic, fine-grained crystalline, and usually very compe-tent.

The technical advantages of having the entire

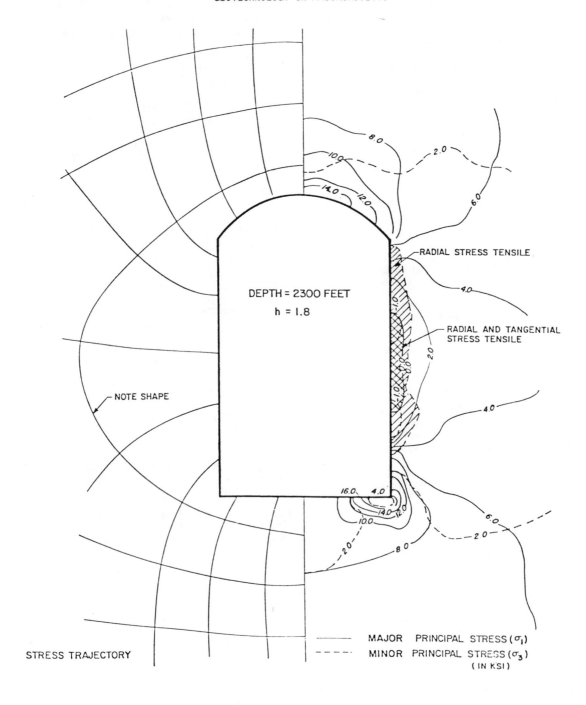

Figure 10. Stress trajectory and principal
stresses for 64 x 111 ft caverns.

underground construction in one single homogeneous geologic body dictates that massive crystalline dolomite bodies should be preferred over thinly laminated limestone layers.

## ENGINEERING PROPERTIES OF CARBONATE ROCK

Engineering classification of intact rock material is usually based on two properties. These are the uniaxial compressive strength, and the modulus of elasticity taken at a stress level equal to one-half the ultimate strength of the rock.

Comprehensive series of tests reported elsewhere in the geological literature have indicated that, under uniaxial compression, a sudden explosive failure occurs in a dolomite core indicating a straight-line stress strain relationship typical of an elastic material. The softer limestones and tuffs exhibit a continually increasing amount of inelastic yielding as the failure load is approached and may be characterized by an elastic-plastic stress-strain relationship.

The uniaxial compressive strengths for limestone and dolomite are known to range from 7 to 40 kips per square inch. According to the engineering classification of intact rock based on uniaxial compressive strength (Table 2), carbonate

rocks fall mostly between class C, Medium strength, and class B, High strength. It should be noted that only a few rocks such as quartzite, diabase, and dense basalt fall in class A, Very high strength.

The second element of the classification system is the modulus of elasticity. However, instead of using the modulus itself, the ratio of the modulus to the uniaxial compressive strength is used (modulus ratio) as shown in Table 3. Most carbonate rocks fall between class M, Average ratio, and class H, High ratio, perhaps as a result of interlocking fabric, little or no anisotropy, and particular mineralogy (calcite and dolomite).

In addition to the above two properties, the shear strength of a rock material plays an important role. Its value reflects the pattern of joints, shear zones, and faults present in a rock mass. The effective shear strength may be reduced much below the intact rock strength, especially in directions parallel to these structural discontinuities. Therefore, the shear strength of an in situ rock mass is usually anisotropic in character depending largely on the direction of measurement in relation to a discontinuity.

Where the directions of loading are such that the potential failure surface must cut across the structural features, the shear strength will

### TABLE 2. ENGINEERING CLASSIFICATION OF INTACT ROCK BASED ON STRENGTH

| Class | Description | Uniaxial compressive strength (KSI) |
|-------|-------------|-------------------------------------|
| A | Very high strength | Over 32 |
| B | High strength | 16 - 32 |
| C | Medium strength | 8 - 16 |
| D | Low strength | 4 - 8 |
| E | Very low strength | Less than 4 |

### TABLE 3. ENGINEERING CLASSIFICATION OF INTACT ROCK BASED ON MODULUS RATIO

| Class | Description | Modulus Ratio |
|-------|-------------|---------------|
| H | High modulus ratio | Over 500 |
| M | Medium modulus ratio | 200 - 500 |
| L | Low modulus ratio | Less than 200 |

TABLE 4.  TYPICAL SHEAR STRENGTH PARAMETERS OF INTACT CARBONATE ROCK

|  | Compressive strength (KSI) | Cohesion (KSI) | $\emptyset$ (Degrees) | $N_q$ = K |
|---|---|---|---|---|
| Range | 7 - 40 | 0.5 - 5.0 | 37 - 58 | 4 - 13 |
| Average value | 15 - 20 | 2.5 - 3.3 | 50 | 8 |

approach that of the intact rock material.  Where the direction of loading is parallel or subparallel to the structural features, the shear strength is governed by the shearing resistance along the discontinuity and will generally be lower.  Table 4 shows the typical shear strength parameters of an intact carbonate rock.

## ADVANTAGES OF CARBONATE ROCK

Most igneous and some metamorphic rocks will be the ideal host rock bodies for a rock cavern. However, because of their irregular shape and size, and general association with regions characterized by intense deformation, it becomes somewhat difficult to predict their subsurface extension with a reasonable degree of confidence without direct observation and data collection.  Only the continuation of massive large pluton bodies can be reasonably predicted to a sufficient depth for energy storage, but such plutons are neither numerous in number, nor abundant in geographical distribution.

On the other hand, most sedimentary rocks are characterized by layered or stratified structure because of their origin by sedimentation (or settling) of particles.  The assumed continuity of sedimentary rocks as a tabular body, and their general association with structurally pristine regions, make it somewhat simple to predict their subsurface distribution with a comfortable level of confidence.

Unlike sandstone and shale, carbonate rocks (especially dolomite) are competent, durable, massive, thick, and mostly homogeneous and isotropic.  However, these rocks are known to have solution cavities and groundwater channels which merit caution and require a careful and detailed examination.

Dolomites possess medium to high strength and high modulus ratio, both properties which favor-

ably influence the cost of artificial support necessary to achieve an adequately stable and safe underground cavity.  In addition, the rock is chiefly composed of the mineral dolomite which has a hardness value of 3.5 to 4 on the Moh's Scale of Hardness.  Thus, dolomite rock is comparatively softer than most igneous/metamorphic rock, which increases its drillability and helps in less wear and tear on construction equipment.

The utilization of sulfur-bearing fuels for steam and power production will require increasing quantities of sulfur sorbent for reduction of sulfur emissions.  Many stack gas scrubber systems utilize limestone or dolomite.  Most concepts for fluidized bed combustion require dolomite for sulfur capture.  If an underground storage plant in dolomite can be phased with a local fossil-fired plant requiring dolomite then the economics of both plants can be improved.

## CONCLUSIONS

The paper has presented various technologies of energy storage and the demand these technologies place on the requirements of a suitably competent rock body to host the facilities.  The use of carbonate rock, especially dolomite, which is a homogeneous, isotropic and competent material, is not only beneficial for short/long term underground cavern stability.  Its use may result in less wear and tear on mechanical equipment, and the excavated rock material can be profitably disposed for utilization in a fossil-fuel fired plant.

## ACKNOWLEDGMENTS

The authors gratefully acknowledge the help provided by the Tennessee Valley Authority during the study, and extend personal thanks to Arnold M. Manaker and Jerry J. Phillips.

# Leakage of compressed air from a storage cavern in hard rock at Ragged Chutes, Cobalt, Ontario

O. C. FARQUHAR
Department of Geology and Geography
University of Massachusetts at Amherst

## ABSTRACT

Air is compressed and stored in a cavern excavated 70 years ago in hard rock at Ragged Chutes on the Montréal River near Cobalt, Ontario. The compressed air is piped from the cavern to operate power tools in nearby mines. Some of the compressed air leaks from the top of the cavern through joints in the enclosing rock and produces intense bubbling in the river above the cavern, particularly at joint intersections. Although the leakage is surplus to requirements at Ragged Chutes, recognition and control of all forms of escaping air are important considerations in the development of modern compressed air plants. In this report comparisons are made between the long established Ragged Chutes type of operation using hydraulic air compression and new concepts for large scale storage of compressed air energy by electric utilities using rotary compressors. Such concepts apply to New England as well as to other areas.

## INTRODUCTION

Underground storage of compressed air in natural or man-made caverns is being evaluated in the northeastern states and other regions as one method for electric utilities to meet the demand for peak power.

Integrity of the cavern to prevent leakage of air is essential for plant economics and equipment safety. Suitable containment may be found in solution cavities, in aquifers, and in hard rock caverns. In the last of these types, air leakage is most likely to occur along joint planes.

This report investigates a case of compressed air escaping from underground at a site in the Canadian shield, where a cavern was excavated 70 years ago. The location is Ragged Chutes on the Montréal River near Cobalt, Ontario.

While modern technology for compressed air storage involves the use of rotary air compressors, the Ragged Chutes plant operates by hydraulic air compression.

At this plant air is entrained by river water, compressed hydraulically at the bottom of a shaft 351 feet (107 m) in depth, stored in the cavern, and then piped as needed to operate power tools in nearby mines. The plant is still functioning and has required a minimum of maintenance.

But the number of active mines using compressed air from this plant has fallen in recent years.

A surplus of compressed air leaks from the cavern through the enclosing rock and quickly reaches the ground surface. Intense bubbling takes place in the river above the cavern, especially along straight lines where joint planes intersect (Figs. 1 and 2). Where sand bars overlie the rock of the river bed, bubbling is more diffused.

## UNDERGROUND STORAGE OF COMPRESSED AIR

The storage of compressed air in underground caverns for later use in turbine generation of electricity has recently become accepted as a valid concept. Operation of the 290 MW plant at Huntorf near the River Weser in West Germany since early 1978 has established the technology on a scale suitable for large utilities throughout the world. Storage of compressed air and gas at that location is in two underground cavities formed by solution in a natural salt formation. Plans were announced in 1972 for underground storage of compressed air in a hard rock cavern near Vaxjo in Sweden, but the project has been delayed.

Research and development programs leading to design work have also been undertaken in Luxembourg and other countries. In the United States, joint ventures formed by electric utilities and turbine manufacturers to undertake preliminary design studies have compared storage in (1) a solution cavity, (2) an aquifer, and (3) a hard rock cavern. The Department of Energy (DOE) and the Electric Power Research Institute (EPRI) are the principal sponsors of these three programs, and other investigations have begun with company funding.

The hard rock study, carried out by the Potomac Electric Power Company (PEPCO), with DOE and EPRI support, involves a site in the metamorphic terrain of eastern Maryland (Acres American, 1981; Thompson and Willett, 1982, this volume).

All three of the programs were completed in the 1980-81 time period, so that interested utilities can now evaluate not only the various compressed air storage (CAS) methods but also different turbomachinery plans for possible use in their own systems. Some have already expressed interest, and parts of Alabama, California, Georgia, Illinois, Indiana, Kansas, Michigan, Mississippi, Missouri, Pennsylvania, and Texas

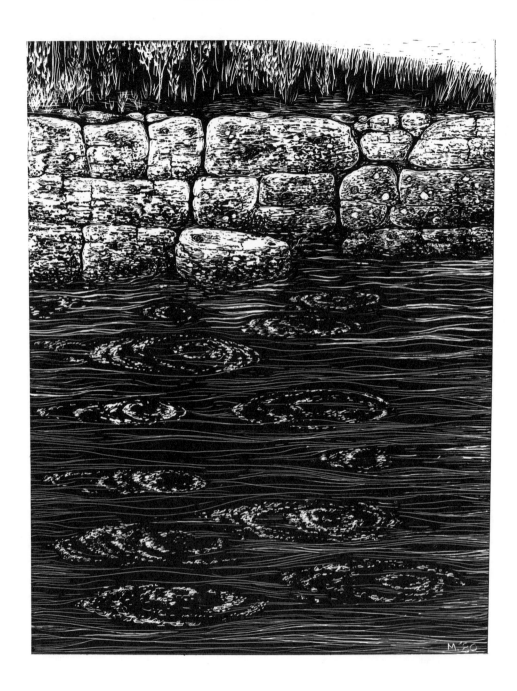

Figure 1. Conglomerate forming the bed and banks of the Montréal River, which in this view is flowing to the left. Compressed air escapes from a man-made cavern over 100 m beneath, moving along openings in the rock. Huge bubbles of the leaking air rise through the water from joint intersections, reaching the river surface in foaming circles up to six meters in diameter. From an 8 mm film.

have been considered, in addition to the Maryland site. Also, a study of potential underground energy storage in eastern Massachusetts for the Boston Edison Company is reported in this volume (Thompson and Vanderburgh, 1982). The various options in underground configuration, machine assembly, and fuel use appear to make widespread adoption of modern CAS technology generally attractive. More detailed assessments will depend upon local conditions which include the generation mix of the utility concerned, subsurface geology, and various economic factors. The three DOE/EPRI studies give a great amount of site-specific information on capital costs, plant efficiency, and operating characteristics.

The reason for converting hydraulic energy into compressed air is to store it for peaking and load leveling service. If the water power was used directly to operate turbines, the electricity generated would only be available on line for immediate consumption.

## HYDRAULIC AIR COMPRESSION

Air can be compressed hydraulically at suitable sites (Farquhar, 1977) as an alternative to the more modern method of using rotary compressors.

The principle of hydraulic air compression by the direct action of water is as follows. If a stream of water falls through a vertical pipe, any air diffused into, mixed with, and entrained in the water as it begins its downward motion will be compressed by the weight of the falling water. If the direction of flow is then changed to the horizontal, suddenly lessening the velocity, much of the air will be liberated and may be stored in a separation chamber. This chamber becomes an air receiver or plenum, the term referring to an enclosed space in which the pressure of the air is greater than that of the outside atmosphere. As used in this report, cavern is the general term for such space underground.

The hydraulic method of compressing large volumes of air is restricted to streams where the necessary quantity and head of water are available. If a pump is used to return the water to its original elevation, topographic relief ceases to be a consideration in siting. Moreover, the same water can be used indefinitely under these conditions, provided losses due to evaporation can be made up. If the water is used over and over again and the depth is sufficient, it may heat up because of repeated contact with the hot compressed air. Then the system will no longer remain isothermal, and provision may have to be made for cooling. At Ragged Chutes, however, advantage is taken of the normal drop in head along the river, and water continually flows through the underground system under the influence of gravity.

The operation of a hydraulic air compression plant is based on several essential features.

- Favorable geologic conditions.

- The construction and size of the dam, reservoir, and intake.

- The quantity of water needed to entrain the required number of cubic feet of air in a given time.

- The diameter of the shaft.

- The depth necessary to furnish the required pressure, and the provision of an air pipe for blow-off when the pressure exceeds a designed maximum.

- Means of separating air entrained in the water.

- The dimensions of the plenum or cavern and its height relative to the shaft.

- The quantity of air compressed.

- The diameter of the distribution pipelines.

- The characteristics of air compression and pressure reduction upon withdrawal, including the impact of any change in temperature.

- Maintenance facilities.

- Overall economic considerations.

Although modern concepts of CAS technology mainly involve rotary compressors, the centuries-old concept of hydraulic air compression has received renewed attention recently (Berghmans and Ahrens, 1978; General Electric Company, 1979; Norton and Huddleston, 1979; Rice and Wood, 1980).

## DESCRIPTION OF THE RAGGED CHUTES PLANT

The plant described in this report is situated on the Montréal River at Ragged Chutes, a few miles south of Cobalt, Ontario, and about 300 miles (483 km) almost due north of Toronto. Figure 3 shows the general plan of the project between the dam on the Montréal River and the outlet. Various pamphlets and articles about the Ragged Chutes plant issued in recent years by Ontario Hydro--and in earlier years by others before Ontario Hydro owned the plant--are listed at the end of this report.

Water flows from the river into an intake chamber measuring 50 by 40 feet (15 by 12 m) (Fig. 4). Within the chamber, there are two heads 16 feet (5 m) in diameter, each with 72 circular metal pipes 14 inches (35 cm) in diameter. Water with entrained air drops into these pipes, the level of which is controlled by a pneumatic lift attached to the heads.

There is a vertical play of 6 feet (about 2

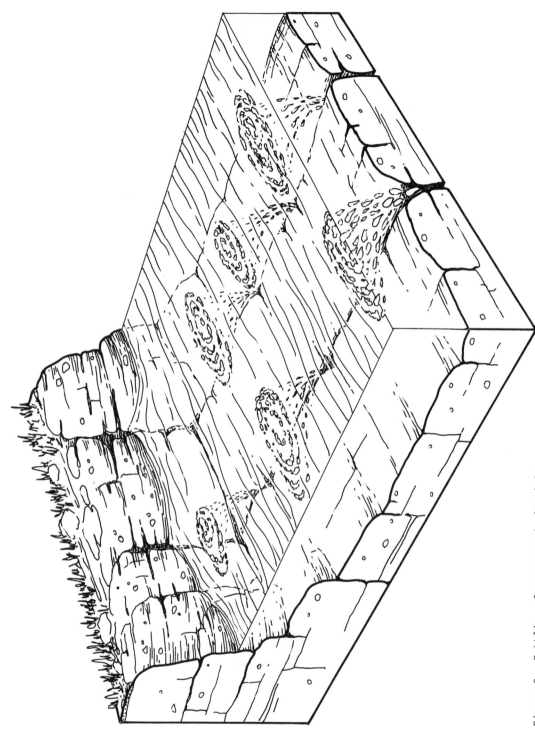

Figure 2. Bubbling of compressed air rising through the Montréal River at Ragged Chutes near Cobalt. The air escapes from a cavern over 100 m beneath and moves along discontinuities in the rock. The bubbles are swept by water currents into elliptical patterns elongated downstream.

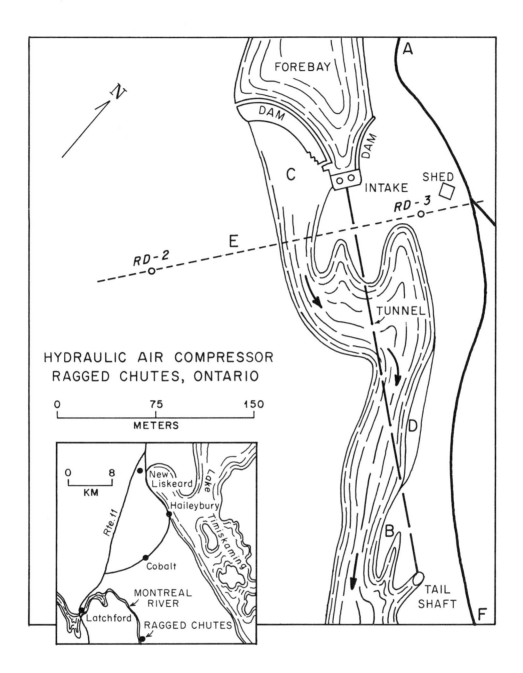

Figure 3. Location of the hydraulic air compression plant at Ragged Chutes on the Montréal
River near Cobalt, Ontario.  A-14.5 km to
Cobalt; B-boulders on river bank; C-conglomer-
ate below the dam (and in RD2); D-diabase dike
along the river bank (and in RD3); E-line of
exploration and drill holes; F-483 km to
Toronto; RD-rotary drill hole.

WATER AND AIR ARE TAKEN
THROUGH 144 PIPES OF 14
IN (35.56 CM) DIAMETER
AND DIRECTED INTO A SHAFT
351 FT (106.98 M) DEEP 10
FT (3.05 M) IN DIAMETER
AT THE TOP AND WIDER BELOW

RAGGED CHUTES
AIR PLANT

COMPRESSED AIR IS PIPED
FROM THE VALVE HOUSE TO
MINES IN THE COBALT AREA

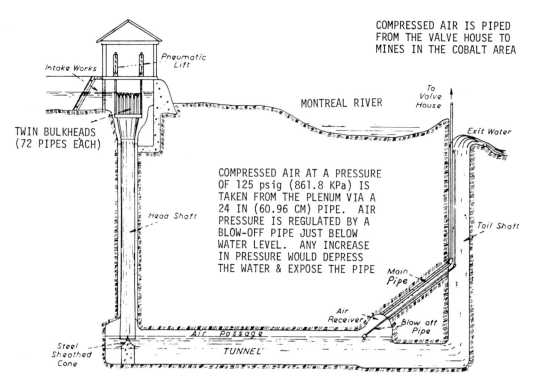

Pneumatic Lift

Intake Works

To Valve House

MONTREAL RIVER

Exit Water

TWIN BULKHEADS
(72 PIPES EACH)

Head Shaft

Tail Shaft

COMPRESSED AIR AT A PRESSURE
OF 125 psig (861.8 KPa) IS
TAKEN FROM THE PLENUM VIA A
24 IN (60.96 CM) PIPE. AIR
PRESSURE IS REGULATED BY A
BLOW-OFF PIPE JUST BELOW
WATER LEVEL. ANY INCREASE
IN PRESSURE WOULD DEPRESS
THE WATER & EXPOSE THE PIPE

Main Pipe

Air Receiver

Blow off Pipe

Steel Sheathed Cone

Air Passage

TUNNEL

TWO STEEL-SHEATHED
CONCRETE CONES AT THE
BOTTOM OF THE SHAFT
ASSIST IN SEPARATING
AIR FROM WATER AND
DIRECTING THE WATER
FLOW INTO A TUNNEL
28 FT (8.5 M) IN
DIAMETER AND 1021 FT
(311.2 M) IN LENGTH

SEPARATED AIR IS
COMPRESSED IN THE
ROOF OF THE TUNNEL
AND IN THE AIR
RECEIVER (PLENUM)
AT ITS DOWNSTREAM
END BY THE WEIGHT
OF THE WATER BODY

WATER CONTINUES
FLOWING ALONG THE
TUNNEL AND IS
DISCHARGED THROUGH
THE DOWNSTREAM
OUTLET SHAFT 298 FT
(90.83 M) IN HEIGHT

Figure 4. Diagrammatic section through Ragged
Chutes air plant, Cobalt, Ontario.

m) at the intake which allows the water entering
the pipes to be maintained at a constant depth
even with large variations in the river flow.
Control gates equipped with trash racks at the
entrance can lower or raise the volume of water
in the plant.

Upon entering the two heads, water falls
into the intake shaft, which is 351 feet (107 m)
in length and nine feet (2.7 m) in diameter at
the top, and which flares to 11-1/2 feet (3.5 m)
at the bottom.  At that point two steel-sheathed
concrete cones assist in separating air from water
and direct both into a horizontal tunnel.  The top
of the outlet shaft is 54 feet (16 m) lower than

the intake, the difference in level being the
effective head.  Thus, water flows by gravity
through the system.

The horizontal tailrace tunnel is 1021 feet
(311.2 m) long and 28 feet (8.5 m) wide.  At the
bottom of the intake it is 16-1/2 feet (5 m) high,
and near the foot of the outlet shaft the height
is 42 feet (13 m).  Compressed air collects in
this rock-enclosed cavern and is stored at 125
psig (862 kPa).  The air pipe leading from the
cavern is 24 inches (61 cm) in diameter.  Figure
5 shows the main part of the network of pipelines
supplying compressed air to metal mines near Cobalt.

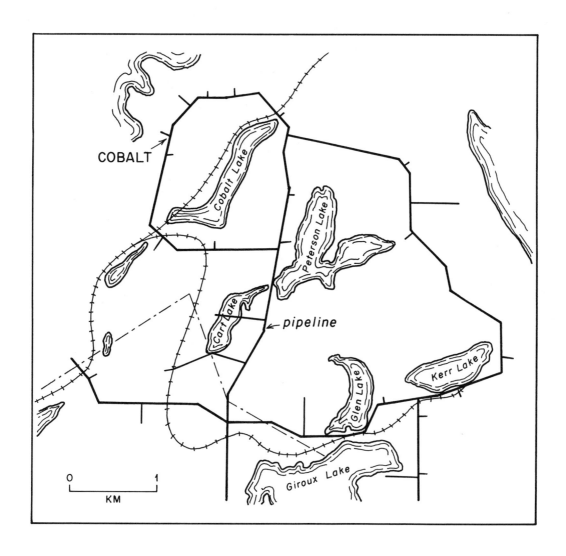

Figure 5.  Main part of the network of pipelines for supplying compressed air to metal
mines near Cobalt, Ontario.

Figure 6.  Working model of the hydraulic air
plant at Ragged Chutes, on display at the
Ontario Science Centre in Toronto.  ABOVE:
Photograph showing the control console.  RIGHT:
Drawing to explain how the model works.

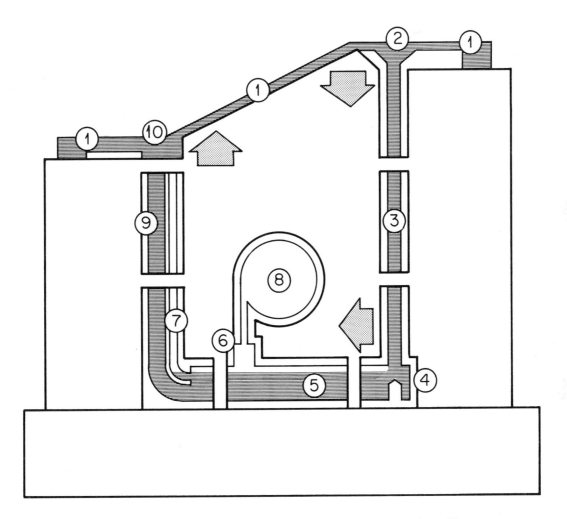

1. The river.

2. Intake: air drawn in with falling water.

3. Air compressed by water.

4. Air and water separated.

5. Air stored.

6. Compressed air released by valve.

7. Small pipe for blow-off to relieve pressure of excess air.

8. Air supply to mines.

9. Tail race.

10. Outlet: water reenters river.

The pneumatic lift is the only moving part in the entire Ragged Chutes installation, and periodic maintenance has kept it in repair. A few of the circular pipes near the upstream side of each of the two heads had to be replaced due to ice damage in 1950 and again in 1979. Otherwise the plant has been nearly maintenance free.

Alongside the air pipe from the cavern lies a 12-inch (30 cm) blow-off pipe. The end is at a precise level in the cavern so that, when the air pressure builds up to over 125 psig (862 kPa), the water level is depressed, and air is then released through the pipe to the atmosphere. The top of the blow-off pipe is 10 feet (3 m) below the surface of the water in the outlet shaft, and the released air blows water to heights of over 100 feet (30 m).

The volume of water diverted from the river into the plant compared with the volume going over the 660-foot (201 m) curved dam, varies according to the flow rate and the season. When the river is high, the water may be somewhat turbulent, entraining some air before entering the intake.

The capacity of the plant is 40,000 cubic feet (1,132 cu m) per minute of free air at 120 psig (827 kPa). The record total use of air in a single year was 523 million cubic feet (1.5 million cu m) at 120 psig (827 kPa) in 1925. Water storage in the forebay above the dam is sufficient to develop 10,000 horsepower (7,457 KW). However, 5,500 horsepower (4,101 KW) was enough to meet demand in the mines even when the plant was first put into operation, and the number of mines to which compressed air is supplied has steadily declined.

Beginning in 1896 other large plants of this type were installed at Norwich, Connecticut; Magog, Québec; Kamloops, British Columbia; and the Victoria Mine in northern Michigan. There may also have been a plant at Fresno, California (Schulze, 1954). Although about half-a-dozen plants were operated in North America in the first part of the twentieth century, Ragged Chutes is believed to be the only one still in use. It provides unique opportunities to observe air leakage. The Ontario Science Center in Toronto has a large working model of the plant (Fig. 6).

## PLANS FOR SITE REDEVELOPMENT

Ontario Hydro, the present owner of the Ragged Chutes plant, has been considering redevelopment of the site for several years. Investigations aimed at several objectives were made in the summer of 1972. The only objective of concern in this report is a preliminary geologic evaluation of the foundation conditions for a newly proposed hydroelectric structure. For the new structure the water level of the head pond would be at an elevation of 908 feet (276 m), or about 48 feet (14 m) above the existing high water level at Ragged Chutes (Ontario Hydro, 1973).

## STRATIGRAPHY AND STRUCTURAL GEOLOGY

Bed rock in the Ragged Chutes area is of Precambrian age and consists mainly of two units, as shown in Figure 7. Below the dam, which has a crest of 860 feet (262 m), the river runs over thick-bedded greenish-gray conglomerate of the Coleman Formation (Lower Huronian), which was intersected in RD-2, a rotary diamond hole, between elevations 850 and 829 feet (260 and 253 m) (Ontario Hydro, 1973). Core recovery from this hole was 100 percent, and water return was 100 percent. On the left bank a diabase of the Keeweenawan (or Nipissing) Group strikes N36°W and dips 75°SW, running almost parallel with the tunnel. This same rock was encountered at 794 feet (242 m) and was penetrated for 26 feet (8 m) to the bottom of RD-3. This is located, as is RD-2, on the east-west exploration line 100 feet (30 m) south of the existing dam. Core recovery from this hole was 83 percent, and water return was 100 percent.

On the right bank near Ragged Chutes are beds of graywacke and quartzite which probably belong to a third unit, the Firstbrook Formation. (The Coleman and the Firstbrook may be equivalent to parts of the widespread Gowganda Formation.) Samples of the conglomerate of the Coleman Formation, which is the main rock of the plant area, were collected from the bed of the river and closely examined. The rock consists of pebbles of many kinds, all of them of very hard rock. The matrix is unweathered and also appears completely sound. The drill samples of the conglomerate were taken more than 300 feet (91 m) above the cavern and some distance to the side, but there is no reason to believe the cavern rocks are different.

The metasedimentary rocks of the Coleman Formation beneath the plant and along the river bed dip gently northward with well-marked bedding planes and two prominent sets of almost vertical joints. The major set strikes N35°W and dips 78°SW, while the minor set strikes N57°E and dips 87°SE. Joint spacing ranges from 2 to 12 feet (60 to 360 cm) and averages 8 feet (245 cm) in the area of the dam.

Both bedding planes and joints permit air leakage to take place from the cavern below the river, particularly through the joints, which are more open than other discontinuities. Presumably escaping air limits the space occupied by water in the joints, which would otherwise be water-filled. The greatest volumes of air are released where joints intersect. Thus, the bubbles rising from the bed of the river tend to occur at points which lie along the joint planes.

There are sand bars in the river and fluvio-glacial materials covering adjacent land. The air permeates more slowly through such overburden, emerging over wide areas in small bubbles resembling the methane gas that rises from vegetation decaying in a pond.

On structural features, there are extensive

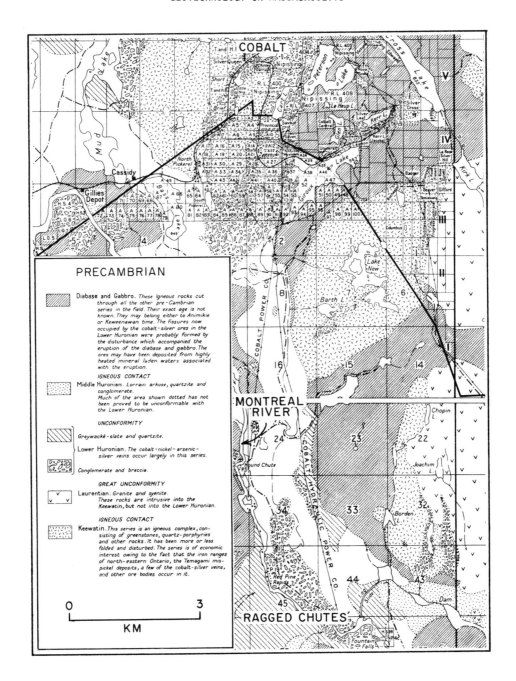

Figure 7. Part of Miller's 1910 geologic map
of the cobalt-nickel-arsenic-silver area west
of Lake Timiskaming, Ontario. This shows the
locations of the town of Cobalt and the site
of the Ragged Chutes compressed air plant on
the Montréal River. The principal rock is
conglomerate, now called the Coleman Formation.
Adjacent rocks include quartzite and diabase.
Areas with glacial and recent deposits are
unshaded.

data from geologic and mining studies. The region is crossed by several major northwest to southeast fractures including the Timiskaming fault and, between the Cross Lake and Latchford faults, the Montréal River fault, as shown on the 1977 Sudbury-Cobalt map on the 1:253,440 scale (no. 2361) in the geological compilation series of the Ontario Geological Survey. The Montréal River fault can be traced across South Lorrain Township, which is down the river from Ragged Chutes, on McIlwaine's 1970 geologic map on the 1:31,680 scale. The contacts of the Firstbrook Formation in that area have been displaced about 5000 feet (1524 m), with the north side moving to the northwest. This and adjacent faults appear also on the much larger scale of 1:15,480 on the 1978 preliminary map of the southern part of Lorrain Township by Lovell and de Grijs.

Another series of maps includes the Ontario Department of Mines provisional map of mining areas on the still larger scale of 1:4840. Additional sheets on the same scale and, therefore, usable as overlays, show "part of the underground workings and approximate structural contours." Although the Cobalt area itself is covered on this scale (Thomson, 1960-63), the Ragged Chutes area lies just to the south. Even so, detailed information available on neighboring rocks (e.g., Thomson, 1957; 1961; and 1964), including their geochemistry, physical properties, and geomechanical behavior, may prove to be of value in any further investigation of the site.

## RELEASE OF COMPRESSED AIR FROM UNDERGROUND STORAGE

During the operation of a plant with an underground storage cavern like Ragged Chutes, there are five ways in which compressed air might be released, although conditions leading to the last of these, no. 5, are most unlikely to occur and are considered only on a hypothetical basis in this particular setting. Nos. 1-3 are normal features of the plant operation. No. 4, air leakage through joints in the rock, is the main subject of this report, which describes the geologic conditions that permit leakage to take place.

### 1. Piped Supply

The main supply of compressed air goes through a large pipe to the valve house. From there it is distributed through about 14 miles of smaller pipes to metal mines in the Cobalt area, returning to the atmosphere after use in pneumatic tools.

### 2. Automatic Blow-off

Quantities of air are automatically released through a blow-off pipe when the pressure exceeds 125 psig (862 kPa). At that pressure the water level is depressed by the larger volume of air, causing the end of the pipe to be exposed. In the 70 years of the plant's operation this arrangement

has apparently always functioned as designed. Blow-off, which is intermittent, usually begins a few hours after the mines shut down at night when the pressure builds up due to lack of demand for compressed air. The longest periods are at the

weekend. The high-angled jet of moist air shooting across the Montréal River from the outlet on the left bank is shown here. Blow-off prevents potential damage by overloading of the underground system, thus eliminating a problem that could destroy the whole air storage concept.

### 3. Via the Tail Race

Air may remain entrained, and a smaller amount may be dissolved, in water leaving the tail race.

### 4. Leakage Through Joints

Compressed air leaks from the walls and roof of the cavern, but presumably not from the floor, which is covered by a considerable depth of tail water. The air escapes through joints in the bed rock, displacing water that would otherwise occupy the joints, and then follows one of three routes.

- Air can move from rocks that form the river bed into the water of the river, where it bubbles upward, usually with considerable force.

- Air can pass into unconsolidated sediments of varying permeability in the river bed.

- Air can escape directly into the atmosphere through rock materials along the river bank. When there are pools and muddy areas, bubbles can be seen. In other places hissing can be heard.

Intense bubbling in the river several hundred feet vertically above the cavern provides dramatic evidence of air leakage through the jointed rock. While the blow-off has always been regarded as spectacular, the bubbling in many respects is even more so. Figures 1 and 2 showing this phenomenon were drawn from a film of the water surface taken from the river bank.

The leakage through joints, while of scientific interest and engineering significance, is in no way hazardous, either to the plant or to the environment. In spite of continuous loss of compressed air, there is adequate pressure at all times to meet demand in local mines. There have been suggestions that the rate of air leakage has increased over the years, but there is no proof of this. The rate is bound to vary with the volume of water and air diverted from the river into the intake shaft, the volume of air being withdrawn, and the closeness of the water level to the mouth of the blow-off pipe. The way in which air reaches the river bed, particularly the size and concentration of the bubbles, is affected by the thickness of any sediment lying over the jointed rocks through which it escapes. Such a sediment cover depends upon the constantly changing balance in the river between erosion and deposition.

The suggestion that leakage has increased has led to the opinion that the cavern is doomed to eventual collapse. There is perhaps a partial precedent for this although with rock conditions and cavern depth that were entirely different. An underground power plant built in 1904 at Fairfax Falls, Vermont, was destroyed by a 1927 flood which broke through the shallow roof. Although the rock surrounding the Ragged Chutes cavern is much jointed there has been no evidence of actual instability. If, indeed, the rock did fall in, the river would continue to flow, and little environmental damage would result, but the plant would cease to operate as an air compressor.

In any event, the leakage at Ragged Chutes could be reduced without much difficulty by dewatering the cavern and pressure-grouting the most obvious of the natural joints in the surrounding rocks of the roof and walls. But with more compressed air available than is needed, there is no incentive to seal the cavern. In fact, dewatering has never been necessary for any reason in the 70-year life of the plant, and there is nothing

to indicate the condition of the cavern, except that it functions as it always has.

5. Upward Bubble Flow (hypothetical only)

Air could move back up the intake shaft if the downward flow of water lessened for any reason and if at the same time the outlet and the blow-off pipes both became blocked. Except when the intake is closed for maintenance, none of these events is likely to occur, and certainly not all at one time. However, some aspects of air escaping upward through a water column are briefly considered. Such reverse flow may be significant in certain underground air storage complexes.

In the PEPCO/DOE/EPRI study on the feasibility of using hard rock caverns for CAS (Acres American, 1981), water from a surface reservoir would be used to maintain pressure on the air as its volume decreases upon withdrawal during the generating cycle. In such a water-compensated cavern, air could diffuse into the water at their interface. Unless precautions are taken during the design of the underground openings, this condition could lead to the champagne effect in which a stream of depressurized air rapidly evacuates the cavern, endangering equipment at the top of the water shaft and resulting in a sudden loss of the stored energy.

Some research has already been undertaken to find ways of eliminating this danger, and more is planned. Specifically, EPRI has initiated new contracts to obtain fundamental data on the champagne effect. The data will be used to develop predictive tools to analyze the effectiveness of control strategies in order to mitigate possible instabilities caused by the champagne effect.

One contract is to identify possible European sites for a high pressure flow facility (about 50 atmospheres) for champagne effect testing and to prepare a detailed design for construction, operation, and testing of such a facility. Another contract is for a similar study considering sites in the United States. In addition, numerical models of the champagne effect will be updated as new data from tests become available. The completion of these and other studies will no doubt lead to further comprehensive and authoritative reports on the phenomenon. One of the latest is by Giramonti and Smith (1981).

The champagne effect is noted in this report, albeit briefly, because the Ragged Chutes operation affords an opportunity to consider some of the conditions under which the reversal of downward air flow to upward air flow could occur.

The phenomenon of air under hydraulic pressure escaping by moving upward faster than the water medium that confines it has been called flooding (Wallis, 1969). Flooding seems to correspond to perceptions of the champagne effect. It is a form of column separation arising from sudden instability of a two-phase mixture. The air would "slip" and the water would be subject to "holdup."

In regard to the movement of air and water mixtures, Berghmans and Ahrens (1978, p. 217) state that "Bubbly flow . . . changes into other flow patterns . . . when the void fraction of the flow becomes larger than 0.3." The void fraction in this case consists of air added in the intake shaft, which has not been dissolved but remains in the form of entrained bubbles. Berghmans and Ahrens go on to say that "For larger values of the void fraction, the flow pattern becomes irregular and may give rise to a net upward flow of air. This has to be avoided." They do not mention the champagne effect per se. The unstable conditions described also have been called backflow, apparently with the same meaning as flooding.

As already emphasized, however, the champagne effect could not occur at a plant with the design of Ragged Chutes, which includes automatic blow-off. In this report the effect is considered only on a hypothetical basis. At one time this plant, unique in North America, might have been suggested as a possible test facility. But the minimum pressure of 50 atm (735 psi) desired to simulate new technologic concepts for compressed air storage is almost six times that at Ragged Chutes (8.5 atm, 125 psi).

## CONCLUDING STATEMENT

In assessing the feasibility of CAS systems, evaluation of air leakage rates and availability of remedial measures are of great importance for economic reasons. This has been noted with increasing emphasis in a series of studies by Bush and others (1976), Giramonti (1976), and Acres American (1981). In the last of these, it was calculated that air leakage quantities range quite widely, depending upon rock conditions. For material having a hydraulic conductivity of $10^{-6}$ cm/s, leakage rates ranged from about 0.25 percent per day to 15 percent per day, depending among other factors on the direction of foliation and fracture planes in the rocks. Further, the depth of the cavern and the pressure of the surrounding ground water are major factors in preventing leakage of gas from unlined reservoirs (Aberg, 1977).

One special point concerns the temperature of the air compressed and stored. If the air can be heated, more energy can be extracted from it when used for generating or other work. If the heat produced during the compression cycle can be reserved and coolers are eliminated, the firing cycle in the case of turbogenerators may function without the addition of fuel. Such an adiabatic operation, with provision for thermal energy storage and using no fuel, is shown in Figure 8. The

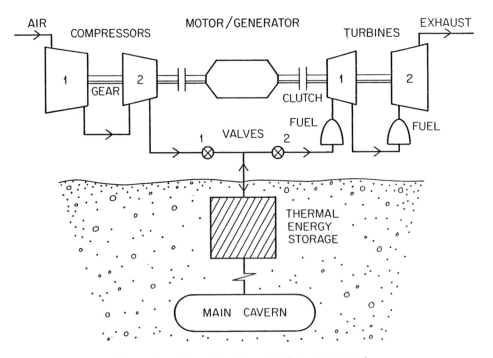

Figure 8. Schematic diagram of a compressed air storage plant showing above-ground facilities, as well as the underground openings. This configuration includes thermal energy storage for adiabatic operation, in which no fuel would be used.

thermal energy storage could be either underground or on the surface, in either case using a pebble bed or other suitable medium. In this configuration the heat would be too great for cycling in and out of the cavern and is removed by the medium before the compressed air enters the cavern, being restored to it upon leaving the cavern. Such adiabatic operation of CAS facilities is one of the newer, so-called second generation, concepts. While Ragged Chutes itself functions at ambient temperature, another rather similar plant in Canada affords some comparison with these adiabatic concepts. This was the Magog plant in Québec, also a hydraulic air compression plant, which has been defunct for many years. This plant had some capability for reheating water-cooled compressed air with steam, although the manipulation of temperature to improve the efficiency of the stored energy was on a very small scale compared with modern CAS designs for electric utilities.

CAS technology depends upon the integrity of each component, especially including the underground reservoir. Air leakage in excess of an acceptable maximum would not only result in a loss of energy, but would tend to lessen confidence in the stability of the underground system. The risk of excessive leakage could adversely affect the overall perception of large scale CAS using rotary compressors as an essentially new engineering development. By contrast, although there is substantial leakage through joints in the cavern rock at Ragged Chutes--where the plant operates by hydraulic air compression--enough compressed air remains to meet requirements, and there is no evidence that leakage is increasing.

## ACKNOWLEDGMENTS

Information and assistance from the Head Office of Ontario Hydro in Toronto and guidance in the field by staff members at Cobalt are gratefully acknowledged. The work was supported in part by Pacific Northwest Laboratories. Discussions with Terrence Doherty and Landis Kannberg were valuable. Comments by John Hubert and Arnold O'Brien, who reviewed the manuscript at different stages, are appreciated. The author alone is responsible for the facts presented and opinions expressed. Marie Litterer prepared several of the illustrations. The photograph in Figure 6 is by Leonard Brown of the Ontario Science Centre in Toronto.

## REFERENCES

Aberg, B., 1977, Prevention of gas leakage from unlined reservoirs in rock: Proceedings of International Symposium on Storage in Excavated Rock Caverns, Stockholm, p. 399-413.

Acres American, 1981, Preliminary design study of underground pumped hydro and compressed air energy storage in hard rock, Final Report; Volume IX, Design Approaches, CAES; Appendix A, Air Storage System; Attachment A, Air Leakage: PEPCO/DOE/EPRI, May 1980. (Date of issue by Electric Power Research Institute, 1981.)

Berghmans, J.A., and Ahrens, F.W., 1978, Performance of a hydraulic air compressor for use in compressed air energy storage power systems, in, Marston, C.H., Fluids engineering in advanced energy systems: American Society of Mechanical Engineers, p. 213-227.

Bush, J.B., Jr., and others, 1976, Economic and technical feasibility study of compressed air storage: U.S. Energy Research and Development Administration, 76-76, and General Electric Company, Schenectady, 9 sections and appendices.

Farquhar, O.C., 1977, Origins of compressed air storage underground: Proceedings, 10th World Energy Conference, Istanbul, v. 1, p. 411-414.

General Electric Company, 1979, Hydro compression gas turbine package power plant: Technical proposal DE-PA-07-79 ID 12055 to DOE Idaho.

Giramonti, A.J., 1976, Preliminary feasibility evaluation of compressed air storage power systems: United Technologies Research Center, NSF Grant AER-74-00242, 2 volumes.

Giramonti, A.J., and Smith, E.B., 1981, Control of the champagne effect in CAES power plants: 16th Annual Intersociety Energy Conversion Engineering Conference, Atlanta, v. 1, p. 984-988.

Lovell, H.L., and de Grijs, J., 1978, Lorrain Township, southern part, Concessions I to VI, District of Timiskaming: Ontario Geological Survey, Preliminary Map P. 1559, Geological Series, scale 1:15,840. Geology 1973, 1974.

McIlwaine, W.H., 1970, Geology of South Lorrain Township: Ontario Department of Mines, Geological Report 83, 95 p., Geologic Map, 1:31,680.

Miller, W.G., 1910, Map of cobalt-nickel-arsenic-silver area, near Lake Timiskaming, Ontario: with Ontario Bureau of Mines Annual Report, v. 19, pt. 2, 4th edition, scale 1:63,360.

Norton, J.R., and Huddleston, C.R., 1979, Exploiting dam potential: Water Power and Dam Construction, v. 31, p. 36-38. (See also, Norton, J.R., 1981: Water Power and Dam Construction, v. 33, no. 9, p. 33-36).

Ontario Geological Survey, 1977, Sudbury-Cobalt: Geological Compilation Series, Map 2361, scale 1:253,440.

Ontario Hydro, 1973, Montréal River, Ragged Chutes redevelopment, preliminary geotechnical feasibility study: Generation Projects Division, Report 119-31, March, 10 p., maps, copyright.

Rice, W., and Wood, B.D., 1980, Characteristics of the hydraulic air compressor as a small hydropower device, in, Small hydro-power fluid machinery: American Society of Mechanical Engineers, p. 81-87.

Schulze, L.E., 1954, Hydraulic air compressors: U.S. Bureau of Mines, Information Circular 7683, 38 p.

Thompson, S.N., and Vanderburgh, M.R., 1982, Preliminary studies of underground energy storage for the Boston Edison Company: this volume.

Thompson, S.N., and Willett, D.C., 1982, DOE/EPRI underground energy storage study: this volume.

Thomson, R., 1957, The Proterozoic of the Cobalt area, in Gill, J.E., ed., The Proterozoic in Canada: Royal Society of Canada, Special Publication, no. 2, p. 40-45.

Thomson, R., 1960-1963, Preliminary reports on parts of Coleman Township and Gillies Limit to the south and southwest of Cobalt: Ontario Department of Mines.

Thomson, R., 1961, Part of Coleman Township, Concessions V & VI, Lots 1-6, District of Timiskaming: Ontario Department of Mines, Provisional Maps P-97 and P-97A, 1:4840.

Thomson, R., 1964, Cobalt silver area: Ontario Department of Mines, Map 2051.

Wallis, G.B., 1969, One-dimensional two-phase flow: McGraw-Hill, 408 p.

BIBLIOGRAPHY

*Ahrens, F.W., and Berghmans, J.A., 1978, Preliminary evaluation of the use of hydraulic air compressors in water-compensated reservoir CAES power plants: Symposium Proceedings, Compressed Air Energy Storage, Volume 1, Pacific Grove, p. 513-534.

#Anderson, W.E., 1963, Historical information on Ragged Chutes: Hydroelectric Power Commission of Ontario, Memorandum, September 10, 3 p.

#Baldwin, D., and Dunn, J.A., 1976, Cobalt--a pictorial history of the development of silver mining: Highway Bookshop, Cobalt, Ontario, 72 p. Popular.

*Barton, N.R., 1972, A model study of air transport from underground openings situated below groundwater level, in, Percolation through fissured rock: Symposium Proceedings, International Society for Rock Mechanics and International Association of Engineering Geology, Stuttgart, Paper T3-A, 20 p.

#Bateman, G.C., 1912, Power development in Cobalt: The Canadian Engineer, p. 815. Not seen.

*Bawden, W.F., and Roegiers, J.C., 1980, Two-phase flow through rock fractures: Proceedings of International Symposium for Environmental Protection, Low-Cost Storage and Energy Savings, Stockholm, Abstract S103.

*Bernell, L., and Lindbo, T., 1965, Tests of air leakage in rock for underground reactor containment: Nuclear Safety, v. 6, no. 3.

*Blecher, W.A., Giramonti, A.J., and Smith, E.B., 1978, The champagne effect in hydraulically compensated compressed air energy storage systems: Symposium Proceedings, Compressed Air Energy Storage, Volume 2, Pacific Grove, p. 635-665.

#Canadian Mining Journal, 1909, The plant and equipment of the Cobalt Hydraulic Power Company: v. 30, October 15, p. 611-617.

#Cassidy, G.L., 1976, Arrow north--the story of Timiskaming: Highway Bookshop, Cobalt, Ontario, 398 p. Popular.

*Clift, R., Grace, J.R., and Weber, M.E., 1978, Bubbles, drops and particles: Academic Press, 380 p.

#Compressed Air Magazine, 1963, An operating Taylor hydraulic compressor: October, p. 24-25.

#Corkill, E.T., 1910, Water power for working mines: Ontario Bureau of Mines, Annual Report, no. 19, pt. 1, p. 131-148.

*Dana, R.T., also Loomis, A.W., 1941, Compressed air practice, in Peele, R., ed., Mining Engineers' Handbook: Wiley, 3rd Edition, v. 2, section 15.

*Di Biagio, E., and Myrvoll, F., 1972, In situ tests for predicting the air and water permeability of rock masses adjacent to underground openings, in, Percolation through fissured rock: Symposium Proceedings, International Society for Rock Mechanics and International Association of Engineering Geology, Stuttgart, Paper T1-B, 15 p.

#Douglas, D.P., 1944, Ragged Chutes plant: Mining Industry (Hydro Electric Development), Bulletin 46, p. 20.

#Eaton, L., 1933, Efficient air compressing: Engineering and Mining Journal, v. 134, no. 6, p. 245-247.

*Ervine, D.A., 1976, The entrainment of air in water: Water Power and Dam Construction, v. 28, no. 12, p. 27-30.

*Glendenning, I., 1979, Compressed air storage: Proceedings of International Conference on Future Energy Concepts, London, England, p. 195-198.

*Govier, G.W., and Aziz, K., 1972, The flow of complex mixtures in pipes: Van Nostrand Reinhold, 792 p.

#Gray, A., 1908, Compressed air for mining in Cobalt District: Mining World, v. 29, December 12, p. 877-879.

#Hartenberg, R.S., and Denavit, J., 1960, The fabulous air compressor: Machine Design, v. 32, no. 15, July 21, p. 168-170.

*Hewitt, G.F., 1978, Measurement of two phase flow parameters: Academic Press, 280 p.

#Hunt, J.R., 1977, Harness hydro power with a trompe: Mother Earth News, Hendersonville, N.C., July/August. Popular.

*Hussain, N.A., and Siegel, R., 1976, Liquid jet pumped by rising gas bubbles: Journal of Fluids Engineering, v. 98, ser. 1, no. 1, p. 49-57.

*Katz, D.L., and Lady, E.R., 1976, Compressed air storage: Ulrich's Books, Ann Arbor, Michigan, 244 p.

#Klein, R., 1977, Cobalt carries on with unique hydraulic plant: The Ontario Technologist, v. 19, no. 6, p. 8-12.

*Lady, E.R., and Katz, D.L., 1978, Underground compressed-air storage for electric utility load leveling: Journal of Petroleum Technology, v. 30, no. 11, p. 1656-1660.

*Lance, M., Charnay, G., and Bataille, J., 1978, A hydrodynamic tunnel for water-air flow turbulence research: La Houille Blanche, v. 33, no. 5, p. 331-335.

*Lundstrom, L., and Stille, H., 1976, Large scale permeability test of the granite in the Stripa mine and thermal conductivity test: Swedish-American Cooperative Program on Radioactive Waste Storage in Mined Caverns in Crystalline Rock, Technical Project Report No. 2, Lawrence Berkeley Laboratory LBL-7052, SAC-02. Date not verified.

*Matikainen, R., 1978, Structure and operation of underground hydraulic compressed-air reservoirs in Finland: Proceedings of International Symposium on Storage in Excavated Rock Caverns, Stockholm, p. 705-710.

*Miller, C.H., and others, 1974, An air injection technique to study intensity of fracturing around a tunnel in volcanic rocks: Bulletin of the Association of Engineering Geologists, v. 11, no. 3, p. 203-217.

*Mollendorf, J.C., Champagne effect phenomena evaluation in hydraulically-compensated compressed air energy storage systems, in, Acres American Final Report; Volume IX, Design Approaches, CAES; Appendix B, Champagne Effect, Attachment A: PEPCO/DOE/EPRI, September 1980. (Date of issue by Electric Power Research Institute, 1981.)

*Morel-Seytoux, H.J., and others, eds., 1979, Modeling hydrologic processes: Proceedings, 3rd International Hydrology Symposium, Fort Collins, 818 p.

*Mundi, E.K., and Wallace, J.R., 1973, On the permeability of some fractured crystalline rocks: Bulletin of the Association of Engineering Geologists, v. 10, no. 4, p. 299-312.

#Murphy, J.P., 1977, Yankee takeover at Cobalt: Highway Bookshop, Cobalt, Ontario, 200 p. Popular.

#Ontario Hydro, Ragged Chutes compressed air plant, New Liskeard area: 3 p. Undated.

*Peele, R., 1930, Compressed air plant: Wiley, 2nd edition, 1910, 502 p. (5th edition, 1930, p. 204-216).

*Pellin, J., 1979, Compressed air power plant--project of the Société Electrique de l'Our: Notes for a meeting on the Resolution of the CAS Champagne Effect, sponsored by the Electric Power Research Institute, Washington, D.C. Unpublished.

#Professional Engineer and Engineering Digest, 1950's, The Cobalt Hydraulic Air Plant: p. 37-38.

*Rice, W., 1976, Performance of hydraulic gas compressors: Journal of Fluids Engineering, v. 98, p. 645-653.

*Sabina, A.P., 1973, Rocks and minerals for the collector, Cobalt-Belleterre-Timmins, Ontario and Québec: Geological Survey of Canada, Paper 73-13, 199 p.

*Salih, A.M.A., and Kenn, M.J., 1974, Entrained air in an accelerating water flow: Water Power and Dam Construction, v. 26, no. 1, p. 34. Letter.

*Savage, W.Z., 1979, A model of the strain response of Barre Granite to wetting and drying: U.S. Geological Survey, Open-File Report 79-768, 17 p.

*Sherwood, T.K., Pigford, R.L., and Wilke, C.R., 1975, Mass transfer: McGraw-Hill, 677 p.

*Smedes, H.W., 1980, The issue of fracture hydrology in crystalline rocks--presumptions versus facts: Geological Society of America, Abstracts with Programs, v. 12, no. 7, p. 524.

*Smith, E.B., Blecher, W.A., and Giramonti, A.J., 1978, Modeling the champagne effect in compressed air energy storage, in, Marston, C.H., Fluids engineering in advanced energy systems: American Society of Mechanical Engineers.

#Standing, G.N., 1955, Ragged Chutes hydraulic air plant: Canadian Institute of Mining and Metallurgy, presented orally at Haileybury, Ontario, October 14, 7 p. Transcript.

#Taylor, C.H., 1910, Cobalt hydraulic air compressor: Mines and Minerals, v. 30, no. 9, April, p. 532-534.

#Taylor, C.H., 1913, The measurement of compressed air delivered by the hydraulic compressor, Cobalt: Canadian Mining and Metallurgical Transactions, v. 16, p. 201-215.

#On the death of Taylor, C.H., 1953, Canadian Mining and Metallurgical Bulletin, December.

*Underground Space, 1979, Notes on compressed air plants in Canada: v. 4, no. 1, p. 29-31.

#W., E.B., 1910, Hydraulic air compression: Mines and Minerals, v. 31, no. 3, October, p. 129-131.

*Watters, G.Z., 1979, Modern analysis and control of unsteady flow in pipelines: Ann Arbor Science, 251 p.

*Wijeyesekera, D.S., 1974, Air entrainment in vertical shafts: Water Power and Dam Construction, v. 26, no. 6, p. 220-223.

*Wittke, W., Pierau, B., and Schetelig, K., 1978, Planning of a compressed-air pumped-storage scheme at Vianden, Luxembourg: Proceedings of International Symposium on Storage in Excavated Rock Caverns, Stockholm, p. 367-376.

#Zienke, P.C., 1944, Water power operated air compressors: Power Plant Engineering, December, p. 77.

# Pamphlets or articles concerning Ragged Chutes.

* Mainly concerning air or water flow.  □

Hors-texte

Quicquid sub terra est, or Whatever is under the earth, is the motto of one of the oldest scientific societies, the Geological Society of London, founded in 1807. The motif is reproduced here by permission.

# System concepts for thermal energy storage in aquifers

M. J. HOBSON
S. BAHADUR
Acres American Incorporated

## ABSTRACT

Thermal energy storage (TES) in aquifers has been studied extensively in recent years and is now undergoing physical testing at selected sites. Attention has been focused mainly on performance of the aquifer as a storage medium. However, for a TES system to function satisfactorily, many additional components are required.

Available sources of low cost heat or cold energy are necessary for charging the aquifer; a purchaser for the energy is required, willing to sign a long-term contract to pay off the investment charges; and subsystems for collection, transmission, storage and distribution of the energy are necessary to link the energy supply to the aquifer and the aquifer to the purchaser.

This paper reviews criteria that aquifer TES systems will be required to meet if the concept is to be developed for commercial application. The information has been drawn from a study performed by Acres American Incorporated for the Tennessee Valley Authority.

## BACKGROUND

Thermal energy storage (TES) in an aquifer is accomplished by withdrawal of water from an underground aquifer, heating or cooling it, then reinjecting the energized water into the aquifer. After a period of storage, which can be in excess of a year, the stored water is withdrawn and the thermal energy removed for either heating or cooling. Figure 1 shows a typical hot water TES system complete with two wells, a heat exchanger, and a transmission system for supply and removal of heat.

In the system shown in Figure 1, the two wells form a doublet which functions as a supply and return couple. As heat is injected, the 'hot' zone around the injection well expands by pushing out the thermocline (division line between hot and cold aquifer water). At the same time, water is being withdrawn by the 'warm' well. The water around this well is warm because during successive cycles the return water is not usually cooled to the ambient temperature of the aquifer but to some intermediate 'warm' temperature between the 'hot' storage temperature and the cold ambient.

The overlying rock masses effectively insulate an aquifer against thermal loss or gain; also, the use of aquifers for storage greatly reduces the problems of environmental restrictions and space limitations associated generally with the construction of storage facilities on the surface. Confining layers above and below the aquifer prevent water migration in a vertical direction. Horizontal migration is possible, and with it loss of stored heat. It is therefore essential to select a storage site where the natural hydraulic gradient is low and water movement in the aquifer is minimal.

Mathematical simulation projections indicate that energy recovery can approach 85 percent, but these estimates have not yet been proven in field tests, possibly due to an insufficient number of cycles and inadequate water flow.

The utilization of the aquifer water in a closed system minimizes the problems associated with contamination which may be caused by mixing two waters of different chemical composition. However, even with this cycle, changing pressure and temperature may cause chemical interaction of the energized water with the aquifer mineral skeleton and aquifer water, and also with the heat exchangers, pumps, and piping of other subsystems.

## THE CONCEPT

The storage of heat or cold energy in aquifers appears to be an attractive method of conserving energy. Waste heat from industrial processes or power generation can be collected, aquifer water can be heated and the warmed water can be stored in the aquifer unit as required. On demand the warm water can be withdrawn from the aquifer and utilized for space heating or for process heating. Alternatively, the aquifer water may be cooled by atmospheric cold or cool river or lake water. The cooled water can be reinjected into the aquifer and stored until required for summer space cooling or process cooling.

These concepts usually have a seasonal time base and are directed toward storage of the thermal energy for periods of up to one year. This long time period raises questions of the ability of an aquifer rock formation to retain energy effectively, and for this reason much attention has been concentrated on the numerical modeling of aquifers in the storage mode and latterly on physical testing.

There are, however, many other requirements that have to be met for an aquifer TES system to be feasible.

- Agreement by local government agencies that an aquifer can be utilized for TES.

- Feasibility of installing a system of injection and production wells, designed to charge and discharge the storage

aquifer.

- Adequate availability of thermal energy at sufficiently high (or low) temperatures for cost effective recovery and utilization.

- Geochemical compatibility between aquifer

## HOT WATER TRANSMISSION SUBSYSTEM

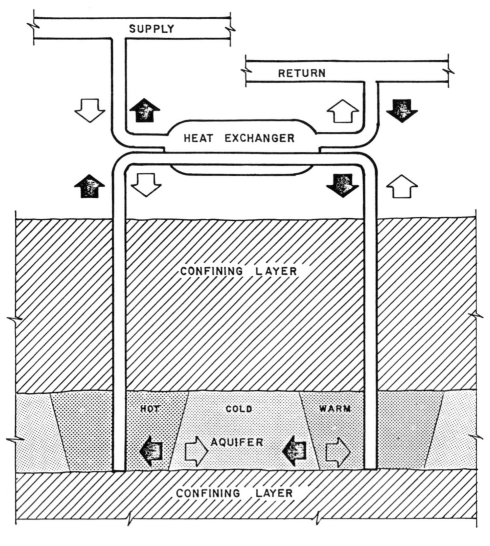

Figure 1. Diagram of doublet well storage concept.

water and mineral skeleton with temperature/pressure changes.

- Sufficient customer demand for the stored thermal energy within acceptable transmission distances.

- Willingness of customers to sign long-term energy supply agreements.

- Availability of acceptable space for installation of surface plant facilities.

- Provision for corrosion and scaling effects in heat exchangers, pumps, etc.

- Ability to obtain rights-of-way for transmission pipelines and/or culverts.

- Ability to gain access to all plant facilities and pipelines for maintenance and repair.

- Ability to comply with all local, state and federal regulations.

- Avoidance of potential environmental damage.

It is apparent, therefore, that both the technical and the economic feasibility of aquifer TES requires careful evaluation before the concept is adopted as a viable conservation strategy.

The major aspects of an aquifer storage system are now examined from the viewpoint of commercial application of the concept.

## POTENTIAL CUSTOMERS

An aquifer TES system requires considerable investment for well drilling, heat exchangers, pumps and piping. It is therefore economically feasible only for relatively large consumers of heat or cold energy. Such large users will be confined to facilities that already purchase energy in the form of fuel or electricity and can show a saving on present supply costs by switching to aquifer TES. Such customers could be airports, hospitals, armed forces bases, schools and universities, institutional complexes, large office and apartment buildings, and similar facilities. Their energy need is likely to be more of a seasonal heating or cooling load than a daily or weekly cycle because shorter cycles can be accommodated more economically in surface tanks or similar storage systems.

The water supply temperatures that heating and cooling systems utilize are between 180°F and 300°F for heating and between 38°F and 50°F for cooling. If these temperatures cannot be attained in an aquifer TES system, it is feasible for the system to function in a support role by bringing the hot or chilled water to a temperature near that required and so alleviate the load on the existing system. Many heating and cooling circuits are designed to operate on a variable temperature basis, so that only on high load days will the backup system be required to cut in.

## THERMAL ENERGY SOURCES

For an aquifer TES system to be economically feasible, the heat or cold energy source must be of low cost. Industrial and power plant waste heat, solar heat, or atmospheric cold are the possibilities that merit examination.

A study (Drexel, 1976) evaluating industrial energy consumption and waste energy identified five waste streams of significant waste heat energy. These waste energy streams, in general applicable to all industries, are defined as:

| | | |
|---|---|---|
| (1) Condenser cooling water (liquid) | 90°F | - 130°F |
| (2) Low pressure steam to condenser (saturated vapor) | 100°F | - 140°F |
| (3) Contaminated process water (liquid) | 140°F | - 200°F |
| (4) Boiler plant exhaust (gas) | 300°F | - 600°F |
| (5) Furnace exhaust (gas) | 500°F | - 1000°F |

Of these five waste energy streams, only the three at higher temperatures are considered practical for providing heat input to aquifer TES. However, the two low temperature supplies may have potential in certain specific applications.

The following industries appear to be candidates for supply of low cost waste heat because flows above $2 \times 10^{12}$ Btu/yr are available. This value is selected as a lower practical limit for injection into a storage system.

| Standard Industrial Code (SIC) | Industry |
|---|---|
| 20 | Food and kindred products |
| 22 | Textile mills |
| 24 | Lumber and wood |
| 26 | Paper and pulp |
| 28 | Chemicals |
| 29 | Petroleum |
| 32 | Stone, clay and glass |
| 33 | Primary metals |
| 37 | Transportation equipment |

Plants producing electric power by a thermal process are also candidates. There are three types of power plants with useful heat discharges: fossil-fueled steam turbines, oil- and gas-fired combustion turbines, and nuclear powered steam turbines. Various approaches for extraction of useful heat are listed below.

- Increased steam flows from existing turbine extraction points. Nuclear and fossil-fuel steam plants.

Figure 2. Distribution of solar energy over
the United States. The figures give solar heat
in Btu/ft$^2$ per average day (insolation).

- Extract steam from the HP/IP crossover
  point (reheat lines) or from the IP/LP
  crossover point. Nuclear and coal-fired
  steam plants.

- Extract heated feedwater from the feedwater system. Nuclear and fossil-fuel
  steam plants.

- Condenser circulating water. Nuclear and
  fossil-fuel steam plants.

- Boiler stack gases. Fossil-fuel steam
  plants.

- Combustion turbine exhaust gases. Oil-
  and gas-fired combustion turbines.

However, each of these approaches requires complicated equipment additions to an already complex
plant.

Cogeneration offers an attractive source of
heat energy. Cogeneration, the simultaneous production of electricity and thermal energy, has a
potentially impressive overall thermal efficiency
compared to conventional thermal power stations.

One of the problems of using cogeneration in
space heating is the low annual load factor of a
typical space heating load. This requires an
investment in heat generation equipment for operation at low load for much of its life. However,
by combining TES with a cogeneration plant, the
heat load can be levelized to match the electric
load of the process system, and investment in
heat-producing equipment can be minimized. The
TES system will then function as a heat absorber
and supplier on a seasonal basis. The heat supply
to the TES system can be from a steam turbine exhaust heat exchanger or gas turbine exhaust water
heater. (Figure 5 shows a typical cogeneration
system with TES balancing.)

Solar energy can provide heat input to aquifer TES for later transmission and distribution
to users remote from industrial waste heat
sources. The solar heat potential within a particular geographic region can be estimated by
defining the following parameters:

- Geographical location.

- Insolation available for the defined area.
  (Insolation is the average incident solar
  energy flux on a horizontal flat surface
  Btu/ft$^2$-day over a 24 hour period.)

- Insolation variation.

TABLE 1.  OUTLET TEMPERATURE AND EFFICIENCY OF A RANGE OF COLLECTION SYSTEMS

| | Single cover pond | Flat-plate collector (tubular) | Commercial one-axis tracking | Advanced one axis | Fully tracking parabolic dish | Heliostat |
|---|---|---|---|---|---|---|
| Concentration ratio | 1 | 1 | 60 | 60 | 1000 | 500 |
| Outlet temperature * (°F) | 90 | 200 | 300 | 600 | 1500 | 950 |
| Efficiency ** | -- | 48 | 45 | 57 | 71 | 77 |

NOTES:  *  Outlet temperature is the temperature of the working fluid (assumed to be water).
       ** Efficiency is the ratio of output energy to input energy (insolation).

● Collector type and respective performance.

Figure 2 shows the distribution of solar energy over the United States.  Various solar heat collection types are available.  Table 1 shows the outlet temperature and efficiency of a range of collection systems.

This table shows that the single cover solar pond is not a suitable collection system for aquifer heat storage because of its low output temperature.  The expected annual performance of each collector type is shown in Figure 3.

The storage of cold energy in an aquifer by chilling aquifer water may also be an economically feasible application of TES.  This cold energy could be used to satisfy space and industrial process cooling requirements.

A previous study at John F. Kennedy Airport, New York City, proposed the concept of atmospheric cold for space cooling utilizing aquifer storage (Thermal Energy Storage in Aquifers, Proceedings, 1978).  Results of the study suggest a chilled water supply temperature of 45°F to 50°F for circulation to building-fan coil units.  To provide this chilled water supply temperature, the storage water temperature within the aquifer is required to be 40°F to 45°F, and the cold water input to the aquifer is to be injected at temperatures of 35°F to 40°F.

Potential sources of cold energy are winter air, cold lakes, cold rivers, and possibly cold ground.  Figure 4 provides a plot of the average Mississippi River water temperatures (at Memphis) throughout the year.  The plot indicates that average temperatures below 50°F are available from mid-November to mid-February.  In such cases, additional cooling, either by chillers or wet cooling towers, would be required.

However, the use of river water/aquifer storage for preliminary cooling of chilled water can save substantial chiller load by reducing the

chilled water temperature from 60°F to 53°F.  For a 500 gpm flow rate, a typical production well flow, chiller load can be reduced by 310 tons continuously for the summer cooling season.

SYSTEM COMPONENTS

The transfer of thermal energy from the source to the end user comprises four subsystems.

● The collection subsystem recovers and transfers waste thermal energy from a given source to a working fluid conveyed in a transmission subsystem.

● The transmission subsystem conveys the recovered thermal energy to the storage subsystem or to the distribution subsystem depending on the load profile of the end user.  The transmission subsystem performs as a central system integrating the collection, storage, and distribution subsystems.  The transmission subsystem is also responsible for the long distance transfer of thermal energy (if required at a particular site).

● The storage subsystem transfers the thermal energy received from the transmission subsystem to an aquifer for storage and produces that energy upon demand by the transmission subsystem.  The preferred storage period for aquifer systems is seasonal, although shorter storage durations are possible.

● The distribution subsystem delivers the thermal energy received from the transmission subsystem to the end users upon demand.

Collection Subsystem

The reclaiming of waste heat from industrial

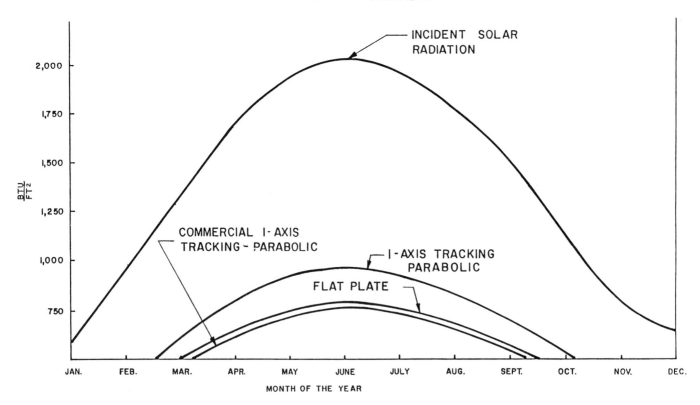

Figure 3.  Expected collector performance.

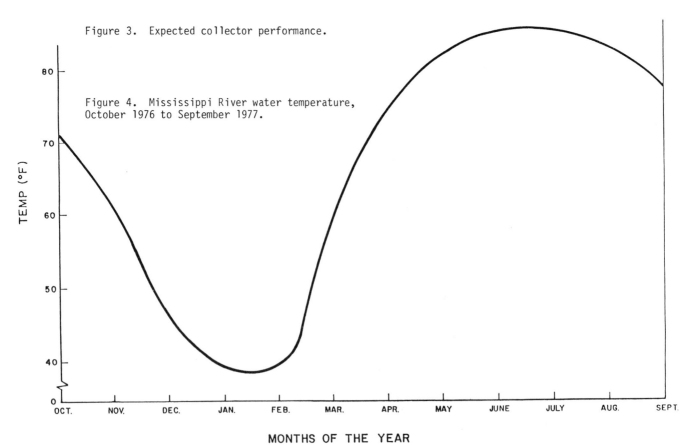

Figure 4.  Mississippi River water temperature,
October 1976 to September 1977.

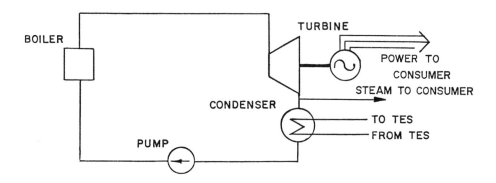

Figure 5. Utilization of thermal energy storage (TES) to balance steam and power loads in a cogeneration system.

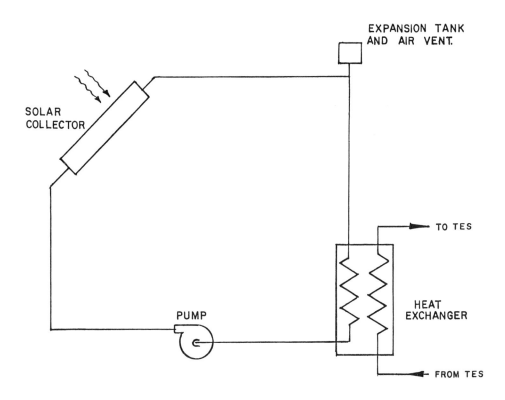

Figure 6. Solar energy collection subsystem for TES supply.

processes is generally achieved by use of heat exchangers. Low temperature water waste heat flows can be recovered by relatively simple water heat exchanger designs. However, the recovery of heat from a boiler exhaust requires an economizer. This device is a gas-to-water heat exchanger installed in the boiler flue gas ductwork ahead of the induced draft fan. The heating surface is critical because boiler exit gases should not be allowed to approach the dewpoint temperature of $H_2SO_4$, where severe corrosion results and sulfur flake deposits occur close to the stack. Furnace exhaust gas heat can also be recovered in an economizer or, possibly, when gas temperatures are high, in a regenerative heat recovery device.

Power plant heat extraction also requires water-to-water or gas-to-water heat exchangers. When both heat and electric power are produced from a power plant it is called cogeneration.

One concept for utilizing heat storage to improve cogeneration is presented in Figure 5. The ability to absorb excess exhaust steam permits flexibility between the production of heat and power, enabling the power plant to respond more satisfactorily to variable electrical power and heating demands.

The advantages of applying aquifer seasonal thermal energy storage in cogeneration include:

- Increased flexibility in the generation of electric power.

- Storage of surplus cogenerated heat.

- Recovery of stored heat to meet peak heating demands.

- Reduction in auxiliary boiler capacity by leveling of peak heating demands.

The recovery of thermal energy from cogeneration plants can be achieved with standard shell and tube exchangers.

Solar energy collection subsystems can interface with other subsystems by the use of gas-liquid or liquid-liquid heat exchangers. Figure 6 shows a simple schematic of a potential solar energy collection subsystem.

Winter cold in atmospheric air and surface water can be stored as cold water in aquifers and withdrawn during the summer for space cooling. Cooling towers (dry or wet) could be utilized for the recovery of cold in atmospheric air, and heat exchangers are applicable for the recovery of cold in surface water. A wet cooling tower utilizes direct contact between the warm cascading water and atmospheric air to achieve the desired cooling effect on the water. Operation of a dry cooling tower involves the flow of fluid through a heat exchanger coil exposed to the forced draft of cold atmospheric air. In this indirect system the working fluid is closed to the surroundings.

Since cooling systems are typically designed to operate between 40°F and 55°F, storage temperatures would be required to be lower to account for system temperature losses in storage, piping and exchangers. Wet towers are more attractive than dry for this application due to lower temperature differentials and lower cost.

Another source of environmental energy that can be used for both space heating and cooling is natural ground water. Since the temperature of water in wells does not deviate greatly from an annual minimum value, the water forms a good natural source of energy for both direct cooling and heat pump cycles. In the summer, the cool water drawn from an aquifer well can be passed through the evaporator of a heat pump system where it is further cooled and then sent to the air-handling units for space cooling. The return water collects the heat rejected at the condenser and then discards it at the surface or reinjects it into a second well located in the aquifer. The injection well must be placed sufficiently distant from the production well to prevent recirculation of injected water with ambient ground water.

In winter, the warm injected aquifer water could be used as the heat source for the evaporator of the heat pump. Because of its elevated temperature the heat rejected from the condenser can be used for space heating.

Conventional air-supplied heat pumps suffer from utilizing warm air in summer and cold air in the winter, both of which work against operational efficiency. By supplying stored warm water to the heat pump during winter and cool water in summer, a considerable reduction in compression power can be realized.

Where aquifer water temperatures cannot be raised to levels suitable for local consumer systems, a heat pump may be utilized to increase the supply temperature. Figure 7 shows one arrangement designed for northern climates where greater energy flows are required during winter than summer. This overcomes the major objection to heat pump systems, namely output reduction during the coldest days, and would meet the requirements of most U.S. locations.

Transmission Subsystem

The transmission subsystem integrates the collection, storage, and distribution subsystems. The transmission subsystem can be defined in terms of fluid medium, temperature, pressure, flow rate, piping arrangement, and transmission distances.

Water in the liquid or steam phase is the working fluid selected for most heat transmission systems. High thermal capacity, widespread availability, low cost, and non-polluting properties are sufficient reasons to justify the use of water.

Hot water is the preferred heating medium for aquifer TES systems for several reasons. At lower temperatures hot water improves the possi-

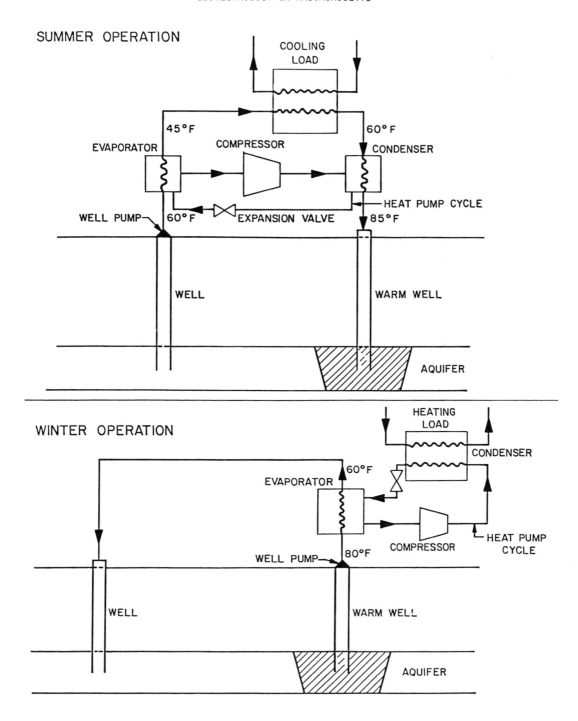

Figure 7.  Combination of heat pump and aquifer
for space heating and cooling.

bilities of collecting industrial waste heat and solar energy. Furthermore, a hot water transmission system provides a better heat exchange interface with the hot water working fluid of the storage subsystem. Other advantages of hot water systems include:

- Overall simpler design.

- Higher thermal storage capacities.

- Smaller transmission pipelines.

- Lower thermal energy losses.

- Longer transmission distances possible.

- Greater flexibility and compatibility with large multiple building complexes.

- Fewer siting restrictions (particularly siting problems related to topography).

- Lower investment costs.

For chilled water cooling systems, water is generally the fluid medium of choice. Antifreeze or brine solutions may be used for systems (usually process applications) that require temperatures below 40°F.

Water transmission systems are commonly classified according to operating temperatures. District hot water systems typically operate between 200°F and 400°F (District Heating, 1978). Because available waste heat temperatures are likely to be moderate and aquifer storage temperature capabilities are likely to be limited by geochemical effects, transmission water temperatures are not anticipated to exceed 250°F as a practical limit. For chilled water cooling systems, temperatures typically range between 40°F and 55°F (ASHRAE, 1976).

The temperature level in the transmission network should be selected to meet the heat demand. From the transmission viewpoint, as low a return temperature and as high a supply temperature as reasonably possible are beneficial. The flows will then be reduced and the pipe sizes will be minimized. The pumping requirements will also be reduced. The same effort toward maximizing temperature difference should be sought for the distribution subsystem. With this design consideration, the sizes of heat exchangers will be minimized.

From the energy collection viewpoint, the supply and return temperatures should be as low as reasonably possible because the opportunities for using waste heat and solar energy increase with decreasing temperature level in the system. In the case of combined power and heat generation, the amount of power generated will also be a maximum if heat rejection temperatures are low. Overall, the selection of heat transmission temperatures is an optimization problem involving a variety of factors, many of which are site-dependent.

The pressure level at all points in a heat transmission network using hot water as the heating medium must be sufficiently high to avoid flashing of water into steam. The lowest permissible pressure in the system is, therefore, determined by the maximum temperature and the prevailing differences in the static head in the network. The pressure drop in the pipe network must be compensated by raising the pressure to a suitable level at the source or at booster pump stations.

Flow rate for a heat transmission subsystem is determined for a given heat load and temperature drop. From the flow rate, allowable heat losses, pipe sizing and pumping power can be estimated for a particular network arrangement.

Hot water transmission subsystems designs are available with piping arrangements utilizing up to four pipelines. The most common arrangement is the two-pipe system involving a supply line and a return line. The required domestic hot water temperature sets the minimum supply temperature for this system at about 140°F in district heating systems (District Heating, 1978). Possible arrangements of the piping for a dual pipe system are shown in Figure 8.

In a three-pipe system, two of the pipes are supply lines. One of the supply lines is used for space heating, and the temperature is controlled in relation to ambient temperature. The other supply line is used for domestic hot water heating and is held at a constant temperature throughout the year. This arrangement is designed to lower the system temperature in order to improve the potential for utilizing low temperature waste heat, or to increase the electrical energy generation in combined power generation and district heating plants.

In a four-pipe system, two pipes are used for space heating and two pipes for domestic hot water distribution. The separate supply and return domestic hot water system allows for continuous recirculation of the hot water to prevent cooling down during low-load periods. The advantages of this system are that numerous local hot water heaters are avoided, and the return temperature in the space heating system is lower.

The transmission distance between the points of supply and end use is the most important parameter in the design and assessment of a heat supply scheme. Transmission distance governs the acceptable supply temperature and the economics of waste heat utilization because, in most cases, it involves a large item of capital expenditure. Pipeline designs are typically optimized with respect to mass flow rates and heat losses, and the limits for heat transmission lines are set by constraints of economic feasibility, rather than by available technology. Transmission distances between 5 and 25 miles appear practical for the transmission of low-grade heat, and distances up to 60 miles have been reported as economically feasible in some cases (Hausz, 1977). The economic practicality of transporting thermal energy

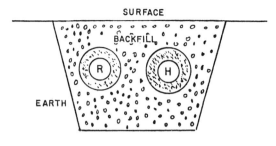

A. DIRECT BURIED PIPE

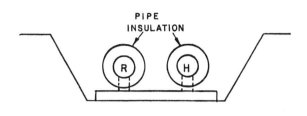

B. STEEL PIPE IN OPEN DITCH

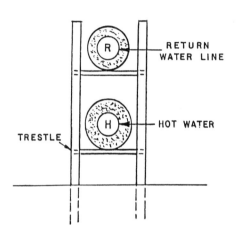

C. ABOVEGROUND TRESTLE

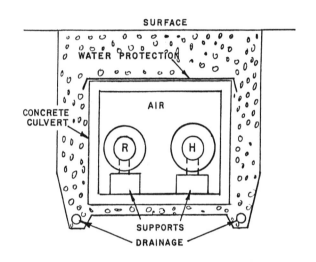

D. BURIED PIPE IN CULVERT

Figure 8. Dual pipe configurations.

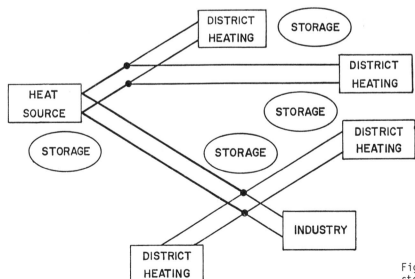

Figure 9. Transmission network with multiple storage centers.

long distances as a response to rising energy costs now lessens the need to co-locate sources of heat with load centers, thereby increasing the opportunities for waste heat utilization. In long distance transport, it might be necessary to install booster pumps between the source and the end user in order to maintain the necessary dynamic flow pressure.

A schematic of a transmission pipeline network incorporating thermal energy storage at various locations is presented in Figure 9 (Hausz, 1977). Multiple locations of storage wells may be desired depending on the configuration and size of the system. Heat storage wells may be located at the thermal energy source, at the end user, and at intermediate points in the transmission subsystem. The location of storage wells will be determined by the availability of suitable aquifers and the heat load requirements of end users. As a general guideline for large systems, the capacity factor for pipeline transmission is maximized to lower transmission costs per unit of energy delivered. This approach is widely used in the pipeline transport of natural gas where, in the off-season, gas is stored near the load end to permit greater use of the pipeline. Locating heat storage wells at the energy source and at various strategic load centers or junctions helps to minimize pipeline size, reduce pumping requirements, and increase system reliability. Multiple storage locations can also help to smooth supply and demand fluctuations and make pipeline flow as uniform as possible.

Storage Subsystem

The storage subsystem comprises components for injection of collected thermal energy into an aquifer for storage and the subsequent production of that energy upon demand by the end user. Single well, double well, and multiple well storage configurations are possible. In the single well system, the well can be designed to act successively as an injection well and a production well.

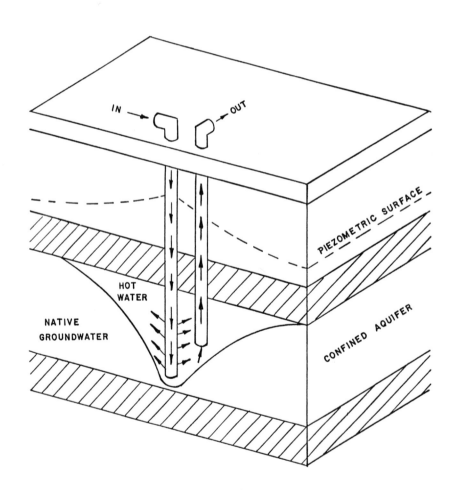

Figure 10. Double well system showing a body of hot water stored within a confined aquifer.

The injected water is provided by another source, preferably from a production well located in the same aquifer to minimize the possibility of geochemical interaction between different waters and between water and the aquifer mineral skeleton.

The double well system is frequently used by the petroleum industry to increase oil recovery. A similar application can be used for hot or cold water storage. The double well system designed for thermal energy storage, shown in Figure 10, comprises two wells which extend into the aquifer. One well is for injection and the other is for production. This system has an advantage over the single well design because simultaneous supply and withdrawal of thermal energy is possible, if the

need ever arises.

A more practical aquifer thermal energy storage subsystem is the doublet storage well concept proposed by General Electric (Meyer and Hausz, 1976; Meyer, 1979). A diagram of this system for hot water storage appears in Figure 1. The doublet system comprises two water wells tapping an aquifer which is confined by low permeability clay or rock formations. The wells are connected by a pipeline which forms a hydraulically closed (and independent) storage configuration. In this concept the storage subsystem is thermally coupled to the transmission subsystem by a heat exchanger. The heat exchanger enables the storage subsystem to be intermittently charged or discharged by

**A. DIRECT CONNECTION**

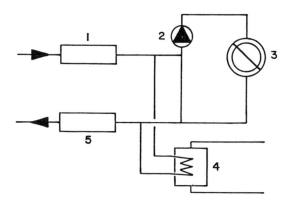

1. SUPPLY FITTING
2. PUMP
3. HEAT CONSUMER
4. WATER HEATER
5. RETURN FITTING

**B. INDIRECT CONNECTION**

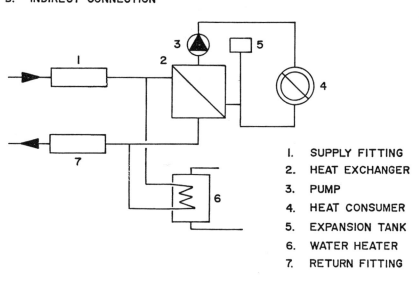

1. SUPPLY FITTING
2. HEAT EXCHANGER
3. PUMP
4. HEAT CONSUMER
5. EXPANSION TANK
6. WATER HEATER
7. RETURN FITTING

Figure 11. Connection of transmission network to the distribution subsystem.

simply reversing the fluid flow from one well to the other.

Major equipment components for storage systems include heat exchangers, pumps, pump drives, valves, piping and controls. Equipment selection problems for the heat storage wells are related to the operating temperatures and corrosive nature of the aquifer ground water which can be brackish or saline. With a closed storage subsystem, these problems are contained because the heat exchanger need only withstand corrosion and scaling effects on the well-water side. The other side of the exchanger interfaces with the treated water of the transmission subsystem.

Pumps for storage subsystems would probably be vertical turbine or submersible types located in the well, depending on the flow of aquifer water required and the working head. This equipment is available from suppliers. Recent geothermal research has advanced heat storage well technology, and equipment is now available to meet most well requirements up to 300°F water temperature (DeBerry, 1978).

Distribution Subsystem

The distribution subsystem receives thermal energy from the transmission subsystem and delivers it to the end user. The distribution subsystem should be designed to meet the customer's instantaneous and continuous heating (or cooling) needs with the largest possible temperature drop across the heat exchanger. A large temperature drop contributes to economical dimensioning of the piping system, reduces pumping requirements, and allows for smaller heat exchange volumes. The temperature drop is controlled by matching the water flow with the load. The distribution subsystem should also permit stable and flexible control of the domestic hot water circuit. Pilot valves should be designed for low noise level and the pressures and temperatures encountered by end users.

The distribution subsystem can be directly or indirectly connected to the transmission network as shown in Figure 11 (District Heating, 1978). In directly connected systems, the thermal energy medium is cycled through the distribution subsystem. In indirect systems, the transmission subsystem is coupled to the distribution subsystem by means of heat exchangers or other heat transfer devices (e.g., absorption chillers), such that the fluid mediums of the two subsystems never come into direct contact. In both cases special water heaters or heat exchangers are used for domestic hot water.

For heating applications where the temperature of the supply water is insufficient to meet the heating needs of the end user, an electrically driven heat pump can be installed to provide the necessary temperature lift. For cooling applications, an absorption cooling system can be adapted to large heating distribution systems with the addition of on-site chillers.

CONCLUSION

This paper has presented various technical aspects and some economic factors to be addressed when assessing the feasibility of an aquifer thermal energy storage system. In addition to the many aspects already reviewed, the designer must also consider environmental trade-offs. Happily, most of the comparisons with alternative energy supply concepts show aquifer TES to be preferable. One area of concern is degradation of the permeable rock media due to mechanical and chemical attack. It is in this area particularly that considerable testing and demonstration investment is also required to prove the long-term performance of the concept.

ACKNOWLEDGMENT

The authors gratefully acknowledge the help provided by the Tennessee Valley Authority during the study, and extend personal thanks to Arnold M. Manaker and Jerry J. Phillips.

REFERENCES

ASHRAE Handbook and Product Directory--1976 Systems: American Society of Heating, Refrigeration and Air-Conditioning Engineers, Inc.

DeBerry D., Willis, P., and Thomas, C., 1978, Materials selection guidelines for geothermal power systems: Radian Corporation, September.

District Heating, 1978, Swedish District Heating Workshop, October 10-20.

Drexel University, 1976, Industrial applications study: Volumes II, III, IV, V, with United Technologies Research Center and Mathematica, Inc., December.

General Electric, 1977, Cool storage assessment study: Corporate Research and Development, May.

Hausz, W., 1977, Seasonal storage in district heating: District Heating, July-August-September.

Meinel, A., 1977, Applied solar energy, an introduction: Addison Wesley.

Merriam, R., 1977, Solar air conditioning study: Arthur D. Little, Inc., Cambridge, Massachusetts, April.

Meyer, C.F., 1979, Potential benefits of thermal energy storage in the proposed Twin Cities district heating-cogeneration system: General Electric, TEMPO, July.

Meyer, C.F., and Hausz, W., 1976, Roles of the heat storage well in future U.S. energy systems: General Electric, TEMPO.

U.S. Geological Survey, 1978, Water resource data book for Tennessee, water year 1977: Water Data Report TN-77-1.

# Gulf Coast salt domes as potential nuclear waste repositories

## J. D. GUSTIN
## Law Engineering Testing Company

ABSTRACT

The U.S. Department of Energy is sponsoring a study of subsurface formations to determine their suitability for long-term storage of radioactive waste. Stable geologic formations including diapiric salt, bedded salt, shale, igneous and metamorphic rocks, carbonates and volcanics are being considered for underground storage of high-level nuclear waste. Eight salt domes formed by the diapiric movement of bedded salt in the Gulf Coast interior salt basins of northeastern Texas, northern Louisiana, and Mississippi are being investigated in order to identify selected domes for additional study and eventual selection for a licensing effort. A brief geologic history of the Gulf Coast interior salt basins and the formation of diapiric salt is presented.

As part of the above study, the geology and hydrology of a 1400 square mile (3730 $km^2$) area in southeast Mississippi, which includes three shallow piercement salt domes under consideration, are being investigated by deep drilling (to depths of 6000 feet, 1829 m), shallow borings (to depths of 600 feet, 183 m), geologic terrace mapping, remote sensing, paleontology, seismic reflection, ground level resistivity, gravity, geophysical logging and deep-aquifer pump tests. The role of these investigative methods in relation to the characterization of the geology and hydrology of the study area is discussed.

# Design requirements for oil and gas storage in salt cavities

H. LORENZEN
PB-KBB, Inc.

# Preliminary design of the Canso salt cavern project for storage of crude oil, Cape Breton, Nova Scotia

H. W. PETRANIK

B. M. LANE

Home Oil Company

## ABSTRACT

Home Oil Company Limited and Gulf Canada Limited are participating in a joint venture proposal to provide underground storage for up to approximately 100 million barrels of crude oil on Cape Breton Island, in the province of Nova Scotia, Canada. The project involves the solution mining of storage caverns in salt deposits near McIntyre Lake and would utilize Gulf Canada's marine terminal at Tupper Point, capable of handling some of the world's largest crude oil tankers. The Gulf dock is approximately 10 miles from the McIntyre Lake deposits; a pipeline system would connect the two locations. Sea water from the Strait of Canso would be used to leach the salt caverns, resulting in negligible impact on fresh water supplies.

Under the terms of the joint venture, Home Oil would operate the underground storage facilities and pipeline. Gulf Canada would continue to own and operate the dock as well as the loading and unloading facilities. Both companies, in particular Home Oil, have experience with developing and operating underground storage facilities in Canada and the United States. Together, both companies account for about one third of the existing underground storage in Canada.

## LOCATION

Figure 1 illustrates the location of the Strait of Canso and Tupper Point in relation to the eastern parts of Canada and the United States. Strategically, this is an ideal location for underground storage since it is only 515 nautical miles from Boston or about 1-1/2 days sailing time. It is only 722 nautical miles from New York and 869 nautical miles from the major east coast refineries in the Philadelphia area.

Several facts of geography and engineering combine to make this location an ideal one for underground storage both for the United States and Canada. It is a large, deep, year-round ice-free harbour, strategically located with respect to the eastern U.S. and to North Atlantic shipping lanes. It is also the only site on the Atlantic Coast of North America that has salt deposits for creating large scale crude oil storage caverns adjacent to an existing ice-free deep water terminal which can handle, and has handled, world-size tankers.

## GEOTECHNICAL/GEOLOGICAL DATA

## Introduction

Numerous salt deposits are known to exist in the Windsor Group of marine sediments in the northern portion of the Nova Scotia peninsula and in the southern part of Cape Breton Island. Tectonic squeezing, folding and faulting of the Paleozoic strata has caused flowing of salt and brecciation of associated anhydrite, shale, and limestone. The result has been the formation of accumulated masses of salt of varying purity, often several hundred feet thick.

Regional geotechical and geological data of an area between longitude 61°00' and 61°30' W and latitude 45°30' and 46°00' N in the general area of Port Hawkesbury, Nova Scotia, indicated the presence of salt deposits of sufficient thickness and depth to allow the development of underground storage caverns.

Between 1972 and 1978 four test holes, NCO Canso Strat 1, Murphy NCO Canso Strat 2, Home et al Canso Strat 3A, and Home et al Canso Strat 4B, were drilled and cored. Geophysical logs (gamma ray, neutron, density, and caliper) were obtained for Nos. 3A and 4B. In addition, regional and microgravity data were obtained for the area of interest. In 1979 two more test holes, 5A and 6, were drilled and cored.

The existence of clean "flow" salt up to 1,000 feet thick with less than 1,500 feet of overburden was confirmed. The salt occurs over an area of just under two square miles and could support cavern development in excess of 250 MM bbl.

Insoluble content of the salt is generally less than 5 percent; a representative analysis from 4B is shown in Tables 1 and 2.

### Regional Geology

The study area lies within the Appalachian geologic region. The rocks present in the southwestern tip of Cape Breton Island range in age from Precambrian to Upper Carboniferous (Pennsylvanian).

Only four rock units, all of sedimentary origin, are present at the surface within a four mile radius of McIntyre Lake. In ascending order, they are the Mississippian Age Horton, Windsor, and Canso Groups and the Pennsylvanian Age Riversdale Group. A major unconformity separates these

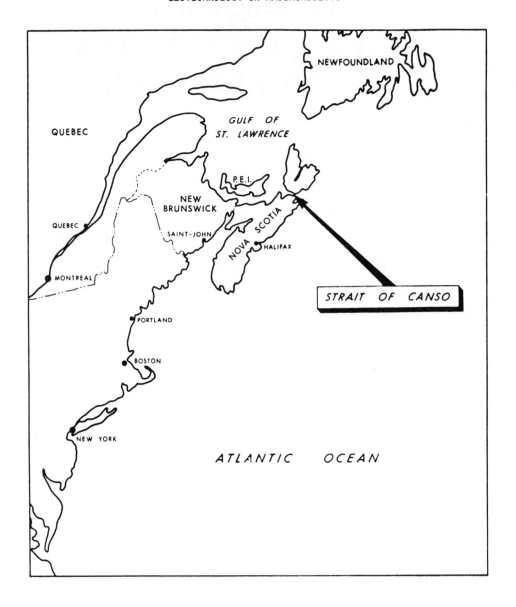

Figure 1.  Location of Strait of Canso.

four rock units from Devonian granites and other pre-Carboniferous rocks.

Horton Group.  This unit is believed to be of continental origin and is found in an outcrop beginning about four miles northwest of McIntyre Lake.  It is comprised of clastic rocks including a lower section of red calcareous conglomerate, sandstone and siltstone and gray to red non-calcareous conglomerate, grading into arkose or gray-wacke, a middle section of gray siltstone and upper layers of conglomerate and red siltstone. Medium-grained gray sandstone and arkosic grits interbedded with red beds of similar lithology are the predominant Horton rock types present.

Windsor Group.  This unit is of marine origin and consists of limestone, evaporites, shaly lime-stone, sandy shale, argillite and limestone con-glomerate.  It overlies the Horton Group.  The Windsor and Horton groups are separated by an unconformity.  The evaporites include halite, gypsum, anhydrite and minor potash salts.

Canso Group.  The Canso strata are comprised of a thick series of red, green, and gray shales and siltstone with thin intercalated red or brown-ish gray sandstone and buff gray limestone layers. These sediments, of continental origin, rest con-formably upon the Windsor Group.

## TABLE 1.  HOME ET AL CANSO 4B: ANALYSIS OF SOLUBLE SALT

A sample was prepared in proportion to the soluble fraction.  The following ratio was maintained.

| Interval (in feet) | Proportion of water soluble material |
|---|---|
| 1163.0 - 1173.0 | 45 percent |
| 1335.5 - 1345.0 | 45 percent |
| 1584.0 - 1657.0 | 5 percent |
| 1801.0 - 1861.0 | 5 percent |

### Composition

| Component | Percentage |
|---|---|
| Sodium | 38.70 |
| Potassium | 0.025 |
| Calcium | 0.45 |
| Magnesium | 0.0003 |
| Chloride | 60.20 |
| Bicarbonate | 0.022 |
| Carbonate | Nil |
| Sulphate | 0.30 |

pH of 10 percent solution          6.6 pH

### Trace Metal Analysis of Water Soluble Portion

| Metal | Concentration milligrams/kilogram (ppm) |
|---|---|
| Iron | 0.01 |
| Nickel | < 0.05 |
| Lead | < 0.03 |
| Copper | 0.4 |
| Chromium | 0.5 |
| Zinc | 0.3 |
| Cadmium | < 0.05 |
| Mercury | < 0.01 |

Riversdale Group.  The youngest rocks in the area are those of the Riversdale Group of continental origin, composed of a thick series of shales, siltstones, sandstones, thin calcareous fragmental beds and minor thin coal seams.

Rocks in the study area have been strongly deformed with folds predominantly oriented in a general north-northwest trend.  These warps are commonly more abrupt in the Horton and Windsor Groups than in the more recent Canso and Riversdale strata.  The first four exploratory core holes drilled are oriented along a northerly trending line roughly parallel to the strike of the Canso/Windsor contact subcrop trace, crudely indicated by sparse outcrop observations made at points over a mile distant from the holes.

Surface mapping has delineated several major faults.  Known faults located close to the core

## TABLE 2.  HOME ET AL  CANSO 4B:  ANALYSIS OF WATER INSOLUBLE PORTION

The water insoluble material was separated by flotation to determine the composition of the clay compounds and the composition of the insoluble fraction.

### Clay Separation by Flotation

| Material less than 2 microns | 4.0 percent |
|---|---|
| Material greater than 2 microns | 96.0 percent |

### X-Ray Diffraction Analysis

| Insoluble material | Material less than 2 microns | Material greater than 2 microns |
|---|---|---|
| Quartz | 2 | 17 |
| Feldspar | 1 | 10 |
| Dolomite | Nil | 6 |
| Calcite | Nil | 4 |
| Anhydrite | 15 | 40 |
| Kaolinite | 60 | 23 |
| Illite | 16 | Trace |
| Chlorite | 6 | Nil |

holes are a major north-south break located about one mile west and an intersecting east-southeast feature located about two miles south of McIntyre Lake.  The tectonics related to these two faults have raised Windsor Group sediments to the level of the Riversdale Group sediments.  The relative vertical displacements of the Windsor sediments immediately west of the north-south fault are in the order of 2,000 feet and dip easterly as indicated by the occurrence of younger Riversdale sediments to the east.

Geotechnical/Geological Interpretation and Assessment

The Acadian disturbance at the close of the Devonian period elevated Appalachia into mountains.  Local folds or mountain ranges supplied source material for carboniferous deposition, dividing the deposits into separate basins when the Appalachian trough subsided during the Mississippian period.

In the McIntyre Lake area of southwestern Cape Breton Island, the ridges controlling deposition were the Creignish Hills, North Mountain, Sporting Mountain and the relatively positive rocks forming the present land surface west of the Strait of Canso.

Varying sea levels combined with sedimentary deposition controlled the access of sea water as the seas progressively flooded the more negative areas and the southwestern Cape Breton area.  The occurrence of thick sections of evaporites, including halite and potash salts together with the preserved thick sections of rocks of the Pennsylvanian Riversdale Group, suggest that the basin center during Carboniferous time was located some few miles east of McIntyre Lake (McIntyre Lake Basin).

Structural deformation within the basin occurred subsequent to the deposition of the rocks of the Riversdale Group of the Pennsylvanian period. Compressional forces parallel to the major regional faults, trending west-southwest, acted on the thicker sections of the Windsor Group evaporites causing a plastic flow to occur. A major fold developed perpendicular to the forces with its axis along a north-northwest line extending north from Inhabitants Harbour through McIntyre Lake to Kingsville.

Subsequent compression of the McIntyre Lake depositional basin resulted in salt piercement structures forming at both ends of the fold axis, one at Inhabitants Bay and the other at Kingsville. A pre-Horton saddle between the southwest end of North Mountain and the Creignish Hills high feature was compressed by the relative south-southwest movement of North Mountain, which forced the Carboniferous rocks in the restricted saddle area upwards.

The Carboniferous rocks in the McIntyre Lake block were displaced westward at least one mile, with the Windsor rocks faulted to the surface. Leaching of the water soluble rocks of the uplifted blocks along the fold axis resulted in formation of collapse breccias. This action protected the water soluble evaporites from further major leaching until the area was glaciated during recent times. Post-glacial solutioning is indicated in the saddle area between North Mountain and the Creignish Hills by the numerous sink holes and surface occurrences of gypsum, but is restricted to this area. It is important to note that there is no surface evidence of post-glacial leaching within one mile of the boundary of the proposed cavern area.

The first three or four core holes drilled for this investigation were located on the gravity low axis which extends north-northeast through McIntyre Lake. Three encountered collapse breccias between the Windsor carbonates and the Windsor evaporites. The fourth core test (Home et al Canso Strat 4B), however, was drilled to the east of the gravity low axis and did not encounter a collapse breccia between the Windsor carbonates and the Windsor evaporites. It is concluded that the Canso Strat holes 1, 2 and 3A were located in the solution front. Water flows encountered in the Windsor carbonates tend to confirm this interpretation. Intermediate casing strings were required to stop the water flow in all of the core holes except the 4B test.

Pre-glacial solutioning or contemporaneous solutioning of the soluble Windsor halite during the recent glaciation may be interpreted from the relative depths of till cover in the Canso Strat holes 3A, 1 and 4B (310 feet, 180 feet and 60 feet respectively). No post-glacial evidence of subsequent solutioning can be interpreted from the

surface geology.

Canso Strat 4B penetrated 1,026 feet of clean flow halite (key halite section) between the depths of 997 feet and 2,023 feet, or 142 feet thicker than the 884 feet to clean flow halite penetrated in Canso Strat 1. This strongly suggests that some portion of the uppermost section of the clean flow halite had been removed by solution from the Canso Strat 1 section.

The solution front generally follows the surface feature located along the Windsor/Canso subcrop trace with minor deviations indicated by the results of the Canso Strat 3A.

The interpretive cross sections indicate the increasing effect of the solution front on the upper section of the Windsor evaporites toward the north-south fault located one mile west of McIntyre Lake. The effects of the solutioning on the "clean flow halite" are still in evidence at the Canso Strat 1 location, where some 884 feet of clean flow halite is preserved. Sections of 1,000 feet or over can be expected to the east of the no. 1 location as well as to the north, as evidenced by the 4B core hole data. In addition, the percentage of insoluble material decreases from the no. 1 location to the no. 4B location suggesting that the north-south axis of the more mobile clean flow halite is located east of the no. 1.

The salt deposits in the proposed storage site were formed by combined northerly and westward salt flows, resulting in differential segregation of the more mobile halites (associated with minor sylvite) from less mobile anhydrites (associated with more competent rocks). These more mobile halites have been termed clean flow halites and occur at the top of the Windsor evaporite section. The clean flow salt is over 1,000 feet thick in the no. 4B core hole and can be expected to maintain this thickness for some distance from the solution front. This interpretation is based on the progressive erosion of the Riversdale, Canso and Windsor sediments to the northwest, indicating that the Carboniferous rocks of the McIntyre Lake Block were tilted upward to the northwest and later eroded by glacial action. The evidence of sink holes as well as surface gypsum to the northeast in the saddle area tends to confirm that the vertical weight of sediments was reduced there, with a resulting salt flow toward the saddle or low pressure area.

PROJECT DESCRIPTION

Dockside Facilities

The additional facilities required at the existing Tupper Point refinery include construction of an extra dock (or docks, depending on ultimate storage capacity) capable of handling tankers up to 100,000 deadweight tons. The existing Gulf dock and berths are capable of handling tankers up to 350,000 deadweight tons.

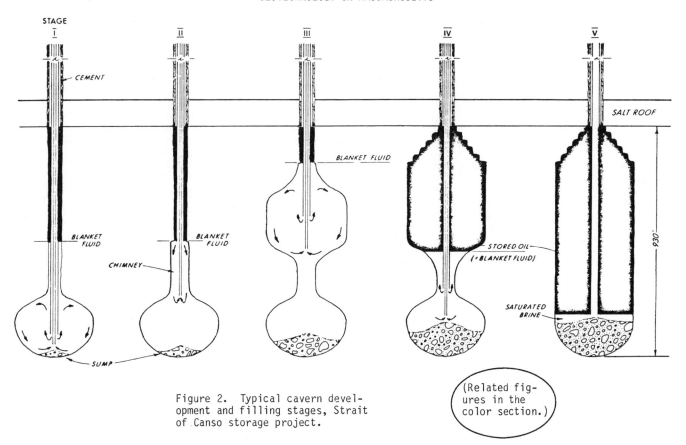

Figure 2. Typical cavern development and filling stages, Strait of Canso storage project.

(Related figures in the color section.)

Other new facilities which will be required in the dock area include a metering station, electrical substation, transfer pumps and ballast tank. This ballast servicing facility is provided to eliminate the discharge of any contaminated water into the strait. All vessels arriving at the terminal to load must discharge ashore all ballast, clean or dirty, as is the case with the Tupper Point refinery.

Two of the existing 450,000 barrel storage tanks in the refinery would be used as part of the project for temporary storage of crude oil in the filling or withdrawal of the storage caverns.

Cavern Development

The storage caverns will be created through the use of the leach/fill technique. This procedure involves partially washing the cavern, filling the completed portion, and then washing the remainder of the cavern (Fig. 2). It allows some product to be stored downhole sooner than in traditional cavern development.

In the first stage of development, a well is drilled through the overburden, and the casing is cemented into the salt. This 20 inch casing is set at a sufficient depth below the top of the salt to provide the minimum safe salt roof thickness, in this case at least 70 feet into salt of less than 20 percent insoluble content. Inter-

mediate casing strings (13 3/8 inch) and 7 inch wash tubing complete the well. Prior to washing, a protective blanket of crude oil is placed in the outer casing annulus. Sea water drawn from the Strait of Canso is then pumped down the tubing to leach the salt, and the resulting brine is returned to the surface through the intermediate tubing annulus.

This is known as direct washing. By injecting sea water through the intermediate string and recovering brine through the 7 inch tubing, indirect or reverse washing is performed. A sump is created at the bottom of the cavern to accommodate any insolubles in the salt deposits.

In the next stage, the tubing will be left on the bottom, and the intermediate string will be raised to the mid point of the cavern. A chimney approximately 40 feet in diameter will be washed from the sump to the mid point of the cavern. This will ensure an unobstructed flow of undissolved materials to the sump during the washing of the upper portion of the cavern.

In order to wash the top portion of the cavern, the intermediate string will be positioned at the point where roof shaping is required. The wash tubing will be located near the mid point of the cavern. Washing will continue until the cavern reaches the desired diameter. The intermediate string and the blanket fluid will be raised in successive stages to effect the desired roof shape. The top portion of the cavern will be ready to accept crude oil for storage when this stage is completed.

The washing of the lower portion of the cavern commences once oil has been pumped into storage in the upper portion of the cavern. To complete the washing of the lower part of the cavern, the wash string is lowered to the bottom of the cavern.

Prior to final filling of the cavern, the inner tubing will be removed, and the washing wellhead will be replaced with a storage wellhead. The intermediate string will be positioned at the bottom of the cavern and will be used for brine removal during filling and sea water or brine injection during withdrawal. To withdraw oil from the cavern, sea water or brine is pumped into the bottom of the cavern to displace the oil floating on top. To refill the cavern after withdrawal, oil is pumped in, forcing brine out. The caverns are never voided, although they are structurally designed to handle that requirement.

## Construction Period

Once a firm commitment has been made it would require approximately 22 months to reach the stage at which it would be possible to commence leaching operations. Partial filling of the caverns could begin 24 months later with the entire storage volume available a further 18 months later.

This type of project is not labour intensive; the entire engineering and construction program would likely require less than 3,500 man-years.

## Environmental Considerations

Wherever possible, both Home and Gulf have incorporated environmental factors into the engineering design and proposed operating methods of the Strait of Canso project. A special environmental sub-committee was established to oversee all environmental studies and measures to be incorporated into the project.

Meetings were held with the Nova Scotia Department of Environment, which is co-ordinating the project with federal environmental agencies. These meetings assisted in identifying any areas of concern, and a number of studies were conducted through outside consultants. Some considerations include brine disposal, tanker traffic, storage cavern acceptability, and pipeline construction.

During leaching of the caverns, 70-80 percent saturated salt brine will be injected on a controlled basis into the Strait of Canso. In order to protect marine life the brine must be diffused in such a way that the salt content of the receiving water does not increase significantly.

The brine would be piped from the storage cavern site, through the brine ponds, along the pipeline system, and would then be forced through a diffuser pipe which would be submerged beneath the existing Gulf dock. The pipe would extend approximately 1,500 feet or almost the length of the dock. The brine would be diffused through approximately 50 nozzles to ensure maximum dispersion. Water depth at this discharge point is in excess of 100 feet.

As a result of the work done to date, conditional environmental approval to proceed with construction of the storage project was granted in October 1979.

## Marine Traffic Control

Navigational suitability and traffic management at the Strait of Canso ranks second after Halifax among 22 Canadian sites on the east coast for overall port acceptability as a crude oil terminal. This assessment was made by the Canadian government which took into consideration ice, tides, winds, navigational aids, visibility, shipping density, wildlife vulnerability, and oil spill clean-up capability.

The Eddy Point Traffic Management Centre maintains radio-telephone communication and radar monitors all marine traffic within the marine traffic regulating zone on a 24-hour-a-day basis. Radar surveillance from the Eddy Point Traffic Management Centre also serves as a backup to shipboard radar.

## SUMMARY

The Strait of Canso storage project offers the following advantages:

- Salt deposits within 10 miles of an existing deep water ice-free port.

- Salt deposits with the potential for 100 MM barrels of storage.

- Proximity to the Atlantic seaboard.

- Existing infrastructure for marine traffic including VLCC's (very large crude carriers).

- Sufficient preparation to receive conditional environmental approval to proceed.

# ADDITION

Upper, Intrusion of Hampden Basalt or Diabase into Granby Tuff.  The vertical jointing is pronounced, and there is a small offshoot of basalt on the left.  The rocks were excavated for Interstate Route 91 east of Bray Lake, Holyoke, and are shown here before the highway was opened with the author, J.R. Hinthorne. (From Bedrock Geology of the Mount Tom Area, Massachusetts, M.S. Thesis in Geology, University of Massachusetts, 1967, p. 43).

Lower, Looking south from Mount Sugarloaf in South Deerfield, Massachusetts.  The flood plain of the Connecticut River occupies the foreground, and the Holyoke Range cuts across the valley in the distance.  Basaltic lavas of Triassic age form the upper part of this range. (From Economic Geology in Massachusetts, O.C. Farquhar, ed., University of Massachusetts Graduate School, 1967, p. 82.)

# Geology in the Connecticut River valley of western Massachusetts

C. KOLTZ
Washington University
St. Louis, Missouri

EDITOR'S FOREWORD

At the conference on Geotechnology in Massachusetts in March 1980, about 75 papers were presented in two full days, beginning and ending with plenary sessions 1, 2, and 14. In between, three sessions were running simultaneously.

If there had been enough time for one more session, the subject probably would have been education in geotechnology. Although not presented at the conference, the following account is concerned with one aspect of learning about the earth sciences and is included here as an addition.

Like geology, geotechnology is a field-based subject and, partly for that reason, will always be of interest to individuals outside the profession. Many of its themes can be followed by people who have no particular qualifications except a strong interest. Scenery, soils, and water are part of life, as are the tales of volcanoes and earthquakes. Everyone can participate in such pursuits as landscape appreciation, mineral collecting, fossil hunting, exploration of caves, stream flow studies, and the depiction of coastlines. Can the non-professional as easily assimilate the rudiments of biochemistry and psychology?

Charles Koltz, author of the following article, discusses the Connecticut River Valley of western Massachusetts, referring not only to its geologic nature but also to the history of studies in the area. With a practised journalistic approach, he describes the rock formations of the Holyoke Range in considerable detail and mentions a number of people involved in research. Some of the scientific, engineering, economic, and environmental conditions that together comprise the geotechnology of the area are also mentioned. Each is important to the citizen and amateur as well as to the professional. From amateur status to professional involvement is only a step, albeit a long one, and whether or not an individual chooses to take that step, he or she can readily develop a lifetime interest in all of the earth sciences. The Connecticut River Valley certainly has its own special attractions for visitors and residents alike.

ABSTRACT (added 1981)

The Pioneer Valley of western Massachusetts, consisting of a wide area on both sides of the Connecticut River between Sugarloaf Mountain in Sunderland and Mount Tom in Easthampton, possesses an unusually interesting geologic landscape. In addition, there are sedimentary rocks with fossil dinosaur prints, there are fine examples of columnar jointing and glacial striations, and there are many locations at which to study the dynamics of floodplain geology. The purpose of this article, written in 1978, was to describe the most attractive geologic features of the Pioneer Valley so that lay persons might be influenced to examine them independently.

## GEOLOGY IN THE CONNECTICUT RIVER VALLEY OF WESTERN MASSACHUSETTS

Daylight dips over the ridge of a lava flow. Below, in the basin, a group of large reptiles, walking erect, waddles through the ooze on a sandy lakeshore. Ranging in size from four to 30 feet tall, the beasts flatten reeds and ferns as they wade into the water.

The lake is shallow, and thick with salt and mud. As the huge animals thrash the swampy water, a pungent aroma from rotting peat fills the air. Through waves of rising heat, other dinosaurs are visible on the expanse of the flat basin. Occasionally, the ground trembles, and in the distance steam rises from volcanic vents. Conifers glisten on far hills. And the sun, now hot, bakes the earth like a kiln.

Where are we? Prehistoric Africa? The opening scene from an Edgar Rice Burroughs novel? Maybe it's a National Geographic special.

Actually, this scenario, or something like it, took place a lot closer to home: adjacent to what is now Route 5, between Northampton and Holyoke in western Massachusetts. About 190 million years ago.

What's more, the geologic evidence for local dinosaur activity and many other exciting events

---

* This article is reprinted from Hampshire Life, with permission of the Daily Hampshire Gazette, Northampton, Massachusetts.

The Riffles, where herds of dinosaurs left their footprints.

Anchisaurus colurus, typical of
dinosaurs passing through the
valley, here seen at the Pratt
Museum in Amherst.

Details of the rock formation
at Titan's Piazza.

from our distant past is easy to find and fun to track down. Hampshire County and its surrounding area is a paradise for both professional and week-end geologists.

Since dinosaurs are such large skeletons in our historical closet, their fossil tracks are a good start for any geological tour.

One of the best fossil track sites in the Pioneer Valley (or anywhere) is the "Riffles," a group of sandstone slabs located about 1/2 mile north of the Mountain Park entrance on Route 5, and adjacent to the Connecticut River. During Triassic time, approximately 190 million years ago, these slabs were soft sediments on the edge of a shallow, salty lake called a playa. Not just one, but a herd or more of dinosaurs, big and small, tracked through these muds on their way to the watering hole.

The result is that today we have many remark-able dinosaur prints. These fossil slabs are to geologists what Hollywood Boulevard is to movie fans. Footprints of the real biggies.

The question is: How on earth did these squishy imprints become preserved? George Bain, author of "The Flow of Time in the Connecticut Valley," has one plausible answer. He says that the climate was very warm and dry, in between periodic rains and floods that caused the playas. The sediments here were perfect for fossils.

These kinds of clays "are baked hard in the hot sun," he says, "and the water (within the clay) contains dissolved mineral matter which crystallizes in the clay and sand as the water evaporates, cementing the particles into a rock-like aggregate." After being cemented in the dry season, the prints were covered (and protected) by additional sediments washed into the basin during flood times.

For such an important hunk of history the Riffles is well hidden. No road signs announce its presence even though many of the prints are located within a brontosaurus stride of the high-way. There is just an inauspicious, turn-in park-ing area, the only such area along that stretch of the road.

Under the circumstances, there might at least be a road sign reading "dinosaur crossing."

Located in an unromantic spot between the highway and the Boston & Maine rail tracks, the dinosaur prints share space with fossils of an-other era. Broken beer bottles. The carved initials of teen-agers. Rubber tire marks on the adjacent road. And the metal tracks of an "iron horse."

In this unlikely setting, the Riffles has become famous. Curious naturalists from far-away places travel here each year to study the distinc-tive, three-toed dinosaur tracks and other fossil evidence trapped in the sandstone.

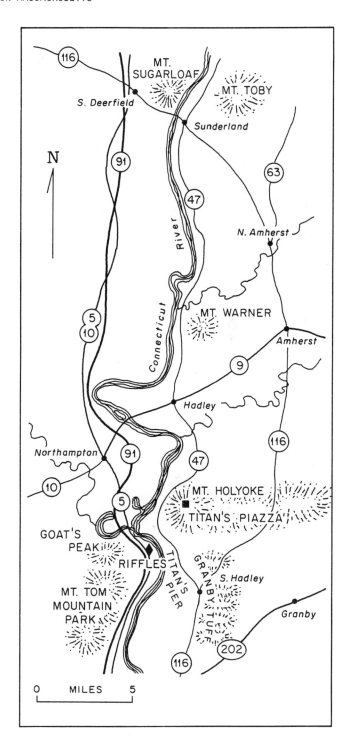

The Connecticut River valley be-tween Sunderland and South Hadley in western Massachusetts.

In several places "petrified" ripple marks, where water made undulating waves in the soft mud, lap the rock as if it were fluid. Nearer the river, reed marks reveal where plants were buried and rotted in the soft sediments of the dinosaur period.

Perhaps even more startling than the dinosaur prints are the delicate pocks of prehistoric rain drops. How astonishing that in these tiny craters we can see where raindrops fell millions of years ago.

From such minute details recorded in geological evidence throughout the valley, investigators have been able to piece together a fairly comprehensive picture of the Connecticut Valley as it was during the reign of reptiles. Bain describes the valley as an arid basin marked by shallow lakes that were fed by seasonal streams. Peat bogs formed near the swampy edges of lakes, and "a bizarre animal population" traveled in herds through the mud. The sedimentary record in the area, says Bain, "suggests a lowland much like some of the tropical valleys in the West Indies, lying in the rain shadow of adjacent mountains."

Of course, as you've doubtless noticed, dinosaurs no longer graze the valley, hunt or herd to the water for drinking. What happened to them?

First off, the climate changed. Over millions of years the weather no longer provided the tropical, playa-filled landscape in which they thrived. In conjunction with shifting climate, the geology of the area underwent drastic upheavals. Volcanic vents spewed lava, forming the Mount Tom and Mount Holyoke ranges. The land tilted and uplifted. Eventually, continental glaciers swept down from Labrador, scouring the mountains and depositing great boulders. Later, a huge glacial lake of dammed icemelt covered western Massachusetts, and, after it drained, the Connecticut and its tributaries eroded the empty lake bed.

By then the gigantic reptiles were long gone, suffering the fate of so many large animals that seem poorly adapted to changing habitat. They all simply died.

As Robie Hubley, the Regional Environmentalist for the Massachusetts Audubon Society, so succinctly puts it: "All living things are at the mercy of the geology."

For one brief period, about the time the dinosaurs were disappearing, living things in the valley were at the mercy of geology's most spectacular force: volcanic activity.

Across Route 5 from the Riffles are dark rock outcrops that begin to tell the story of this fiery episode. These are "fire rocks." They were deposited during volcanic outpourings sometime after a similar process created the Mount Holyoke and Mount Tom ranges. Geologists have named this second lava flow, which stretches along the south side of the Holyoke Range and the east side of

the Mount Tom Range, "Granby Tuff." Take note of these rocks' appearance.

You'll probably be jolted when you compare this modest example of Granby Tuff with the most popular specimen of the older, Holyoke lava flow, Titan's Piazza, the next stop on our tour. As you have probably guessed by its name, the piazza is no ordinary hunk of rock.

The piazza was named in the mid-19th century by Dr. Edward Hitchcock, then president of Amherst College, to replace earlier names that attributed the odd formation to the devil's work. Its location is on the western cliff of Mount Holyoke, to the right of the dirt entrance road leading to Skinner State Park. One Hampshire County Gazetteer, which is admittedly prone to exaggeration, calls the piazza "one of the eight wonders of the world."

The place is called a piazza for good reason. At its formation, when basalt lava, heated to a temperature near 1,300 degrees centigrade, poured out from a three-mile long fissure, the rock cooled in a distinctive way. Cooling caused the rock to contract, cracking the entire formation in a regular pattern. The result is a spectacular example of a common lava shape: a network of hexagonal columns. The product looks like classical architecture chiseled into a mountain side.

Such a formation is called columnar jointing, and the piazza rivals even the most tourist-infested lava structures in the American west.

A similar phenomenon, Titan's Pier, is situated nearby, on the banks of the Connecticut, directly across the river from the Mount Tom power plant. Unfortunately, access to the pier is on private property, and visitors are prohibited. Through binoculars, a good view of the pier is possible from the west bank of the river and hardcore rock hounds can get a close-up look by boat, just as Titan did when he was docking his mythical vessel.

Up the mountain from Titan's Piazza and the Pier is the inoperative Mount Holyoke Hotel, now the location of a spectacular park at the peak. From this spot Thomas Cole painted his famous landscape of the Ox Bow on the Connecticut River.

Oxbow formation, which occurs when a river meanders and then floods, is a big deal in the valley. By wandering back and forth in its flood plain, which encompasses virtually the entire valley, the Connecticut constantly reshapes the landscape we inhabit.

In fact, erosion by the Connecticut River and its tributaries has shaped most of the topography of our area, and is the most important geological process along the length of the Connecticut Valley.

Nowhere is the work of the river more evident than from Mount Holyoke. Look north. The river snakes past the two Sugarloafs and beneath the Sunderland Bridge. Several miles to the south it turns abruptly to avoid Hadley, but its powerful currents punish the outside of the curve by lashing into the banks. At this point the town has constructed a rip rap of pots, kitchen utensils and other paraphernalia that possibly will dissuade the river from relocating huge chunks of Hadley land.

A large meander skirts Hadley, bringing the river under the Coolidge Bridge. Downstream from the bridge, the Connecticut takes another hairpin turn--the sharp meander you see directly below as you face northward.

This curve is a good example of how a river migrates, or wanders from side to side. Here, current strikes the outside curve with more force than against any curve on the river. Constantly gouging hunks of river bank, currents then wash this eroded material downstream. Much of it is deposited on the inside of the next curve and, presto, the river migrates.

The Connecticut may not have the speed of a sidewinder, but, year by year, inch by inch, it snakes back and forth across the valley with the same coiling motion.

An oxbow is simply one curve of the river that has been cut off and abandoned during the flood season, thus leaving the meander a circular lake. The Ox Bow in Easthampton is an excellent example, because it was cut off only about 150 years ago. Looking west, you can see this curving pond, now bisected by Route 91.

When the river flooded in 1830, its channel followed a few plowed furrows that stretched across the narrow neck of land between the two ends of the meander loop. This action abandoned the loop. Northampton declared a day of thanksgiving, because the town was now three miles (the length of the meander loop) closer to sea. However, those farmers who had suddenly been transferred from Hadley to Northampton were not so happy.

By using binoculars, you can scan the panorama below and pick out many characteristic landforms on the floodplain. Just east of the Ox Bow, for instance, is a second, older oxbow that was cut off from the channel a few hundred years ago. This older oxbow is not nearly as distinct as The Ox Bow.

Having filled with sediments deposited by incoming streams and seasonal flooding, this old oxbow is now a marsh. It's also the home of Arcadia Wildlife Sanctuary, which you can tour later if you want to study floodplain topography up close.

The inside of the sharp meander directly to your north is called Rainbow Beach. Located where it is, the beach is the fastest growing piece of land on the Connecticut. One report claims that in this spot the river is migrating at the rate

of six meters per year. Scanning inland from Rainbow Beach you can actually see long curving lowlands that are past locations of the river channel. These old channels are called "meander scars."

If you scan eastward from the Rainbow Beach curve, you should be able to find terraces which the meandering river once carved into the floodplain.

Another floodplain feature is the river's natural levees. These river banks have been built up by the deposition of sediments during flood times.

According to one geologist, Marshall Schalk of Smith College, the hard lava ridges of the Mount Holyoke and Mount Tom ranges are responsible for the wide valley we live in. "The ridge is why we are here now," he says matter-of-factly. The reason for this effect is the narrow gap between the two ridges. "That is all the Connecticut has been able to cut in 40,000 years of carving in hard stone," he explains.

During the season of spring flooding, ice flows catch in the narrow "water gap" between the two ridges. The Connecticut often backs up behind these trapped flows, spilling its flood waters in a wide area across the valley. Increased meandering is one result. The deposition of fertile soil is another. Such flooding necessitated the long, manmade dikes that protect Northampton from flooding. The Army Corps of Engineers built these embankments, which you can see on the edges of Northampton, in 1940 after several disastrous floods in the 1930s.

If the Connecticut River landscapes our area today, the continental glacier did so in the past. Glacial action has left many calling cards from thousands of years ago.

Glacial "erratics" are one type of ice age leftover. Erratics are boulders that are transported by moving ice sheets and, as George Bain says, deposited "promiscuously" over the countryside after the ice melts. Such a rock is a kind of glacial hitch-hiker.

Most of the rocks used in New England's stone walls are erratics. Evidence suggests that pioneer farmers did not build these walls for the reason suggested by Robert Frost: that "Stone walls make good neighbors." Rather, the befuddled farmers just couldn't think of anything better to do with the thousands of mysterious rocks littering their fields.

Geologist Marshall Schalk found one huge erratic on top of Mount Warner (North Hadley). This boulder hobo, he says, is a lava rock that hitch-hiked from Greenfield.

Go to Amherst College for more glacial evidence. The hill upon which the school was built is a drumlin, or low rounded hill made of ground-up glacial till. When the glacier became over-loaded with eroded rock debris, it simply dumped the stuff. Amherst College, therefore, has a glacial dump for its foundation. Other drumlins in the area are Round Hill in Northampton and Prospect Hill at Mount Holyoke College.

From the south side of the Amherst drumlin, at the site of the school's war memorial, more glacial littering is evident. As part of this beautiful view, you can see the shapes of various ridges, eroded by glacial pressure as ice moved southward. Early settlers called the configura-tions of these ridges roches moutonnées, after the wigs of sheepskin worn by jurists of the day.

This overlook is a good place to sit and read Bain, who has something fascinating to say about any place you might visit locally. He also tells what sorts of rock and minerals you can expect to find.

Amherst College has a fine geology museum, although at the time of writing it was closed temporarily for alterations. When it reopens, be sure to see the dinosaur and rock exhibits, and Dr. Hitchcock's incredible collection of fossil prints.

Nice as the view from Amherst College is, there are other high places in the valley that are interesting geologically and spectacular aes-thetically. Mount Sugarloaf, home of a famous kind of red rock--Sugarloaf arkose--is one over-look not to pass up.

Mount Tom's Goat Peak features rocks that were "autographed" by the glacier. Where the paved asphalt approach walk ends near the top of the peak, two flat rocks display glacial "stria-tions"--parallel grooves, pointed north and south, that were scoured into the stones when the glacier moved across their faces. Goat Peak also contains miniature versions of Titan's Piazza in which basaltic lava cooled into interesting formations, though not the perfect kind of hexagonal columns found at the piazza.

A good example of how geology influences

wildlife is the hawk migration, visible from Goat Peak. The projection of the Mount Holyoke and Mount Tom ridges above the lowlying valley creates thermal updrafts over the mountains. Hawks use these thermals for gliding during mi-gration. So, each spring and fall, thousands of hawks converge on these ridges, using them as air corridors to fly north or south. The ridges act something like a wind tunnel for hawks.

Another place where wildlife has been drama-tically influenced by geology is Arcadia Wildlife Sanctuary, the best floodplain learning center in the valley. Here, the river has sculpted marshes, streams, forests and meadows that act as a varied and attractive habitat for all sorts of beasts and plants.

The nature center at Arcadia provides a good trail guide that explains the relationship between geology and wildlife. Soon, says sanctuary direc-tor Judy Hubley, there will also be a Massachu-setts Audubon Society booklet dealing specifically with Arcadia's unique floodplain geology.

Arcadia is a good climax for a day of red-hot geology. One last assignment, should you choose to accept it, will complete your whirlwind tour. Pick a time when the spring sun is warm and relax-ing. Lie on the grass or sit in a pleasant loca-tion, such as on one of Arcadia's trail benches. Think about the volcanoes, the coming and going of the dinosaurs, glaciers and the huge glacial lake, how the Connecticut now shapes the valley, and all the changes that your habitat has under-gone in the last few million years.

Then, with these things in mind, read this poem by Alfred Lord Tennyson.

There rolls the deep where grew the tree.
O, earth, what changes has thou seen!
There where the long street roars hath been
The stillness of the central sea.
The hills are shadows, and they flow
From form to form, and nothing stands;
They melt like mist, the solid lands,
Like clouds they shape themselves and go.

# AFTER DINNER

Boston Harbor, looking northwest from Weymouth.  Quincy is in the left foreground.
In this 1966 photograph, a circle shows the position of Columbia Point in Dorches-
ter, now the site of the Harbor Campus (University of Massachusetts) and the John
Fitzgerald Kennedy Library.  Across the Inner Harbor in the far center is Logan
Airport.  (Courtesy, Aerial Photos of New England.)

# BANQUET

## THE COPLEY PLAZA HOTEL

**THURSDAY
MARCH 20, 1980**

AFTER DINNER

After the dinner in the Copley Plaza Hotel, the program was opened by Oswald Farquhar. He began by noting that the conference on geotechnology involved two of the major branches of the University of Massachusetts; it had been planned at the Amherst campus, but was being held at the Boston campus. He acknowledged the help of the conference services and the community affairs groups of both branches.

He then continued: "The conference has been supported by the University of Massachusetts, by professional societies and foundations, by government, and by industry. It deals with many projects that affect people's lives. The contributions of those presenting papers today and tomorrow are much appreciated, and it is hoped that the papers will later be useful in print.

"This also seems to be a time to remember the past. In 1980, Boston is celebrating its 350th anniversary. (The photograph on the next page shows part of the Tall Ships Parade later in the summer, with Boston skyscrapers in the background.) And the first official state geological survey of Massachusetts started 150 years ago, as one of the earliest in the country.

"In 1979, the U.S. Geological Survey completed its first century. That organization--as evident at this conference, particularly in sessions 1, 2, 3, and 14--has undertaken extensive work in Massachusetts, much of it under a cooperative program with the Commonwealth. Major projects have dealt with both basic and applied geology.

"Year by year the scope and influence of geologic studies everywhere are increasing, as shown in these proceedings which deal with a typical region. The emphasis is upon industry's need for this important science and, in turn, upon sizeable benefits from combining it with engineering. Are discoveries in geotechnology equal to the task, and do they keep pace with those in other disciplines? These are fundamental questions for which the conference papers perhaps provide some answers.

"This message to conference participants was received today from the President of the Association of Engineering Geologists, John B. Ivey, of Denver, Colorado.

> I would like to extend my best wishes to all of the participants in the conference, Geotechnology in Massachusetts. Much of the program reads like a textbook in its organization and content, and it seems certain that in the years to come the abstracts and preprints will receive great use.

> It is particularly important, in an area where engineering geology and geotechnics are receiving increasing attention, that you will bring to the conference papers which touch on a wide variety of subjects. Most of the papers are related to practical applications of aspects of our endeavors as engineering geologists and geotechnical engineers. The program is comprehensive.

> In covering the subject matter outlined, even the casual observer in the engineering field should be impressed with the importance of geology to virtually all civil works. The non-geologists in attendance should readily see areas in which their disciplines interface with those of the engineering geologist and the geotechnical engineer. This is perhaps one of the most significant achievements of your conference.

- 343 -

# GEOTECHNOLOGY IN MASSACHUSETTS

It is hard not to envy those of you in attendance at this meeting. Please be assured that, speaking for myself and the Association of Engineering Geologists, you have our very best wishes for a successful conference.

"A similar message of good wishes was sent by Senator Paul Tsongas.

"Governor Edward King and the Secretary for Environmental Affairs regret that they are unable to be present. We are pleased that Joseph Sinnott, State Geologist, can attend the dinner and is presenting a paper at the conference."

———————————

David Knapp, President of the University of Massachusetts, also spoke.

———————————

Vincent Murphy, Weston Geophysical Corporation, then introduced Randolph Bromery, who gave the main address.

Dr. Bromery is Commonwealth Professor of Geophysics at the University of Massachusetts and is a former chancellor of the University's Amherst campus. He is a former regional geophysicist with the United States Geological Survey and is currently a Director of the Exxon Corporation.

Boston Harbor during the Parade of Tall Ships in the summer of 1980, one of the city's 350th Anniversary celebrations. (Courtesy, The Boston Globe.)

# Outer continental margin hydrocarbon possibilities and problems

RANDOLPH W. BROMERY
Department of Geology and Geography
University of Massachusetts at Amherst

I recently spent a few weeks visiting the Aramco facilities located at Dhahran, Saudi Arabia. At the 1979 rate of production, Saudi Arabia produces 3 billion barrels of crude oil per year and has produced nearly 37 billion barrels of oil since the first producing well was discovered along the margin of a small sand hill 42 years ago. Since March, 1938, Saudi Arabia has discovered more than 40 additional oil fields with nearly one half of them currently producing. Among these Saudi Arabian oil fields are the largest onshore and offshore oil fields in the world. The onshore Ghawar field is 240 kilometers long and 40 kilometers wide at its widest point. (For those of you who have not yet acquired a metric facility, the Ghawar field is 150 miles long and 25 miles wide at its widest point.) The largest offshore oil field in the world is the Safaniya field which is 80 kilometers long and 30 kilometers wide at its widest point; again, this field is 50 miles long and 20 miles wide. Finally, at the present time Saudi Arabia has proven reserves of oil that are estimated to exceed 113 billion barrels and conducts an active and aggressive exploration program to expand those reserves.

Several of the world's experts estimate that there are two trillion barrels of oil somewhere in the world, and to date we have discovered slightly over one half of this amount or approximately one trillion barrels. Now, if these estimates are nearly correct, then slightly less than one trillion barrels of oil remain to be discovered.

Halbouty and Moody, two of these world experts, estimate that of this one trillion barrels of undiscovered oil, nearly one third will come from the world's mature producing areas in the form of (1) extensions to known fields, (2) new horizons in new stratigraphic zones or in deeper structures, and (3) newly developed enhanced recovery techniques from known fields or lower-grade deposits. Examples of new production in mature areas are the gas discoveries on known structures in the Middle East, Lake Maricaibo in Venezuela, and the Volga-Ural Basin of the U.S.S.R.

Halbouty and Moody, in a recent paper delivered at the World Petroleum Congress in Bucharest, Romania, further estimate that several new exploratory "hot spots" contain another one third of the undiscovered hydrocarbons of the world. Examples in this case are the Moray Firth part of the North Sea, Upper Jurassic discoveries in the central parts of the North Sea, the Carboniferous discoveries in western Siberia, and the Cretaceous-Jurassic discoveries in the Reforma area of Mexico.

These estimates, then, indicate that over two thirds of the world's undiscovered hydrocarbon deposits are to be found in existing producing basins. However, it is of interest to note that none of the occurrences described so far are located within the continental United States or its territories.

It also appears that the remaining one third of the world's undiscovered oil is going to be found in areas of difficult access. These areas have moderately-harsh to harsh environments and will therefore require large costs to explore and exploit their hydrocarbon potential. If these areas show promise, they will then require fairly long lead times to fully develop. One of the major problems facing us today is that there appear to be very few people in important decision-making positions who seem to be aware of the large costs, the extreme complexity, and the lead times associated with these programs. I realize, however, that the comprehension of these important factors seems to diminish in four year cycles. To reach into these new frontiers, less politics and a closer cooperation between government and private industry will be required. The proper role for government will be to encourage industry, with its expertise and experience in the profession of finding oil, to invest its capital in exploring these areas of harsh environments and high risks.

Other important pieces of information to keep in mind are that, at the end of 1978, the world's crude oil reserves amounted to approximately 650 billion barrels, and that, at the current rate of consumption of slightly over 20 billion barrels per year coupled with a world-wide decline in both discoveries and reserves, we will be in serious trouble fairly soon. Our only hope for the future depends upon increased discoveries or alternate energy sources. Most of the world's experts estimate that alternate energy sources will take another 30 to 40 years to develop to meaningful levels, and therefore the one trillion barrels of undiscovered oil in the world will be needed to bridge this gap. In this case, I personally think that the experts are not conservative enough in their estimates. I believe that it will be closer to 50 years before these alternate energy sources, such as fusion processes or solar power, can be developed and brought on line.

Closer to home, in the United States' quest for this undiscovered oil, we have just begun to lease and explore on our Continental Shelves in several promising hydrocarbon provinces. In one of these areas, the Baltimore Canyon, the results have not been as encouraging to date as was hoped earlier. Other data, however, indicate that the offshore extensions of the Alaskan North Slope and Beaufort Sea are quite similar geologically and in their hydrocarbon potential to the onshore areas that are currently productive. A similar promising area is believed to exist in the deeper parts of the Gulf of Mexico. Based on this moderate to poor showing on the Continental Shelf, experts feel that it tends to increase the chances of finding new hydrocarbon provinces farther seaward on the Outer Continental Margins. The question still remains as to whether these fields, if they exist, will be of sufficient size to be commercial at these greater water depths.

Although we know very little concerning the geology and the hydrocarbon potential of the vast expanses of our domestic Outer Continental Margins, recent deep sea drilling results and geophysical data indicate that the hydrocarbons are there. The Outer Continental Margin, the transitional zone between the continental and oceanic regimes, includes the deepest parts of the Gulf of Mexico which are approximately 12,000 feet, and the Bering Sea off Alaska, which is approximately 13,000 feet. The O.C.M. contains a considerable thickness of sedimentary rocks and covers nearly four times the area of our Continental Shelves. In fact, the volume of sediments contained in the O.C.M. nearly equals the total volume of sediments contained within the continental United States and its Continental Shelf combined.

Just offshore, on the Continental Shelf, we know that we have hydrocarbon productive basins, as has been indicated in recent exploration and drilling programs. We also know that there are no hydrocarbon possibilities in the deep sea sediments. To date, we can only speculate on hydrocarbon possibilities on the Outer Continental Margins. However, many of you in the audience here tonight are aware that the geophysical professions have a natural affinity for speculation. If you will permit me, I would like to engage in some speculation at this time. Considering our current domestic energy situation and our dependence on a very fragile and vulnerable Middle East connection, I believe that some speculation is in order.

Based on recent reports from the U.S. Geological Survey, drilling in the deep Atlantic Basins has revealed Cretaceous Age sediments composed in part of a thick sequence containing black organic-rich clays that are oil and gas prone. Further, the reports state that seismic data has traced these organic-rich zones back toward the continent across the O.C.M. to the Continental Slope, where they appear to end against a reef-like structure or carbonate bank; normally reefs are good reservoirs for oil and gas. In addition, scientists speculate that the thick Tertiary sediments that comprise a major part of the modern Continental Rise may contain

sand bodies with promising reservoir characteristics.

Other U.S. Geological Survey reports reveal that in a deep part of the Gulf of Mexico, sediments 6 to 8 kilometers thick are pierced by salt domes. Recent drilling by the Glomar Challenger penetrated the sediments overlying one of these salt domes and discovered an oil-stained caprock buried just 400 feet below the sea floor. Age determinations date the oil as Jurassic, suggesting a more deeply buried source for the oil. At the present time, while we still have incomplete results of the drilling from the Glomar Challenger, we do have information on the sediments surrounding the salt dome. However, we know almost nothing concerning the underlying sediments and whether those oil stains indicate hydrocarbon possibilities within the older, more deeply buried deposits.

Another even more promising indicator was recently discovered in the Bering Sea off Alaska. Here, the U.S. Geological Survey reported that seismic data suggests the presence of gas in the 4 to 6 kilometer thick sediments contained within the deep basin of the Bering Sea. These seismic gas anomalies are abundant over an area equal in size to the state of Washington, nearly 70,000 square miles. As with other parts of our domestic Outer Continental Margin areas, we know very little about the sediments underlying the Bering Sea.

Returning again to the east coast of the United States, the Continental Shelf extends south from the Canadian Border to the southern tip of Florida. The northern part of the Continental Shelf is underlain by clastic sediments which thicken to the south, reaching more than 40,000 feet in the Baltimore Canyon area. The sediments then thin southward and interfinger with the carbonate sediments flanking the Florida peninsula. The carbonate rocks of the Florida platform contain productive hydrocarbon reservoirs onshore; and these same carbonate sediments grade westward from the Florida platform into the clastic sediments that contain highly productive reservoirs off the Louisiana coast and moderately productive reservoirs off the Texas Gulf Coast.

Along the Pacific coast of the United States, the southern California borderlands and the Santa Barbara Channel north of Mexico are highly productive in hydrocarbons from deposits within the clastic sediments that extend offshore from the Los Angeles and Ventura Basins. Farther to the north along the coast of Oregon and Washington, these same types of sediments are unproductive to date. Many scientists, however, wonder if we may find channel sands and turbidites off the northwest coast similar to those in the California basins to the south.

Onshore carbonate rocks in Alaska extend offshore and may have significant hydrocarbon possibilities beneath the Arctic Ocean, the Bering Sea, and the Pacific margin of southern Alaska. However, in this latter area close proximity to a developing deep ocean trench diminishes the potential. The same carbonate rocks are productive under Cook Inlet in southern Alaska.

Considering the oil and gas production in parts of the U.S. Continental Shelf and studies by the Glomar Challenger which indicate that hydrocarbons are present in other parts of the Outer Continental Margins, it would seem that the next step for us is to develop an exploration program for this extremely large area adjacent to our shorelines. Remember, when you consider the probabilities for oil deposits, that the Outer Continental Margins contain over 21 million cubic kilometers of sediments, which is five times the volume of sediments that are contained in the Continental Shelves. In summary, the Glomar Challenger data suggest that the sediment conditions, types, thicknesses, and thermal history are all favorable for the occurrence of hydrocarbons in this area. Time is far too limited here to even touch upon the mineral possibilities of the Outer Continental Margins.

Last year, while visiting South Africa, I went down a gold mine in the Transvaal where gold is presently mined at a depth of 12,400 feet below the surface of the ground. I must say that I am not enthusiastic about going underground since I figure that I have an eternity ahead of me to experience that condition. However, my scientific curiosity literally pushed me down the shaft. Less than a decade ago, the technology had not been fully developed to mine the gold at these depths, and the price of gold did not warrant the cost. Now both the price of gold and the mining technology make this a fairly routine operation. The ventilation systems are complex, and the working conditions are no worse than operations at far shallower depths. In fact, they are better than in some of our domestic coal mines. I was informed that new drill holes had intersected the same gold zone at a depth of 20,000 feet, and the mining company was confident that, by the time it became necessary to mine the gold at 20,000 feet, the technology would be developed and ready to go on line, and the price of gold would be the limiting factor. I fully recognize the associated social problems involved in this mining operation in South Africa; however, an important mineral is being mined by men more than two miles below the surface.

A major problem with offshore drilling and production of hydrocarbon deposits has been the development of the technology for deep water drilling. In fact, the exploration program, which begins far ahead of drilling for production, requires deep water drilling technology. Based on what I have seen and what has been related to me from those associated with several petroleum companies, deep water drilling and production technology is fast advancing in the development of new techniques, and water depth records are being set every few months. Within the last several months, these companies have developed and demonstrated the ability to drill in waters deeper than 1300 meters, or 4,200 feet, and plans are well

advanced to reach water depths of 1600 meters, or 5,300 feet. During the research for the development of these methods, it appears that 1,000 meters of water is the point where systems take a large jump in sophistication, and much higher strength components are required. In deep water drilling, for example, the drilling vessel has to have a larger load capacity, a sophisticated and reliable dynamic positioning system for staying on location at the drilling site, and the ability to quickly disconnect and move off position in the case of an emergency. New weather satellites and better weather forecasting techniques have diminished emergencies due to changing and severe weather. Most emergencies today are failures of computers or other equipment. The ship, in any case, must be able to return, relocate the drill hole on the ocean floor, reenter the hole, and continue drilling. New drilling risers have to be developed, and a multiplex electrohydraulic blowout preventer system of a new breed will have to be designed.

Production systems for use once the hydrocarbons are found are even more complex. However, private industry has made great strides in this developmental area over the last few years. One of the more promising types has been the subsea production system developed, constructed, and tested by a research group with Exxon. This particular system is ready for commercial use and contains all of the required equipment for drilling and producing. When production ceases, the entire system can be safely disconnected and abandoned. It has a complete hydrocarbon handling capability and is remotely installed, controlled, and maintained.

Thus, we have the current capability to drill and produce hydrocarbons in water depths that exceed 1,300 meters, and the technology is far advanced to drill and produce at even greater depths. This will be required in order to explore and develop most of the areas of the Outer Continental Margin.

In a recent exchange of letters in the New York Times, Professor Hollis Hedberg, a respected geoscientist, pointed out that one of the major impediments in an expanded offshore exploration program by the private oil companies is the current U.S. system of requiring very large outlays of capital to lease small parcels of land in the less promising parts of our vast offshore areas. Most other countries of the world grant exploration and development leases for far larger blocks of land, especially in areas of moderately-harsh to harsh environments. These countries, Hedberg goes on to say, require specific drilling obligations and have developed a reasonable set of petroleum laws that protect their governments. Our present domestic system is to grant leases for parcels of land only nine square miles in area, and over the last 25 years less than one seventh of the areas with hydrocarbon potential have been leased. Two relatively uncomplicated steps could be taken by the federal government that would surely lead to greatly expanded offshore exploration activity. The first step would be to increase the size of the leased offshore parcels from the current nine square miles up to the world average of 3,000 square miles per parcel. The second step would be to open up those offshore areas with a greater promise for desperately needed hydrocarbon deposits.

U.S. Congressman John M. Murphy (D-NY), who responded to Professor Hedberg's push for a greatly expanded offshore activity, pointed out that in September, 1978, Congress passed a set of amendments to the O.C.S. (Outer Continental Shelf) Lands Act which empowered the Secretary of the Interior to lease tracts in excess of the old nine square mile limit. However, Congressman Murphy went on to say that the Departments of Interior and Energy have been slow in making the changes permitted by these amendments. It seems that someone in Washington has managed to reverse the priorities established when the amendments were enacted. The reason Congress made the changes was to stimulate an increase in offshore leasing and exploration by private industry, and not merely to increase revenues to the federal government through this offshore leasing program. I am sure that Congress was hoping that these changes would encourage private industry to expand its exploration activity in the offshore, because they recognize that the risk factor is related to the size of the leased tract.

Finally, we must take note of the growing concern for possible environmental hazards in conducting exploration and development programs in these deep water areas. I believe that U.S. technology leadership has advanced to the point that these programs can be implemented while protecting the environment of the ocean margins. The recent Gulf of Mexico disaster was a perfect case of lack of professional experience in deep water drilling combined with lack of advanced technologies in blowout preventer systems.

In this context, I recall that about ten years ago I read an interesting article in the 1966 issue of the American Scholar. (I know it will come as a surprise to many of you here tonight that scientists read material other than their own set of scientific journals.) However, the specific article which had caught my attention was a philosophical discussion of one of Emerson's essays by Phillip Hallie, a distinguished professor of philosophy at Wesleyan University. Hallie quoted from Emerson as follows: "Every fact is related on one side to sensation and on the other to morals. The game of thought is, on the appearance of one of these two sides, to find the other . . .". Hallie then went on to remark: "Living

intelligently and living well are not separate enterprises." He also said: "The main concerns of the scientific philosophers and the main concerns of the wisdom philosophers are two sides of a very thin coin, but still some men are quite content to spend most of their lives looking on the side of objective knowledge, and others are quite content to spend most of the time of their lives looking on the side of objective knowledge, and others are quite content to spend most of the time of their lives putting into words the business of living well." Further in the article, Hallie said that he found he was a wisdom philosopher stranded in a community of scientific philosophers. (Perhaps my experience has been different, due primarily to my ten years in university administration, because there I found that I was a scientific philosopher stranded in a community of wisdom philosophers.) Returning to Emerson, it seems that the popular belief in this country is that the development of our technological expertise--particularly in the area of energy research and exploration--and a deep abiding concern for the protection of our environment are in conflict, and these two concerns are not at all compatible. I do not subscribe to the perceived gap between these two legitimate concerns, because I believe that, in reality, these two concerns are two sides of a very thin coin. I find that we are often guilty of ignoring Emerson's charge, i.e., "The game of thought is, on the appearance of one of these two sides, to find the other . . .".

The demand for petroleum in this decade is expected to exceed the supplies that are available. This fact, combined with a decline in world petroleum reserves, will cause us for the first time to experience a true "energy crisis." If we greatly expanded our exploration programs tomorrow morning, it would be sometime in 1990 or the 21st century before this newly discovered oil would help in our then acute "energy crisis."

But most of you out there are aware of this problem. In fact, it is at conferences like this that scientists and policymakers contribute to a better understanding of rational resource assessment and better communication with the populace. All of these groups must acknowledge the pressing need for a greatly expanded, quickly implemented exploration program designed to safely exploit our natural resources. Along with severe geopolitical considerations, the abstract concept of being cold and the actual condition are far removed from each other. If I have only made you think about it tonight, then I will consider that a start. Thank you for your time and attention.

# 8

# ENERGY AND THE GEOSCIENCES

Session moderators

A. A. Qazilbash
C. E. Maguire, Inc.

L. Morgenstern
Massachusetts Executive Office of Energy Resources

# The Lawrence hydroelectric project, Lawrence, Massachusetts

D. K. HOLWAY
W. R. Holway and Associates

## ABSTRACT

The Lawrence hydroelectric project, located in the center of Lawrence, Massachusetts, is now well underway with the powerhouse excavation completed during January 1980. Concrete work is in progress, with completion scheduled this fall to allow generating units and auxiliaries to be installed and tested for operation in July 1981.*

This date represents an extremely short six-year period from project conception to completion, including all preliminary studies, procurement of the essential federal license (major project), arrangements for financing and for sale of the output, and formation of the construction team.

The project was conceived and promoted by a group of private businessmen with no utility or governmental connections. Financing was entirely private, with several banks providing the various funds required. The construction team composed of the manufacturers, engineering consultants, and the contractor is providing an operating project on a turnkey basis. All of the output will be sold to the New England Power Company.

The project was located by the promoters in a search for feasible alternate energy sources. They found an existing dam with most of the hydraulic potential unused and declining. The Essex (or "Great Stone") dam in Lawrence was built in 1845-48 by New England investors to establish a new industrial development about 24 miles north of Boston on the New Hampshire turnpike. The development was extremely successful. A new town, Lawrence, was founded. Mills were built along canals fed by the dam. Adjoining land was sold for residential and commercial use, and the final result was an operating textile, machinery, and paper manufacturing center that grew into the world center for woolen cloth production by 1900. Today most of the mills have moved away or closed, and the hydraulic power potential of the Merrimack River is unused.

---

\* The project was dedicated in August 1981.--ed.

Inquiries regarding permission to reproduce this paper should be directed to the author.

## THE SITE

As general background, the existing dam is located on the Merrimack River in Lawrence (Fig. 1). It is the last dam in a series that extends up the river (Fig. 2), which is fed by a drainage area of some 5,000 square miles (the fourth largest in New England).

The dam was built on a granite outcropping known as Bodwell's Falls. It was a considerable engineering undertaking in its day, as it was to be three times as high as any previous dam built in the United States. A tribute to its designer, Charles S. Storrow, it was constructed without serious incident and has survived to this day without repair or maintenance. The dam was built of rubble masonry with cut and fitted granite blocks for facing and the crest. It was keyed into excavated rock, with the lower courses bolted to the foundation. The highest portion of the dam is about 40 feet with an average of 32 feet.

The dam itself extends about 26 feet above the low water level at its base, with four or five feet of flashboards to produce additional head. In the original project a single canal extended along the north side of the river below the dam (Fig. 3), controlled by a gate house at the entrance.

This canal produced a guaranteed head of 25 feet for use by the mills. A second canal was completed in 1866 on the south side of the river to serve more mills. Essex was also responsible for constructing each mill (complete with a hydraulic turbine), highway and railroad bridges, a navigation lock, a crude fish ladder, and a hydraulic research facility.

The main highway bridge and a railroad bridge were built adjacent to the dam, and many years later the site was leased to a motel and restaurant.

## THE NEW PROJECT

In 1975 the group of business men now known as the Lawrence Hydroelectric Associates recognized the potential of the dam for redevelopment, and obtained an option to purchase the property with all its water rights, subject to a favorable feasibility study and successful financing.

During the next few years the study was completed, a federal license was obtained, further

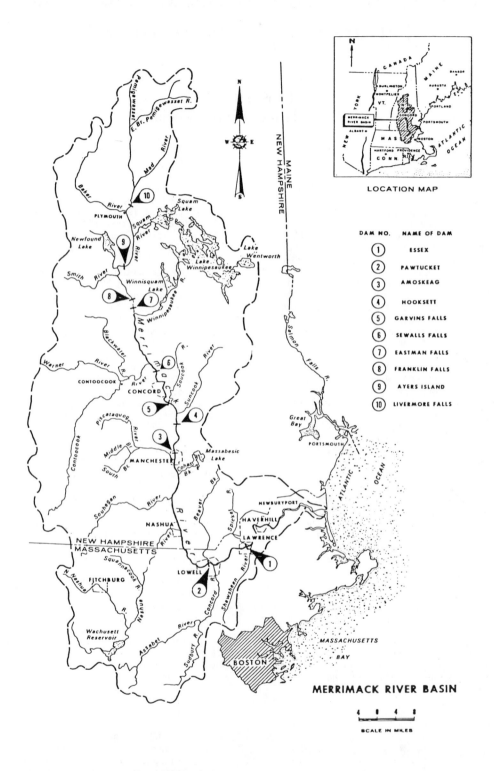

Figure 1.  Merrimack River basin.

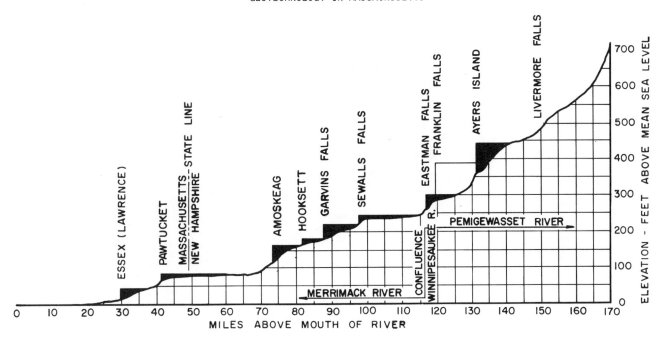

Figure 2. Merrimack River profile.

Figure 3. Essex dam and canal system, location map, Lawrence, Massachusetts.

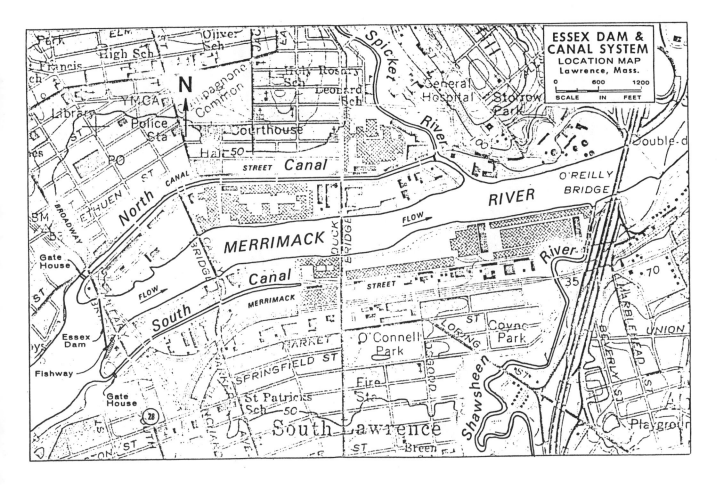

Figure 4. Aerial view of Essex dam, looking southwest.

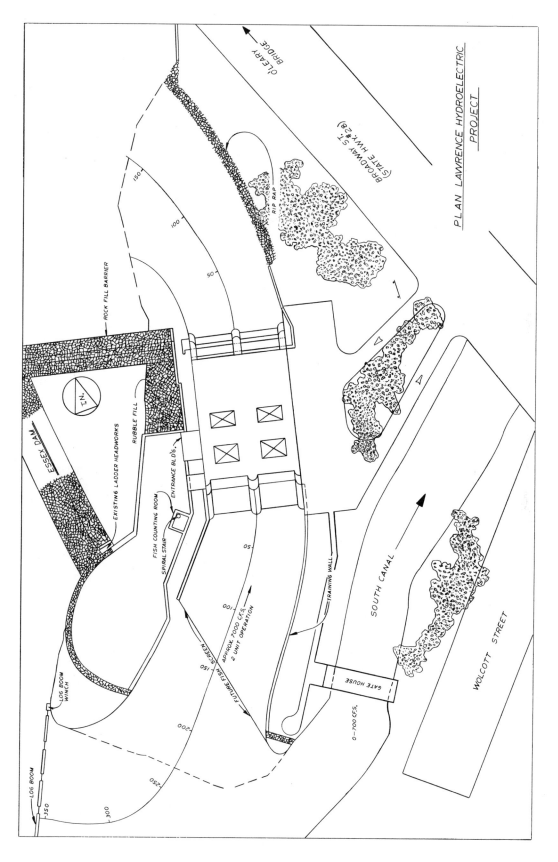

Figure 5. Plan view of Lawrence hydroelectric project.

water rights were acquired, a sales contract for the electric energy was negotiated, support of municipal, state and federal agencies was obtained, financing was arranged and Allis-Chalmers Corporation and W.R. Holway & Associates were enlisted to provide all civil, mechanical, and electrical design and the turbine design and construction support for the project. The Westinghouse Electric Corporation and the Perini Corporation were added to the team to provide the electric generator equipment and the civil construction capability for a complete turnkey proposal. This proposal limited the ultimate cost of the project.

This turnkey contract arrangement provided an early-on interaction between the principals to optimize the ultimate design in ways unachievable under usual construction contracting. Early and continual, frank and constructive communication between them concerning the total project both saved considerable time in concluding various contracts and permits and produced a simplified, low-cost hydropower project design.

An important feature of the licensing process was early involvement of the local, state, and regional federal agencies. Their valuable impact and cooperation during preparation and refinement of the license application greatly helped to reduce the time necessary for issuance.

A most significant decision arrived at by this process was selection of the bulb-type turbine-generator set, rather than the tube-type arrangement originally selected. Another, resulting from both a group evaluation of civil and erection costs and a group visit to the Urstein plant in Austria, was to utilize a horizontal, rather than an inclined, bulb arrangement to avoid the complexities and hidden costs of the latter.

Figure 4 shows the project area, "The Great Stone Dam," with the O'Leary (Broadway Street) and railway bridges immediately downstream from the dam and the North and South Canals with their intake control gate houses. The only structures to be removed from the site are the home of the control gate house keeper and an old motel which, in recent years, has been used as a private nursing home.

Figure 5 shows the planned redevelopment with its intake channel (forebay) beginning at the entrance of the South Canal, the 14.8 MW, 2-bulb-unit power house and the tailrace discharge back into the river between "The Great Stone Dam" and the O'Leary (Broadway Street) Bridge. Also shown are the upstream migrant fish handling facilities to be built on the downstream and the river sides of the power house. Underground power cables, 23-kV and 600-700 feet in length, will run from the power house to a tower to be erected just east of the railway by the South Canal to connect the power plant to the existing 23-kV utility transmission system.

Because of the historic aspect of both "The

Great Stone Dam" and the South Canal control gate house, as well as the location of the project in the center of the City of Lawrence, the turnkey contract also includes landscaping the project site, west of Broadway Street, to give the people of Lawrence an interesting and attractive park. In addition to grass, paved paths and shrubbery, there will be public lavatory facilities, picnic tables, benches and security fencing of waterways.

As can be seen from the project elevation drawing, Figure 6, both the power plant and fish facilities will have a very low, clean profile, with a pleasing appearance from O'Leary (Broadway Street) Bridge and surrounding areas. In fact, the power house discharge will enhance the river at the foot of the dam, especially when water is not being spilled along its crest.

PROJECT DATA

```
Number and type of units.....................2 bulb
Plant annual energy output....100,000,000 kW hours
Unit capacity (rated).......................7,400 kW
Unit capacity (maximum)....................9,120 kW
Head range........................22.0 to 31.5 feet
Unit speed..............................128.6 rpm
Generator voltage.....................4,160 volts
Transmission voltage.......................23.0 kV
Start of construction.................June 1, 1979
Scheduled commercial operation........July 1, 1981
```

HYDRAULIC TURBINES

Bulb generating units are being furnished for reasons of high efficiency and low total project cost, resulting from the shallow, narrow, straight water passageway they require as compared with other types of units. Initially a tube-type unit was proposed with an inclined shaft and a direct-driven open generator. Further studies by all parties working closely together, on both a design and total project cost basis, led instead to a bulb generator arrangement, first slightly inclined, then to the present horizontal bulb generator arrangement (Fig. 6). Hydraulic, mechanical, electrical, and civil engineering costs had to be thoroughly considered when making the selection.

In resulting project design, the water will enter each unit through inclined trash racks mounted on the upstream face of the power house; into the rectangular water passageway, which becomes circular in the region of the generator bulb with its top and bottom piers (and access tube); through the conical wicket gate arrangement; over the conventional-appearing, adjustable, blade-propeller runner; and out through the straight conical/rectangular draft tube into the tailrace channel. Every effort has been made to ensure that hydraulic losses throughout will be minimal to obtain maximum possible conversion of energy from water power to mechanical power for spinning the bulb generator.

The total generating unit, turbine and

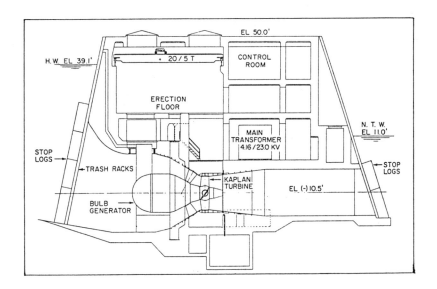

Figure 6.  Power house elevation,
Lawrence hydroelectric project.

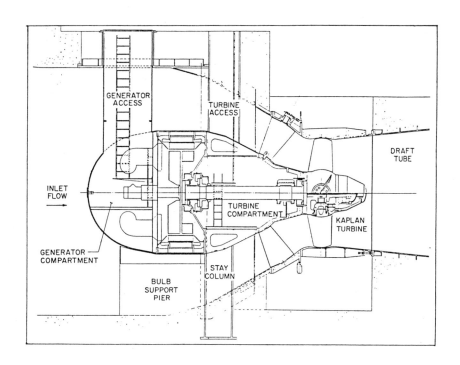

Figure 7.  Vertical section,
Lawrence bulb/turbine generator.

generator, resembling a giant stubby submarine (Fig. 7), is supported in the center of the water passageway by means of a streamlined, vertical, heavy, fabricated steel stay column (Fig. 8), as well as a sole plate under the bulb nose section, both of which are firmly embedded and anchored into the powerhouse substructure. These bulb units do not have a multi-vaned supporting structure, similar to the stay ring of a conventional vertical Kaplan turbine, for both hydraulic and cost reasons. The turbine is cantilevered from the downstream face of the stay column and the generator from its upstream face, additionally supported by its sole plate. All loads, normal and short circuit, gravity and buoyancy, from the turbine and generator, will be carried by the stay column structure and the pier under the bulb. In the areas where the stay column crosses the water passageway, both below and above the bulb, it is streamlined for hydraulic reasons. The top section of the stay column also serves as the access tube from the power house into the turbine compartment of the bulb.

The cooperation between the engineers and the manufacturers during the early conceptual design period allowed more rapid selection of alternate design approaches and brought more concepts to the table as discussion of each feature developed. The crane facilities selection is another example of the cooperation among all the parties. The material handling equipment for permanent use in the plant will be required to lift less than five tons (for all except extraordinary maintenance), and jib cranes would appear to be the best solution. The construction requirements, however, are much greater, requiring 175-ton mobile equipment for 60-ton lifts at short radius. Other construction activities will probably require a 100-ton mobile crane most of the time for concrete forms and miscellaneous work. Conference table discussions showed that a permanent 32-ton bridge crane of simplest possible design can be installed in the power house to provide for indoor winter assembly of smaller parts into larger units at less total cost than using jib cranes and outdoor assembly with a mobile crane. In addition, during plant operation, the overhead bridge crane will facilitate both ordinary and extraordinary operations. Other project features have been developed in a similar manner, both during conceptual and during detailed design stages.

## ELECTRICAL SYSTEM

The electrical systems are not conventional by today's standards. Thus, the project is to be operated manually rather than unattended and remote controlled, because the existing canals and remaining water powers served by the dam require regular manual attendance. Provision will be made for future remote operation.

The generator voltage choice in a bulb generator is limited for optimum design, 4,160 volts being chosen for these units. The unit rating of 9.6 MVA required 2,000-ampere main breakers in the metalclad switchgear. The interconnection voltage of 23-kV dictates a step-up transformer. One is to be supplied for each unit--of the indoor, self-cooled dry type. Station service is taken from each 4-kV bus, and is backed up with a diesel generator set capable of providing for safe shutdown. The 23-kV bus consisting of two (2) OCB's and the interconnection metering equipment will be housed indoors to conform with the project description calling for no outdoor stations. Conventional lighting and small power systems will be furnished along with the necessary mechanical systems for drainage, dewatering, ventilation, fire protection, etc.

## SITE PROBLEMS

The site chosen in the initial feasibility study, adjacent to the south abutment of the dam, was extremely restricted in area, and the restraints of turbine design dictated a narrow, deep (89 feet) power house to properly develop the hydraulic resource. As noted above, the power house is entirely below the original grade level. It extends to 60 feet below the rock line, resulting in a major portion of the excavation being in rock. This rock has been described as layered metamorphic, consisting predominantly of quartzite which dips at angles from 60 to 80 degrees and is approximately parallel to the length of the excavation. There has been a large slope failure on the east side of the powerhouse excavation (the power house runs approximately north and south), amounting to about 2000 cubic yards. Fortunately, this has occurred on the face of the excavation that is away from the dam abutment, and the other face is unaffected. The stability of the remaining portions of the east face was seriously questioned, and a rock reinforcement program was adopted consisting of 10-foot long, 1-inch diameter, fully resin-grouted rock bolts spaced on patterned 5-foot centers. Two-inch square wire mesh is secured to the face with the rock bolts, which are subsequently torqued to 400-450 foot pounds. The failure was ascribed to the existence of a clay seam in the rock layers. No such seam was noted in the extensive core-drilling program conducted during the early design work. It should also be noted that at full excavation depth no significant leakage occurred from the dam abutments. The only leakage appeared to originate in the ungrouted hundred-year-old rock walls of the adjacent south canal.

In conjunction with the experience of the Perini Corporation, a marine piling wall design was adopted to restrain the earth section between the new headwater canal and the existing South Canal. This design allowed the South Gate House to be undisturbed, because no backslope was required in the overburden for the deep rock excavation in the headwater canal. A similar wall was used for the same reason to protect the dam abutment on the other side and to provide the maximum distance between the dam and the rock excavation.

All rock blasting was carefully controlled and monitored with seismic instruments to limit

Figure 8.  Urstein partial stay
column assembly (portions of outer
stay column missing).

the risk of working near a 130-year old dam. Rock splitting techniques were used to separate the rock before major blasting operations. No other problems developed from these techniques.

Additional excavation will be required to remove the plugs left above and below the power house as cofferdams.

\*   \*   \*

Lawrence hydroelectric project.

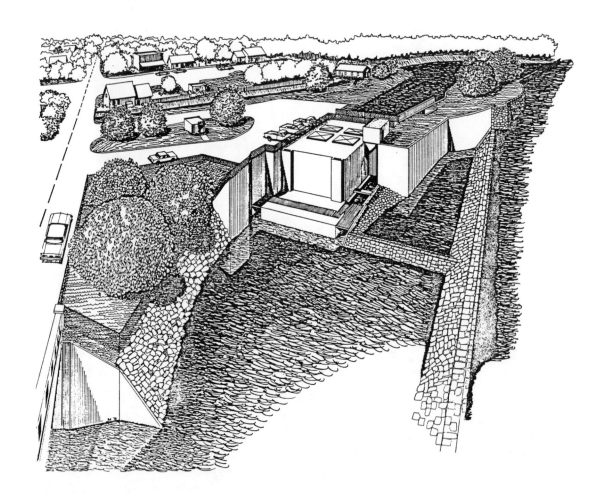

# Hydro and tidal power development in Maine—Small scale projects

## N. L. LABERGE
Passamaquoddy Tribal Council, Pleasant Point Reservation
Perry, Maine

## I. SMALL-SCALE HYDROELECTRIC PROJECTS

### ABSTRACT

The U.S. Army Corps of Engineers recently released a report entitled, "Hydroelectric Potential of Existing Dams in the New England Region," which assessed the power production potential of 10,670 dams. The results of their analysis based on an engineering practicability test determined that 1,748 sites could be developed with a capacity factor of 40 per cent. Of these, 1,154 sites would have a capacity factor of 70 per cent. New England as a region could theoretically obtain 1,002 MW and 419 MW for projects with capacity factors of 40 per cent and 70 per cent, respectively. In the case of the lower capacity factor, the region could save approximately 4,900,000 barrels of oil per year. The average plant size is around 560 KW ranging from 2 KW up to 5,000 KW.

* * *

However, the engineering practicability test only serves to identify the technically feasible sites. To determine a realistic estimate of the small-scale hydroelectric potential an assessment of environmental, institutional, and economic issues would be required. For the state of Maine, the Corps report listed 367 MW and 154 MW of hydro potential for capacity factors of 40 per cent and 70 per cent, respectively. This figure represents the upper limit of total capacity able to be developed. In my opinion, only 25 per cent to 50 per cent of this total could be placed on-line within the constraints of environmental, economic, and institutional factors.

The East Machias hydro redevelopment project has conducted a number of studies related to their hydro station which generated electricity from 1926 to the mid 1950's. It has been estimated that the project, if placed on-line during 1980, could produce power for 4.5¢/KWh. This number has been determined on the basis of engineering, environmental, and institutional studies. I feel that the fishway design was the most critical environmental and institutional issue resolved for approval by state, federal, and local agencies and also by fishermen and other residents of East Machias.

However, before the project can enter the construction phase, it will be necessary to: (1) receive licenses from the Federal Energy Regulatory Commission and from the state of Maine; (2) work out an acceptable agreement for the sale of power; (3) formulate the plan for revenue bond financing; (4) attempt to secure federal assistance to reduce the town's share of the construction cost; and (5) hold a referendum vote to obtain legal jurisdiction to construct the project. In summary, the development of small-scale hydro is not a simple exercise. It involves a great deal of time and effort to address site-specific issues and to properly analyze the project's impact on the affected communities.

## II. TIDAL POWER: AN UNTAPPED ENERGY RESOURCE

### ABSTRACT

The tides of Passamaquoddy Bay and Cobscook Bay have intrigued energy developers over the many years since Dexter Cooper first proposed his tidal power project. The occurrence here of the highest tides of any site along the east coast of the United States has attracted this interest and desire to harness the tidal forces as an energy resource. In order to appreciate the power production potential from the amount of water flowing in and out of the bay, it has been estimated that the tidal exchange measured at Head Harbor during a two week period is equal to the total discharge of the Mississippi River at New Orleans during one year.

* * *

Today, the U.S. Army Corps of Engineers is once again studying large-scale tidal projects capable of being constructed completely in Maine. The so-called All American schemes are virtually the same configurations proposed by Dexter Cooper in the 1920's. Will the results be different now than they were nearly sixty years ago? Probably not. The effects of an observed fuel cost escalation rate rising faster than inflation and the desired transition to environmentally clean sources of electricity will undoubtedly enhance the attractiveness of tidal power, but probably not enough to overcome the economic constraints imposed by a capital intensive project which initially produces power at a rate exceeding the cost of electricity paid by the average consumer in Maine.

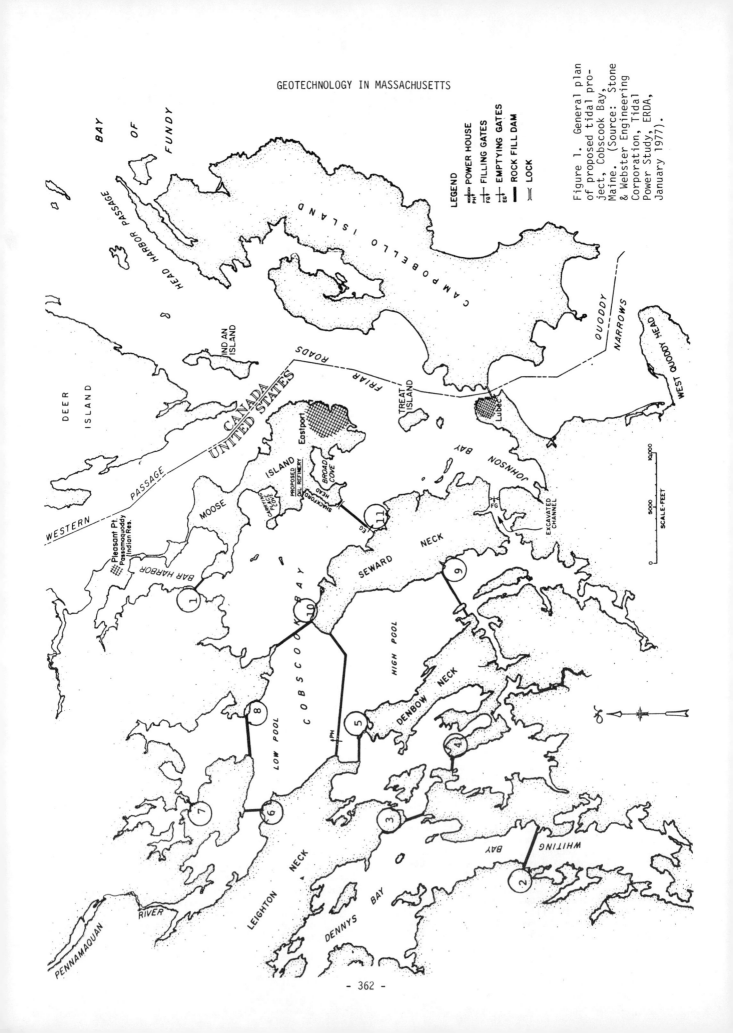

Figure 1. General plan of proposed tidal project, Cobscook Bay, Maine. (Source: Stone & Webster Engineering Corporation, Tidal Power Study, ERDA, January 1977).

TABLE 1. POWER PRODUCTION POTENTIAL AT SITES PROPOSED FOR DEVELOPMENT OF TIDAL PROJECTS, COBSCOOK BAY REGION, MAINE (SEE FIG. 1); FROM A REPORT PREPARED BY STONE AND WEBSTER ENGINEERING CORPORATION FOR THE CORPS OF ENGINEERS.

* Calculations based on an optimized operating mode which has a 0.4325 capacity factor.

| Site | Area at mean high tide (acre) | Entrance span-ft. | Maximum depth at mean low tide-ft. | Capacity (MW) | Annual energy output * (10⁶ KWh) |
|---|---|---|---|---|---|
| 1. Half-Moon Cove | 795 | 1220 | 27 | 8 | 30.315 |
| 2. Bar Isle | 1630 | 3430 | 33 | 16 | 60.619 |
| 3. Mahar Point | 5850 | 2170 | 52 | 58 | 219.745 |
| 4. Coffin's Point | 1200 | 750 | 28 | 8 | 30.315 |
| 5. Denbow Point | 8760 | 2030 | 102 | 88 | 333.405 |
| 6. Two-Hour Point | 870 | 1740 | 39 | 8 | 30.315 |
| 7. Sipp Bay | 300 | 300 | 10 | 2.5 | 9.472 |
| 8. Clement Point | 1270 | 3400 | 34 | 13 | 49.253 |
| 9. Long Isle | 425 | 3660 | 15 | 3 | 11.366 |
| 10. Gove Point | 17250 | 3830 | 120 | 180 | 681.966 |
| 11. Shackford Head | 21200 | 4370 | 151 | 230 | 871.401 |

TABLE 2. FOUR SCHEMES FOR THE DEVELOPMENT OF TIDAL POWER IN COBSCOOK BAY

** Figures in parentheses represent the amount of oil-fired electricity displaced in barrels.

| | Total capacity (MW) | Capacity dependable (MW) | Annual total energy production** (10⁶ KWh) |
|---|---|---|---|
| SCHEME 1 - Paired basin mode | | | |
| Half-Moon Cove and Coffin's Point | 16 | 1.6 | 16.630 (106,870 BBL) |
| SCHEME 2 - Small Tidal Plants | | | |
| Coffin's Point, Clement Point, Two-Hour Point, Long Isle, Half-Moon Cove | 40 | 8.0 | 151.564 (267,160 BBL) |
| SCHEME 3 - Small and Intermediate | | | |
| Two-Hour Point, Clement Point, Long Isle, Half-Moon Cove, Denbow Point | 120 | 6.4 | 454.654 (801,425 BBL) |
| SCHEME 4 - Small and Large | | | |
| Mahar Point, Shackford Head, Half-Moon Cove, Coffin's Point | 304 | 1.6 | 1151.776 (2030,250 BBL) |

If the results are predictable, why should additional time and effort be expended on the investigation of tidal power? The answer is that tidal power can be proven economically feasible if steps are taken to properly evaluate and promote this renewable source of energy.

In order to properly evaluate the true potential of tidal power, an economic assessment should consider the value of a tidal project in relation to its long-term return and also make comparisons with an appropriate alternative. If the Corps of Engineers had been able to complete the tidal project started in 1936, we would be paying less than one cent per kilowatt-hour (1¢/KWh) for tidal power, which is far below the approximate value of 5.5¢/KWh presently being paid by the average residential user of electricity. In theory, the production cost from the tidal project would have increased by less than 1/2¢/KWh during a forty-year period. The reason for this "inflation proof" behavior is that the fuel (tidal water) is free once the project is placed in operation. The capital intensive nature of the project dictates a high initial investment, i.e., annual cost, which remains constant during the project's lifetime. Therefore, in practice the production cost of a tidal project remains relatively constant with time as opposed to sources of energy that are drastically affected by inflation and by environmental concerns, e.g., nuclear plants.

The value of a tidal project can be determined in various ways. One method considers how a project displaces the most expensive sources of fuel that are presently being used for the production of electricity within the utility network. However, this method does not adequately consider a tidal project with respect to a comparable alternative which would be required for future demands and also does not properly consider the total replacement, or displacement, cost of the capital needed for each additional unit of capacity. In summary, the realization of the region's tidal power potential will involve a balance between the long-term benefits and short-term deficits by establishing an equitable value as an incentive for development.

The promotion of tidal power needs a new approach that reflects local initiative and regional support. I feel that the objectives of tidal power development can be served best by placing primary attention on the construction of small tidal projects that are designed for demonstration purposes and for regional energy supplies. The Half-Moon Cove tidal project being proposed by the Passamaquoddy Tribe at the Pleasant Point Reservation exemplifies this philosophy. The recent formation of the Cobscook Bay Tidal Power Committee with membership from the bordering communities is another positive step which broadens the support base and encourages the development of tidal power for the many potential sites in the region. Hopes for the realization of tidal power objectives have languished for too long with groups external and insensitive to the region's concerns. The time

has arrived to initiate the driving force from within the region for projects which are realistic and achievable.

HALF-MOON COVE TIDAL POWER PROJECT

The Passamaquoddy Tribe at the Pleasant Point Reservation in Perry, Maine, has been actively involved in the development of tidal power since 1976. This effort has been directed at the construction of a small tidal power plant which would harness the tidal forces of Half-Moon Cove. The average range is 18.1 ft. The power plant would serve the following purposes.

● Generate electricity from a renewable and environmentally safe energy resource for local and regional electricity demand.

● Research and develop tidal power at an operating demonstration installation.

● Establish an economic base from project-related industries, e.g., aquaculture development, tourism, and research laboratories.

● Develop tidal power, a non-depletable resource, as a substitute for conventional energy supplies.

Half-Moon Cove, adjacent to the Reservation and Cobscook Bay, would serve as the tidal basin for the proposed tidal power plant. A dam constructed across the entrance would hold back tidal water flowing in both directions, generating electricity when released through the turbines. This project, when completed and operational, would mark the first-ever tidal plant of this type constructed in the United States and would initiate the wide-scale development of tidal power.

Since 1919, when tidal power development for Passamaquoddy Bay and Cobscook Bay was first proposed, the Passamaquoddy Tribe and the regional community have patiently awaited the development of this indigenous natural resource. But meaningful progress never materialized. Instead, periodic studies were conducted to assess the technical and economic feasibility of tidal power plants. Technical feasibility has invariably been affirmed and recognized, but economic feasibility has been critically questioned and inevitably formed the basis for the rejection of project construction. The Half-Moon Cove tidal project has been proposed as a logical phase of development which would demonstrate technical and scientific aspects before constructing a large tidal power plant. The inclusion of an extensive research and development program would also enhance economic feasibility for any future projects by decreasing the high capital costs associated with generating equipment and by resolving environmental, engineering, and operating uncertainties at an "on-line" facility.

Today, with increasing energy prices and geopolitical uncertainties of supply, tidal power is once again being seriously considered as an alter-

nate energy source because of its renewable quality. In a U.S. Department of Energy report
(March, 1977) prepared by the Stone & Webster
Engineering Corporation, which asssessed the potential for tidal power development, it was concluded that large tidal power plants were still
not economically feasible as based on conventional
economic analyses. However, when considered in
terms of life cycle cost and long-term capital
return investment taken over a project's economic
lifetime, tidal power appears to be economically
feasible. Many believe that the most expedient
method of developing this valuable energy resource
is to construct a demonstration project.

POWER PRODUCTION POTENTIAL

The Cobscook Bay region offers a number of
attractive sites for the development of small-
scale, intermediate-sized, and large tidal power
projects. Figure 1, reproduced from a Corps of
Engineers report on the proposed International
Passamaquoddy Tidal project, depicts the location
of these sites in Cobscook Bay. The eleven potential projects identified in Table 1 are mutually
exclusive in some instances. The degree of com-
patability would depend on such factors as available tidal exchange, hydrodynamics, land-use conflicts, and environmental considerations.

Four schemes for the development of tidal
power in Cobscook Bay are indicated in Table 2.
For reference, the various sites are described in
terms of their respective physical parameters and
operating characteristics. It will be useful at
this time to discuss the more relevant aspects of
the various development scenarios.

- Scheme 1. The paired basin system represents the foundation for tidal power plans
  capable of producing dependable, or continuous, electrical generation. In this
  case, dependable capacity of 1.6 MW would
  supply continous production for nearly
  2,200 homes in the region as based on an
  average residential demand of 6,400 KWh
  per year. The remaining output would
  enter the electrical grid network as predictable and well defined energy generation. It should also be noted that the
  tandem plants would operate at full capacity (i.e., 8 MW) for nearly 85 per cent
  of the time for an average tidal range of
  18 ft.

- Scheme 2. This plan would establish an
  integrated system of small scale tidal
  plants as a continuation of scheme 1.
  The level of dependable capacity would
  increase to 8 MW, thereby increasing the
  immediate service area capable of receiving continuous tidal production and also
  supplying larger amounts of intermittent
  energy into the interconnected grid.

- Scheme 3. The construction of an intermediate-sized tidal power plant (88 MW)

at Denbow Point would be compatible with
the operation of several small tidal
plants within Cobscook Bay. In this case,
more surplus power would be produced for
a larger service area outside the communities bordering the plants. Dependable
capacity would still be available at a
level sufficient for local demand.

- Scheme 4. This plan represents the full
  utilization of the tidal power potential
  of Cobscook by incorporating scheme 1
  with the construction of an intermediate-
  sized plant at Mahar Point (58 MW) and a
  large facility at Shackford Head (230 MW).
  The implementation of this plan will depend on a number of interrelated factors
  which include the efficient integration
  of tidal power with a public utility network and the satisfactory mitigation of
  environmental factors associated with
  large installations.

The figures listed in Table 1 were based on an
operating mode which optimized production for
long-time duration. The capacity factor of 0.4325
reflects this decision. By decreasing the capacity factor to 0.25 the installed capacity would
increase from 8 MW to 24 MW for the Half-Moon Cove
project. This flexibility could conceivably lead
to improved utilization factors if the demand for
narrower bands of electrical generation were economically justified by the interconnected network.

The previously derived estimates of tidal
power production reflect the potential of sites
within Cobscook Bay. This area has the highest
tidal range of any site located in Maine. However, the upper Maine coast where tidal ranges
exceed 15 ft also offers potential locations for
tidal power projects. Future conditions might
favorably affect project economics and permit
development at sites outside the Cobscook Bay
region.

OTHER CONSIDERATIONS: ENVIRONMENTAL AND ECONOMICS

The construction of any tidal power plant
will undoubtedly produce some adverse environmental effects. However, the relative impact is
expected to be much less than observed at conventional power plants, e.g., nuclear, or coal-fired.
Tidal power does not pollute the air nor dump
waste into the water-ways. For small tidal projects, the major concern centers on the potential
changes imposed on the tidal basin's ecological
balance. The proposed Half-Moon Cove project is
expected to quantify the actual environmental consequences for this type of development. The relationship between the various physical, biological,
and chemical parameters deserves site-specific
research in order to fully understand the controlled environment established by the basin's
impoundment.

The total cost of constructing an 8 MW station at Half-Moon Cove has been estimated at
approximately $21,250,000 (1978 dollars). This

figure assumes financing at 7 per cent over a 50-year period. The project would then be expected to generate electricity at the rate of 5.7¢/KWh. However, the economic justification for this project will have to be stated not only in relation to the immediate returns that are marginal when compared to new, conventional plants, but also in relation to long-term benefits and the desire to conserve supplies of fossil fuels by substituting renewable resources. Because the Half-Moon Cove project would be the first of its type constructed in the United States, the initial investment is expected to be higher than for future projects that can take advantage of the results derived from a demonstration project.

## PRESENT STATUS OF TIDAL POWER DEVELOPMENT

Feasibility studies for the Half-Moon Cove project are in the final stages. The various investigations will be completed by the end of the summer (1980). In the event that the results prove positive, future plans will be drafted for the demonstration project and will incorporate the concept of the interconnected energy network presently being refined by the Cobscook Bay Tidal Power Committee. Preliminary results indicate that the project will be feasible if sufficient federal assistance can be committed in order to absorb the losses expected during the first several years of operation.  □

Hors-texte

The Arledge 1-17 well in west Texas, recently drilled by Tenneco. Tree growth in the foreground follows the patterns of geologic structure and rock outcrop.

# 9

# INDUSTRIAL ROCKS

Session moderators

L. Morgenstern
Massachusetts Executive Office of Energy Resources

A. A. Qazilbash
C. E. Maguire, Inc.

# Peat and water pollution problems

J. A. SINNOTT
State Geologist, Massachusetts

## ABSTRACT

Early settlers of Block Island, Rhode Island, a prosperous farming and fishing community, commonly were deeded "tug" rights when they purchased their home or farm. "Tug" is apparently derived from an Irish word for peat, and it was taken for granted that each home had an almost communal interest in a source of fuel for the home. Located adjacent to most properties on the island are peat bogs varing in size from small to large. The total number appears to be in the hundreds.

## DISCUSSION

Block Island is a glacial moraine representing the southern terminus of Pleistocene glacial ice advance. It is very similar to the islands of Nantucket and Martha's Vineyard in Massachusetts.

The topography is gently rolling with deep melted ice-block depressions and hills two hundred feet high. The original forests were cut down and used for timber and fuel. The shore exposes wave-cut cliffs which are constantly changing as the ocean works to reshape the outline of the island, taking soil in one area and depositing it in another.

Water supply to the island is almost exclusively from wells drilled into the glacial soil. The depth of the wells varies considerably, as does the surface elevation of existing ponds and bogs. Since no rivers exist on the island, reservoirs are not a viable water source.

Water quality in private water wells can be very poor, requiring two and three stages of treatment procedures. Iron (Fe) and manganese (Mn) are two of the principal pollutants in the private systems. The same two minerals are the

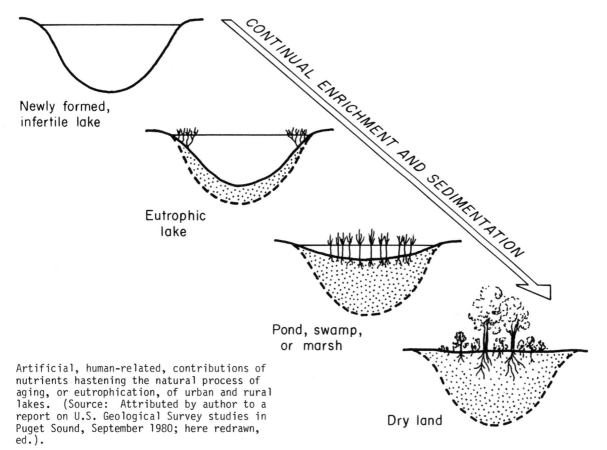

Newly formed, infertile lake

Eutrophic lake

Pond, swamp, or marsh

CONTINUAL ENRICHMENT AND SEDIMENTATION

Dry land

Artificial, human-related, contributions of nutrients hastening the natural process of aging, or eutrophication, of urban and rural lakes. (Source: Attributed by author to a report on U.S. Geological Survey studies in Puget Sound, September 1980; here redrawn, ed.).

main leachates and runoffs from peat bogs. Personal experience and observations on Block Island indicate that the runoff of ground water from bog areas contains enough naturally occurring mineral matter to cement grains of sand and gravel together, forming a pavement of black to rusty soil that forms a "true" hardpan type of deposit. I hesitate in using the word hardpan because in everyday language it has come to have a meaning different from that initially intended. Downstream, both vertically and horizontally, a plume of iron and manganese remain in the groundwater flow in both dissolved and solid states. If a homeowner pumps water downstream from the bog, he is certain to have unwanted minerals in his drinking water supply.

Peat, an accumulation of plant and other organic matter, started to form in depressions and in perched water table areas immediately after glacial age temperatures began to moderate. The thickness of the deposits has been tested in a few instances and found to be 4 feet to 11 feet thick. As a general geologic principle, maximum thickness can be taken as 18 feet unless very unusual conditions exist.

Peat is used as a fuel or source of power worldwide, especially in the northern hemisphere. It is often made into barbeque-like briquettes, burned loose, or gasified. It is an extremely clean burning, low sulfur, smokeless type of energy resource. The ash content is very low and of little value.

Computations by Joseph Pecoraro of the Department of Energy indicate that a few acres of peat just five feet deep can sustain a power generating station of 1 MW for a full year. Very preliminary calculations of acreage indicate a possible one hundred year supply. Thirty years' supply could amortize a specialized generating station. Whether the peat is used for energy purposes or for a new industry which would export its product to the mainland and provide local jobs, the overall effects of extraction would be:

- a cleaner, less polluted environment;

- the creation of an energy resource not dependent on imports of fuel; and

- the provision of new jobs no matter how the peat is used.

BIBLIOGRAPHY

Hem, J.D., 1960, Restraints on dissolved ferrous iron imposed by bicarbonate redox potential, and pH: Geological Survey Water-Supply Paper 1459-B, p. 33-55.

Hem, J.D., 1960, Some chemical relationships among sulfur species and dissolved ferrous iron: Geological Survey Water-Supply Paper 1459-C, p. 57-73.

Hem, J.D., 1960, Complexes of ferrous iron with tannic acid: Geological Survey Water-Supply Paper 1459-D, p. 75-94.

Hem, J.D., 1963, Chemical equilibria and rates of manganese oxidation: Geological Survey Water-Supply Paper 1667-A, p. A1-A64.

Hem, J.D., 1964, Deposition and solution of manganese oxides: Geological Survey Water-Supply Paper 1667-B, p. B1-B42.

Hem, J.D., 1965, Reduction and complexing of manganese by gallic acids: Geological Survey Water-Supply Paper 1667-D, p. D1-D28.

Hem, J.D., 1972, Chemical factors that influence the availability of iron and manganese in aqueous systems: Geological Society of America, Special Paper 140.

Hem, J.D., and Cropper, W.H., 1959, Survey of ferrous-ferric chemical equilibria and redox potentials: Geological Survey Water-Supply Paper 1459-A, p. 1-31.

Institute of Public Administration, Northeastern United States Water Supply Study. Regional water supply: institutional aspects, Volume I, July 1972, Report.

Institution of Public Administration, Northeastern United States Water Supply Study. Regional water supply: institutional aspects, Volume II, July 1972, Organizational and Legal Alternatives.

Institution of Public Administration, Northeastern United States Water Supply Study. Regional water supply: institutional aspects, Volume III, July 1972, State Surveys.

Koljonen, T., and others, 1976, Origin, mineralogy, and chemistry of manganiferous and ferruginous precipitates found in sand and gravel deposits in Finland: Bulletin of the Geological Society of Finland 48, p. 111-135.

Oborn, E.T., 1960, A survey of pertinent biochemical literature: Geological Survey Water-Supply Paper 1459-F, p. 111-190.

Oborn, E.T., 1960, Iron content of selected water and land plants: Geological Survey Water-Supply Paper 1459-G, p. 191-211.

Oborn, E.T., 1964, Intracellular and extracellular concentration of manganese and other elements by aquatic organisms: Geological Survey Water-Supply Paper 1667-C, p. C1-C18.

Oborn, E.T., and Hem, J.D., 1961, Microbiologic factors in the solution and transport of iron: Geological Survey Water-Supply Paper 1459-H, p. 213-235.

Mitchell, J.H., From peat to pavement: Public Service Information, Massachusetts Audubon Society, Lincoln, MA. Undated.

# AUTHORS AND ADDRESSES

J.M. Aaron
U.S. Geological Survey
Reston, VA 22092

D.D. Adrian
Department of Civil Engineering
University of Massachusetts
Amherst, MA 01003

R.P. Allen
Weston Geophysical Corporation
P.O. Box 550
Westboro, MA 01581

F.J. Anders
National Park Service
Cooperative Research Unit
University of Massachusetts
Amherst, MA 01003

D.D. Ashenden
Metropolitan District Commission
20 Somerset Street
Boston, MA 02108

J.E. Ayres
Goldberg, Zoino & Associates, Inc.
30 Tower Road
Newton Upper Falls, MA 02164

S. Bahadur
Acres American Incorporated
Suite 329, The Clark Building
Columbia, MD 21044

J.J. Balco
U.S. Water Resources Council
2120 L Street, N.W.
Washington, DC 20037

P.J. Barosh
Weston Observatory
Department of Geology and Geophysics
Boston College
Weston, MA 02193

W.R. Barton
(formerly: U.S. Bureau of Mines)
ERDE, Inc.
78 Whitehouse Road
Rochester, NH 03867

M. Barvenik
Goldberg, Zoino & Associates, Inc.
30 Tower Road
Newton Upper Falls, MA 02164

P. Beal
Hanover Water Department
Hanover, MA 02339

F.X. Bellini
Yankee Atomic Electric Company
P.O. Box 700
Seabrook, NH 03874

M.P. Billings
Department of Geological Sciences
Harvard University
Cambridge, MA 02138

C. Bjork
Skanska (USA) Inc.
Tycon 11, Suite 500
8330 Old Courthouse Road
Vienna, VA 22180

E.A. Blackey, Jr.
New England Division
Corps of Engineers
424 Trapelo Road
Waltham, MA 02154

J.S. Booth
U.S. Geological Survey
Woods Hole, MA 02543

M.H. Bothner
U.S. Geological Survey
Woods Hole, MA 02543

B.A. Bouley
Callahan Mining Corporation
6245 North 24th Street
Phoenix, AZ 85016

O.C. Braids
Geraghty & Miller, Inc.
6800 Jericho Turnpike
Syosset, NY 11791

F.M. Brasier
Office of Drinking Water
U.S. EPA
Washington, DC

B.M. Brenninkmeyer, S.J.
Coastal Research Institute
Department of Geology and Geophysics
Boston College
Chestnut Hill, MA 02167

Randolph W. Bromery
Department of Geology and Geography
University of Massachusetts
Amherst, MA 01003

A.H. Brownlow
Department of Geology
Boston University
Boston, MA 02215

D.H. Bruehl
Metcalf & Eddy, Inc.
50 Staniford Street
Boston, MA 02114

B. Butman
U.S. Geological Survey
Woods Hole, MA 02543

R.M. Cadwgan
Environmental Research and Technology, Inc.
696 Virginia Road
Concord, MA 01742

N.A. Campagna, Jr.
Goldberg, Zoino & Associates, Inc.
30 Tower Road
Newton Upper Falls, MA 02164

H.B. Chase, Jr.
18 Beech Street
Mansfield, MA 02048

C. Chow
Drinking Water Branch
U.S. EPA, Region 1
JFK Building
Boston, MA 02203

D.H. Corkum
Morrison-Knudsen Company
P.O. Box 121
Cambridge, MA 02140

Robert A. Corrigan
Chancellor, University of Massachusetts
Harbor Campus
Boston, MA 02125

A.D. Cortese
Dept. of Environmental Quality Engineering
Commonwealth of Massachusetts
1 Winter Street
Boston, MA 02108

T.R. Cullen
Bechtel Civil & Minerals, Inc.
58 Day Street, P.O. Box 487
West Somerville, MA 02144

S.L. Dean
Whitman & Howard, Inc.
45 William Street
Wellesley, MA 02181

J.P. Dugan, Jr.
Haley & Aldrich, Inc.
238 Main Street
Cambridge, MA 02142

O.C. Farquhar
Department of Geology and Geography
University of Massachusetts
Amherst, MA 01003

L. Feldman
Goldberg, Zoino & Associates, Inc.
30 Tower Road
Newton Upper Falls, MA 02164

A. Ferreira
Electric Power Research Institute
c/o Northeast Utilities
174 Brush Hill Avenue
West Springfield, MA 01089

J.J. Fisher
Department of Geology
University of Rhode Island
Kingston, RI 02881

J.A. Focht, Jr.
McClelland Engineers, Inc.
P.O. Box 37321
Houston, TX 77036

B.K. Fowler
Pike Industries, Inc.
U.S. Route #3
Tilton, NH 03276

M.H. Frimpter
Water Resources Division
U.S. Geological Survey
150 Causeway Street, Suite 1001
Boston, MA 02114

J.D. Gustin
Law Engineering Testing Company
2749 Delk Road
Marietta, GA 30067

S.E. Haggerty
Department of Geology and Geography
University of Massachusetts
Amherst, MA 01003

J.C. Hampson, Jr.
U.S. Geological Survey
Woods Hole, MA 02543

J.H. Hartshorn
Department of Geology and Geography
University of Massachusetts
Amherst, MA 01003

A.W. Hatheway
(now:  University of Missouri
Rolla, MO 65401)
Haley & Aldrich, Inc.
238 Main Street
Cambridge, MA 02142

R.W. Heeley
Lycott Environmental Research, Inc.
Box 535
Southbridge, MA 01566

J.R. Hight
Haley & Aldrich, Inc.
238 Main Street
Cambridge, MA 02142

R.P. Hight
Norton Company
7 New Bond Street
Worcester, MA 01606

M.J. Hobson
Acres American Incorporated
Suite 239, The Clark Building
Columbia, MD 21044

R.J. Holt
Weston Geophysical Corporation
P.O. Box 550
Westboro, MA 01581

D.K. Holway
W.R. Holway and Associates
5300 South Yale Avenue
Tulsa, OK 74135

A.A. Jennings
Department of Civil Engineering
University of Notre Dame
Notre Dame, IN 46556

J.C. Johnston
Weston Geophysical Corporation
P.O. Box 550
Westboro, MA 01581

J.R. Jones
Department of Geography
University of Texas
Austin, TX 78712

F.M. Keville
Massachusetts Bay Transportation Authority
45 High Street
Boston, MA

J.F. Kick
P.O. Box 6
Dunstable, MA 01827

J.R. Kirby
U.S. Geological Survey
Woods Hole, MA 02543

G. Klimciewiez
Weston Geophysical Corporation
P.O. Box 550
Westboro, MA 01581

C. Koltz
Office of Public Relations
Washington University
Campus Box 1070
St. Louis, MO 63130

N.L. Laberge
Passamaquoddy Tribal Council
Pleasant Point Reservation
Perry, ME 04667

D.M. Lane
Home Oil Company Limited
2300 Home Oil Tower
324 Eighth Avenue SW
Calgary, Alberta T2P 2Z5
Canada

F.D. Larsen
Department of Earth Sciences
Norwich University
Northfield, VT 05663

D.R. LeBlanc
Water Resources Division
U.S. Geological Survey
150 Causeway Street, Suite 1001
Boston, MA 02114

G. Leblanc
Weston Geophysical Corporation
P.O. Box 550
Westboro, MA 01581

S.P. Leatherman
National Park Service
Cooperative Research Unit
University of Massachusetts
Amherst, MA 01003

E.N. Levine
Weston Geophysical Corporation
P.O. Box 550
Westboro, MA 01581

Harro Lorenzen
(formerly: PB-KBB, Inc.
Houston, TX)
Billiton International Metals
P.O. Box 190
2501 AS The Hague
The Netherlands

T.F. McLoughlin
Department of Environmental
  Quality Engineering
Commonwealth of Massachusetts
1 Winter Street
Boston, MA 02108

L.P. Meade
Geomapping Associates, Ltd.
P.O. Box 133
Pittsford, VT 05763

W.S. Motts
Department of Geology and Geography
University of Massachusetts
Amherst, MA 01003

V.J. Murphy
Weston Geophysical Corporation
P.O. Box 550
Westboro, MA 01581

D.P. Murray
Weston Observatory
Department of Geology and Geophysics
Boston College
Weston, MA 02193

T.L. Neff
Department of Engineering
  and Applied Science
P.O. Box 751
Portland, OR 97207

C.J. O'Hara
U.S. Geological Survey
Woods Hole, MA 02543

R.N. Oldale
U.S. Geological Survey
Woods Hole, MA 02543

W.C. Paris, Jr.
Bechtel Associates Professional Corporation
777 East Eisenhower Parkway, P.O. Box 1000
Ann Arbor, MI 48106

J.M. Peck
Stone & Webster Engineering Corporation
245 Summer Street, P.O. Box 2325
Boston, MA 02107

J.M. Pecoraro
Executive Office of Energy Resources
Commonwealth of Massachusetts
73 Tremont Street
Boston, MA 02108
(on loan from the US DOE)

H.W. Petranik
Home Oil Company Limited
2300 Home Oil Tower
324 Eighth Avenue SW
Calgary, Alberta T2P 2Z5, Canada
(now with Dome Petroleum Limited)

R.B. Pojasek
Roy F. Weston, Inc.
289 New Boston Park
Woburn, MA 01801

J.D. Raben
Weston Observatory
Department of Geology and Geophysics
Boston College
Weston, MA 02193 (see next entry)

also:
New England Geotechnical Consultants, Inc.
6 Ridgeway Road
Winchester, MA 01890

J.R. Rand
Cundy's Harbor
RD 2-2476
Brunswick, ME 04011

T.L. Rice
U.S. Geological Survey
P.O. Box 25046, M.S. 903
Denver Federal Center
Denver, CO 80225

J.M. Robb
U.S. Geological Survey
Woods Hole, MA 02543

P. Robinson
Department of Geology and Geography
University of Massachusetts
Amherst, MA 01003

H.A. Russell
Parsons, Brinckerhoff, Quade &
   Douglas, Inc.
177 Milk Street
Boston, MA 02109

A.A.G. Sa da Costa
Ralph M. Parsons Laboratory
Department of Civil Engineering
Massachusetts Institute of Technology
Cambridge, MA 02139

T.F. Sexton
Weston Geophysical Corporation
P.O. Box 550
Westboro, MA 01581

L.R. Silka
Office of Drinking Water
U.S. EPA
Washington, DC

G. Simmons
Department of Earth and Planetary Sciences
Massachusetts Institute of Technology
Cambridge, MA 02139

J.A. Sinnott
State Geologist
Department of Environmental Quality
   Engineering
100 Cambridge Street
Boston, MA 02202

J.W. Skehan, S.J.
Weston Observatory
Department of Geology and Geophysics
Boston College
Weston, MA 02193

L. Söderberg
Skanska Cementgjuteriet
S-182 25 Danderyd
Stockholm, Sweden

A.J. Stewart
United Engineers & Constructors, Inc.
P.O. Box 700
Seabrook, NH 03874

W.E. Stimpson
Haley & Aldrich, Inc.
238 Main Street
Cambridge, MA 02142

B.D. Stone
U.S. Geological Survey
National Center, MS 928
Reston, VA 22092

D.E. Thompson
Haley & Aldrich, Inc.
238 Main Street
Cambridge, MA 02142

S.N. Thompson
Acres American Incorporated
The Liberty Bank Building
Main at Court
Buffalo, NY 14202

F.S. Tirsch
Department of Civil Engineering
University of Massachusetts
Amherst, MA 01003

D.C. Twichell
U.S. Geological Survey
Woods Hole, MA 02543

M.R. Vanderburgh
Acres American Incorporated
The Liberty Bank Building
Main at Court
Buffalo, NY 14202

R.V. Varnum
Haley & Aldrich, Inc.
238 Main Street
Cambridge, MA 02142

R.A. Weimar
Camp, Dresser & McKee, Inc.
One Center Plaza
Boston, MA 02108

D.C. Willett
Acres American Incorporated
The Liberty Bank Building
Main at Court
Buffalo, NY 14202

J.L. Wilson
Ralph M. Parsons Laboratory
Department of Civil Engineering
Massachusetts Institute of Technology
Cambridge, MA 02139

D.U. Wise
Department of Geology and Geography
University of Massachusetts
Amherst, MA 01003

D.J. Worth
School of Medicine
Tufts University
171 Harrison Avenue
Medford, MA

L.W. Young, Jr.
Bechtel Incorporated
15740 Shady Grove Road
Gaithersburg, MD 20760

W.S. Zoino
Goldberg, Zoino & Associates, Inc.
30 Tower Road
Newton Upper Falls, MA 02164

GEOTECHNOLOGY in MASSACHUSETTS

# FIRST AUTHORS IN KWIC INDEX

| Name | Page | | Name | | Page |
|------|------|---|------|---|------|
| AARON | 521 | | FARQUHAR | air leakage | 293 |
| ANDERS | 501 | | " | pegmatites | 401 |
| ASHENDEN | 213 | | FELDMAN | | 64 |
| AYRES | 436 | | FERREIRA | | 135 |
| BAHADUR | 279 | | FISHER | | 511 |
| BALCO | 57 | | FOCHT | | 605 |
| BAROSH | 455 | | FOWLER | | 141 |
| BARTON | 375 | | FRIMPTER | | 73 |
| BEAL | 77 | | GUSTIN | | 325 |
| BELLINI | 109 | | HAGGERTY | | 425 |
| BILLINGS | 229 | | HAMPSON | | 551 |
| BLACKEY | 97 | | HATHEWAY | geologic assessments | 121 |
| BOOTH | 567 | | " | excavation | 151 |
| BOULEY | 403 | | " | glacial till | 193 |
| BRAIDS | 440 | | " | hardrock mapping | 238 |
| BRENNINKMEYER, S.J. | 479 | | " | waste disposal | 411 |
| BROMERY | 345 | | HEELEY | | 83 |
| BROWNLOW | 477 | | HIGHT, R. | | 402 |
| BRUEHL | 87 | | HOBSON | | 311 |
| CADWGAN | 436 | | HOLWAY | | 351 |
| CHOW | 429 | | JENNINGS | | 413 |
| CORTESE | 437 | | KICK | | 91 |
| CULLEN | 197 | | KOLTZ | | 335 |
| DEAN | 47 | | LABERGE | | 361 |
| DUGAN | 221 | | LARSEN | | 29 |

| Name | Page |
|---|---|
| LEBLANC, D. | 75 |
| LEBLANC, G. | 467 |
| LORENZEN | 326 |
| MEADE | 404 |
| MOTTS | 55 |
| MURPHY | 119 |
| NEFF | 171 |
| O'HARA | 539 |
| PARIS | 231 |
| PECK    waste disposal | 427 |
| "    dating faults | 443 |
| PECORARO | 371 |
| PETRANIK | 327 |
| POJASEK | 407 |

| Name | Page |
|---|---|
| RAND | 461 |
| ROBINSON | 7 |
| RUSSELL | 127 |
| SINNOTT | 369 |
| SKEHAN, S.J. | 381 |
| SÖDERBERG | 255 |
| STONE | 11 |
| THOMPSON    energy storage, Boston | 249 |
| "    DOE/EPRI study | 273 |
| WEIMAR | 410 |
| WILSON | 65 |
| WISE | 447 |
| WORTH | 428 |
| ZOINO | 183 |

# KWIC INDEX

Sample of Key Word in Center (KWIC) Index

MINERAL . . . . . . . . . . . . CHEMISTRY AND GEOLOGICAL DISTRIBUTION OF PHASES IN SYNROC * HAGGERTY * THE

CHEMISTRY AND . . . . . . . . . . GEOLOGICAL DISTRIBUTION OF PHASES IN SYNROC * HAGGERTY * THE MINERAL

THE . . . . . . . . . . . . . . MINERAL CHEMISTRY AND GEOLOGICAL DISTRIBUTION OF PHASES IN SYNROC * HAGGERTY *

PHASES IN . . . . . . . . . . . SYNROC * HAGGERTY * THE MINERAL CHEMISTRY AND GEOLOGICAL DISTRIBUTION OF

ENGINEERED CONSTRUCTION * HATHEWAY * SIGNIFICANCE OF GLACIAL TILL TERMINOLOGY
ENGINEERING AND APPLIED GEOCHEMISTRY * HAGGERTY * RADWASTE--ASPECTS OF
ENGINEERING BEHAVIOR OF THE TAUNTON RIVER CLAYS * ZOINO *
ENGINEERING GEOLOGY * BLACKEY * REMOTE SENSING APPLICATIONS IN
ENGINEERING--PLACEBO, PARADIGM, OR PANACEA? * NEFF * PREVENTIVE GEOTECHNICAL
ENGINEERING PROBLEMS RELATED TO THE DEVELOPMENT OF GROUNDWATER SUPPLIES ON
ENGINEERING'S ROLE IN THE REGULATION OF HAZARDOUS WASTE DISPOSAL IN
ENVIRONMENTAL ATLAS--WHAT DO WE TELL THE PLANNERS, AND HOW? * BROWNLOW *
ENVIRONMENTAL QUALITY ENGINEERING'S ROLE IN THE REGULATION OF HAZARDOUS WASTE
ENVIRONMENTAL STUDIES ON THE CONTINENTAL SHELF AND SLOPE OFF NEW ENGLAND *
EPRI UNDERGROUND ENERGY STORAGE STUDY * THOMPSON * DOE/
EROSION AND SHINGLE MOVEMENT AT MANN HILL BEACH, SCITUATE, MASSACHUSETTS,
EXCAVATION PROGRAMS IN NEW ENGLAND * HATHEWAY * DESIGNING
EXCAVATIONS AT SEABROOK STATION, SEABROOK, NEW HAMPSHIRE, BELLINI * GEOLOGY
EXPLOITATION OF THE NARRAGANSETT COAL BASIN, MASSACHUSETTS AND RHODE ISLAND
EXPLORATION AND EXPLOITATION OF THE NARRAGANSETT COAL BASIN, MASSACHUSETTS
EXPLORATION AND SAMPLING OF CONTAMINATED GROUND WATER (TITLE ONLY) * AYRES *
EXPLORATION * BEAL * GEOSCIENCE IN MUNICIPAL GROUNDWATER
EXPLORATION IN MASSACHUSETTS * BRUEHL * USE OF GEOPHYSICS IN GROUNDWATER
FAILURE OF THE CONCRETE LINING IN THE DORCHESTER TUNNEL (DISCUSSION) *
FAILURE OF THE DORCHESTER TUNNEL, BOSTON * ASHENDEN * GEOLOGIC FACTORS
FAULT AND FRACTURE DOMAINS OF SOUTHWESTERN NEW ENGLAND--HINTS ON
FAULT MOVEMENT * PECK * FLUID INCLUSION STUDIES FOR DATING
FILTER BEDS (ABSTRACT) * LEBLANC D * DISTRIBUTION OF DISSOLVED SUBSTANCES IN
FLUID INCLUSION STUDIES FOR DATING FAULT MOVEMENT * PECK *
FORELAND AT GRAPE ISLAND, BOSTON HARBOR, MASSACHUSETTS * FISHER * ORIGIN
FOUNDATION EXCAVATIONS AT SEABROOK STATION, SEABROOK, NEW HAMPSHIRE *
FRACTURE DOMAINS OF SOUTHWESTERN NEW ENGLAND--HINTS ON LOCALIZATION OF THE
GAS STORAGE IN SALT CAVITIES (TITLE ONLY) * LORENZEN * DESIGN REQUIREMENTS
GENESIS, WITH SPECIAL REFERENCE TO NEW ENGLAND (ABSTRACT) * BOULEY *
GEOCHEMISTRY OF HAZARDOUS WASTE DISPOSAL * BRAIDS *
GEOCHEMISTRY * HAGGERTY * RADWASTE--ASPECTS OF MOLECULAR ENGINEERING AND
GEOLOGIC ASSESSMENTS FOR REAL ESTATE APPRAISALS * HATHEWAY *
GEOLOGIC FACTORS AFFECTING FAILURE OF THE DORCHESTER TUNNEL, BOSTON *
GEOLOGIC MAP OF MASSACHUSETTS (ABSTRACT) * ROBINSON * THE BEDROCK
GEOLOGIC MAP * STONE * THE MASSACHUSETTS STATE SURFICIAL
GEOLOGIC MAPPING FOR UNDERGROUND CONSTRUCTION IN THE BOSTON BASIN * HATHEWAY *
GEOLOGIC STUDIES OF THE INNER CONTINENTAL SHELF OFF MASSACHUSETTS * O'HARA *
GEOLOGIST * BALCO * GROUNDWATER PROTECTION--LEGAL MECHANISMS, INSTITUTIONS,

IN.
MOLECULAR # title changed # new key words in sample #
. . . . . . . . . . .
CAPE COD, MASSACHUSETTS * DEAN * . . .
MASSACHUSETTS * CORTESE * THE DEPARTMENT OF ENVIRONMENTAL QUALITY
THE CAPE COD.
DISPOSAL IN MASSACHUSETTS * CORTESE * THE DEPARTMENT OF
AARON * U.S. GEOLOGICAL SURVEY.
. . . . . . . . . .
DURING THE BLIZZARD OF FEBRUARY 1978 * BRENNINKMEYER *.
. . . . . . . . . .
OF FOUNDATION . . .
* SKEHAN * EXPLORATION AND.
BELLINI * GEOLOGY OF.
AND RHODE ISLAND * SKEHAN *
METHODS FOR . . .
. . . . . . . . . .
BILLINGS *
AFFECTING . . .
LOCALIZATION OF THE MESOZOIC BASINS * WISE * NEW.
. . . . . . . . . .
GROUND WATER RESULTING FROM INFILTRATION OF TREATED SEWAGE THROUGH SAND
. . . . . . . . . .
AND DEVELOPMENT OF A CUSPATE.
BELLINI * GEOLOGY OF.
MESOZOIC BASINS * WISE * NEW FAULT AND.
FOR OIL AND.
VOLCANISM AND ORE.
APPLIED # title changed # new key words in sample #
. . . . . . . . . .
ASHENDEN *.
. . . . . . . . . .
HARDROCK.
MARINE.
ATTITUDES, AND THE.

GEOLOGY AND RADIOACTIVE WASTE DISPOSAL (ABSTRACT) * PECK *
GEOLOGY IN THE CONNECTICUT RIVER VALLEY OF WESTERN MASSACHUSETTS * KOLTZ *
GEOLOGY OF FOUNDATION EXCAVATIONS AT SEABROOK STATION, SEABROOK, NEW
GEOLOGY * BLACKEY * REMOTE SENSING APPLICATIONS IN ENGINEERING
GEOMORPHOLOGY OF THE CONTINENTAL SLOPE OFF NEW JERSEY * HAMPSON * MASS
GEOPHYSICAL STUDIES AND MEASUREMENTS IN EASTERN MASSACHUSETTS * MURPHY *
GEOPHYSICS IN GROUNDWATER EXPLORATION IN MASSACHUSETTS * BRUEHL * USE OF
GEORGES BANK AND BALTIMORE CANYON * BOOTH * GEOTECHNICAL PROPERTIES AND SLOPE
GEOSCIENCE IN MUNICIPAL GROUNDWATER EXPLORATION * BEAL *
GEOTECHNICAL ENGINEERING--PLACEBO, PARADIGM, OR PANACEA? * NEFF * PREVENTIVE
GEOTECHNICAL PROPERTIES AND SLOPE STABILITY ANALYSIS OF SURFICIAL SEDIMENTS ON
GLACIAL TILL TERMINOLOGY IN ENGINEERED CONSTRUCTION * HATHEWAY * SIGNIFICANCE
GRAPE ISLAND, BOSTON HARBOR, MASSACHUSETTS * FISHER * ORIGIN AND DEVELOPMENT
GRAVITY METHOD IN MASSACHUSETTS * KICK * APPLICATION OF THE
GROUND WATER (TITLE ONLY) * CADWGAN * MEASUREMENT AND MONITORING OF ORGANIC
GROUND WATER (TITLE ONLY) * AYRES * METHODS FOR EXPLORATION AND SAMPLING OF
GROUND WATER RESULTING FROM INFILTRATION OF TREATED SEWAGE THROUGH SAND FILTER
GROUNDWATER EXPLORATION * BEAL * GEOSCIENCE IN MUNICIPAL
GROUNDWATER EXPLORATION IN MASSACHUSETTS * BRUEHL * USE OF GEOPHYSICS IN
GROUNDWATER HYDROLOGY OF MARTHA'S VINEYARD ISLAND, MASSACHUSETTS * WILSON *
GROUNDWATER LEVELS FROM OBSERVED WATER LEVELS IN MASSACHUSETTS (ABSTRACT) *
GROUNDWATER PROTECTION--LEGAL MECHANISMS, INSTITUTIONS, ATTITUDES, AND THE
GROUNDWATER SUPPLIES ON CAPE COD, MASSACHUSETTS * DEAN * ENGINEERING PROBLEMS
GROUTING TO REPAIR THE DORCHESTER WATER TUNNEL, BOSTON * DUGAN * PRESSURE
GULF COAST SALT DOMES AT POTENTIAL NUCLEAR WASTE REPOSITORIES (ABSTRACT) *
HARDROCK GEOLOGIC MAPPING FOR UNDERGROUND CONSTRUCTION IN THE BOSTON BASIN *
HAZARDOUS WASTE DISPOSAL * BRAIDS * GEOCHEMISTRY OF
HAZARDOUS WASTE DISPOSAL IN MASSACHUSETTS * POJASEK *
HAZARDOUS WASTE DISPOSAL IN MASSACHUSETTS * CORTESE * THE DEPARTMENT OF
HIGHWAY CUT * FERREIRA * ROCK SLIPPAGE ON THE UPPER SLOPE OF A
HYDRO AND TIDAL POWER DEVELOPMENT IN MAINE--SMALL SCALE PROJECTS * LABERGE *
HYDROCARBON POSSIBILITIES AND PROBLEMS * BROMERY * OUTER CONTINENTAL MARGIN
HYDROELECTRIC PROJECT, LAWRENCE, MASSACHUSETTS * HOLWAY * THE LAWRENCE
HYDROGEOLOGY OF THE LAWRENCE SWAMP AQUIFER SYSTEM, AMHERST, MASSACHUSETTS
HYDROLOGY OF MARTHA'S VINEYARD ISLAND, MASSACHUSETTS * WILSON * GROUNDWATER
IMPOUNDMENT ASSESSMENT IN THE NEW ENGLAND STATES * CHOW * SURFACE
INCLUSION STUDIES FOR DATING FAULT MOVEMENT * PECK * FLUID
INFILTRATION OF TREATED SEWAGE THROUGH SAND FILTER BEDS (ABSTRACT) * LEBLANC
INNER CONTINENTAL SHELF OFF MASSACHUSETTS * O'HARA * MARINE GEOLOGIC STUDIES
INTEGRAL ROCK SAMPLING--A TECHNIQUE OF ORIENTED ROCK CORE RECOVERY * RUSSELL *

HAMPSHIRE * BELLINI *
MOVEMENT FEATURES AND
STABILITY ANALYSIS OF SURFICIAL SEDIMENTS ON THE ATLANTIC CONT SLOPE:
THE ATLANTIC CONT SLOPE--GEORGES BANK AND BALTIMORE CANYON * BOOTH * .
OF .
OF A CUSPATE FORELAND AT.
CONTAMINATION IN.
CONTAMINATED.
BEDS (ABSTRACT) * LEBLANC D * DISTRIBUTION OF DISSOLVED SUBSTANCES IN

FRIMPTER * ESTIMATING HIGH.
GEOLOGIST * BALCO * .
RELATED TO THE DEVELOPMENT OF
GUSTIN * .
HATHEWAY * .

ENVIRONMENTAL QUALITY ENGINEERING'S ROLE IN THE REGULATION OF .

(ABSTRACT) * MOTTS * .

D * DISTRIBUTION OF DISSOLVED SUBSTANCES IN GROUND WATER RESULTING FROM
OF THE.

# title changed # new key words in sample #

RADIOACTIVE WASTE DISPOSAL (ABSTRACT) * PECK * GEOLOGY AND
STORAGE CAVERN IN HARD ROCK AT . . . . RADWASTE--ASPECTS OF MOLECULAR ENGINEERING AND APPLIED GEOCHEMISTRY * HAGGERTY *
RAGGED CHUTES, COBALT, ONTARIO * FARQUHAR * LEAKAGE OF COMPRESSED AIR FROM A
THE STUDY OF ABRASIVE AND . . . . REAL ESTATE APPRAISALS * HATHEWAY * GEOLOGIC ASSESSMENTS FOR
DEPARTMENT OF ENVIRONMENTAL QUALITY ENGINEERING'S ROLE IN THE . . . . REFRACTORY MINERALS (TITLE ONLY) * HIGHT * PETROGRAPHIC TECHNIQUES USED IN
REGULATION OF HAZARDOUS WASTE DISPOSAL IN MASSACHUSETTS * CORTESE * THE
NUCLEAR WASTE . . . . REMOTE SENSING APPLICATIONS IN ENGINEERING GEOLOGY * BLACKEY *
BASIN, MASSACHUSETTS AND . . . . REPOSITORIES (ABSTRACT) * GUSTIN * GULF COAST SALT DOMES AS POTENTIAL
FROM A STORAGE CAVERN IN HARD . . . . RHODE ISLAND * SKEHAN * EXPLORATION AND EXPLOITATION OF THE NARRAGANSETT COAL
ROCK AT RAGGED CHUTES, COBALT, ONTARIO * FARQUHAR * LEAKAGE OF COMPRESSED AIR
FOR DETERMINING . . . . ROCK EXCAVATION PROGRAMS IN NEW ENGLAND * HATHEWAY * DESIGNING
ROCK LOADS FOR MODERATELY SIZED, SHALLOW-DEPTH ROCK TUNNELS * PARIS * METHOD
ROCK SAMPLING--A TECHNIQUE OF ORIENTED ROCK CORE RECOVERY * RUSSELL * INTEGRAL
ROCK SLIPPAGE ON THE UPPER SLOPE OF A HIGHWAY CUT * FERREIRA *
SIZED, SHALLOW-DEPTH . . . . ROCK TUNNELS * PARIS * METHOD FOR DETERMINING ROCK LOADS FOR MODERATELY
ROCK * BAHADUR * UNDERGROUND ENERGY STORAGE PLANT SITING IN CARBONATE
PETRANIK * PRELIMINARY DESIGN OF THE CANSO . . . . SALT CAVERN PROJECT FOR STORAGE OF CRUDE OIL, CAPE BRETON, NOVA SCOTIA *
STORAGE IN . . . . SALT CAVITIES (TITLE ONLY) * LORENZEN * DESIGN REQUIREMENTS FOR OIL AND GAS
COAST . . . . SALT DOMES AS POTENTIAL NUCLEAR WASTE REPOSITORIES (ABSTRACT) * GUSTIN * GULF
EXPLORATION AND . . . . SAMPLING OF CONTAMINATED GROUND WATER (TITLE ONLY) * AYRES * METHODS FOR
IN GROUND WATER RESULTING FROM INFILTRATION OF TREATED SEWAGE THROUGH . . . . SAND FILTER BEDS (ABSTRACT) * LEBLANC D * DISTRIBUTION OF DISSOLVED SUBSTANCES
EROSION AND SHINGLE MOVEMENT AT MANN HILL BEACH, . . . . SCITUATE, MASSACHUSETTS, DURING THE BLIZZARD OF FEBRUARY 1978 * BRENNINKMEYER *
EXCAVATIONS AT . . . . SEABROOK STATION, SEABROOK, NEW HAMPSHIRE * BELLINI * GEOLOGY OF FOUNDATION
SEDIMENTS ON THE ATLANTIC CONT SLOPE--GEORGES BANK AND BALTIMORE CANYON * BOOTH
* GEOTECHNICAL PROPERTIES AND SLOPE STABILITY ANALYSIS OF SURFICIAL . . . . SEWAGE THROUGH SAND FILTER BEDS (ABSTRACT) * LEBLANC D * DISTRIBUTION OF DISSOLVED
SUBSTANCES IN GROUND WATER RESULTING FROM INFILTRATION OF TREATED . . . . SHELF AND SLOPE OFF NEW ENGLAND * AARON * U.S. GEOLOGICAL SURVEY
ENVIRONMENTAL STUDIES ON THE CONTINENTAL . . . . SHELF OFF MASSACHUSETTS * O'HARA * MARINE GEOLOGIC STUDIES OF THE INNER
CONTINENTAL . . . . SHINGLE MOVEMENT AT MANN HILL BEACH, SCITUATE, MASSACHUSETTS, DURING THE
BLIZZARD OF FEBRUARY 1978 * BRENNINKMEYER * EROSION AND . . . . SHORELINE ANALYSIS--NAUSET SPIT, MASSACHUSETTS * ANDERS * MAPPING TECHNIQUES
AND HISTORICAL . . . . SITE INVESTIGATIONS FOR BOTTOM-SEATED STRUCTURES * FOCHT * MARINE
SITING FOR AGGREGATE PRODUCTION IN NEW ENGLAND * BARTON *
SITING IN CARBONATE ROCK * BAHADUR * UNDERGROUND ENERGY STORAGE PLANT
SLOPE STABILITY ANALYSIS OF SURFICIAL SEDIMENTS ON THE ATLANTIC CONT . . . . SITING PARAMETERS FOR NEW ENGLAND * HATHEWAY * SOME REASONABLE WASTE DISPOSAL
SLOPE--GEORGES BANK AND BALTIMORE CANYON * BOOTH * GEOTECHNICAL PROPERTIES AND
ON THE CONTINENTAL SHELF AND . . . . SLOPE OF A HIGHWAY CUT * FERREIRA * ROCK SLIPPAGE ON THE UPPER
THE CONTINENTAL . . . . SLOPE OFF NEW ENGLAND * AARON * U.S. GEOLOGICAL SURVEY ENVIRONMENTAL STUDIES
SLOPE OFF NEW JERSEY * HAMPSON * MASS MOVEMENT FEATURES AND GEOMORPHOLOGY OF
GEORGES BANK AND BALTIMORE CANYON * BOOTH * GEOTECHNICAL PROPERTIES AND . . . . SLOPE STABILITY ANALYSIS OF SURFICIAL SEDIMENTS ON THE ATLANTIC CONT SLOPE--
SOIL * JENNINGS * METHODS FOR EVALUATING THE LEACHATE ATTENUATIVE CAPACITY OF
TECHNIQUES FOR DATA GATHERING AND ANALYSIS (ABSTRACT) * HEELEY * SOLUTE TRANSPORT IN NEW ENGLAND'S UNCONSOLIDATED AQUIFERS--RECOMMENDED

# CONVERSION FACTORS FROM U.S.-BRITISH UNITS TO SI UNITS

| To Convert From— | To— | Multiply By— |
|---|---|---|
| **Acceleration** | | |
| foot/second$^2$(ft/s$^2$) | metre/second$^2$(m/s$^2$) | $3.048 \times 10^{-1}$ |
| inch/second$^2$(in/s$^2$) | metre/second$^2$(m/s$^2$) | $2.54 \times 10^{-2}$ |
| **Area** | | |
| foot$^2$(ft$^2$) | metre$^2$(m$^2$) | $9.2903 \times 10^{-2}$ |
| inch$^2$(in$^2$) | metre$^2$(m$^2$) | $6.4516 \times 10^{-4}$ |
| yard$^2$(yd$^2$) | metre$^2$(m$^2$) | $8.3613 \times 10^{-1}$ |
| **Density** | | |
| pound mass/inch$^3$(lbm/in$^3$) | kilogram/metre$^3$(kg/m$^3$) | $2.7680 \times 10^4$ |
| pound mass/foot$^3$(lbm/ft$^3$) | kilogram/metre$^3$(kg/m$^3$) | $1.6018 \times 10$ |
| **Energy, Work** | | |
| British thermal unit (BTU) | joule (J) | $1.055 \times 10^3$ |
| foot-pound force (ft-lbf) | joule (J) | $1.3558$ |
| kilowatt-hour (kw-h) | joule (J) | $3.60 \times 10^6$ |
| **Force** | | |
| kip (1000 lbf) | newton (N) | $4.4482 \times 10^3$ |
| pound force (lbf) | newton (N) | $4.4482$ |
| ounce force | newton (N) | $2.7801 \times 10^{-1}$ |
| **Length** | | |
| foot (ft) | metre (m) | $3.048 \times 10^{-1}$ |
| inch (in) | metre (m) | $2.54 \times 10^{-2}$ |
| mile (mi) (U.S. statute) | metre (m) | $1.6093 \times 10^3$ |
| mile (mi) (international nautical) | metre (m) | $1.852 \times 10^3$ |
| yard (yd) | metre (m) | $9.144 \times 10^{-1}$ |
| **Mass** | | |
| pound mass (lbm) | kilogram (kg) | $4.5359 \times 10^{-1}$ |
| slug (lbf-s$^2$/ft) | kilogram (kg) | $1.4594 \times 10$ |
| ton (2000 lbm) | kilogram (kg) | $9.0718 \times 10^2$ |
| **Power** | | |
| foot-pound/minute (ft-lbf/min) | watt (W) | $2.2597 \times 10^{-2}$ |
| horsepower (550 ft-lbf/s) | watt (W) | $7.4570 \times 10^2$ |
| **Pressure, Stress** | | |
| atmosphere (std)(14.7 lbf/in$^2$) | newton/metre$^2$(N/m$^2$ or Pa) | $1.0133 \times 10^5$ |
| pound/foot$^2$(lbf/ft$^2$) | newton/metre$^2$(N/m$^2$ or Pa) | $4.7880 \times 10$ |
| pound/inch$^2$(lbf/in$^2$ or psi) | newton/metre (N/m$^2$ or Pa) | $6.8948 \times 10^3$ |
| **Velocity** | | |
| foot/minute (ft/min) | metre/second (m/s) | $5.08 \times 10^{-3}$ |
| foot/second (ft/s) | metre/second (m/s) | $3.048 \times 10^{-1}$ |
| knot (nautical mi/h) | metre/second (m/s) | $5.144 \times 10^{-1}$ |
| mile/hour (mi/h) | metre/second (m/s) | $4.4704 \times 10^{-1}$ |
| mile/hour (mi/h) | kilometre/hour (km/h) | $1.6093$ |
| mile/second (mi/s) | kilometre/second (km/s) | $1.6093$ |
| **Volume** | | |
| foot$^3$(ft$^3$) | metre$^3$(m$^3$) | $2.8317 \times 10^{-2}$ |
| inch$^3$(in$^3$) | metre$^3$(m$^3$) | $1.6387 \times 10^{-5}$ |

# Peat as an energy source

## J. M. PECORARO
### U.S. Department of Energy

ABSTRACT

Peat, a potential indigenous fuel source, is beginning to loom larger on the New England energy scene. For centuries, in Europe, its use has been a normal occurrence. As the price of fuel oil escalates, the possibility is developing that New England in general, and Massachusetts in particular, may tap this valuable resource for electrical generation and space heating.

DISCUSSION

Since 1973 when the Arab embargo was imposed on the United States, literally thousands of energy ideas and millions of words have been directed toward the American public. It is my guess that the sheer volume of these efforts has left the populace in a completely confused state. One concept, however, has persisted and, up to this moment, everyone is waiting for the "big bang," or major breakthrough, which will answer all of our energy woes. Unfortunately, at this point in time, such a development does not appear in the cards. The macro answer to an immense problem is just not there. However, a series of micro steps can lead to an overall positive response to our nation's dilemma. The old geometric axiom that the whole is equal to the sum of its parts is as valid today as it was in Grecian times, and it is in this context that I suggest that New England in general, and Massachusetts and Maine in particular, take a close look at an indigenous energy resource, peat.

Joe Sinnott, the Massachusetts State Geologist, has devoted his paper to an overall view of Massachusetts peat resources, and I shall attempt to define the potential of peat as an energy alternative. In every conceivable sense it is a viable component within the overall energy framework.

It is necessary, however, to place in perspective why, as a nation, we are where we find ourselves today. The basic "given" is that our country is in its present dilemma because we were the beneficiary of cheap energy. Therefore, this low cost element of our economic life led to many of the inefficient and high cost systems that plague us today. For example, when residual oil was $1.39 per barrel, the designer of a system pretty well had his course of action determined for him. Who, for example, would have considered using a fuel with a heat content of 6-7000 BTU/lb versus approximately 18,700 BTU/lb for residual oil and 11-12,000 BTU/lb for coal? The picture has changed, and what was not so attractive a few years ago is now a strong candidate for use as an alternate energy.

Why can't we here in New England follow the lead of other nations which have used peat as an energy source for centuries? Russia, with the largest reserves in the world, fuels 76 electrical generation plants with peat, some of which are in the 730 MW class. The technology is on the shelf and is currently in use in Finland, Ireland, Denmark, and Germany.

The United States, which has the second largest peat resources in the world, is estimated to have approximately 1400 quads ($10^{15}$) locked up in this national asset. In terms of oil equivalent, this represents 240 billion barrels of oil.

Our own New England states of Maine and Massachusetts rank 8th and 13th among the 50 in order of their estimated reserves. To put it in potential energy terms, Maine has 21 quads and Massachusetts has 10 quads stored up in its bogs. The combined peat energy potential of these two states represents almost 12 percent of the energy content of the proved petroleum reserves of the United States. Obviously, this regional and national energy source should be used, and I am glad to say that New England is now moving strongly in that direction.

Let me set forth a few of the peat initiatives now underway in our area. The University of Rhode Island (URI) has recently completed a resource definition of the peat deposits on Block Island. This was done under the sponsorship of the Department of Energy in Boston in conjunction with the State Energy Office. A unique problem had developed on the island centering on abnormally high electrical generating costs. As Block Island is not connected to the mainland electrical grid, all of its power needs are met through the use of diesel driven generators. With the cost of diesel fuel approaching $1.00 per gallon and still going up, I need say little about the economic effects of this situation. The islanders, however, recall that in Colonial times heat requirements were met by burning local peat. This raises a question. Can these same deposits be utilized today by the local power company for electrical generation?

We were most interested in a possible answer

to this question, for Block Island is New England in microcosm. It has high energy costs due to its overdependence on petroleum and apparently has no other energy resource in common use. DOE ascertained that if sufficient peat reserves were still in place, and if the quality lent itself to efficient combustion, peat could be used in the power plant.

Here we must look at a different facet of our energy story. There is another energy effort underway on the island, which could complement peat combustion, and that is the use of a DOE-NASA designed wind turbine of 200 KW capacity. This unit can supply the island's needs during the winter when the wind blows constantly. During the summer when there is relatively little wind, the use of peat could be adapted either to power a boiler or to be gasified in an appropriate gasifier for use by diesel engines. These two native resources, wind and peat, could be adapted to a local energy need, therefore, backing out the use of expensive imported petroleum.

The URI study defined the seven largest bogs on the island and, in conjunction with the Department of Energy Pittsburgh Energy Lab, had all samples analyzed for heat values, sulphur content, and ash. Generally speaking, the best fuel grade samples averaged 5,500 BTU/lb with sulphur contents of less than 1 percent and ash values at approximately 10 percent.

An estimate of the proved deposits indicated that the best grade peats could fuel a 3 MW power plant for approximately 20 years, but we would like to point out that this is a very conservative estimate; in all likelihood this reserve is twice as large as now indicated. Incidentally, the summer peak demand is 1 MW.

A further study now underway on the island is to consider the use of this peat as a space heating substitute for bottled gas and electricity. It appears quite logical that the use of this supply could be applied to both electrical generation and home fuel. In addition, development of a small industrial base for the island is a definite option. Where there is little or no work available locally, this is a real plus.

A while back, I mentioned that the State of Maine looms large on the New England peat scene, and under the leadership of Walt Anderson, the State Geologist, a very aggressive resource evaluation program is underway. Both the Department of Energy and the U.S. Geological Survey are cooperating in this venture. The most recent investigations have revealed that commercial quality deposits in Maine contain less than 10 percent ash, very low sulphur and a very high hydrogen component as compared with lignite and subbituminous coal. Low sulphur appears favorable to attaining air standards, and the high hydrogen certainly favors the gasification process.

I would like to mention at this point that the Maine study is very wide in scope and is devoted additionally to the determination of geo-

chemical trace elements, ph, and degrees of decomposition. Also, Carbon-14 radiometric dating and pollen studies are being conducted at the University of Maine.

The Department of Energy has recognized from the beginning of its peat interest that the requirements of the National Environmental Protection Act must be addressed if this fuel source is to be used. Although I have directed my remarks to the New England area, there are large programs underway in Minnesota, North Carolina and Michigan, and extensive environmental impact issues are being studied. Our Block Island study is now being supplemented by an Environmental Impact Assessment under the auspices of the Bureau of Mines. I have few doubts, because of the delicate nature and balance of environmental factors on the island, that the bureau's efforts will be most productive and beneficial to the future of peat development. If it can work in Rhode Island, it can work anywhere!

CONCLUSION

I would like to touch on one more technology that lends itself to efficient local peat usage. This is the close coupled gasifier that can be retrofitted to an existing boiler at an industrial installation or domicile. This unit was developed by a New Hampshire firm for use with wood chips. There appear to be few, if any, impediments to its use as a peat gasifier. The University of New Hampshire is now conducting tests for us to establish base line data for equipment and fuel size modifications leading to a large scale test at an apartment complex. We feel that the retrofitting of a gasifier for such a use can point the way to the real coming of peat as an alternative energy resource for our region. Although each individual installation of this type appears small in itself, every one of them knocks down petroleum usage. If enough of these steps are taken, they, in conjunction with conservation measures and greater usage of coal, can go a long way toward providing energy independence for our country. Certainly peat is not the complete answer, but it is one of the micro steps we can and should take as soon as possible.

BIBLIOGRAPHY

Barton, W.R., and Pecoraro, J.M., 1978, Peat as an energy resource in New England: Federal Regional Council.

Bastin, E.S., and Davis, C.A., 1909, Peat deposits of Maine: U.S. Geological Survey, Bulletin 376, 127 p.

Bowles, W.D., ed., 1956, The Soviet peat industry: New York, F.A. Praeger.

Cameron, C.C., 1975, Some peat deposits in Washington and southeastern Aroostook Counties, Maine: U.S. Geological Survey, Bulletin 1317-C.

Institute of Gas Technology, 1978, Experimental
program for development of peat gasification:
Institute of Gas Technology, January.

Sheridan, J.T., and DeCarlo, J.A., 1957, Peat in
the United States: U.S. Bureau of Mines,
Information Circular 7799.

☐

Hors-texte

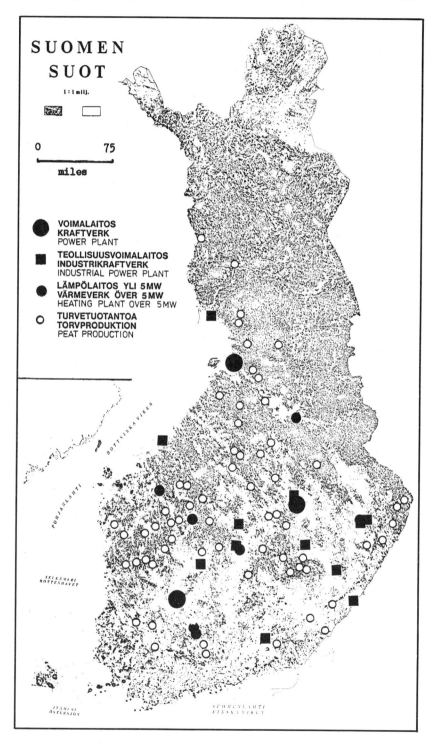

Map of Finland, showing the considerable extent
of peat production and the location of some
industrial plants using this important energy
resource. (Courtesy, Ekono Oy, Helsinki.)

Hors-texte

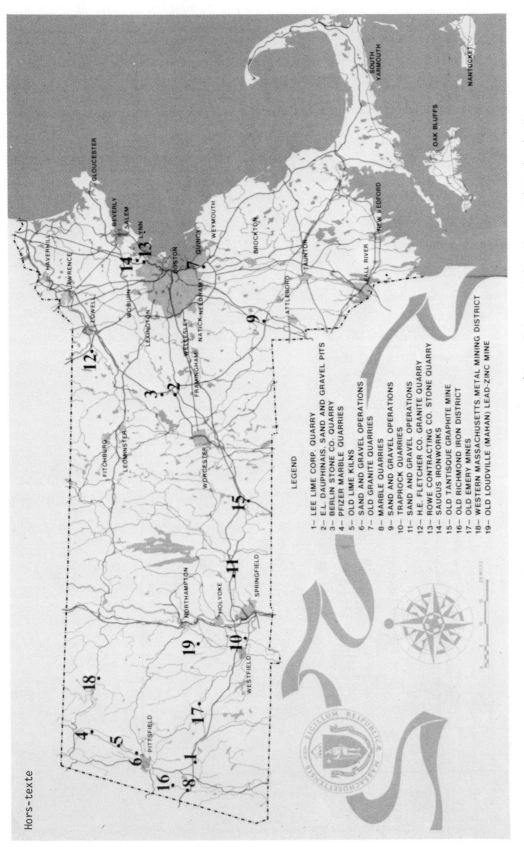

LEGEND

1— LEE LIME CORP. QUARRY
2— E.L. DAUPHINAIS, SAND AND GRAVEL PITS
3— BERLIN STONE CO. QUARRY
4— PFIZER MARBLE QUARRIES
5— OLD LIME KILNS
6— SAND AND GRAVEL OPERATIONS
7— OLD GRANITE QUARRIES
8— MARBLE QUARRIES
9— SAND AND GRAVEL OPERATIONS
10— TRAPROCK QUARRIES
11— SAND AND GRAVEL OPERATIONS
12— H.E. FLETCHER CO. GRANITE QUARRY
13— ROWE CONTRACTING CO. STONE QUARRY
14— SAUGUS IRONWORKS
15— OLD TANTISQUE GRAPHITE MINE
16— OLD RICHMOND IRON DISTRICT
17— OLD EMERY MINES
18— WESTERN MASSACHUSETTS METAL MINING DISTRICT
19— OLD LOUDVILLE (MAHAN) LEAD-ZINC MINE

Map of mining and mineral operations in Massachusetts. (From mining and mineral operations in the New England and Mid-Atlantic states: a visitor guide, Bureau of Mines, 72 p., 1976; Massachusetts portion by W. R. Barton.) The guide contains the following CAUTION. (1) Remember that abandoned mines are death traps. Stay out of them. Old shafts often cave near the surface and form a funnel-shaped opening. Unwary visitors have been trapped in these funnels. Stay away from old shafts! (2) Always use available guide services. Mine openings (tunnels, adits, open pits) should never be entered except with a competent guide. (3) Sometimes the air is bad in abandoned mines and is not safe to breathe. Explosive gas may also be present. Gases frequently come from the rocks themselves, but during active operations they are swept out of the mine by the controlled ventilating current. (4) Remember, too, that even the oldest mines usually are private property. Most mine owners do not object to the collection of a few mineral specimens (some do charge a fee), but all object to touring vandals, who wantonly destroy buildings and equipment, or to inexperienced trespassers, who present a hazard to themselves, the property, and the owners.

# Siting for aggregate production in New England

## W. R. BARTON
### U.S. Bureau of Mines

ABSTRACT

Land use conflicts between aggregate producers and New England urban centers are discussed
and placed in economic perspective. Strategies
for proper site location are reviewed, and feasible solutions to problems are suggested.

THE PROBLEM

Sand, gravel, and stone are made into aggregates to serve the needs of society. Society does
not always serve the aggregate producer well in
return. Many planners, zoners, and members of the
general public consider it axiomatic that the
aggregate producer and the average urban resident
have incompatible goals. The producer wants to
be near his mass market, and the average resident
wants him as far away as possible.

The traditional economic decision to mine
local material to avoid transportation costs is
increasingly challenged by zoning and planning
bodies and by citizens' groups. This conflict has
generated much written and spoken word and offered
opportunity for flights of rhetoric. The pressure
on the producer also has forced reappraisal of the
need for this classic confrontation, with indications that much of the conflict is more apparent
than substantive.

In much of New England several factors combine to increase complexity of the siting problem.
It is a region of high land values and considerable population density. Due to the proximity of
metropolitan areas, even rural communities have
experienced a proliferation of environmental
groups with concomitant enthusiasm for regional
planning and critical watch over land use. In New
England, where there is little public understanding of the necessity for, and the realities of,
mineral production a sophisticated approach to
locating sites for aggregate production is
required.

A metropolitan area, such as Boston, greatly
influences the fortunes of an aggregate producer.
It gives him a mass market and assures that if he
manages his affairs well he may reasonably hope
to earn a substantial profit. Profit, after all,
is the primary objective in any business enter-
prise including aggregate production. And profit,
or perhaps more correctly the prudent reinvestment
of profit, is generally accepted as the long-term,
socially most useful objective of business in a
capitalistic society.

However, the aggregate producer has little
apparent mass effect or influence upon the city,
its people, its economy, or its social milieu.
Generally aggregate production accounts for much
less than one percent of the gross metropolitan
product, and the raw materials produced account
for only a few percent of finished building or
other construction costs. Because the essential
nature of his product does not have high visibility, the aggregate producer is, unfortunately,
often perceived as a fair target for resident ire.
His trucks, his noise, and his perceived-as-ugly
plant, are often singled out as fair game for a
campaign to close down the operation.

PERSPECTIVE

Actually few good undeveloped aggregate deposits remain within the metropolitan Boston area.
All deposits that can conceivably exist in the
area are well known. For the most part, those
deposits that remain occupy land that is more
valuable for other uses. It may have social value for open space or possess scenic attributes.
It may not be economical to develop such areas for
aggregate production. Offshore sand and gravel,
use of other materials, and longer haulage provide
three alternatives to lessened consumption.

Ocean mining is broadly opposed by New
England environmentalists and, in fact, many of
the new coastal zone management regulations outlaw
ocean mining on a de facto if not entirely on a
de jure basis. Mass use of alternative materials
within metropolitan areas is faced with the same
operational constraints as when processing natural
aggregates. Little progress has been made except
for recycling old pavements and limited demonstra-
tions of materials such as glassphalt. Transportation from more distant sites has been the classical New England solution. The trick is to maintain profits in the face of the increased haulage
cost.

Not only profit, but profit maximization, are
the goals of an astute businessman. Cost engineering principles applied from a corporate cost-
benefit perspective not only help to minimize
costs and maximize profits, but also place the
aggregate production site in perspective--as an
essentially suburban-rural industry which economically should not sustain itself in urbanizing
areas.

## EFFICIENCY OF USE

The key to resolution of the mineral producer-urban confrontation is to recall a basic economic precept: "The cost of using something in a particular venture is the benefit foregone (or opportunity lost) by not using it in its best alternative use."

Urbanization raises alternative use values of land and makes mining economically less sensible and more difficult. The land-use conflict then is not just social or aesthetic, it is economic as well. Urban land becomes worth more for purposes other than mining. If urban land is not used for its best alternative use, larger profits from the land may be foregone, that is, the opportunity to make such profits is lost. By deferring income that might be earned from higher land use, the producer is in effect paying interest for using improper sites to produce aggregates, because deferred income is less income. Quantitatively this concept is expressed by the equation, that we might term an "Efficiency of use" equation, as:

$$S = P (1 + i)^{n-1}$$

where P = the present value of a piece of land

i = the prevailing rate you expect to earn with capital

n = the number of years that sale or reuse is delayed

S = the sum that would have to be realized in n years to equal real present value (P)

Substituting one million dollars for P and 10 per cent for i the equation says that in 10 years you would have to sell the site for $2,594,000 just to obtain interest on the use of the one million dollars for which the site could be divested today. This does not take into account other variables such as increasing taxes, legal fees, inflation, etc., normally encountered in an urbanizing area. All payments in excess of alternate use value are termed economic rent and constitute increased calls on capital for each ton of product realized from the site.

The operational value of the site to the producer lies in the cash flow generated by his investment, typically calculated by an equation that may be simply expressed:

$$V = (p) \frac{a}{n|} + R$$

where: p = the annual profit realized from the resource

$\frac{a}{n|}$ = the coefficient for present value at a selected discount rate

R = the value of the real estate after operations cease

V = the present value of the resource and site

The coefficient $\frac{a}{n|}$ at 10 per cent over 10 years is 6.145, which means $100,000 profit per year over the next 10 years is worth today $614,500, not the total $1,000,000 to be realized.

Many concerns are expressed that, as aggregate producers retreat to rural sites, the price of aggregates to city center consumers will rise exorbitantly. This is not necessarily true either in economic theory or in hard reality. Profit, the bottomline reason for being in business, is determined by factors expressed in the following equation:

$$P = NQ - F - NV$$

where N = the number of units sold
Q = price per unit
F = fixed costs
V = variable cost per unit
P = profit

## LOCATION COST

Site retention beyond a time when the land should be put to an economically higher use is a constantly increasing cost which serves to reduce profitability or increase price. The opportunity costs associated with high value sites remaining in production can more than offset added transportation costs from a more distant site. In addition, the lower land costs and possibly lower operating costs at a rural site offer other cost advantages. Location cost is a fixed cost that is a design variable generally inversely proportional to the distance from the city center, which can be expressed abstractly in the equation:

$$C = AX + \frac{B}{X} + k$$

where
X = represents the design variable

A, B, and k = constants with positive values or equal to zero

C = represents total location costs

Thus, the interest of producer, consumer, and city may coincide. The producer makes an acceptable profit, the consumer obtains an assured aggregate supply possibly at reduced cost, and the city is unsullied by a pit or quarry when economically prudent site redevelopment has run its course. And site reuse such as for a high-rise building will generate far more cash flow per acre than a residual urban sand pit.

## ANCILLARY CONSIDERATIONS

As noted earlier, however, the producer's life will not be entirely free of vexation at his new rural retreat in New England.

Assuming he has an aggregate source that will permit meeting product specifications, that plant wash water is available, and that economic transportation is available (and, in this time of high New England fuel costs, that generally indicates railroad or water for anything over a 25 mile haul), his problems are still not over. He must obtain the necessary zoning and production permits and obtain approval of his plans from sundry environmentally-oriented boards. These include air pollution, water pollution, water supply, regional planning, conservation board, etc. His site must be screened from adjoining properties, he must provide satisfactory means for control of all sorts of real or perceived pollution, such as air, water, noise, visual and traffic, and he must have an approved site rehabilitation or site reuse plan. Note that I said approved plan, rather than sensible or reasonable, although the terms are not necessarily mutually exclusive.

Technology can reduce some of the undesirable side effects of aggregate production. The producer also might reduce conflict with neighbors at his new site and shift site location economics to his favor by attracting as neighbors industrial users of his product. This includes industries such as precast concrete components, block plants, pre-bagged concrete and mortar mix products, etc. These ancillary industries are more labor intensive and ship a higher unit value product which can stand greater shipping charges. In addition, by pre-planning the subsequent use of his site 10, 20, 30 or 40 years hence, a producer can practice landscape architecture as he digs and as he rehabilitates and landscapes his worked-out site.

Emotionalism is another factor which must be faced. Local environmentalists and politicians may become impassioned over their precious aggregate going out of town or out of state. In New Hampshire bills are annually introduced to the state legislature to embargo exports of sand and gravel to Massachusetts. So far the bills have been rejected as unconstitutional restraint of interstate commerce. The feelings of New Hampshire residents are not assuaged when they see several million tons of aggregate moved from southern New Hampshire to Boston's northern border

for road base and then have a former Governor of Massachusetts decide not to finish the road. During rush hour commuters can travel the old road and see New Hampshire sand and gravel sitting on top of a Massachusetts salt marsh. Massachusetts taxpayers have the consolation that the sand and gravel appreciates in value as it sits there, and someday it may be put to use.

## A FUTURE MODEL

Boston is supplied with aggregates from numerous sites including one which is about 110 miles away in Ossipee, New Hampshire. The Boston and Maine Railroad operates unit-trains over its tracks for Boston Sand and Gravel Company from its subsidiary, Ossipee Aggregates, Inc. It is probably the longest haul sand and gravel unit-train operation in the country and, as far as I know, in the world. The rural site at Ossipee is well-screened, it causes no discernible pollution (even though a trout stream flows through the property), it is Ossipee's highest taxpayer, and it provides freight traffic for the railroad. When operations are completed, the level site remaining will be a prime candidate for redevelopment. In place of sand hills covered with scrub pine, the town will have a level site producing revenue and jobs or places of residence. The site location, believed typical of future New England aggregate production modes, was indicated not only by the location of markets, transportation routes, and deposits, but also by economic wisdom superimposed on physical and social facts.

## CONCLUSIONS

Aggregate producers and urban areas share a symbiotic producer-consumer relationship. They also share in competition for available land. Because many land uses in urban centers yield higher economic benefit than the use of a tract for aggregate production, the producer is faced with a retreat to a production site more removed from his marketing center or faces lost opportunity costs on his site investment. When such economic concepts are considered, the more rural site may prove to be more cost effective in supplying aggregates for urban needs.

Hors-texte

An esker in Pelham, Massachusetts, looking north. Locally this has been called the great serpent esker. (From Geology of Old Hampshire County, Massachusetts, by B.K. Emerson, U.S. Geological Survey, Monograph, Vol. 29, 1898, p. 579).

# 10

# MINERAL RESOURCES

Session moderator

W. J. Mallio
Resource Engineering, Inc.

# Exploration and exploitation of the Narragansett coal basin

J. W. SKEHAN, S. J.      D. P. MURRAY      J. D. RABEN

Weston Observatory, Department of Geology and Geophysics,
Boston College; and, J. D. R. only, New England Geotechnical Consultants, Inc.

H. B. CHASE, JR.
Mansfield, Massachusetts

## ABSTRACT

The Narragansett Basin supported intermittent mining of coal and graphite principally in the 19th century. The coal is contained in the Rhode Island Formation of Pennsylvanian age, which is folded, faulted and variably metamorphosed, ranging from the diagenetic zone in the northern part of the basin to the upper sillimanite zone in the southwestern part. Coal has been mined from rocks of the diagenetic zone, anchizone and greenschist facies, and graphite from the amphibolite facies.

Prospecting and mining of coal date back to 1736, with an estimated 1.1 million tons of good quality coal having been produced from several mines in Portsmouth, Rhode Island, in the 19th and 20th centuries, notably for copper smelting. Coal for raising steam and household use was mined in both Massachusetts and Rhode Island, and "graphite" or natural carbon, chiefly for foundry and crucible facings, was mined in Rhode Island. Coal as a fuel is currently being quarried together with rock in Plainville, Massachusetts, for the production of lightweight aggregate.

Illite crystallinity and coal petrography have proven to be useful guides in the drilling program. Coal characteristics are variable throughout the basin, but some practical indicators of coal quality include its reported uses, ash and hydrogen content, petrographic features, and ignition characteristics. Preliminary results suggest that the Narragansett Basin coal, although inferior in quality to Pennsylvania anthracite, has characteristics which make further exploration highly desirable. Its characteristics are keys to future exploitation of anthracite, meta-anthracite and possibly also of "graphite".

## INTRODUCTION

The Narragansett Basin of southeastern Massachusetts and Rhode Island is a topographic lowland of approximately 960 square miles which supported intermittent and limited coal mining during the 19th and, to a lesser extent, the 18th and 20th centuries. For the most part, the basin consists of woodlands, farms and wetlands with scattered villages and towns, and a few larger cities such as Providence, Cranston, Pawtucket, Newport and Bristol in Rhode Island, and Attleborough, Brockton, Taunton and Bridgewater in Massachusetts (Fig. 1). Due to extensive glacial deposits, exposures of bedrock tend to be limited, especially for the finer-grained rocks.

## SUMMARY OF GEOLOGY

The distribution of Pennsylvanian rock formations in the Narragansett and adjacent Norfolk Basins is shown in Figure 2. Table 1 summarizes the age relations and estimated thickness of these non-marine clastic sedimentary rock units. Coal appears to be restricted to the Rhode Island Formation, the thickest (probably in excess of 10,000 ft) and most extensive formation. Lyons (1977) has estimated the thickness of the Rhode Island Formation as 20,000 feet. The Rhode Island Formation consists of sandstone, siltstone, shale, conglomerate, and coal, arranged in decreasing abundance based on drill core data, and is interpreted as a non-marine, primarily braided stream complex. Known coal occurrences (Fig. 1) are chiefly concentrated along or near the western, northwestern and southeastern margins of the basin. It is unclear whether this pattern reflects the representative distribution of coal in the basin or merely a relative abundance of near-surface coal discoveries made in populated areas in the course of digging for wells and building foundations. It appears that the younger coal-bearing rocks (Stephanian A) may be older than the coarse-grained Dighton Conglomerate (Lyons, 1979). Alternatively, the Dighton Conglomerate may be the coarse-grained time equivalent of the finer-grained coal-bearing strata (J. Boothroyd, pers. comm., 1980).

Structurally the basin is characterized by relatively gently folded and faulted rocks in its northern part (chiefly Massachusetts). The southern region (Fig. 3), however, is more intensely and complexly deformed (Skehan and Murray, 1979; and Murray and Skehan, 1979). Sedimentary rocks and coal have also been progressively metamorphosed, the grade of metamorphism ranging from the prehnite-pumpellyite zone in the north to the sillimanite zone in the southwestern part (Fig. 4) near the contact with the Permian-aged (ca. 275 million years old) Narragansett Pier Granite. Coal has been mined from rocks of the chloritoid zone and below, and "graphite" from the chloritoid zone and above.

## HISTORICAL MINING ACTIVITIES

Records show prospecting and mining activities for coal in the Narragansett Basin since 1736 when the Leonard's mine was opened in Mansfield (then Norton). "Graphite" was also mined in the Colonial era. Table 2 summarizes historically known mining, quarrying, and prospecting activi-

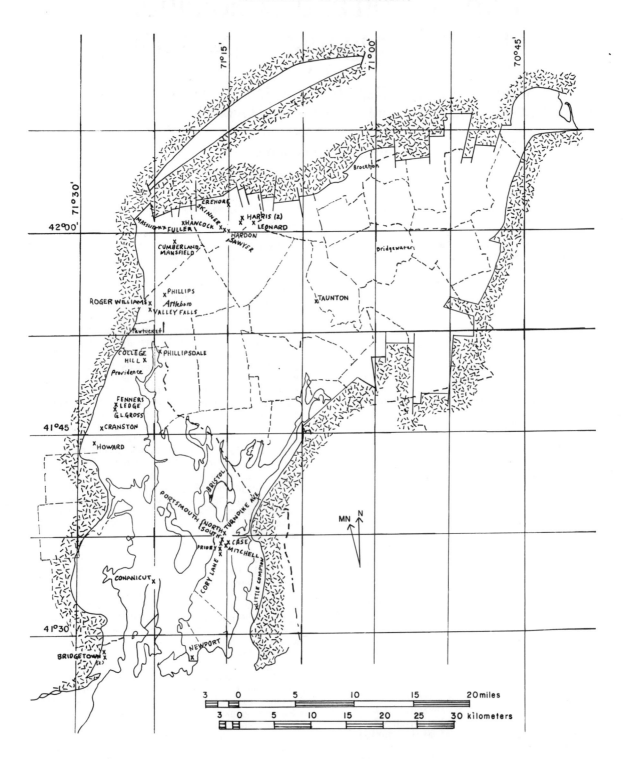

Figure 1. Map of the Narragansett Basin showing the location of coal and graphite mines,
prospects and quarries. Modified from Chase
(1978 and 1979).

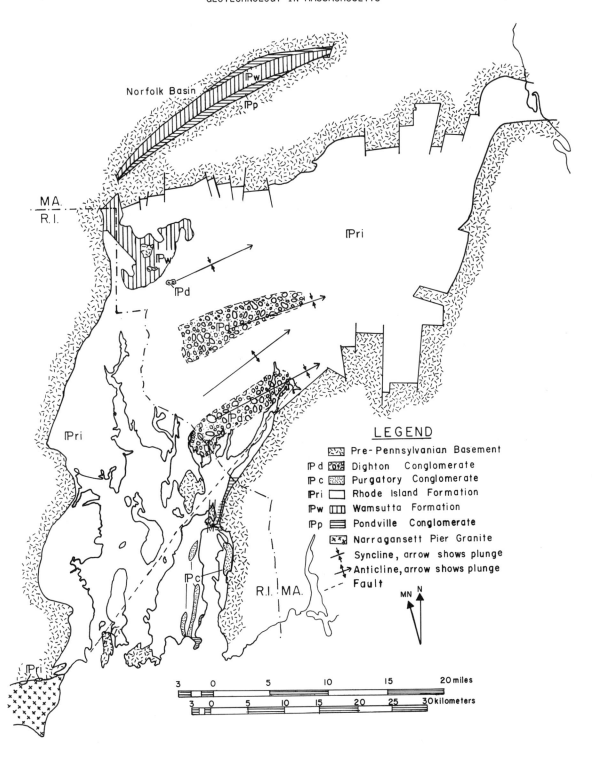

Figure 2. Geologic map of the Narragansett and Norfolk Basins. Modified from Quinn (1971); Quinn and Moore (1968); Lyons (1977); Skehan and others (1978); Skehan and Murray (1979); and Murray and Skehan (1979).

## TABLE 1. DESCRIPTION OF STRATIGRAPHIC UNITS OF THE NARRAGANSETT BAY GROUP

| Lithology | Sedimentary and other distinguishing features | Approximate thickness (m) | Age | References |
|---|---|---|---|---|
| **Pondville Conglomerate**<br>At type locality: interbedded red and green slate, silt-stone, arkose and quartzite-pebble conglomerate; elsewhere may also include gray to greenish coarse conglomerate, most pebbles being quartzite with some granite and schist; abundant sandy matrix; and dark gray granule conglomerate containing pebbles of smoky quartz 5mm in diameter; irregularly bedded with sandstone and lithic graywacke. | There is a general absence of basal conglomerate, the first deposited beds commonly being siltstone or arkosic sandstone; but sandstones and shales of the Wamsutta Formation or Rhode Island Formation may lie directly on older rocks; pebbles 15-60 cm in diameter. | 0-150 | Namurian C (?) to Late Westphalian (?) | Lyons, 1979 |
| **Wamsutta Formation**<br>Interbedded red, coarse-grained conglomerate, lithic graywacke, sandstone, and shale; conglom-erate layers contain felsite pebbles < 1.2m; a few lenses of limestone, one rhyolite flow and several sheets of basalt. | Crossbedding and interfingering of layers is characteristic. | 300 | Partly equivalent to the Rhode Island Formation as the red layers inter-finger with gray and black; contains a few plant fossils. Westphalian A or B to late Westphalian. | Lidback, 1977<br>Lyons, 1979 |
| **Rhode Island Formation**<br>Gray sandstone and siltstone with lesser amounts of gray to black shale, gray conglom-erate and coal ≤10m thick. Quartz forms the major com-ponents of the sandstones (Mutch, 1968, Fig. 5) and conglomerates. | Both fining- and coarsening upward sequences are present; paleocurrents have been defined only locally; conglomerate is relatively less abundant than in Dighton. | <3000 | Westphalian A or B to Stephanian A or B. | Lyons, 1979;<br>Skehan and others, 1978;<br>Lyons and Chase, 1976 |
| **Dighton Conglomerate**<br>Gray conglomerate consisting primarily of rounded quartzite cobbles to boulders with subordinate rounded granite cobbles and slate pebbles; very little sand matrix; lenses of medium sandstone form less than 20 percent of the unit. | The sandstone lenses are faintly cross bedded and coarser both upward and downward into adjacent conglomerate. | <300-450 | Small isolated amounts of alloch-thonous (?) non diagnostic plant debris; Stephanian (?) or C (?). | Lyons, 1979;<br>Skehan and others, 1976 |
| **Purgatory Conglomerate**<br>Coarse- to very coarse-grained conglomerate, interbedded with thin sandstones and magnetite-rich sandstone lenses; clasts in conglomerate are almost entirely quartzite, but there are several varieties of quartzite. | | > 30 | No Pennsylvanian flora yet known; several distinctive Lower Paleozoic fauna are present in quartzite clasts; stratigraphic arguments suggest time equivalence with Dighton. | Skehan and Murray, 1979b;<br>Mosher and Wood, 1976 |

NOTE: Modified from Skehan and Murray, 1979B, which includes references to the authors listed on the right. Other references which apply to the entire chart: Quinn and Oliver, 1962; Mutch, 1968; Quinn, 1971.

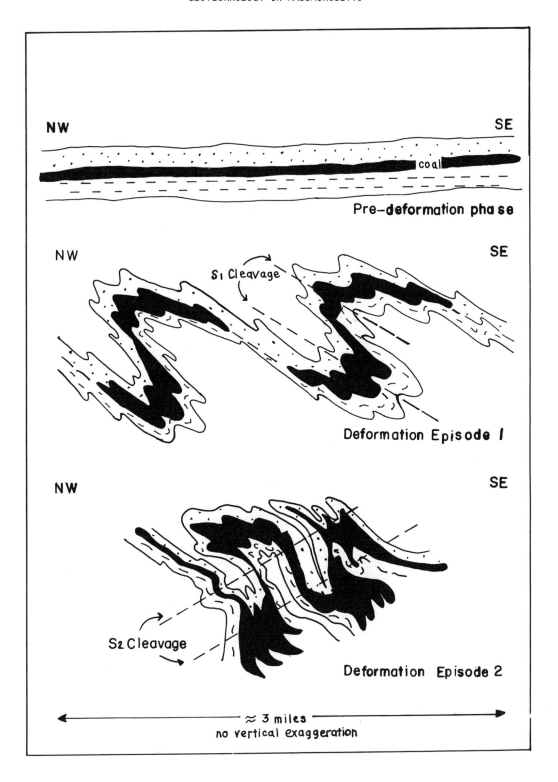

Figure 3. Generalized model for the structural
evolution of the southern Narragansett Basin
(Skehan and Murray, 1979; and Murray and
Skehan, 1979).

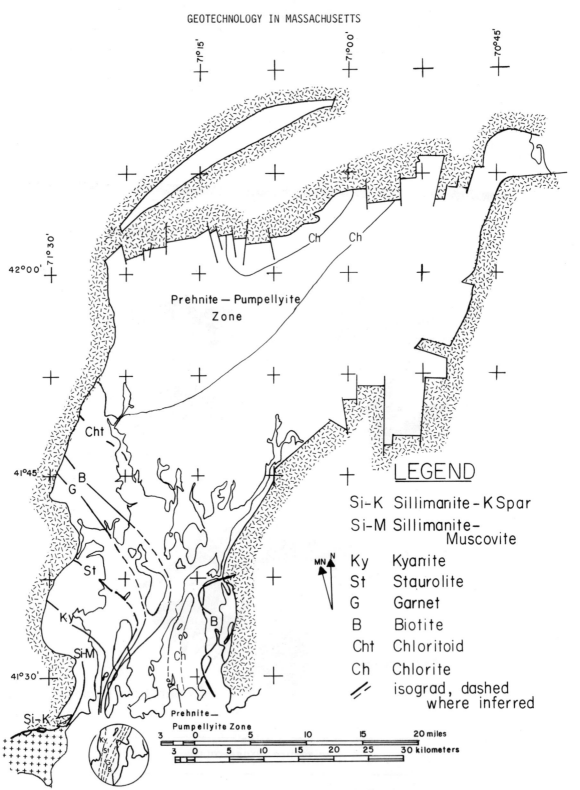

LEGEND

Si-K  Sillimanite-K Spar
Si-M  Sillimanite-
          Muscovite
Ky    Kyanite
St    Staurolite
G     Garnet
B     Biotite
Cht   Chloritoid
Ch    Chlorite
//    isograd, dashed
           where inferred

3    0       5        10        15        20 miles
3  0   5   10   15   20   25   30 kilometers

Figure 4. Metamorphic zones for the Narragansett Basin, based on data from outcrop and drill core and Quinn (1971); Grew and Day (1972); Grew (1974); Rehmer and others (1978); Murray and others (1979); Murray and Hepburn (1979); Smith (1977); Murray and Rehmer, unpub. data; and Skehan and Murray (1979).

- 386 -

TABLE 2. HISTORICAL MINING, QUARRYING AND PROSPECTING ACTIVITIES IN THE
NARRAGANSETT BASIN (AFTER CHASE, 1978 AND 1979, AND CHUTE, 1979)

| Location | Name | Dates operated | Production | Use | Comments |
|---|---|---|---|---|---|
| MASSACHUSETTS | | | | | |
| Attleboro | Phillips Mine | | coal & iron | | |
| Foxborough | Crehore Prospects | 1836-1840 | several tons | | Two shafts; one encountered in drilling by Boston College, 1977. |
| Mansfield | Carpenter Prospect | 1852 | some coal | | |
| | Hardon Mine | 1835 | | fired steam engine on site; to heat steamship President, 1842 | Vertical shaft encountered main coal seam at 64 ft. |
| | | 1838 | 1200-1500 tons (10 tons/day max) | raising steam and household uses | |
| | | 1838 | 200 tons from back bed | | "Back" bed reached 40 ft SE of shaft. Mining stopped in 1838 due to accessible coal being mined out and groundwater problems, lack of operator skill and general economic depression. |
| | | 1839, 1841 | State House lobby heated for a week with coal from SE bed during petitions to Massachusetts General Court for funding | | |
| | | 1910 | some coal | | In 1909 Massachusetts Coal and Power Company bought 803 acres and leased 1135 to set up mine mouth, producer-gas, electric generating plant. In 1910, 253 ft slope shaft followed main coal bed. MC&P passed into receivership. |
| | | 1920 | 25 tons  total, 1500-2100 tons | coal from dump used in engine | Slope unwatered and 20 ft pocket of coal mined. Mining rights expired in 1926. |
| | Harris Prospects | 1835 | | | Two vertical shafts 64 and 92-100 ft deep, 450 ft apart; 1 graphitic coal bed encountered. 1838-mine abandoned. |
| | Leonard Mine | 1736-1745 | unknown | in iron smelting works | 19 years before first recorded use of Pennsylvania anthracite. |
| | Sawyer Mine | 1848-1854 | 2500 tons from "North Seam" in NW cross cut; 2500 tons from SE cross cut for smelting and heating in Mansfield and Foxborough | | 162 ft shaft sunk; cross cuts driven 660 ft SE, 832 ft NW; 13 coal beds but only 2 worked; failed due to irregular seams and inferior quality of coal. Mine pumped out in 1883 and 1909-1910 with small production. |

| Location | Name | Dates operated | Production | Use | Comments |
|---|---|---|---|---|---|
| | Skinner Mine | 1836-1837 | little | | |
| | (Tremont or Wading Mine) | 1838 | 25 tons | blacksmithing, heating and raising steam, 6 hp steam engine used mix of Skinner coal and wood | Vertical shaft to 40 ft. From bottom of 84 ft shaft cross cut carried SE to lens of good coal, the "Wading Vein." |
| | | 1923 | 5 tons/day from NE gangway off SE cross cut | 40 tons for household stoves and furnaces | In 1925, 10 tons left piled at mine mouth. |
| | | 1835-1925 | total, 100-160 tons | | |
| North Attleboro | Cumberland-Mansfield Mine (Southern Massachusetts or North Attleboro Mine) | | | | Coal discovered on Turnpike Hill (date unknown). |
| | | 1910 | 60 tons | home heating | Vertical shaft to 60 ft |
| | | 1922 | | | Shaft deepened to 100 ft; a second shaft started 100 ft to NE. |
| | | 1924 | 70-100 tons | | Shaft to 105 ft with 2 cross cuts; property sold 1928. |
| Plainville (until 1905 Plainville was part of Wrentham) | Fuller Prospect | before 1841 | | | Excavation. |
| | Guild Prospect | before 1840 | | | Bed of poor coal found in 22 ft shaft or well, but not worked. |
| | Hancock Prospect | before 1840 | | | Several shafts; the deepest 60 ft were sunk near Hancock House reaching graphitic coalbeds. |
| | Masslite Quarry (Erickson or Bird Quarry) | 1885 approx | | | Six or Seven adits driven in Blake Hill in search of coal. |
| | | 1934 | | | One of these 40-60 ft long, encountered coal bed. |
| | | 1934-1945 | | | Bird and Son took out 440,000 tons of slate for roofing granules, using only a small amount of coal for heating. |

| Location | Name | Dates operated | Production | Use | Comments |
|----------|------|----------------|------------|-----|----------|
| | | 1961-present | 400 tons per day mixed coal and shale quarried in 1975, from two coal beds; a third bed was worked out; total production more than 50,000 tons | from 1967-78 as a heat source; mixed with Penn. anthracite to produce light weight aggregate from shale; since 1979 a mixture of Masslite coal and/or carbonaceous shale and fuel oil used | |
| | Plainville Prospect | before 1841 | | | A shaft 170-180 ft deep encountered several beds of poor coal, but was abandoned. |
| | Taunton Mine | 1800's | small production from shaft | blacksmithing and in copper smelting furnace | |
| **RHODE ISLAND** | | | | | |
| Bristol | Bristol Prospect | 1849-1851 | | | Coal found in well and on Church farm and Thames St. "Excellent quality" coal mined in 1849. Sinking of 70 ft shaft on Thames St. in 1852. Changes in water level with the tides suggests that water problems may have been an important factor in developing the mine. |
| Cranston | Cranston (Budlong or Sackanosset Mine) | 1857 as open pit | | to strengthen iron | Exploratory pits before 1840. |
| | | 1868 | 3600 tons | used by Mt. Hope Iron Works and Hicks Boiler Works and others | |
| | | 1874 | | in facing works | Mining on small scale. |
| | | 1886-1887 | 250-300 tons/week for time shipped to Pittsburgh | billets for blooms | N.Y Carbon Iron Co. of Pittsburgh reopened open cut mine 225 ft long, and 40 ft deep; also a 75 ft vertical shaft equipped to raise 30/tons/day, 5 chambers at bottom; 30 miners. |
| | | 1910 | | briquets unsuccessfully tried as fuel during coal strike | |
| | | 1913-1916 | 10,000-15,000 tons | fuel for household use, in Budlong nursery | Open cut was 300 ft long; slope less than 100 ft deep; 12 miners produced 60 tons. |
| | | 1919 | | fuel | |
| | | 1920 | | briquet coal with navy fuel oil amalgam | |

| Location | Name | Dates operated | Production | Use | Comments |
|---|---|---|---|---|---|
| | | 1921- 1923 | | for household use | One million dollars for modernization of mine. |
| | | | | briquets | By 1927 old surface plant torn down, new one erected and machinery installed. |
| | | 1927- 1929(?) | | "graphite" for lubricant, paint pigment and pencils | |
| | | 1929(?)- 1932 | | briquets of poor quality | |
| | | 1935 | 850 tons | graphite | Sold to N.J. and Ohio. |
| | | 1940- 1957 | 600-700 tons/ year; 3500 tons in 1944; 4000 tons in 1945; total to 1945 was about 115,000 tons of coal and graphite | foundry and crucible facings, as carbon raiser in steel batches and in paint pigments | In 1945 slope was 450 ft long; working extended 810 ft north of slope; old silted-in workings 450 ft south; single coal bed 6-40 ft thick; mine map published (Toenges and others, 1948). 5-9 employees. After fatality mine ordered closed by State. |
| | | 1958 | Cranston was one of two producers of "natural" graphite in U.S. Total to 1959, 175,000 tons. | | |
| | Fenner's Ledge Mine | after 1848 | 3 cars per month | graphite mine opened as open cut for foundry facings and paint; and in "Rising Sun Stove Polish" | |
| | G.L. Gross Mine | may be older than Fenner's Ledge Mine | | | Before 1909 buildings and machinery installed. Graphite crushed and screened but fine quartz was difficult to separate and process was unsuccessful. |
| | | 1909 | several hundred tons from Gross and Fenner's Ledge Mines combined | | Graphitic shale bed followed 200 ft underground and reached by 30 ft vertical shaft. Mine closed by 1913. |
| | Howard Prospect | closed before 1920 | | | |
| Cumberland | Robert Williams Mine (Cumber land Mine) | 1808 | several hundred tons | used at mine and locally | 80-ft shaft sunk but mining abandoned; wood abundant and coal use not understood. |
| | | 1828 | 50 tons | | New 60-ft shaft to coal. Abandoned after fatal roof fall. |

| Location | Name | Dates operated | Production | Use | Comments |
|----------|------|----------------|------------|-----|----------|
| | | 1836 | 600 tons | | 40-ft slope sunk in 1835, continued to 67-78 ft; drifts driven 300 ft. Coal generally accepted but not properly cleansed. |
| | | before 1853 | | | 300 ft vertical shaft; abandoned old coal bed and carried drift 260 ft to new pocket; soon abandoned. |
| | Valley Falls Mine | 1847 | 500 tons | | Coal found and 120 ft slope driven; by 1853 slope was 500 ft deep, crossed 5 coal beds and a 30 ft nest of coal. |
| | | after 1853 | | foundry facings and furnace linings | Chiefly worked for graphite. |
| East Providence | Phillipsdale Mine | about 1800 | | | Quarry worked for graphite. |
| Jamestown | Conanicut Prospect (?) | | | | Graphite. |
| Little Compton | Little Compton Mine (Tiverton Mine) | 1909-before 1912 | 200 tons graphite | basis for paints | Open cut on Sakonnet River. |
| Newport | Newport Prospects | 1776-1779 | unknown | heating barracks | British troops mined impure coal from outcrops near Sheep Point on Newport Neck. |
| Portsmouth | British Lustre Pits | 1841 | | used for purposes of graphite | Trial openings near Portsmouth Mine yielded light cellular coal sold under name "British Lustre." |
| | Case Mine (Aquidneck, Hazard, Mt. Hope or Butts Hill Mine) | 1809-1811 | 1 1/2 tons/day; 2400 tons (estimate by J.W.S., S.J.) | blacksmithing, and used in steam engine; N.Y. brewery and home heating | 35 ft thick coalbed found in 1808, operated sporadically due to shortage of funds and poor management. |
| | | 1826 | | | William Cullen Bryant wrote poem "A Meditation on Rhode Island Coal." |
| | (Mt. Hope Mine) | 1850 | 100,000 tons of coal and rock "principally the former" | household use | Leases lapsed in 1889 |
| | Cory Lane Prospect | | | | No data. |
| | Mitchell Mine | | | | 80 ft shaft on west slope of Butts Hill, abandoned 1889. |

| Location | Name | Dates operated | Production | Use | Comments |
|----------|------|----------------|------------|-----|----------|
| Portsmouth (Rhode Island, Aquidneck, Mt. Hope or South Mine): Portsmouth, Eddy, New England, Crocker, New or North Maine; Arnolds Point Mines. | | mid 1700's | in 1820 about 15-30 tons/day raised | domestic fuel | Coal dug from outcrops; in in 1809 R.I. Mine dug near later Portsmouth South shaft and abandoned in 1816 but resumed in 1819. |
| | | 1827 | 2200 long tons | for burning lime and bricks; for cooking, raising steam, air forges and in N.Y. for glass making | Mine operated sporadically with 4 shafts driven 1/2 mile NE of R.I. mine. |
| | | 1840-1848 | 2800 tons in 1844; 165 tons shipped to Boston in 1846 | brickmaking and fuel; blacksmithing | North Mine deepened from 100 to 300-500 ft down main bed and drifted along coal bed 1200 ft NE and 800 ft SW; front bed opened. |
| | | 1850- | 3100 tons from middle bed | loaded on schooners | 40-50 men employed in raising coal; middle bed followed to 623 ft; 6 gangways 80-844 ft long crosscut to "back" bed. |
| | | | 1010 tons loaded aboard vessels | | In 1857 gangway extended 1500 ft NE through good coal bed; cross cut from 500 ft level in Aquidneck Mine to "front" bed. In 1858-9 south slope operated at Mt. Hope Mine. |
| | | | | in Taunton used in smelting copper ore | Before 1860 the north slope opened as Crocker or New Mine at or near Portsmouth or Eddy Mine site; on 400 ft level gangway ran NE over 1800 ft; slope deepened to 770 ft and better coal obtained. |
| | | | 1862-3, 4000-5000 tons shipped to N.Y.; other shipments to Boston, Providence, and Taunton | | |
| | | | 1863-Mt. Hope Mine producing 50 tons/day | in furnaces of Poughkeepsie Iron Co., and domestic uses. | South slope deepened crossing 6 coalbeds. In 1964 new charter granted to mine coal and smelt copper, zinc, and iron. |

| Location | Name | Dates operated | Production | Use | Comments |
|---|---|---|---|---|---|
| | | | 1866-10,000 tons coal/year mainly from North slope | smelting copper ore and matte | Taunton Copper Manufacturing Company began building smelting works on shore west of mines; 8 furnaces, 22 kilns; new dock and rail connections; 4000 tons of copper and 1000 tons of matte smelted annually. |
| | | | 1858-70, 150,000 tons from Mt. Hope and 100,000 tons from New Mine; 30-40 tons/ day by 1870 from Mt. Hope Mine; 600 tons/month from New Mine | Mt. Hope Mine coal delivered to shipper to rail cars; all coal from new mine used in smelting works | By 1870 shaft reached 1240 ft depth on middle bed; 7 gangways totalling 3.5 miles; copper smelter and coal mines closed in 1883 due to protective tariff on copper imports and scarcity of domestic ores. |
| | | | 1897-8 briquets from culm produced in new North Slope plant | | |
| | | 1904 | | | Mine at North Slope worked. |
| | | 1909-1913 | | | Rhode Island Coal incorporated with plans to mine 4000-5000 tons/day, for briquets of coal treated with calcium chloride and build producer-gas, electric generating plant at mine mouth. |
| | | 1909 | 765,000 tons from middle bed; 240,000 tons from back bed with 80 percent recovery | | Mining exposed 1200 ft of coal down dip, 3800 ft on strike; in 1909-10 south slope deepened to 2100 ft. |
| | | 1911 | few hundred tons/week; total from both slopes 1,061,000 tons | | 82 miners; 14 miles underground; mine abandoned in 1913. |
| | Priory Prospect Turnpike Avenue Prospect | 1800's | | | No data. Few small pits dug along strike of coal bed. |
| Providence | College Hill Prospects | 1700's | | | During wartime fuel storages, coaly shales were successfully tried as fuel. |
| South Kingstown | Bridgewater Mines (Tower Hill or Cojoot Black Lead Mine) | Colonial Era | | | John Watson bought "Lead Mine Ferm" from Indians who used graphite to smear faces as signs of mourning. Before 1909 best graphite worked out and mine abandoned. |
| | | before 1840 | graphite mined in 2 or 3 small cuts; at one time 30 tons of pure graphite dug from 4 ft in bedrock | molding dust for iron founders | |

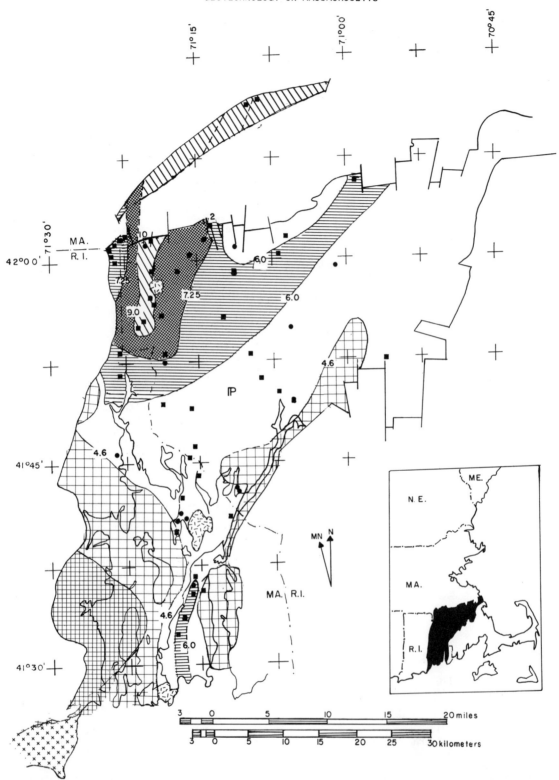

Figure 5. Map of illite isocrystallinity sub-divisions within the Narragansett Basin (Rehmer and others, 1979; Rehmer and Hepburn, written comm., 1978; and as Figure 8 in Skehan and Murray, 1979).

# LEGEND

⬚ Narragansett Pier Granite

⬚ Pennsylvanian

⬚ Pre Pennsylvanian

⬚ DIAGENETIC ZONE

⬚ ANCHIZONE
    ▤ lower
    ▢ upper

⬚ GREENSCHIST FACIES

⬚ AMPHIBOLITE FACIES

⟋6.0 ILLITE ISOCRYSTALLINITY CONTOUR

ARGILLACEOUS SAMPLE ANALYZED

• FROM CORE

■ FROM SURFACE EXPOSURE

•⁵ AVERAGE FOR 5 SAMPLES AT ONE LOCALITY

ties in the Narragansett Basin. These have been discussed in four progressively more detailed accounts (Chase, 1978, p. 20-24; Chase, 1978, Appendix B, 31 p.; Chute, 1979; and Chase, 1979, unpublished manuscript, 79 pages). This analysis indicates that an estimated 1.1 million tons of good quality coal was produced from several mines in Portsmouth, Rhode Island, in the 19th and early 20th centuries for a variety of purposes, notably for copper smelting (Table 2).

Coal suitable for raising steam and for household use was mined in limited quantities in: the Mansfield, Massachusetts, area, especially from the Sawyer and Hardon Mines; the Cumberland-Mansfield Mine in North Attleborough, Massachusetts; the Roger Williams Mine, Cumberland, Rhode Island; and possibly from the Bristol prospect in Bristol, Rhode Island (Table 2). The Cranston Mine, Cranston, Rhode Island, was by far the biggest producer of meta-anthracite and "graphite", predominantly for foundry and crucible facings and as a carbon raiser in steel batches. Additionally, it would appear that at various times hand-picked benches within the 6 to 40 ft thick seam were selected for briquet coal mixed with fuel oil amalgams. Other producing graphite mines were: the Fenners Ledge and the Gross Mines, Cranston, Rhode Island; the Little Compton Mine, Little Compton, Rhode Island; and the Valley Falls Mine, Cumberland, Rhode Island, which primarily produced coal as a fuel, but at least certain seams or benches were used chiefly in foundry activities (Table 2). The Masslite Quarry, Plainville, Massachusetts, is currently heating shale and siltstone by igniting a coal-oil mixture to produce a lightweight aggregate. The rock and coal have both been quarried on the site from 1961 to present.

## METAMORPHIC HISTORY OF THE BASIN

Although the Narragansett Basin is relatively restricted in area, the metamorphic effects vary in a relatively systematic way from place to place within it. It is not possible, however, to categorize the metamorphism of the basin or the coal in any simple way. Quinn (1971) presented metamorphic isograds for the Rhode Island part of the Narragansett Basin. Subsequent studies of the metamorphism by Grew and Day (1972), Grew (1974), Murray and others (1978 and 1979), Murray and Hepburn (1979), Rehmer and others (1978), Skehan and Murray (1979), and Murray and Skehan (1979) have added to an understanding of certain aspects of the metamorphic evolution of the basin but have not changed the basic picture of metamorphic isograd distribution presented by Quinn. Rehmer and others (1979), however, have developed a contour map of isocrystallinity of illite (Fig. 5) within those parts of the basin below the biotite and chloritoid zones of metamorphism. This reconnaissance isocrystallinity map cannot be directly converted to an isograd map in a precise way. Nevertheless, these data can be incorporated into a preliminary metamorphic isograd map of the entire basin (Fig. 4).

Preliminary illite crystallinity and coal petrography studies suggest that these are important guides to generally favorable drilling exploration localities for the basin within the chlorite and subchlorite zones of metamorphism. There is a relatively consistent relationship between illite crystallinity values and coal petrographic data throughout the lower metamorphic zones and subzones of the basin. Studies by Raben and Gray (1979a, 1979b, and 1979c; and other studies in progress) suggest that coalification to ranks as high as low volatile bituminous coal or possibly semi-anthracite was followed by a thermal episode or episodes which affected much of the basin. These processes, to varying extents, altered the coal (Raben and Gray, 1979a).

Alteration features include incipient mosaic texture, granular texture, coke structures, and graphitic depositional carbon. The coals which have not developed pronounced thermal alteration

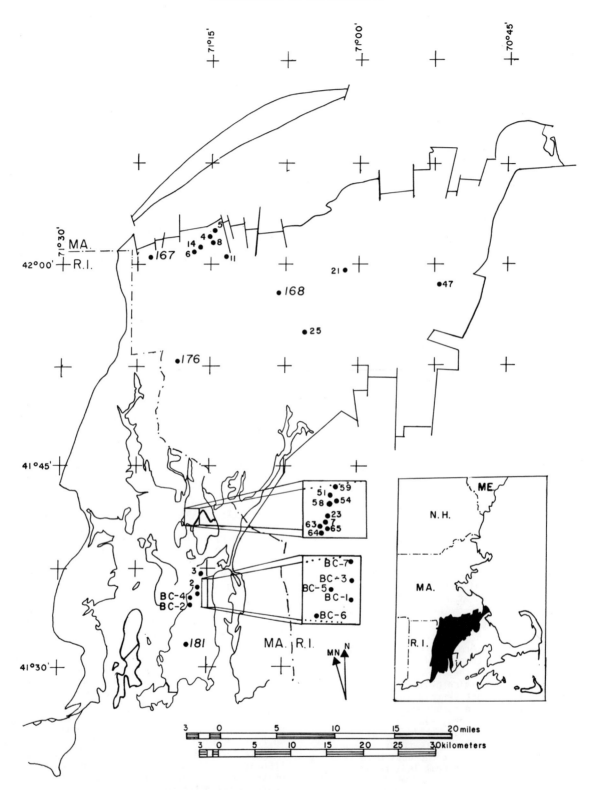

Figure 6.  Location of drill sites in the
Narragansett Basin, southeastern New England.
Small numbers indicate drilling by Boston
College in 1976-1978, large numbers drilling
in 1979, medium numbers drilling in 1980.

textures are those which, on the basis of reconnaissance illite crystallinity studies, fall chiefly in the diagenetic zone or lower anchizone. Thus, preliminary studies of illite crystallinity combined with coal petrography suggest that they may be a helpful guide in the development of exploration programs for better quality anthracite.

## COAL CHARACTERISTICS

The coals of the Narragansett Basin are highly variable in quality. This variability is pronounced when comparing coal characteristics from one part of the basin to another, but is also obvious when comparing several coal samples even within a specific part of the basin. Quantifying the coals of the basin in terms of standard parameters is insufficient to characterize the coal in a fully meaningful manner. Some practical indicators of coal quality are listed below:

- The reported use of the material in historic time.

- The ash content as reported in proximate and ultimate chemical analyses.

- The hydrogen content as reported in ultimate analyses.

- Petrographic characteristics.

- Ignition characteristics.

It should be noted that routine chemical analyses of volatile matter and carbon content are insufficient to quantify coal rank. There are several reasons for this, the most important being the nature of the volatile components of the coals, the nature and amount of mineral matter, and pervasive secondary graphitic depositional carbon found in many of the coals within the basin. The hydrogen content of a particular sample is possibly the best chemical indicator of coal rank, although there are several factors which bias the hydrogen content in chemical analyses, such as the amount of moisture and the manner in which it is held.

For preliminary discussions of the petrography of the coals of the Narragansett Basin, the reader is referred to Raben (1979), Raben and Gray, (1979a, 1979b, 1979c, and 1979d), Murray and Rabin (1980, in press), and Raben and others (1978). Preliminary ignition tests suggest that these coals burn at temperatures in excess of those of Pennsylvania anthracite.

Compared to Pennsylvania anthracites, Narragansett Basin coals are characterized by the following features.

- Generally higher ash content derived from syngenetic (normal ash) and epigenetic (chiefly veins) processes.

- Low sulfur values (generally less than 0.5 percent).

- Very low hydrogen content.

- Unusual petrographic features (Raben and Gray, 1979c, and Murray and Raben, 1980).

- Coals in thick (up to 40 ft.) laterally discontinuous beds with evidence of faulting and folding associated with deformation along the upper and lower contacts of a seam.

## DRILLING PROGRAM

In response to increasing demands for indigenous energy resources in the Northeast, an evaluation of the coal deposits has been underway at Boston College. This exploration program was funded originally by the National Science Foundation in 1976, subsequently by the U.S. Bureau of Mines, and currently by the Department of Energy (Anthracite Office). The program has relied heavily upon continuous core drilling, and to date approximately 28,000 feet of NX (2 1/4 inch diameter) core has been obtained from 35 drillsites (Fig. 6). More precise locations and descriptions of the cores of the first 28 holes are given in Skehan and Murray (eds., 1978) and Skehan and others (eds., 1979). The summary of locations and descriptions of the seven cores of the 1980 drilling program are in preparation. All sites were chosen so as to determine the extent or verify the presence of coal sightings, mines or prospects. In general, the results have tended to confirm the assumption that the greatest concentrations of coal in the basin are found in the vicinity of the larger, previously known coal occurrences, such as Portsmouth, Rhode Island.

The present 1980 drilling program, largely concentrated in the eastern part of Portsmouth, Rhode Island, has focused on relatively closely spaced drill holes. These have been placed so as to permit correlation of coal beds between holes and three dimensional stratigraphic reconstruction, thus providing a basis for computation of resource tonnages in a contiguous coal field on northern Aquidneck Island.

## CONCLUSION

Studies to date have shown that thick coal seams have been drilled, mined, and quarried in several widely spaced parts of the Narragansett Basin. Preliminary petrographic and other analytical results suggest that Narragansett Basin coal, ranging from anthracite to meta-anthracite, is inferior in quality to Pennsylvania anthracite because it has had a more intense and complicated thermal and deformational history than the latter. Nevertheless, preliminary results suggest that further exploration should be undertaken to provide information on the extent and quality of this potentially important and extensive energy resource.

## ACKNOWLEDGMENTS

Research conducted in the Narragansett Basin has been supported by National Science Foundation Grant No. AER-76-02147, U.S. Bureau of Mines Contract No. J0188022 and U.S. Department of Energy Contracts Nos. DE-AC01-79RA20020 and DE-AC01-79RA20029. A number of elected officials played prominent roles in the bipartisan effort to make this possible, notably Honorable Thomas P. O'Neill, III, Lieutenant Governor of Massachusetts; Thomas P. ("Tip") O'Neill, Jr., Speaker of the House (D-MA); Senator Edward M. ("Ted") Kennedy (D-MA); and former Senator Edward W. Brooke (R-MA). Special recognition is due to Representative Margaret M. Heckler (R-MA) for her extraordinary concern and untiring efforts to ensure the continuation of the project, and to Senator Clairborne Pell (D-RI) for efforts to undertake a substantial program of exploration for these deposits. We are grateful also to the entire New England Congressional Caucus. We extend our gratitude as well to the many Congressional staff members who have been most helpful in this effort to explore the indigenous energy resources of Massachusetts and Rhode Island. In addition, we are grateful to a number of Federal, State (Massachusetts and Rhode Island) and regional agencies, private companies and individuals too numerous to mention, who have contributed financial help and expertise in support of this project.

Judith Rehmer and J.C. Hepburn have provided helpful discussions, and a review of the manuscript by Rehmer materially improved its contents. We wish to thank Greta E. Gill and Kathryn A. Proko for drafting the illustrations.

# REFERENCES

Chase, H.B., Jr., 1978, Summary history of coal and graphite mines and prospects of Massachusetts and Rhode Island, in Skehan, S.J., J.W., and Murray, D.P., eds., The coal-bearing Narragansett Basin of Massachusetts and Rhode Island: v. 1, Geology, NSF Grant No. AER-76-02147, Final Report, p. 20-24, and Appendix B.

Chase, H.B., Jr., 1979, History of exploration for coal and graphite in New England: unpublished manuscript, 79 p.

Chute, N.E., 1979, Coal resources of southeastern Massachusetts assessed in 1942: U.S. Geological Survey, Open-file report 79-1140, 32 p.

Grew, E.S., 1974, Carbonaceous material in some metamorphic rocks of New England and other areas: Journal of Geology, v. 82, p. 50-73.

Grew, E.S., and Day, H.W., 1972, Staurolite, kyanite, and sillimanite from the Narragansett Basin of Rhode Island: U.S. Geological Survey Professional Paper 800-D, p. D151-167.

Lyons, P.C., 1977, Report on the bedrock geology of the Narragansett Basin, Massachusetts and Rhode Island: U.S. Geological Survey, Open-File Report OF-77-816, 24 maps, 38 p.

Lyons, P.C., 1979, Biostratigraphy of the Pennsylvanian of Massachusetts and Rhode Island, in Skehan, S.J., J.W., and others, The Mississippian and Pennsylvanian (Carboniferous) systems in the United States--Massachusetts, Rhode Island, and Maine: U.S. Geological Survey Paper 1110-A-1, p. A1-A30.

Murray, D.P., and Hepburn, J.C., 1979, Preliminary description of the metamorphic evolution of the Narragansett Basin, southeastern New England: Geological Society of America, Abstracts with Programs, v. 11, no. 1, p. 46.

Murray, D.P., and Raben, J.D., 1980, The metamorphism of carbonaceous material, Narragansett Basin, southeastern New England, U.S.A.: 26th International Geological Congress, in press.

Murray, D.P., Raben, J.D., and Rehmer, J., 1979, The Alleghenian metamorphism of the Narragansett Basin, southeastern New England: Ninth International Congress of Carboniferous Stratigraphy and Geology, Urbana, Illinois, Abstracts with Programs, p. 145-146.

Murray, D.P., Rast, N., and Skehan S.J., J.W., 1978, The convergence of the Caledonian and Variscan (Alleghenian) episodes in the northern Appalachians: International Geological Correlation Programme, Project Caledonide Orogen Conference, Dublin, Ireland, Abstracts with Programs, v. 10, p. 51-52.

Murray, D.P., and Skehan, S.J., J.W., 1979, A traverse across the eastern margin of the Appalachian-Caledonide Orogen, southeastern New England, in Skehan, S.J., J.W., and Osberg, P.H., editors, The Caledonides in the U.S.A., Geological excursions in the northeast Appalachians: International Geological Correlation Program, Project 27, Weston Observatory, Weston, Massachusetts, p. 1-35.

Quinn, A.W., 1971, Bedrock geology of Rhode Island: U.S. Geological Survey, Bulletin 1295, 69 p.

Quinn, A.W., and Moore, G.E., Jr., 1968, Sedimentation, tectonism, and plutonism of the Narragansett Basin region, in Zen, E-an, White, W.S., Hadley, J.B., and Thompson, J.B., editors, Studies in Appalachian geology --northern maritimes: New York, Wiley Interscience Publishers, p. 269-280.

Raben, J.D., 1979, Coal: chemistry, petrography, rank and stratigraphy, in Skehan, S.J., J.W., Murray, D.P., and Rider, T.H., editors, Evaluation of coal deposits in the Narragansett Basin, Massachusetts and Rhode Island: U.S. Bureau of Mines, Contract No. J0188022, Final Report, p. 48-64.

Raben, J.D., and Gray, R.J., 1979a, Deformational

textures in Narragansett Basin coals and their implications for utilization: Geological Society of America, Abstracts with Programs, v. 11, no. 1, p. 46.

Raben, J.D., and Gray, R.J., 1979b, The geology and petrology of anthracites and meta-anthracites in the Narragansett Basin, southeastern New England, in Cameron, B., Geology of southeastern New England: Field Trip Guidebook, New England Intercollegiate Geolocial Conference, 68th Annual Meeting, p. 93-108.

Raben, J.D., and Gray, R.J., 1979c, The nature of highly deformed anthracites and meta-anthracites in southern New England: Ninth International Congress of Carboniferous Stratigraphy and Geology, Urbana, Illinois, Abstracts with Programs, p. 169.

Raben, J.D., and Gray, R.J., 1979d, Simplified classification and optical characteristics of meta-coals in the Narragansett Basin, southeastern New England: Geological Society of America, Abstracts with Programs, v. 11, no. 1, p. 49.

Raben, J.D., Rushworth, P.A., and Murray, D.P., 1978, Coal, in Skehan, S.J., J.W., and Murray, D.P., editors, The coal-bearing Narragansett Basin of Massachusetts and Rhode Island: v. 1, Geology, NSF Grant No. AER-76-02147, Final Report, p. 66-72.

Rehmer, J., Hepburn, J.C., and Ostrawski, M., 1979, Illite crystallinity in subgreenschist argillaceous rocks and coal, Narragansett and Norfolk Basins, U.S.A.: Ninth International Congress of Carboniferous Stratigraphy and Geology, Urbana, Illinois, Abstracts with Programs, p. 176.

Rehmer, J., Hepburn, J.D., and Schulman, J., 1978, The diagenetic to metamorphic transition in an Appalachian coal basin: Geological Society of America, Abstracts with Programs, v. 10, no. 7, p. 477.

Skehan, S.J., J.W., Murray, D.P., Palmer, A.R., Smith, A.T., and Belt, E.S., 1978, Significance of fossiliferous Middle Cambrian rocks of Rhode Island to the history of the Avalonian microcontinent: Geology, v. 6, no. 11, p. 694-698.

Skehan, S.J., J.W., Murray, D.P., editors, 1978, The coal-bearing Narragansett Basin of Massachusetts and Rhode Island: v. 1, Geology, NSF Grant No. AER-76-02147, Final Report, 99 p.

Skehan, S.J., J.W., Murray, D.P., 1979, Geology of the Narragansett Basin, southeastern Rhode Island, in Cameron, B., editor, Carboniferous basins of southeastern New England: Ninth International Congress of Carboniferous Stratigraphy and Geology, Field Trip Guidebook no. 5, American Geological Institute, Falls Church, Virginia, p. 7-35.

Skehan, S.J., J.W., Murray, D.P., and Rider, T.H., editors, 1979, Evaluation of coal deposits in the Narragansett Basin, Massachusetts and Rhode Island: U.S. Bureau of Mines, Contract No. J0188022, Final Report, 333 p.

Smith, A.T., 1977, The geology of Conanicut Island, Rhode Island: Senior Thesis, Amherst College, Amherst, Massachusetts.

Toenges and others, 1948, Map of Cranston mine, Rhode Island. See Chase, 1979, and Table 2.

Hors-texte

Folded rocks on the north side of Interstate
84 near Brewster, New York.

# Rationale for reappraisal of New England pegmatites

O. C. FARQUHAR
Department of Geology and Geography
University of Massachusetts at Amherst

ABSTRACT

The last wide-ranging investigation of New England pegmatites was by Cameron and others in 1954, using maps with scales as large as one inch to 40 feet (1:480). In the past 25 years the terms of reference for examining such mineral-producers have been radically altered in several ways: (1) the scale of the general base maps has greatly increased (from 1:125,000 [and 1:126,720] through 1:63,360, 1:48,000, and 1:31,680 to 1:24,000), thus extending facilities for recording pegmatites not previously noted; (2) the latest geological survey maps on these larger scales may show additional pegmatites, but detailed analysis of them is not normally a mapping objective; (3) major new geochemical, geophysical, and geological methods for studying pegmatites and other hydrothermal deposits have been devised in recent years; (4) the state-of-the-art may have advanced more rapidly overseas than in North America, as shown through the work in Russia alone of Zavaritsky, Kuleshov, Solodov, Nikanorov, Zakharchenko, Vlasov, Uspensky, Ermakov, Nikitin, Rodionov, Shmakin, and many others; (5) more searchers are available now, including people who are interested, knowledgeable, motivated, mobile, and sometimes, especially in the case of uranium pegmatites, employed; (6) market values have improved, not only for precious and other metals but also for many non-metals in pegmatites, with the selling price of gold now well above mining costs; (7) knowledge about reserves of pegmatite minerals has not advanced, compared for instance with the case of oil and gas, components of a much later industry whose health and growth depend upon continued exploration; (8) better knowledge of subsurface stratigraphy exists in many areas, and there are novel petrographic and numerical techniques for solving geochemical problems; (9) reasonable means have been developed for dealing with environmental and legislative constraints; and (10) there is, as well, the attraction of examining some of the coarsest-grained rocks in the world, now enhanced by modern theories about their place in crustal sequences. A combination of these reasons may provide a rationale for reexamination of pegmatites, especially in the crystalline basement of New England. With the conditions for exploitation notably changed since the industry declined at the end of World War II, it may be determined that other pegmatite masses like those that were once productive also possess an economic potential.

# Petrographic techniques used in the study of abrasive and refractory minerals

R. P. HIGHT
Norton Company

# Volcanism and ore genesis, with special reference to New England

## B. A. BOULEY
### Callahan Mining Corporation

ABSTRACT

Volcanogenic exhalative massive sulfide deposits have much in common with fossil organisms: they represent fossil fumarolic systems that are as diagnostic of their paleo-environment as are certain fossils. A number of features, including contemporaneity with enclosing volcanism, stratigraphic control of the distribution of sulfide minerals, lateral equivalence with chemical sedimentary horizons, vertical and lateral element zonation, sharp hanging wall contacts, diffuse footwall contacts, and other features, are used to support syngenesis of this important class of metal sulfide deposits. Recently, discovery of exhalative brines on the floor of the Red Sea--in the form of metalliferous sediments near ridge axes--have unequivocally documented the existence of this process. Integration of these oceanographic studies, with centuries of land-based observation in important mining camps, supports the idea that the forms and metal contents of massive sulfide deposits are indeed a function of their environment of formation. That is, deposits related to sea floor tholeiitic volcanism are distinguishable from those attributable to volcanic processes involved in calc-alkalic felsic volcanism, and are further separable from those related to sedimentary processes near volcanic arcs. Furthermore, each of these broader categories is divisible into a number of sub-categories.

This has important stratigraphic and tectonic implications inasmuch as discovery of a deposit is analogous to discovery of an index fossil within any given terrain. For example, in west central Maine, the Chain Lakes Massif is considered by some authors to be in part an ophiolitic remnant of sea-floor volcanism. If this hypothesis is correct, then massive sulfide deposits within this terrain should have a copper/zinc assemblage and a form compatible with those deposits characteristic of tholeiitic volcanism. Farther south in New England, where more intense metamorphic overprinting has obscured most primary volcanic features, the discovery of base-metal deposits may well serve an important function in understanding the geotectonic environment of lower Paleozoic sequences.

# Critique on life and death of mines

L. P. MEADE
Geomapping Associates, Ltd.

# 11

# ENVIRONMENTAL AND GEOCHEMICAL PROBLEMS

Session moderators

J. Hager
Bentley College

D. S. Hunnewell
Massachusetts Department of Environmental Quality Engineering

L. D. Lyman
Lycott Environmental Research Incorporated

F. G. Wolf
U.S. Environmental Protection Agency

# Hazardous waste disposal in Massachusetts

R. B. POJASEK
Roy F. Weston, Inc.

## ABSTRACT

With the enactment of the Massachusetts
Hazardous Waste Management Act and the issuance
of final Federal regulations under the Resource
Conservation and Recovery Act (RCRA), the stark
reality of locating suitable treatment and disposal sites for chemical wastes is with us at
last. There has been and is today a big problem
in siting hazardous waste disposal facilities.
Now that industries must notify the U.S. Environmental Protection Agency (EPA) of the generation
of any hazardous wastes and must track these
wastes from generation through disposal, it will
not be as easy for waste chemicals to get into the
hands of midnight dumpers. Perhaps the economic
incentive has been given to select disposal technology that will enable the industrial community
to continue with its operation.

## INTRODUCTION

Most treatment/disposal options fall into
the following general categories.

- Treatment or processing for recovery of
  valuable components for recycling.

- Utilization as a fuel source for energy
  production.

- Treatment for discharge to surface waters.

- Treatment and/or incineration for discharge to atmosphere.

- Treatment and/or disposal onto or into
  the land.

These options are listed in a general priority
sequence, i.e., most favorable options listed
first. The least desirable option is the one of
greatest interest to geologists and many others.
Therefore, emphasis will be placed on land disposal in this article. Several references are
listed (Pojasek, ed., 1978-80; New England Regional Commission, 1979; Pojasek, 1979) that will
provide the reader with more detailed information
on this and other disposal options.

## LANDFILL DISPOSAL

A secured landfill is an ultimate disposal
site specifically designed to contain hazardous
waste and minimize environmental contamination
when operated and maintained properly. These
facilities are usually located in thick natural
clay deposits where the hydraulic transport of
leachate to an aquifer is unlikely. Section 3004
of RCRA has placed strict specifications on the
siting, design, operation, closure, and post-
closure care of these facilities (U.S. EPA, 1978).
Specifications are included for secured landfills
in regions, such as Massachusetts, where there is
no substantial clay. These engineered facilities
use imported clay and synthetic liners and are
equipped with leachate collection devices.

Because of the random location of existing
sites and the exorbitant cost of engineering a
site in a geologically unfavorable area, wastes
are often transported great distances for this
form of ultimate disposal. In the case of Massachusetts, the nearest existing sites are in western New York state. Despite these facts, this
alternative remains the dominant method of disposal for a wide variety of chemical wastes. It
has been argued that, for the foreseeable future,
there will be need for these facilities for certain wastes which cannot be disposed of in other
ways. However, there are problems associated with
the continued and future use of these facilities.

In a recent symposium on hazardous waste disposal (Pojasek, 1978-80), an official of an EPA
Office of Solid Waste cited some of the problem
areas of secured landfilling.

- Landfilling costs under RCRA will escalate
  significantly above present costs, making
  this alternative less financially attractive than it is now.

- Landfill methods are generally dependent
  on local conditions (e.g., soil properties, rainfall, geology, hydrology).
  There may well be areas where landfills
  are not suitable at all.

- Since many hazardous wastes are essentially indestructible in a landfill environment, the true cost of secured land disposal includes monitoring and maintenance
  activities and legal liability long after
  the landfill has been closed. In the
  past, these costs have not been recognized, estimated or charged.

- Because the problems of inadequate past
  landfill practices are now gaining public attention, citizen opposition to new

landfill facilities is overwhelming.

This last issue has led to popular legal challenges such as the Wilsonville, Illinois, decision which closed down an operating secured landfill and ordered the removal of the entire contents. If this decision is upheld, it will become virtually impossible to construct facilities in the future. Conscious business judgments that every secured landfill operator has to make, no matter how good the site, are (1) will he eventually get into trouble with the public and (2) is it worth the hassle?

A New Jersey study (N.J. Governor's Hazardous Waste Advisory Commission, 1979) lists four reasons why reliance on secured landfilling of hazardous wastes should be minimized.

- "The first is that landfilling of hazardous wastes (unless they are first 'fixed,' 'stabilized' or rendered innocuous) only isolates them from the rest of the environment. They remain forever as a threat. Should the containment system fail, the health of future generations could be harmed. Although new designs for secured landfills hold the promise of perpetual containment, no one can be certain they will live up to that promise. EPA's proposed RCRA standards for secured landfills, for example, cannot guarantee containment beyond 50 years if one of the liners is perforated."

- "Second, stewardship of a secured landfill calls for perpetual monitoring and perpetual protection of the site from disturbance. Human institutions, including nations, do not last forever. There is no way to predict with confidence what will happen to a landfill site 500 to 1,000 years from now."

- "Third, landfilling uses up land and limits its usefulness thereafter. Because of the possibility of containment failure, it is not prudent to build habitations over a closed landfill. Furthermore, there can be no use of a site that would risk damaging the containment system. Any substantial development on the site risks economic dislocation later on if a containment failure requires major remedial work."

- "Finally, because of New Jersey's dense population and land use patterns, and the difficulties that can be anticipated in acquiring sites for secured landfills, there will probably be only a few such sites available. When they are filled up, it will be even more difficult to find others. As with any other scarce resource, prudence dictates they be stretched as far as possible."

One operator of a secured landfill has stated that landfills for chemicals are wrong by nature,

and that we fill them up and then have to look for new sites repeatedly. Process sites have to be set down only once, since they never become filled. If wastes could be detoxified to a greater extent by various treatment techniques and the solid portion of the wastes tied up in a solid matrix, these wastes could be landfilled in a site that need not exactly duplicate the rigorous specifications of RCRA secured landfill. This would enable the disposal site to be located at or close to the waste treatment facility. Ideally, each waste should be reviewed relative to its particular hazardous properties, and the most effective destruction technologies should be given primary consideration before a simple secured landfill storage approach is selected.

Because concern with secured landfills is more widespread, research on methods of securing sites is more significant now than in the past. Studies are being conducted on types and combinations of liners, on leachate control and treatment, on monitoring methods, on solidification methods, and on other landfill-associated parameters. Results of these development activities will need to be factored into constantly improving design and operating practices. The initial New England Regional Commission report (New England Regional Commission, 1979) states that 40 percent of all hazardous wastes in the region must be disposed of in a secured landfill. However, there is another land disposal option.

SOLIDIFICATION

The term solidification collectively defines disposal technologies that fixate or encapsulate waste in a solid matrix end-product suitable for land disposal. Fixation techniques chemically and physically bind the waste with a solidification agent. Encapsulation methods physically surround the waste with the agent. Both techniques reduce waste permeability and produce an end-product having significant shear strength.

Solidification has been extensively practiced in Europe and Japan, but until recently it was too expensive relative to other available (adequate and inadequate) disposal methods in the United States. A couple of review articles (Pojasek, 1978; Pojasek, 1979) discuss this option in detail. Its use has been almost exclusively for radioactive wastes and flue gas desulfurization sludges. However, RCRA has spurred increased interest in solidification techniques because hazardous waste (RCRA Section 3001 definition) can be converted into a nonhazardous substance.

The subsequent reduction in waste surface area brought about by solidification may enable many wastes to pass the EPA toxicity test even though they might fail in a presolidification form. These wastes are now legally nonhazardous and subject to a less stringent set of disposal regulations under RCRA Section 4004. It is not acceptable for these nonhazardous wastes to be placed in a sanitary landfill. The Commonwealth of Massachusetts should specify geological and operational criteria for such a fill. These criteria could be similar to, though less stringent than, those specified for stabilized metallic sludge disposal in Massachusetts (Massachusetts Department of Environmental Quality Engineering, 1978).

There are many interesting geological considerations involved in placing a monolithic mass in the ground. Some of these are discussed in a review (Mulica and Pojasek, 1978) on local site conditions and their amenability to accepting solidified wastes. The geological stability of the monolith also presents an interesting situation on which to speculate.

The solidified end product may offer interesting reuse potential for the waste. This reuse may bring a return on investment or simply reduce the cost of disposal. Among the examples of reuse applications of solidified waste are the following.

- Road bed aggregate.

- Parking lot pavement.

- Impermeable liners.

- Artificial reefs.

- Land reclamation.

- Landfill capping.

## WASTE TREATMENT

Solidification represents one treatment technology wherein a waste can be detoxified prior to landfilling in a less rigorously designed landfill. This paper would not be complete unless it pointed out that there are numerous other technologies that can convert hazardous wastes into nonhazardous wastes. Some of these technologies are sufficiently developed to permit present use at some scale. Others will require substantial development for general use in hazardous waste treatment. Many treatment technologies offer potential for resource and/or energy recovery. This is highly desirable from both an operational and siting point of view.

Not all treatment technologies produce a nonhazardous waste with all waste streams all the time. Incineration, for example, produces an ash which may be deemed hazardous when tested against Federal and State standards. This form of thermal treatment did detoxify the organic components and reduce the volume of the waste. However, the ash would have to be solidified and retested to determine whether it is nonhazardous.

## CONCLUSIONS

There are other geological means of waste disposal such as deep-well injection, geological deposit isolation, and ocean bed emplacement. However, these disposal means offer little potential for use in New England at the present time. Solidification or other treatment of hazardous wastes to render them nonhazardous under Federal and State guidelines offer the greatest potential for handling such materials here in Massachusetts. Special consideration must be given to the geological aspects of land disposal of the residues from these processes.

## REFERENCES

Massachusetts Department of Environmental Quality Engineering, 1978, Interim policy for disposal of stabilized metallic sludges: Boston, June 19.

Mulica, W.S., and Pojasek, R.B., 1978, Developing disposal site criteria for stabilized and solidified hazardous wastes, in Pojasek, R.B., ed., Stabilization/solidification options for hazardous waste disposal: Ann Arbor Science Publishers, Michigan.

New England Regional Commission, 1979, A plan for development of hazardous wastes management facilities in the New England region; Volume II, Boston, September.

N.J. Governor's Hazardous Waste Advisory Commission, 1979, Report on Governor Brendan Byrne's hazardous waste advisory commission: Preliminary draft, Trenton, October 31.

Pojasek, R.B., 1979, Disposing of hazardous chemical wastes: Environmental Science and Technology, v. 13, p. 810-814.

Pojasek, R.B., 1979, A novel approach to hazardous waste disposal in New England: Journal of New England Water Pollution Control Association, v. 13, no. 1, p. 36.

Pojasek, R.B., 1979, Solid waste disposal solidification: Chemical Engineering, v. 86, no. 17, p. 141-145.

Pojasek, R.B., 1978, Stabilization, solidification of hazardous wates: Environmental Science and Technology, v. 12, p. 382-386.

Pojasek, R.B., ed., 1978-80, Toxic and hazardous waste disposal series: Ann Arbor Science Publishers, Michigan, 4 volumes.

U.S. EPA, 1978, Standards for owners and operators of hazardous waste treatment storage and disposal faciltities: Federal register, v. 43, no. 243, p. 58994-59016.

# The polluted aquifer
# at Provincetown, Massachusetts

R. A. WEIMAR
Camp, Dresser & McKee, Inc.

# Some reasonable waste disposal siting parameters for New England

A. W. HATHEWAY
W. E. STIMPSON
Haley & Aldrich, Inc.

## ABSTRACT

Public officials, townspeople, consulting engineers, and geologists are striving to meet environmental goals for waste disposal, in ways that are economically and socially acceptable. States are presently empowered to safeguard public health from adverse impacts of solid waste disposal. Federal involvement comes mainly in the form of injunctions against towns that operate landfills which are deemed to be polluting the air or ground water. Solid waste disposal regulations of individual New England states vary considerably, in content, intent, and administration. This is in the autonomous tradition of old New England, and perhaps we should be thankful for having this luxury and burden of regional self-determination. However, there is much misunderstanding about the nature of geological parameters of disposal site selection, design, and the regulatory approval process.

## DISCUSSION

Let us consider the case of a waste disposal location that has been cited as unacceptable in an individual New England town. It has been cited either because it is not a sanitary landfill (operated in accordance with present state regulations), or because some adverse impact has resulted from its operation (such as visible leachate generation). The next step in the scenario is that the town is placed under injunction by the State or Region 1 of the U.S. Environmental Protection Agency to cease operation of the landfill and begin operation at an approved site within a specified period of time. It should be pointed out here that EPA is far too busy with implementation of numerous federally-mandated programs to undertake the specific inspection and enforcement of waste disposal objectives in the towns. Rather, EPA generally acts in response to a formal complaint by a concerned citizen or citizen's group.

At any rate, what is the town to do? Within their own democratic structures, the towns of New England have been rising to the challenge as best they can. The main obstacles have been austere operating budgets and uncooperative attitudes of some of their citizenry. The town finds a consultant in environmental engineering and sets about to find a "new place" to dispose of the waste. Several misunderstandings can arise to plague this effort. The first misunderstanding is that the sanitary landfill regulations are unalterable, and it is useless to discuss siting with state officials. A sorry situation, indeed! Secondly, it is often felt that the important siting parameters are only those mentioned in the regulations. Wrong again! Also, the well recognized concern for quality of ground water in New England is misunderstood by many citizens and some public officials. Those who are first to rise in indignation at the thought of burying waste are commonly those who do not understand the rudiments of hydrogeology. Much of this concern develops around occurrences of perched water.

A fourth misunderstanding centers around what is acceptable pollution. Few sanitary engineers will argue that some leachate will not be generated in an operating landfill. There is a growing commitment among some individuals (in and out of state government) toward zero pollution. What is extremely difficult about this concept is defining just what constitutes "zero pollution". Seldom do regulatory officials ask for baseline water quality studies to determine what is in the ground water prior to initiation of the new landfill operation.

For those most concerned with the impact of solid waste landfilling, the only answer is complete resource-recovery conversion of refuse or installation of a "failproof" liner and leachate collection system for the landfill. How is a town of 5000 to finance and support a two-million-dollar facility?

We propose that some reasonable parameters for landfill siting and design are as follows.

- A town should never be forced to develop an alternate or replacement disposal site with less than one year of actual ground-water observations. This would establish at least the seasonal fluctuation of the year of record. Discussions should be held as to the risk impact of this determination as an element of long-term fluctuation in precipitation.

- Perched water should not be considered as ground water, especially if operating conditions at the landfill can be maintained at a sufficiently low hydrostatic head to avoid driving leachate from the perched zone and to avoid affecting hydraulic connection with ground water.

- Zero pollution is not attainable in the

terms of landfill design that is afford-
able by most New England communities, and
acceptable levels of long-term ion migration from the landfill, down-gradient in
the hydrogeologic regime, should be negotiated with the state regulatory agency.

- It should be recognized that federal
drinking water standards are sensitive to
pollutants in the parts-per-billion (ppb)
range and that some ppb-level ion migration may be expected.

- Landfill life may be purposefully short-
ened on the basis that properly operated
and decommissioned landfills are graded
for maximum runoff and negligible infiltration. Although there is a cost penalty
for site development for relatively small
landfills, the driving head of inadvertent
infiltration occurring during operation
is removed at an earlier time, and leachate generation is decreased and its down-
gradient movement reduced measurably.

- The manner in which the landfill is operated is the single most crucial aspect of
fulfilling environmental concerns of regulation. Most important of the operating
factors are the nature and density of
daily and final cover; perimeter surface
drainage features which are designed to
divert additional surface water from entering the landfill; surface slope conditions consistent with promoting absolute
runoff of all rainfall and snowmelt; and
screening of incoming waste to exclude
toxic or hazardous substances.

- Topographic setting should be considered
as a separate siting factor. Those sites
which are topographically isolated from
outside groundwater recharge are inherently more desirable locations for the
conduct of siting studies.

- Reasonable dispensation should be allowed
for sites in regions which have suffered
abnormally high precipitation and which
are not expected to receive equivalent
amounts in subsequent years. Transport
of leachate under these conditions of
increased hydrostatic head will advance a
developing leachate plume to a degree, but
the driving head should diminish rapidly
in a following dryer year.

CONCLUSION

Geologists have learned that certain types
of surficial geologic materials possess physical
properties which are adverse to the retention and
attenuation of leachate. These types of materials
should be avoided, or the price of extensive
engineered protection should be accepted by the
town.

Parties undertaking to answer the challenge
of waste disposal in New England should willingly
and cooperatively discuss the nature of each problem and strive to develop a commonly-acceptable
solution for the town. To "let George do it" is
to invite a protracted and bitter conflict at town
meeting; to avoid close contact with state regulatory personnel is to invite further misunderstanding and bitterness. We advise early discussion among the town's citizenry, its geological
and environmental engineering consultants, and
state regulatory officials--before commitments
are made to philosophy or to sites. We would
hope that these discussions might consider the
reasonable parameters . . .

# Methods for evaluating the leachate attenuative capacity of soil

A. A. JENNINGS
Department of Civil Engineering
University of Notre Dame

F. S. TIRSCH
D. D. ADRIAN
Department of Civil Engineering
University of Massachusetts at Amherst

## ABSTRACT

If soil attenuation is not effective, leachates released from solid waste disposal sites pose a serious threat to groundwater quality. Experimental and analytical methods are presented which allow for the identification and quantification of mechanisms of attenuation. Comparisons and contrasts between batch equilibrium and dynamic simulation results are illustrated. A method for gauging reversibility is discussed. For the leachates and soils examined, batch methods were found to produce accurate results but failed to unmask time variability of effects. Simulation was found to be the superior method. The soils' overall attenuative capacities were found to be ineffective in reducing the leachates' total ionic strength. Active sorptive removals were found to be reversible.

## INTRODUCTION

It has been documented beyond question that leachates produced from the land disposal of solid waste can be severely contaminated. Therefore, whenever leachate migration into the subsurface regime is possible, groundwater quality is threatened. However, opinion is scattered on the degree to which this pollution potential may be realized, and the concept of soil attenuation is the focus of much of the disagreement. If soil attenuation can effectively alleviate the problem, then concern for groundwater quality may be abated. If it cannot, then a great deal of concern is clearly justified.

In this context, attenuation is most successfully defined as the effect of a physical, chemical, or biological mechanism altering the liquid-phase mass of a leachate constituent. By this definition, attenuations other than the soil's are possible but, as discussed by Fuller and Korte (1976), Phillips and Nathwani (1976), and others, soil attenuations are by far the most numerous and powerful. Potential mechanisms of soil attenuation include surface and depth filtrations, chemical reactions, biological transformations, and a group of soil interactions known collectively as sorptions. Unfortunately, little is known of the capacities of these mechanisms to attenuate specific leachate constituents and of how these properties vary from soil to soil.

This condition demands resolution. Without this knowledge, site evaluations must be made presuming conservative leachate transport. Migration predictions based on more optimistic models can be justified only after their propriety has been validated and their descriptive coefficients have been measured. The current paucity of this information attests to the difficulties involved. In its absence, decisions seriously affecting land disposal practices and groundwater quality must be made based on little better than guesswork. There is a clear need for additional research in this area. Capacities for many of the leachate's constituents must be evaluated. The variability among soils must be explored. Effects of the different flow regimes and electrochemical environments must be investigated. The permanence or reversibility of attenuations must be established.

The research reported here was undertaken to investigate interactions of specific soils and leachate from a waste disposal site in Barre, Massachusetts. In this paper, it is the intent of the authors to concentrate on the methodology developed during their study. Examples of empirical results will be given but with the object of illustrating analytical techniques. With these, the authors hope to demonstrate that capacity verification and quantification are possible within the bounds of established experimental practice.

## MATERIALS

All leachates originated from a privately owned sanitary landfill operated by the Martone Trucking Company, Barre, Massachusetts. At this site, leachate is generated by a three-acre fill area which received municipal solid waste from 1970 to 1976. Table 1 presents a characterization of this leachate. Batch "A" represents a winter leachate collected during the month of January by breaking through surface ice and intercepting leachate as it flowed from the toe of the fill area. Batch "B" was collected at the same location the following September from pools standing under a thick surface crust. Site conditions prohibited the acquisition of leachate directly from within the landfill. Upon standing under anoxic conditions, both samples clarified to clear, pale yellow solutions typical of anaerobic leachate.

Soils used were taken from the base of the Solid Waste Disposal Research Facility located on the grounds of the Martone landfill. The "Barre sand" was selected because it had been placed under the facility to collect and attenuate leachate before passing it on to downstream treatment units. The "Barre clay" (clay loam) was used be-

TABLE 1.  CHARACTERIZATION OF BARRE LEACHATES AND SURFACE WATER SAMPLE

| | Batch "A" | Batch "B" | Surface water |
|---|---|---|---|
| Specific conductance ($\mu$MHOS/cm) | 16,000 | 11,800 | 70 |
| pH | 5.50 | 6.00 | 5.70 |
| Alkalinity (mg/l as $CaCO_3$) | 2,700 | 1,790 | 2.10 |
| Chemical oxygen demand (mg/l) | 12,500 | 7,690 | 7.40 |
| Total organic carbon (mg/l) | ND | 2,640 | ND |
| Ammonia (mg/l) | 270 | 175 | 0.18 |
| Sulfate (mg/l) | 128 | 56.3 | 0.0 |
| Nitrate (mg/l) | 2.60 | ND | 0.1 |
| Phosphate (mg/l) | 0.18 | ND | 0.0 |
| Chloride (mg/l) | ND | 450 | ND |
| Iron (total mg/l) | 1,000 | 360 | trace (< 0.05) |
| Manganese (total mg/l) | 42.2 | 16.2 | trace (< 0.05) |
| Calcium (total mg/l) | 875 | 480 | 1.15 |
| Magnesium (total mg/l) | 200 | 134 | 0.57 |
| Copper (total mg/l) | 2.65 | ND | 0.0 |
| Zinc (total mg/l) | 0.71 | 1.00 | 0.08 |
| Dissolved oxygen (mg/l) | ND | ND | 8.05 |

ND - Not determined

TABLE 2.  CHARACTERIZATION OF BARRE SOILS

| | Barre Sand | Barre Clay |
|---|---|---|
| Percent sand | 96.3 | 36.0 |
| Percent silt | 2.5 | 36.8 |
| Percent clay | 1.2 | 27.2 |
| Mean diameter ($d_{50}$) (cm) | 0.045 | 0.10 |
| Uniformity coefficient ($d_{60}/d_{10}$) | 3.2 | 12.0 |
| Specific gravity (g/cm$^3$) | 2.63 | ND |
| Percent organic matter | 0.11 | 0.10 |
| pH (20 g + 20 ml 0.01M $CaCl_2$) | 5.10 | 4.82 |
| Cation exchange capacity (CEC) (meq/100g) | 1.69 | 4.71 |
| Exchangeable calcium (meq/100g) | 0.08 | 1.64 |
| Exchangeable magnesium (meq/100g) | 0.03 | 0.67 |
| Exchangeable acidity (meq/100g) | 0.09 | 0.08 |
| Exchangeable aluminum (meq/100g) | 0.04 | 0.06 |

ND - Not determined

cause it composed the barrier stratum placed under the sand to confine the leachate flow. A characterization of these Barre soils is presented in Table 2. Soil classification was based solely on grain size distribution. Mineralogical classification was not attempted.

For evaluating the reversibility of attenuations, a very clean but otherwise typical New England surface water was used. A characterization of this water has also been included in Table 1.

METHODS

The interactions of the Barre soils and the Barre leachate were studied in two parallel phases of experimentation. Batch equilibrations were conducted to evaluate this technique and to determine if useful measures of attenuation could be retrieved. Concurrently, soil column experimentation was performed to simulate contact under dynamic flow conditions and to evaluate the leachate's true transport potential. Anaerobic conditions were maintained in all phases because this represents both the worst case and the most frequent condition of leachate/soil contacts.

Batch Equilibration

Equilibrations were performed for a wide range of leachate mass to soil mass ratios. Flexibility was achieved by varying both the volume or concentration of leachate and the weight of

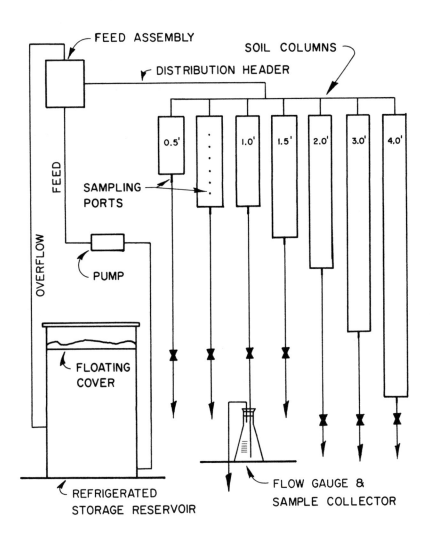

Figure 1. Soil column apparatus.

soil used. Maintaining anaerobic conditions proved to be difficult but its importance must not be disregarded. When anaerobic leachate is exposed to the atmosphere, metal precipitates form rapidly. In an equilibration, these are either retained directly by the soil or are removed during phase separation. Attributing this removal to sorption would erroneously inflate the soil's attenuative capacity.

Equilibrations were accomplished by weighing out soil aliquots into 1 liter glass sample bottles. These were thoroughly evacuated of oxygen by flushing with nitrogen gas. Leachate was then siphoned into the bottles under continuous nitrogen purging. Where dilutions were required they were prepared with continuous nitrogen gas flushing of the volumetric flasks. Oxygen-purged deionized water was used for all dilutions. Reactors were equilibrated at constant temperature for five days. Liquid and solid phases were then separated by centrifugation and filtration. Filtrates were analyzed for COD, TOC, ammonia, Fe, Mn, Ca, and Mg. Equilibrium distributions of mass removed or released as a function of equilibrium concentration were constructed. Duplicate equilibrations and a full set of blanks were carried through all steps of the procedure.

## Column Simulation

For contacting the Barre sand and leachate, a multiple-column apparatus was developed (Fig. 1) rather than using a single column having multiple sampling taps. This approach was selected because single columns require high application rates to produce adequate sample volumes at multiple depth increments. Also, "tapping" a column alters, with depth, its volume applied per soil mass ratio and distorts breakthrough characteristics. The multiple-column approach eliminates this problem. It also makes possible the simulation of unsaturated flow without sampling complexity.

Leachate of sufficient volume to accomplish one "run" was stored in the air-sealed 40-gallon (150 ℓ) reservoir and refrigerated to approximately 4.5°C. From storage, leachate was pumped at 5.0 ml/min to a constant head feed assembly. This provided residence time for the flow to warm to room temperature. It also pressurized the delivery system to exclude the atmosphere and drive the column feeds. Leachate was applied to seven parallel 4 in (10.2 cm) diameter soil columns at a rate of 0.20 ml/min (10 in per week per unit surface area). Column lengths were arranged to provide data on soil depth increments of 0.0 to 4.0 ft (0.0 to 0.91 m).

Using this apparatus, conditions of saturated and unsaturated leachate flow through clean soil, and clean water flow through leachate-equilibrated soil, were simulated. Column effluents were analyzed for changes in COD, inorganic carbon, specific conductance, total alkalinity, total carbon, total Cu, Ca, Fe, Mg, Mn, Zn, chloride, ammonia, sulfate, phosphate, nitrate, and pH.

Intrinsic to this experimental design is the assumption that all columns act similarly. To improve on the validity of this assumption, a vibrating packing apparatus was developed so that disturbed soil could be placed uniformly with depth and uniformly from column to column. For the Barre sand, vibration was found to improve its in-place void ratio from 0.725 to 0.427 and its porosity from 42.0 percent to 29.9 percent over unvibrated columns. As a final check on technique, two 1.0 ft (30.4 cm) columns were incorporated into the apparatus design.

## DATA ANALYSIS

To extract full benefit from column study data, analysis must distinguish between results of true attenuations and those of non-attenuating transport phenomena. In the soil transport of any solute, hydrodynamic dispersions and molecular diffusion distort a plane source into an S-shaped breakthrough curve. However, dispersions are only spatial redistributions of mass. They should not be confused with attenuations which alter the solution phase mass burden. Accounting for dispersion takes on added importance if columns of varying lengths are used or when a single column is sampled at several depths. Because dispersive effects vary with distance, curves from different levels gauge both attenuation and dispersion over the space increments. If the difference is attributed only to soil attenuation, its capacity will be overestimated.

The column transport of an active solute through attenuating porous medium may be described by:

$$\frac{\partial C}{\partial t} + a \frac{\rho}{\varepsilon} \frac{\partial S}{\partial t} = -V \frac{\partial C}{\partial Z} + [D(mech)+D(mole)] \frac{\partial^2 C}{\partial Z^2} + bKC^n \quad (1)$$

where:

$C$ = solute concentration ($ML^{-3}$)

$Z$ = depth ($L$)

$V$ = interstitial velocity ($LT^{-1}$)

$D(mech)$ = coefficient of mechanical dispersion ($L^2T^{-1}$)

$D(mole)$ = coefficient of molecular diffusion ($L^2T^{-1}$)

$K$ = reaction rate constant (units vary with n)

$n$ = reaction order exponent

$S$ = mass of solute exchanged per unit mass of solid phase exchanger ($MM^{-1}$)

$\rho$ = solid phase bulk density ($ML^{-3}$)

$\varepsilon$ = solid phase pore fraction ($L^3L^{-3}$)

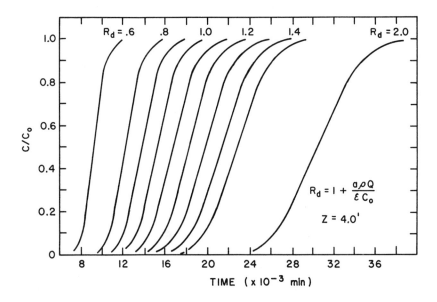

Figure 2. Typical linear sorption breakthrough curves.

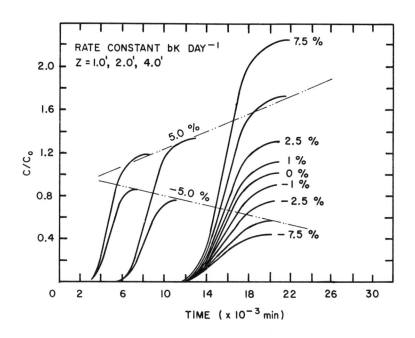

Figure 3. Typical reaction break-through curves.

a,b = + 1 depending on the direction (positive or negative) of the mechanism

Obviously, this formulation contains tacit assumptions about dispersion and is less than exhaustive with respect to attenuation mechanisms. Nevertheless, it incorporates simultaneous convection, dispersion, sorption, and reaction, and al-

lows for both positive and negative attenuations. It also has merit in that under the appropriate assumption, analytical solutions are possible. If it is assumed that the reaction is of first-order and that sorption may be approximated by a linear isotherm, then by applying infinite-length boundary conditions,

$$C(Z,0) = 0 \qquad (2a)$$
$$C(0,t) = C_o \qquad (2b)$$
$$C(\infty,t) = 0 \qquad (2c)$$

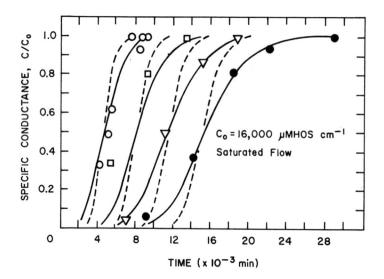

Figure 4A. Specific conductance breakthrough.

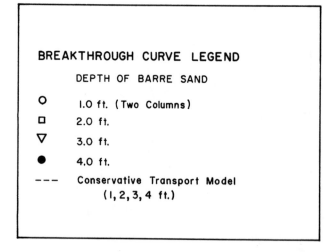

Figure 4B. Breakthrough curve legend.

$$\frac{C(Z,t)}{C_0} = \frac{1}{2} \exp\left(\frac{VZ}{2D}\right)\left\{\exp\left[-Z\sqrt{\left(\frac{V}{2D}\right)^2 - \frac{bK}{D}}\right] \mathrm{erfc}\left[\frac{Z - \sqrt{V'^2 - 4bK'D'}\ t}{2\sqrt{D't}}\right]\right.$$

$$\left.+ \exp\left[Z\sqrt{\left(\frac{V}{2D}\right)^2 - \frac{bK}{D}}\right] \mathrm{erfc}\left[\frac{Z + \sqrt{V'^2 - 4bK'D'}\ t}{2\sqrt{D't}}\right]\right\} \qquad (3)$$

where:  $C_0$ = initial solute concentration $(ML^{-3})$

$$V' = V/\left(1 + \frac{a\ \rho Q}{\varepsilon C_0}\right) \qquad K' = K/\left(1 + \frac{a\ \rho Q}{\varepsilon C_0}\right) \qquad D' = D/\left(1 + \frac{a\ \rho Q}{\varepsilon C_0}\right) \qquad -1.0 < \frac{a\ \rho Q}{\varepsilon C_0}$$

$Q$ = mass of solute removed by sorption in equilibrium with $C_0$ $(MM^{-1})$

$D$ = overall dispersion coefficient [D(mech) + D(mole)]  $(L^2T^{-1})$

$$\frac{C(Z,t)}{C_0} = \frac{1}{2}\left\{\mathrm{erfc}\left[\frac{Z-Vt}{2\sqrt{Dt}}\right] + \exp\left[\frac{VZ}{D}\right] \mathrm{erfc}\left[\frac{Z + Vt}{2\sqrt{Dt}}\right]\right\} \qquad (4)$$

the solution is given by Equation (3) (Bear, 1972).

For the case of no sorption (Q = 0.0) and no reaction (K = 0.0), Equation (3) reduces to the solution for conservative mass transport (Equation (4)). The overall dispersion coefficient (D) for a soil may be evaluated by generating a conservative tracer breakthrough curve at some fixed depth and velocity. The tracer selected should approximate the leachate's ionic strength so that diffusivity is also approximated. By fitting Equation (4) to the generated curve, a value for D may be extracted.

Once D is known, Equation (3) may be used to identify and quantify mechanisms of attenuation. Figure 2 presents a family of curves generated from Equation (3) for the case of no reaction (K = 0) but varying degree of sorptive capacity (Q ≠ 0). From these, it can be seen that use of the linear sorption approximation simply delays or advances in time the appearance of dispersion-like breakthrough curves. The identifying characteristic of the curve family is that, at equilibrium, they are always asymptotic to C/C$_0$ = 1.00. This is due to the eventual exhaustion of the soil's finite capacity to receive mass from the liquid phase, and will occur regardless of the sorption distribution relationship. Obviously, if the sorption type is linear, Equation (3) may be used to extract a value for Q.

Figure 3 presents curves characteristic of reactive attenuation. Mass formation or consumption demands that at equilibrium C/C$_0$ cannot equal 1.00. By this characteristic and by the fact that the equilibrium asymptote will be a

function of depth, reactive attenuations may be identified. Furthermore, K may be calculated directly when the asymptotic value is known. By taking the limit of Equation (3) as time goes to infinity, it can be shown that:

$$bK = \ln(C/C_0)_\infty \left[\frac{V}{Z} - \frac{D}{Z^2}\ln(C/C_0)_\infty\right] \qquad (5)$$

Obviously, this leaves many cases uncovered, but similar arguments can be constructed to identify curves typical of other mechanisms (Jennings, 1977).

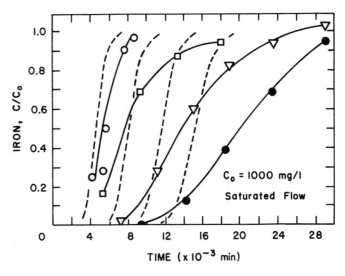

Figure 5.  Iron breakthrough.  (See Figure 4B for legend).

## RESULTS

### Ionic Strength

Experiments with the Barre soils produced surprising results. It had been anticipated that the soils would be unsuccessful in completely renovating leachate. Still, nothing had been encountered in the literature to suggest just how poor the soil's effect would be. Saturated flow experimentation indicated that the soil's overall attenuative capacity was virtually zero.

Figure 4A presents specific conductance breakthrough curves for the saturated flow of Batch "A" leachate through Barre sand. The dashed lines correspond to the theoretical breakthrough of a conservative solute. If this background dispersion is neglected, the data would appear to indicate attenuation. By accounting for dispersive effect, it can be seen that true attenuation is very limited. Simply by increasing the coefficient of dispersion from the measured value of $7.20 \times 10^{-3}$ cm$^2$/min (dashed lines) to $3.00 \times 10^{-2}$ cm$^2$/min (solid lines), the observed data are satisfactorily fitted. Obviously, if any mechanisms of attenuation are active, then total ionic strength does not act conservatively. Co-attenuations affecting Fe, Mg, Ca, Mn, ammonia, sulfate and alkalinity were observed and others undoubtedly occurred. However, all were of minor magnitude and included both positive and negative removals. Their net effect (i.e., the transport of total ionic strength) may be modeled as if transport was conservative.

Based on this evidence, four or more feet of Barre sand could do nothing to prevent the pollution of underlying ground water. It is not known how well this result generalizes to other soils. The Barre clay did accomplish better removals than the sand. Also, unsaturated flow experimentation with the less concentrated leachate Batch "B" showed that, under some conditions, the Barre sand could attenuate some ionic strength. Still, both soils could only be ranked as poor on any qualitative scale. This underscores the necessity for investigating a soil's attenuative capacity rather than relying on literature values. Knowledge of these capacities is only beginning to be developed but, if the Barre sand is included, then suggested capacities range from "nothing less than miraculous" (Zanoni, 1972) to virtually zero.

### Iron

The saturated flow of leachate through Barre sand produced iron breakthrough curves characteristic of positive sorptive attenuation. From Figure 5 it can be seen that the time to 50 percent breakthrough was significantly delayed behind the conservative model prediction. Also, divergence increases with depth, implying depth-dependency, and the curves are asymptotic to $C/C_0 = 1.00$, indicating the consumption of a finite capacity. These properties all identify a sorptive mechanism, but comparisons to the linear isotherm model are not favorable. If forced upon these data, the linear model produces a removal capacity estimate of Q = 0.065 mg Fe/g soil, but the quality of fit is poor. Indications are that iron undergoes non-linear sorption.

Another estimate of this capacity may be retrieved from a mass balance on column influents and effluents. Because removals in depth increments should be equal once equilibrium is achieved, a plot of mass removed versus depth should produce a straight line passing through the origin. Figure 6 presents such a plot for the

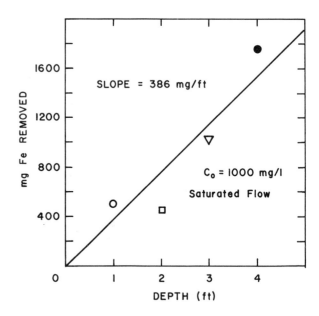

Figure 6. Iron removal with depth. (See Figure 4B for legend).

Figure 5 data. The slope of 386 mg Fe/ft soil (0.09 mg Fe/g soil) provides the removal capacity estimate.

The necessity for reducing column simulation to equilibrium analysis makes a case for the substitution of equilibration procedures. Figure 7 presents iron removal distributions constructed for these two soils. The favorability of the clay to attenuate iron can be clearly seen. It also responds well to Langmuir isotherm analysis which is a boon to its transport simulation. Although the results for the sand are not as well-behaved, removal capacity is also demonstrated. Its distribution predicts that in equilibrium with a concentration of 1,000 mg/$\ell$ about 0.18 mg Fe/g soil should be removed. Although this is twice the value predicted from the columns, it would serve as a reasonable estimate if it told the whole story. Unfortunately, it does not. Results of

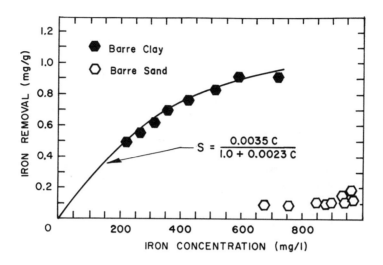

Figure 7. Batch iron removal.

unsaturated flow experimentation (Fig. 8) illustrate the full value of simulation. During this run, the decision was made to operate beyond 100 percent breakthrough to determine if a biological removal mechanism would become established. This produced the unexpected discovery that the soil's equilibrium removal capacity can vary considerably with time. After an initial period of sorptive

removal, the soil's capacity to retain iron declined until virtually all of the previously attenuated iron was released back to solution.

Explanations for this capacity change have been postulated (Tirsch, 1977; Jennings, 1977) linking the changes to sulfur transformations, but details of the mechanism remain unknown. This

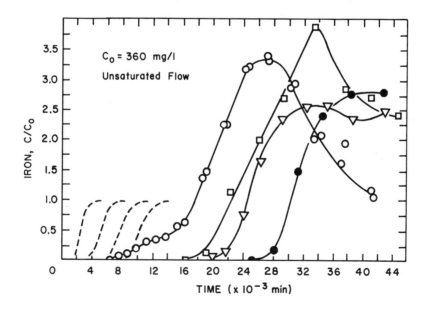

Figure 8. Iron breakthrough, unsaturated flow. (See Figure 4B for legend).

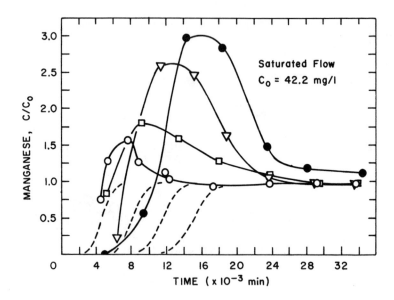

Figure 9. Manganese breakthrough.
(See Figure 4B for legend).

suggests that the fate of leachate's separate constituents cannot be dissociated. The leachate/soil interaction is a complex chain of events, and a simplistic element by element approach cannot detail the complete story. It may well be that equilibrium is reached only after months or years, if it is reached at all. Reliance on batch equilibrations can only yield information about a short

portion of this very long history.

Manganese

The properties of negative attenuation are illustrated by the saturated flow breakthrough curves of manganese (Fig. 9). In contrast to a

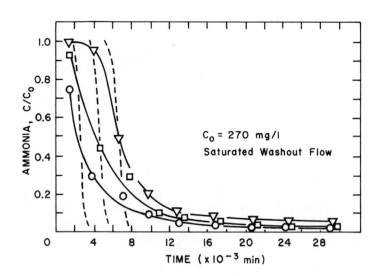

Figure 10. Ammonia "washout."
(See Figure 4B for legend).

positive mechanism, negative sorption leads to an increased apparent transport velocity. But depth dependency is still evidenced, and the curves still converge on $C/C_0 = 1.00$, typical of sorption curves. The obvious feature identifying these as the product of a negative attenuation is that effluent concentration exceeds influent concentration ($C/C_0 > 1.0$) over the history of the event.

Clearly, the linear sorption model cannot quantify or simulate this behavior. By mass balance, Figure 9 data return 0.012 mg Mn/g soil as the release capacity. Unsaturated flow simulation resulted in a release of 0.010 mg Mn/g soil. These values are in good agreement with the soil's manganese equilibrium distribution. Batch methods predicted that in equilibrium with a concentration of 42.2 mg/ℓ Mn, a release of 0.009 mg Mn/g soil would result. Unlike iron, no additional interactions were observed when columns were run past 100 percent breakthrough.

Reversibility

Reversibility was gauged by simulating the flow of clean water through leachate-equilibrated soil. This was accomplished by stepping in a water feed to the soil columns of the saturated leachate flow experiment. The batch study analog would be to completely replace the leachate liquid phase with clean water, but the logistics of the procedure would be difficult. A theoretical examination of the step change input leads to a conservative "washout" model, which is a simple complementation of Equation (4). This ignores effects such as solutes diffusing back out of dead-end pores, but all such effects would probably be minor. Given this simplification, a conservative or positively attenuating solute would be flushed from the porous medium within the bounds of the model prediction. Solute concentrations would persist only if negative attenuation was originally occurring or if a positive mechanism reversed direction.

Figure 10 represents washout curves observed for ammonia. During leachate contact the Barre soils demonstrated positive sorptive attenuation very similar to that for iron. The saturated flow removal capacity for the sand was calculated to be 0.016 mg ammonia/g soil. The washout curves demonstrated that this removal was not permanent. With the penetration of clean water, the soil responded to the concentration decrease by releasing ammonia back into solution. Thus, it was observed to persist in column effluents long after it should have disappeared. The value of $C/C_0$ appears to become quite small, but a value of 0.01 in Figure 10 corresponds to an ammonia concentration of 2.70 mg/ℓ which alone could degrade water quality. Concentrations remained above 1.0 mg/ℓ until the experiment was terminated at 100,000 minutes.

Very similar washout curves were observed for iron, sulfate, specific conductance, and alkalin-ity, all of which appeared to be attenuated to some degree during initial contact. Unattenuated solutes washed out rapidly as predicted. These results forced the conclusion that the Barre sand would accomplish no significant permanent attenuations.

SUMMARY AND CONCLUSION

The method of flow simulation under anaerobic conditions proved to be the superior method for evaluating attenuative capacity of a soil. Although batch equilibrations produce accurate and useful results, they provide no information on the time variations of the effects and are too constrained to model all the stages of contact. Simulations return all the information of batch studies. They also gauge the potential for capacity changes with time, i.e., the reversibility of mechanisms, and they can return information on non-sorptive attenuations.

The effectiveness of the Barre sand for mitigating leachate strength was found to be virtually zero. Although selected parameters were attenuated, gross ionic strength traversed the soil unchanged. Sorptive removals were found to be reversible. Four feet of Barre sand would pose no barrier to the leachate's pollution potential, and that potential would be rapidly realized.

Unfortunately, these major inadequacies of the Barre sand probably generalize well to similar soils and may be far more universal than the authors would care to believe.

ACKNOWLEDGMENTS

This research was supported by Massachusetts Division of Water Pollution Control, Grant 76-10(2) and the U.S. Forest Service, Northeastern Forest Experiment Station, Pinchot Institute Grant USDA 23-591. The cooperation of Leonard Martone, owner of the Barre Landfill, and graduate research assistants, Robert Pease, Ronald Lavigne, George Lombardo, and Sandra Ferry, is gratefully acknowledged. The bulk of the data and analysis contained herein was presented at the First Annual Conference of Applied Research and Practice on Municipal and Industrial Wastes at Madison, Madison, Wisconsin, September 10-13, 1978.

REFERENCES

Bear, J., 1972, Dynamics of fluids in porous media: American Elsevier Publishing Co., Inc.

Fuller, W.H., and Korte, N., 1976, Attenuation mechanisms of pollutants through soils; gas and leachate from landfills; formation, collection, and treatment: EPA-600/9-76-004, p. 111-121.

Jennings, A.A., 1977, The leachate attenuation properties of soil under anaerobic conditions: M.S.C.E. Thesis, University of Massachusetts, Amherst, Massachusetts.

Phillips, C.R., and Nathwani, J., 1976, Solid waste interactions: a state-of-the-art review: Environment Canada, Solid Waste Management Report EPS-3-EC-76-14.

Tirsch, F., 1977, Leachate reactions with soils: M.S. Thesis, University of Massachusetts, Amherst, Massachusetts.

Zanoni, A.E., 1972, Ground water pollution and sanitary landfills - a critical review: Groundwater, v. 10, no. 1, p. 3-16.

# The mineral chemistry and geological distribution of phases in SYNROC

## S. E. HAGGERTY
### Department of Geology and Geography
### University of Massachusetts at Amherst

## ABSTRACT

SYNROC is a synthetic rock designed for the safe immobilization of high level radioactive nuclear wastes (Ringwood et al., 1979, Nature, 278, 219-223). The principal constituents are: 35% of a phase that is isostructural with hollandite $Ba(Mn^{2+}Mn^{4+})_8O_{16}$, but having the formula $BaAl_2Ti_6O_{16}$; 31% zirconolite ($CaZrTi_2O_7$); 22% perovskite ($CaTiO_3$); 7% $TiO_2$; and 5% $Al_2O_3$. A common factor among minerals that are present in high modal proportions is their structural ability to accommodate many of the fission products (REE, Zr, Mo, Te, Tc, Rh, Ru, I, Cs, Pb, Sr, Ba, Rb), the actinides (Th, Pa, U, Np, Pu, Am), and the processing contaminants (Fe, $PO_4$, Na, Cr, Ni), that constitute a typical calcine (radwaste). The strategy of immobilization in crystalline solids has been adopted because of the potential advantage of long term stabilization in a suitably sited geological repository. This cannot be guaranteed with the more widely accepted viewpoint that alkali borosilicate glasses or Cermet (metallic glasses) are suitable alternatives to SYNROC. Amorphous receptors do, however, have a number of advantages: Radwaste products are variable in composition and, hence, elemental partitioning among a fixed mineral assemblage does not need to be considered. In addition, the relative proportions of the inactive media and the active waste can probably be varied over a wider range than that proposed for SYNROC in which a 9:1 ratio appears to be optimum. However, these apparent advantages are negated by the inherent instability of glass over historic, let alone geological, time. It appears, therefore, that SYNROC, or the principle of a mineralogical barrier, is most likely to be adopted for radwaste immobilization.

Our contribution to this effort has focused on several questions: (1) What are the environments in which SYNROC minerals occur? (2) How stable are these minerals in natural settings? (3) How do radwaste specific elements partition? (4) Are there other minerals that may be considered in SYNROC? (5) What are the intensive parameters necessary for the experimental and subsequently the mass production of SYNROC? In essence, how does nature deal with the problem?

## DISCUSSION

Modified hollandite has not been recognized in nature but two closely related minerals, freudenbergite and priderite (Table 1) are constituents

TABLE 1. SYNROC B AND SOME RELATED MINERALS IN NATURE

| SYNROC B | |
|---|---|
| "Hollandite" | $BaAl_2Ti_6O_{16}$ |
| Zirconolite | $CaZrTi_2O_7$ |
| Perovskite | $CaTiO_3$ |

| Some Related Minerals in Nature | |
|---|---|
| 1. Freudenbergite | $Na_2FeTi_7O_{16}$ |
| 2. Priderite | $(K, Ba)_8(TiFe)_8O_{16}$ |
| 3. Loparite | $(Ce, Na, Ca)_2(Ti, Nb)_2O_6$ |
| 4. Pyrochlore group | $A_{2-m}B_2O_6$ |
| | (A = Na, Ca, K, Sn, Ba, REE, Pb, Bi, U) |
| | (B = Nb, Ta, Ti) |
| (a) | Pyrochlore Nb + Ta > 2Ti and Nb > Ti |
| (b) | Microlite Nb + Ta > 2Ti and Ta > Nb |
| (c) | Betafite 2 Ti > Nb + Ta |
| 5. Transitional armalcolites | $(FeMgCa)(TiZrCrAl)_2O_5$ |
| 6. Crichtonite group | $AB_{21}O_{38}$ |
| | (A = Sr, Ca, Na, REE, Pb, Ba, K) |
| | (B = Ti, Zr, Cr, Al, Fe, Mg, Mn) |
| (a) | Crichtonite - Sr |
| (b) | Senaite - Pb |
| (c) | Davidite - REE |
| (d) | Loveringite - Ca |
| (e) | Landauite - Na |
| (f) | "Lindsleyite" - Ba |
| (g) | "Mathiasite" - K |

of carbonatites and kimberlites. Zirconolite is an extremely rare mineral in gabbros but is somewhat more abundant in kimberlites and in lunar highland basalts where it is associated with ilmenite, rutile, baddeleyite ($ZrO_2$) and armalcolite. Perovskite is a common and widespread mineral in all kimberlites and carbonatites, but it is also present as an accessory phase in other highly undersaturated igneous rocks. Based on the abundances and on the partitioning of fission and actinide elements in nature (Table 2), we propose that several other minerals are probable candidates for SYNROC in which a high degree of stabilization can be demonstrated over geological time. In particular, we draw attention to members of the crichtonite mineral group and to pyrochlore, in which high concentrations of REE and actinides have been retained for periods of at least 90 my. These minerals have the added advantage that a higher degree of flexibility is introduced to SYNROC in the context of accommodating the wide variety of elements that are present in radwaste. We conclude that SYNROC minerals have restricted geological settings and are constrained to crystallization conditions of low $fO_2$ and high temperatures ($<$ FMQ for kimberlites and carbonatites, and $<$ IW for lunar highland basalts), factors that ought to be considered in the production sequence, and perhaps even in the final repository.

CONCLUSION

A considerable amount of additional geochemical and experimental data is required to establish the phase relationships of SYNROC, the partitioning coefficients of radwaste elements among SYNROC minerals, and the mobility of these elements under the most severe conditions of leaching in a variety of potentially stable geological settings.

TABLE 2.  RADWASTE FISSION PRODUCTS AND ACTINIDES IN SOME NATURALLY OCCURRING OXIDES

|  | Fission | Actinides |
|---|---|---|
|  | (weight percent) | |
| Zirconolite |  |  |
| Gabbros (Zr, REE) | 32-33 | 1-2.5 |
| Lunar basalts (Zr, REE) | 32-39 | 0.3-2.5 |
| Kimberlites (Zr, REE) | 41-71 | 0 |
| Perovskite |  |  |
| Kimberlites | 3-13 | ND |
| Crichtonite group |  |  |
| Crichtonite (Sr) | 5.0 | ND |
| Senaite (Pb) | 10.5 | ND |
| Davidite (REE) | 10.0 | 4 |
| Loveringite (REE, Zr) | 7.5 | 0.3 |
| Landauite (Pb) | 2.5 | ND |
| "Lindsleyite" (Ba, REE) | 5-10 | ND |
| "Mathiasite" (Ba, REE) | 5-10 | ND |
| Transitional armalcolites |  |  |
| (REE, Ba, Sr, Pb) | 0.5-3.5 | ND |
| Pyrochlore group |  |  |
| (REE, Pb, Sr, Zr) | 10-15 | 20-25 |

# Geology and radioactive waste disposal

J. H. PECK
Stone & Webster Engineering Corporation

ABSTRACT

The safe disposal of radioactive waste is a pressing national issue. Low-level radioactive waste presents somewhat different problems than high-level waste and has been handled much like other hazardous wastes; shallow burial in soil or sedimentary rocks. High-level waste has been accumulating since the Manhattan Project in the early 1940's, and no disposal scheme has been adopted by the federal government to date. The currently favored scheme is deep burial in stable geologic formations, in repositories designed and excavated solely for waste isolation.

New England produces both high- and low-level radioactive waste but has no facility for disposal. Low-level waste is shipped elsewhere. High-level waste is stored on nuclear reactor sites where it is produced, primarily as spent fuel rods.

The National Waste Terminal Storage Program has the objective of locating suitable sites for building and operating repositories for the iso-lation of commercial high-level waste. Most siting studies to date have concentrated on regions underlain by salt. However, crystalline rocks, shales, and tuffaceous rocks are considered to be adequate alternatives to salt. Siting requires a systematic approach with a number of phases of geologic investigation. The objective is to identify one or more locations which meet minimum requirements for acceptance on the basis of tectonic stability, structural integrity, hydrogeologic suitability, and geochemical compatibility. Potential sites first have to meet all geologic specifications for safe isolation of waste. These sites are then evaluated on secondary geologic attributes and environmental, economic, engineering, and political factors.

Swedish and Canadian studies have identified granitic plutons as potential sites for nuclear repositories in geologic terrains similar to New England's. Massachusetts and the New England region have abundant crystalline rocks with geologic characteristics that may make the region attractive for future investigation.

# Lead in drinking water—
# A study in metropolitan Boston

D. J. WORTH
School of Medicine
Tufts University

# Surface impoundment assessment in the New England states

C. CHOW
L. R. SILKA
F. M. BRASIER
U.S. Environmental Protection Agency

## ABSTRACT

The Surface Impoundment Assessment (SIA) is a study conducted by the Environmental Protection Agency, through grants to the States, to locate and identify impoundments (pits, ponds and lagoons) used for storage, treatment or disposal of fluid wastes. In addition, the States assessed the groundwater contamination potential of these sites using methodology devised for the SIA.

The SIA has been completed in all of the New England states. A total of 1,321 sites has been located which contain 4,340 impoundments. Of these sites 1,163 have been assessed. These figures represent 80-90 percent of the actual situation.

Preliminary analysis of the data shows that 66 percent of these sites are located over thin or highly permeable unsaturated zones underlain by thick or very permeable aquifers containing water of fewer than 1000 mg/l total dissolved solids, and therefore have a high potential to contaminate usable ground water. Further, the data show that 86 percent of the impoundments at these sites are unlined, 91 percent are unmonitored, and 9 percent are within 200 meters of downgradient water wells which could be affected by seepage from the impoundments, while 48 percent are within 200 meters of a surface water body into which potentially contaminated ground water discharges.

The SIA methodology can be used in the future as a planning tool for siting of waste facilities, and to this end sensitive aquifer maps combining the SIA data with available hydrogeologic information will be prepared.

## SURFACE IMPOUNDMENT ASSESSMENT PROGRAM

Groundwater contamination is not an uncommon occurrence, and yet little is known about the extent of this problem and its relationship to drinking water, the methods of protecting ground water, and the science of controlling the contamination. Many federal programs have recognized this lack of knowledge and, therefore, have supported various programs in order to understand and manage ground water and its associated problems.

One such program instituted through the Safe Drinking Water Act (SDWA) was the Surface Impoundment Assessment (SIA). The principal objectives of the assessment program were to rate the contamination potential of ground water from surface impoundments[1] (pits, ponds, lagoons) and to develop practices for the evaluation of different surface impoundments. Other supporting activities included location and counting of these impoundments, documentation of actual contamination cases related to impoundments, and evaluation of existing state legislation, regulations, and programs for impoundment practices. The information collected through the SIA program would indicate the extent of the actual and potential groundwater contamination problems resulting from pits, ponds, and lagoons and would also provide a foundation for future State and Federal legislation of groundwater protection programs and impoundment management programs.

The methodology for data collection is by means of an evaluation system that yields a first round approximation of the relative groundwater contamination potential at these impoundments.

## THE EVALUATION SYSTEM

The evaluation system uses hydrogeological and drinking water parameters to rank the impoundments in terms of their relative groundwater contamination potential. The first group of parameters examines the hydrogeologic conditions and the waste characteristics of the site in order to rate the site's overall contamination potential. These parameters consist of the thickness of the unsaturated zone and the type of earth material of that zone, the quality and quantity of the drinking water source beneath the site, and the waste hazard potential of the impoundments and sites. The second set of parameters rates the relative magnitude of potential endangerment to drinking water supplies. Parameters corresponding to this group are the type of water source, i.e., ground water or surface water, whether the water

---

[1] For this program, a surface impoundment is defined as either a natural topographic depression, artificial excavation, or dike arrangement with the following characteristics: (1) it is used primarily for storage, treatment or disposal of wastes in the form of fluids; (2) it may be constructed above, below, or partially in the ground; (3) it may or may not have a permeable bottom and/ or sides potentially allowing contamination of ground water by infiltration of its contents.

source is in the anticipated flow direction of contaminated ground water, and the distance between the water source and the potential contamination source.

Since the evaluation is carried out in sequence, each rating step relates to the next one, leading to the final determinations of the overall contamination potential and the potential health hazard. The first four steps assess the site's hydrogeology and the nature of the waste. Step 1 rates the unsaturated zone by the thickness and the type of earth material. The thickness of the unsaturated zone is measured from the base of the surface impoundment to the water table or to the top of a confined aquifer if no water table exists. In the case of perched water tables, the depth measured, whether it be to the underlying regional water table, will depend upon the usefulness of the lens or the underlying aquifer as a drinking water source. In determining the earth material below the impoundment, several factors have to be considered: the permeability, the sorption, and the complexity of the geological conditions. Step 2 determines the groundwater availability ranking according to the thickness and the type of earth material in the saturated zone. The thickness of the aquifer is estimated using geologic maps and cross-sections and driller's logs. Selection of the earth material category is similar to that in Step 1. Following this, the groundwater quality is rated in Step 3. The quality is a determinant of the ultimate usefulness of the ground water, i.e., its suitability as a drinking water source. It is ranked in terms of the total dissolved solids content.[2]

Step 4 evaluates and ranks the waste hazard potential, which is defined as the potential for causing harm to human health. The rating for contaminants (waste constituents) ranges from 1 to 9, with 9 being the most hazardous. When an impoundment accepts a multitude of wastes, the most severe contaminant is rated. Step 5 combines the four previous steps according to their numerical rating and determines the site's overall groundwater contamination potential. The rating of Step 5 ranges from 1 to 29, with 29 being the greatest contamination potential. Finally, Step 6 ties together the contamination potential with the health hazard potential by relating the two in terms of the magnitude of endangerment to the water supplies. The criteria for this determination are based upon priority ranking of waste plume movement and surface water or well water location. For example, if the nearest water well is less than 200 meters from the site and is situated in the anticipated direction of the waste plume movement, it is treated as the highest priority; i.e., the most threatening case regarding

contamination of the drinking water source.

All of the steps outlined in this section appear to require detailed and precise data. Conducting extensive research to collect comprehensive information on geological and hydrological conditions, as well as on the waste constituents, is a lengthy and costly process. Furthermore, this is not the objective of the SIA program. The purpose of the SIA evaluation is to sort and use the best available information for developing a first-round approximation of the groundwater contamination problems associated with surface impoundments. Precise data are not necessary for satisfactory results when the assessment is an estimate and a rating of contamination potentials.

SIA IN THE NEW ENGLAND STATES

In March 1978, the administrator of EPA granted the six New England states, along with the rest of the nation, funds to conduct this assessment program. The project period began in June 1978 with the first phase being the location and count of both impoundments and sites. All of the states initially performed a literature search of the existing information. This gave the agencies who are involved in the program a better perspective of the scope of work and tasks necessary in order to gather the required data for the inventory. Three of the six states commissioned aerial photographs to assist them in locating and counting the impoundments. Some states used mailed questionnaires and telephone polling to collect the inventory data regarding the facility type, construction, and operational purposes. Information collected by these two means served not only to verify but to enhance existing data. Random site investigations were also performed for the same purposes.

Upon completing the inventory, the impoundments/sites were assessed according to the rating system previously described. Both facility descriptions and evaluation parameters are then entered into a computer data base. From this data base, various analyses, tabulations, and trends could be generated. This information could then be used as a management or decision tool in groundwater programs and other surface impoundment related activities.

Examining the impoundment inventory of New England, it can be seen that most of the sites and impoundments, both those presently in use and abandoned ones, are of the industrial and municipal category (Table 1). The remaining impoundments, which include agricultural and oil and gas practices, make up only 20 percent of the total number of sites in New England.

Further investigation of facility descriptions from the inventory data reveals that only a small percentage of the sites have groundwater protection measures such as impoundment liners or monitoring wells (Table 2). Although there are slightly more active municipal sites (483) than active industrial sites (418), these industrial

---

[2] Proposed Underground Injection Control Regulations (40 CFR Part 146) of the Safe Drinking Water Act as amended in 1977 (P.L. 93-523 and P.L. 95-190)

TABLE 1. SUMMARY OF SITES IN THE DATA BASE
AS OF 2-18-80

| Category | Sites Located | Assessed | Impoundments Located | Assessed |
|---|---|---|---|---|
| Active Industrial | 418 | 366 | 1129 | 481 |
| Active Municipal | 483 | 409 | 2069 | 550 |
| Active Agricultural | 205 | 198 | 241 | 216 |
| Other | 48 | 35 | 358 | 36 |
| Abandoned Industrial | 102 | 97 | 277 | 116 |
| Abandoned Municipal | 51 | 45 | 220 | 45 |
| Abandoned Agricultural | 5 | 5 | 5 | 5 |
| Other | 6 | 6 | 6 | 6 |
| Unknown | 3 | 2 | 6 | 2 |
| Total | 1321 | 1163 | 4340 | 1457 |

With this inventory information in hand, an evaluation is performed according to the designed system. From an examination of steps 1 through 3 (the hydrologic characteristics of the assessed sites), it appears that the New England states have geological conditions susceptible to contamination, but the underlying aquifers are of good quantity and quality (Table 3). Most of this re-

TABLE 3. HYDROGEOLOGIC CHARACTERISTICS
OF ASSESSED SITES

| | Characteristics | Number of sites | Percentage |
|---|---|---|---|
| Unsaturated zone | 1 M thick of high permeability | 909 | 78 |
| | Moderate permeability | 137 | 12 |
| | Relatively impermeable | 114 | 10 |
| Aquifer | Thick & high permeability | 880 | 76 |
| | 3 M thick or moderate permeability | 137 | 12 |
| | Relatively impermeable | 138 | 12 |
| Groundwater quality | 1000 MG/L TDS | 1142 | 98 |
| | 1,000-10,000 | 2 | 0 |
| | 10,000 or no ground water | 28 | 1.5 |

sites exhibit more protection measures than the municipal sites. But that is little consolation when, collectively, only 2-18 percent of the three major categories (industrial, municipal, agricultural) of active sites protect the ground water with either earthen or synthetic liners, or monitoring wells, or both devices.

More critical as a threat to ground water is the high percentage of abandoned sites, especially industrial ones, which do not have any contamination control mechanisms. Sixty-two percent of the abandoned sites are from industrial practices and only 6 percent of the sites are lined, 12 percent of them are monitored, and 3 percent have both of these protection measures. Considering the chemical constituents of industrial wastes, the associated high potential health hazard, and the high percentage of these sites without monitoring or control, abandoned industrial impoundments rate as having one of the highest groundwater contamination potentials in New England.

TABLE 2. GROUNDWATER PROTECTION MEASURES AT ASSESSED SITES

| Category | Liners Number of sites | Percentage | Monitoring wells Number of sites | Percentage | Liners & monitoring wells Number of sites | Percentage |
|---|---|---|---|---|---|---|
| Active Industrial | 68 | 19 | 43 | 12 | 10 | 3 |
| Abandoned Industrial | 6 | 6 | 12 | 12 | 3 | 3 |
| Active Municipal | 61 | 15 | 32 | 8 | 5 | 1 |
| Active Agricultural | 51 | 26 | 1 | 0.5 | 0 | 0 |
| All Categories | 193 | 17 | 91 | 8 | 18 | 1 |

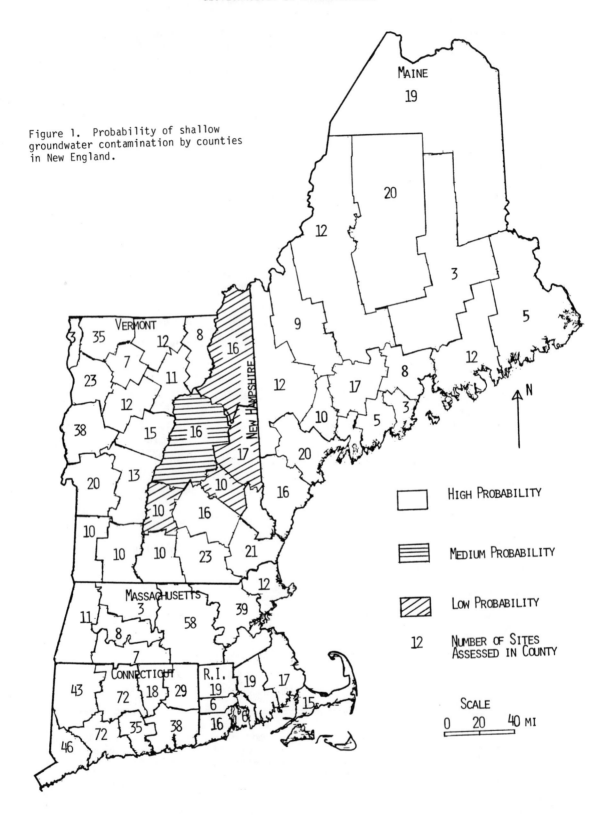

Figure 1. Probability of shallow groundwater contamination by counties in New England.

gion's saturated zones (78 percent) consist of high permeable earth material with a thickness of approximately two meters. Seventy-six percent of the saturated zones have good aquifer conditions; i.e., the thickness and high permeability of earth material in this zone implies a capability of producing moderate to high quantities of water. As for the quality of these aquifers, 98 percent of them rate as potential or present drinking water sources. The potential water supply sources, according to the proposed Underground Injection Control Regulation, are defined as all ground water containing up to 10,000 mg/l total dissolved solids (TDS). Putting these three hydrogeological characteristics into perspective, it can be seen that over three-quarters of the New England area has earth material where leachates from various disposal practices can readily permeate into potential underground drinking water sources.

Comparing the hydrogeological characteristics and the summary of sites assessed, the conclusion that industrial sites, both active and abandoned, have the highest contamination potential is confirmed (Table 4). Out of 366 active industrial sites assessed, 73 percent are located above both a highly permeable unsaturated zone as well as a good aquifer. Only 37 of these sites are lined; 32 are monitored; and 3 have both liners and monitoring wells. On the other hand, 81 percent of the abandoned industrial sites were evaluated as having high contamination potential. The protection measures at abandoned sites were also inadequate. In fact, they were even slightly lower than those for active sites--25 percent of the abandoned sites had liners or monitoring wells versus 27 percent of the active sites with the same protection measures. This clearly defines and emphasizes that the major potential contamination problem in New England is associated with abandoned industrial sites. Similarly, active municipal sites, although their hazard potential rating is lower than industrial wastes, are a substantial threat to ground water, particularly when only 54 out of the 231 high contamination potential sites have groundwater protection measures. Active agricultural sites rank the lowest among the three major impoundment categories in contamination potential. Even so, approximately 50 percent of these sites pose a potential contamination problem to the underlying aquifer.

All three impoundment categories possess a significant threat to aquifers which are suitable for drinking water sources. The crucial question then becomes whether there exists a potential endangerment to current water supplies attributed by these surface impoundments. General state regulations in New England recommend an estimated 125 meter radius protection zone around an existing well used for water supply. If that figure is used as an approximation of the most severe case of a water supply endangerment zone, there are 116 sites which would fall under this case (Tables 5 and 6), 83 sites being those having high contamination potential. Where surface waters are concerned, the protection zone varies from state to state, but is generally less than that for

ground water. An examination of the data reveals that 601 sites represent a significant endangerment to drinking water reservoirs, and 416 of these sites have high potential for movement of the contaminated plume in the direction of the surface source. Therefore, within New England, 62 percent of the surface impoundment sites exist on extremely sensitive land where the waste plume movement would intersect the ground and surface water supplies.

Since a protection zone for either well or reservoir is a function of hydrological and geological conditions, it is difficult to assume, as general state regulations do, that a finite distance around these sources would be sufficient in preserving the water quality. However, if the protection zone were to be defined according to hydrogeological configuration and pumping rates, the area of concern around the source would range from 100 to 400 meters. Using this range, an additional 15.5 percent of the sites endanger either ground or surface water sources. A closer examination of these sites reveals that only 11 percent are lined. Therefore, 89 percent of the sites have the highest potential for contaminating either a current ground source or surface water source of drinking water.

The data discussed in this section are the result of a first-round evaluation of the situation made with the best available information. Even so, the New England state agencies which conducted the assessment program are confident that the inventory data represent 80-90 percent of the actual situation. Therefore, the analyses performed with the information gathered from the evaluation system indicate a valid set of conclusions which reveal a high potential for groundwater contamination and endangerment to water supplies from surface impoundments. The probability of groundwater contamination throughout the majority of New England is high, as seen pictorially in Figure 1.

The data and assessment generated through this program can serve these important functions:

- a foundation for management and decision-making purposes regarding the control of existing impoundments/sites,

- development of new techniques and methodologies for future impoundment construction, and

- establishment of legislation and regulation of existing and future impoundments/sites.

SIA AS A MANAGEMENT AND DECISION TOOL

This assessment program has indicated that there exist substantial groundwater contamination problems associated with surface impoundments. It also pointed out the lack of scientific knowledge and regulatory abilities for controlling these impoundments and sites.

TABLE 4.  SUMMARY OF SITES HAVING HIGH CONTAMINATION POTENTIAL

| Category | Number of sites | Percentage of category | Number lined | Number monitored | Number lined and monitored |
|---|---|---|---|---|---|
| Industrial | 268 | 73 | 37 | 32 | 3 |
| Abandoned Industrial | 79 | 81 | 5 | 12 | 3 |
| Municipal | 231 | 57 | 32 | 22 | 0 |
| Agricultural | 110 | 56 | 31 | 1 | 0 |
| All Categories | 753 | 66 | 110 | 70 | 6 |

TABLE 5.  POTENTIAL ENDANGERMENT TO WATER SUPPLY FROM ALL ASSESSED SITES

| Distance in meters | CASE A | | CASE B | | CASE C | | CASE D | |
|---|---|---|---|---|---|---|---|---|
| | Number of sites | Percentage | Number of sites | Percentage | Number of sites | Percentage | Number of sites | Percentage |
| $\leq 200$ | 116 | 10 | 601 | 52 | 18 | 1.5 | | |
| $> 200, \leq 400$ | 53 | 4.5 | 129 | 11 | 11 | 1 | | |
| $> 400, \leq 800$ | 34 | 3 | 89 | 8 | 10 | 1 | | |
| $> 800, \leq 1600$ | 26 | 2 | 33 | 3 | 14 | 1.2 | | |
| Total | 229 | 20 | 852 | 74 | 53 | 4 | 21 | 2 |

NOTES:

Case A =  The potentially contaminated plume would intersect a water well.

Case B =  The potentially contaminated plume would intersect a surface water body.

Case C =  A water well or surface water body is located near the site but not in the anticipated direction of the plume.

Case D =  There are no water wells or surface water bodies within 1600 meters of the site.

TABLE 6.  POTENTIAL ENDANGERMENT TO WATER SUPPLY FROM SITES HAVING HIGH CONTAMINATION POTENTIAL

| Distance in Meters | CASE A | | CASE B | | CASE C | |
|---|---|---|---|---|---|---|
| | Number of Sites | Number Lined | Number of Sites | Number Lined | Number of Sites | Number Lined |
| $\leq 200$ | 83 | 16 | 416 | 53 | 10 | 3 |
| $> 200, \leq 400$ | 41 | 11 | 79 | 15 | 4 | 1 |
| $> 400, \leq 800$ | 20 | 5 | 42 | 5 | 3 | 0 |
| $> 800, \leq 1600$ | 15 | 0 | 17 | 0 | 7 | 1 |
| Total | 159 | | 554 | | 24 | |

The obvious course to follow as a continuing mode of the SIA program is first to develop detailed data of the original inventory, then to expand the existing aquifer maps, and finally to develop methodologies and techniques for impoundment location and construction. Also, the assessment can serve as a guide for the development of related regulations and their implementation. Results of the evaluation could also disclose weaknesses in current regulations and, therefore, lead to suggested amendments to strengthen these regulations. All of these activities are associated with correction measures or better management practices of existing and future surface impoundments and sites. In addition, the assessment contains valuable information which is useful in developing or supplementing other programs.

Consider, for example, the Areawide Wastewater Management Plan as defined under Section 208 of the Clean Water Act. This program deals with many water quality issues ranging from controlling a multitude of point and non-point sources of pollutants to protecting surface and groundwater quality. Many of the strategies for non-point source pollutants evolving from these areawide Section 208 plans will be influenced by the surface impoundment assessment. Decision factors for "208" land use criteria, particularly for water supply protection, will also have to incorporate the high probability of groundwater contamination in most of New England as indicated in the assessment.

In the water supply decision matrix, there is more to consider than the high contamination potential resulting from the sites. Developing and protecting a drinking water source depends upon water quality, safe yield of source, projected population demands, and the projected population itself. Population demands will not only influence water supply alternatives but also influence, and be influenced by, the situation created by the surface impoundments. If the alternatives for drinking water souces are to flourish, waste disposal practices by means of surface impoundments should be curtailed, and other viable disposal alternatives must be sought. If economics come into play due to an increase of popula-

tion, and if surface impoundments are the most economically feasible waste disposal method, then restrictions would be required on various land uses and restrictions placed on certain drinking water sources. In such cases, the suitability of land use, i.e., the groundwater contamination potential, must be closely examined. Priorities can then be assigned according to the practicality and economics of the alternative before a decision on future resource commitments is made.

Groundwater management plans will also be initially dictated by the findings of this assessment because such surface activities, like the poorly controlled waste disposal impoundments, affect the subsurface environment. Results from the SIA will focus attention on specific areas of concern. Once these problem areas are defined, methods of regulating and managing them can be formulated. When a final systematic groundwater management plan has been developed, changes in surface impoundment practices as well as other waste disposal practices will inevitably occur.

We see through these three examples that waste disposal practices by means of surface impoundments, ground and surface water supply, and land use management planning are closely aligned. Decisions in one area will eventually affect the others; therefore, whether at design level or at management level, consideration of all these areas is necessary for an overall view of possible cause and effect situations.

CONCLUSION

The surface impoundment assessment, a first-round approximation, has exposed the order of magnitude of the contamination of pits, ponds, and lagoons, a nebulous notion two years ago. The assessment also revealed the extensive potential contamination problem and, in turn, brought about an awareness of ground water and its need for protection. Finally, the assessment served as a mechanism for creating programs and changing regulations related to groundwater protection and surface impoundment management.

# Methods for exploration and sampling
# of contaminated ground water

J. E. AYRES
M. BARVENIK
Goldberg, Zoino & Associates, Inc.

# Measurement and monitoring
# of organic contamination in ground water

R. M. CADWGAN
Environmental Research and Technology, Inc.

# The Department of Environmental Quality Engineering's role in the regulation of hazardous waste disposal

A. D. CORTESE    Department of Environmental Quality Engineering
T. F. McLOUGHLIN            Commonwealth of Massachusetts

ABSTRACT

This paper discusses the application of the 1976 federal Resource, Conservation and Recovery Act to Massachusetts and the 1979 state Hazardous Waste Management Act. A new division in the Massachusetts Department of Environmental Quality Engineering administers the program.

INTRODUCTION

When I looked at the advance copy of the program for this session, I realized that problems associated with hazardous waste disposal would have been fully documented by previous speakers; that you would have heard about the most recent state-of-the-art techniques for monitoring groundwater pollution; and that you would be fully aware of the public health and environmental consequences if the present situation were allowed to continue in an uncontrolled manner. By now you should be asking yourselves: What can be done about this problem? In the few minutes available, I shall attempt to answer this question.

RESOURCE CONSERVATION AND RECOVERY ACT (RCRA)

In a report to Congress in 1973, EPA first recommended passage of a federal law to regulate the handling of hazardous waste. EPA reported that although existing federal legislation was adequate to protect the air, surface waters, and oceans from improper disposal of hazardous waste, there were no national controls over its disposal on land. Moreover, the air and water pollution laws requiring industry to adopt environmentally acceptable treatment and disposal practices had increased the amounts of hazardous waste being dumped on the land. Thus, a law was needed to close the circle of federal environmental protection by providing, for the first time, control over disposal of hazardous waste on land and protection of ground water.

Congress responded in 1976 with passage of the Resource Conservation and Recovery Act (RCRA) - a law establishing a national program to protect human health and the environment from improper handling of solid waste and hazardous waste, and to encourage conservation of natural resources. Of primary interest to us today are those provisions of the act which address the hazardous waste issue. The hazardous waste management program outlined in the act and implemented by regulations developed by EPA is to be a national "cradle-to-grave" control system to track all significant quantities of hazardous waste from the point of generation as a waste to the point of ultimate disposal. By the way, radioactive wastes, which are regulated by the Nuclear Regulatory Commission, are excluded from the category of hazardous wastes regulated by the Resource Conservation and Recovery act. EPA's regulatory program, as first proposed on December 18, 1978, will include the following.

- Identification of hazardous waste.

- Standards for generators and transporters of hazardous waste.

- Performance, design, and operating requirements for facilities that treat, store, or dispose of hazardous waste.

- A system for issuing permits to such facilities.

- Guidelines describing conditions under which state governments can be authorized to carry out their new hazardous waste management programs.

Although EPA has not yet promulgated the final regulation identifying hazardous waste, we understand that it will consist, in part, of a list of substances regarded as hazardous, and, in part, of tests for four characteristics: ignitability, corrosivity, reactivity (or explosiveness), and toxicity. Since not all hazardous substances pose an equal danger to human health, many of us have urged EPA to incorporate a "degree-of-hazard" concept in the final regulations - requiring more stringent controls for the more hazardous substances.

Final regulations setting forth standards for generators and transporters were promulgated on February 26, 1980. Companies that generate wastes which are determined to be hazardous may either dispose of their wastes on-site or transport the wastes off-site for disposal. On-site disposal requires a permit, but not a manifest. Off-site disposal requires generators to originate a transport manifest, describing the amount, origin, routing, and destination of each shipment; to use approved containers and label them properly; to select a responsible company to transport the waste; to specify the facility to which the waste is to be delivered and to make certain that it has a valid permit; to confirm that a waste reaches the designated facility; to keep records of information in the manifest and report it to an authorized state or EPA; and to notify authorities of international shipments.

Transporters must deliver hazardous waste shipments to the facility designated by the generator, keep appropriate records, and report any spills enroute. Hazardous waste haulers do not need permits in the federal system, but some states, such as Massachusetts, require transporters to be licensed. It is EPA's hope and our hope that the manifest system will discourage such irresponsible actions by waste haulers as indiscriminate dumping into sewer systems, illegal midnight dumping of waste loads, and abandonment of consigned wastes.

Final regulations covering performance, design, and operating requirements for facilities that treat, store, or dispose of hazardous waste and the regulations for issuance of a permit to such facilities have not yet been promulgated. We know, however, that the final regulations will include standards which cover containing, testing, and destroying wastes so that they cannot contaminate ground water, surface water, or the atmosphere. There will also be standards for safety, emergency procedures in case of accidents, personnel training, record keeping, and demonstration of financial responsibility. To receive a permit, an applicant must meet the standards set for the specific type of facility (landfill, incinerator, etc.).

The hazardous waste management program can either be conducted by EPA or by a state authorized by EPA to conduct its own program. In order to receive authorization, the state program must be equivalent to the national program. Among other things, the state must have legislation and regulations that are no less stringent than the federal standards, and the state must show that it has the resources to administer and enforce the program. If a state's program does not fully comply with EPA requirements, EPA may grant the state interim authorization for two years, during which time the state program is to be further developed to meet the requirements for full authorization.

Massachusetts is now in the process of submitting its request to obtain interim authorization. As one of the steps in this process, the legislature last year enacted Chapter 704 of the Acts of 1979 (the so-called Hazardous Waste Management Act), which is now incorporated as Chapter 21C of the General Laws of the Commonwealth.

CHAPTER 21C

The purpose of the new law is "to provide adequate safeguards from the point of generation, through handling, processing, and final disposition of certain hazardous wastes which threaten the public health and safety and the environment, and to establish a statewide program to provide for the safe management of hazardous wastes."

To accomplish this, the act assigns responsibility for regulating hazardous wastes to the Department of Environmental Quality Engineering and establishes a new division of hazardous waste within DEQE to develop and administer the program.

DEQE is required to develop a regulatory program to carefully track and stringently control hazardous wastes from cradle-to-grave. The bill imposes penalties of up to $25,000 per offense

per day, and/or up to five years imprisonment for violation of the regulations. This means that offenses will be a felony.

Closely paralleling the federal legislation, the act says that DEQE must identify hazardous wastes; develop regulations and standards for those who generate, use, transport, treat, store, and dispose of such wastes; establish a cradle-to-grave manifest system; and require evidence of financial responsibility from hazardous waste licensees. In carrying out these tasks we are directed to be as consistent as possible with the federal Resource Conservation and Recovery Act.

The new act also:

1. Charges DEQE with responsibility for adopting standards and procedures for a hazardous waste licensing program, with fees of up to $500.

2. Requires the department to conduct a survey and publish a list of sites where hazardous wastes have been deposited or abandoned.

3. Establishes a special 19-member legislative commission to study the sensitive issue of siting hazardous waste treatment and disposal facilities. Senator Robert D. Wetmore (D-Barre) and Representative Richard J. Dwinell (D-Millbury) are co-chairmen of the commission, which must complete its study, draft appropriate legislation, and make other recommendations before July 1, 1980. At the present time the siting of hazardous waste facilities is subject to approval by local boards of health.

4. Establishes a Hazardous Waste Advisory Committee to review the development of standards, rules, and regulations required by the act, and to make recommendations to DEQE. The Governor has appointed 14 members to this committee.

5. Prohibits the siting of hazardous waste landfills over an aquifer which is or can be used for drinking water purposes. While the provision may limit the number of available landfill sites, it is estimated that no more than 20 percent of the state's land would be affected. The bill also directs the legislative commission to investigate the siting of hazardous waste landfills over aquifers.

6. Suspends the state's authority to take land for hazardous waste facilities until January 1, 1981, unless DEQE adopts hazardous waste regulations and siting criteria that are acceptable to the legislature before then. Private facilities can still be established if the local board of health first approves the site.

7. Finally, the act provides for a great deal of public participation throughout this whole process. In addition to having an advisory committee, we are required to hold at least six public hearings throughout the state before any regulations are promulgated. Furthermore, we must

notify local communities through the board of health about applications for hazardous waste licenses and about the quantities and types of wastes handled in each community annually.

The Department of Environmental Quality Engineering feels that we now have a strong legislative mandate to make certain that hazardous wastes are disposed of legally and safely. Last year the department issued orders to close 22 public water supply wells because of contamination by organic chemicals. But we have certain reservations about the short-term consequences of enforcing the new hazardous waste program, which we would like to share with you.

First, we are concerned about the shortage of legal disposal alternatives within the state. Without adequate, nearby facilities for storage, treatment or disposal, our waste generators must ship their wastes out-of-state to a limited number of facilities with a limited capacity. Already the market is responding to this facility shortage. One Massachusetts firm, which last year paid $400 a truckload for out-of-state disposal, is now paying $4,000 a truckload. This imposes an undue economic hardship upon industries located in this state who seek to comply with the law.

Second, as the cost of legal disposal becomes more expensive, the business of illegal midnight dumping becomes more attractive. In spite of stiff fines for violations of the new law, it will require a greatly expanded enforcement staff, plus the assistance of all existing state and local law enforcement personnel, to prevent and prosecute cases of illegal dumping. As reported in the newspapers in March of 1980, shipments of hazardous waste from as far away as Ohio and Delaware are now being transported into New England for illegal disposal. Again, this illegal activity is basically related to a shortage of available, legal disposal alternatives.

Finally, we are convinced that there must be a change in the institutional arrangements for siting facilities for the storage, treatment and disposal of hazardous wastes. In Massachusetts, the site assignment process is largely subject to control by the local board of health, under Chapter 111, section 150A, of the General Laws. Although the Department of Environmental Quality Engineering has the power to develop disposal policies, only the local boards of health have the power to implement the policy. This has already created a bottleneck in the asbestos removal program in schools. Asbestos is classified as a hazardous waste because it is a potentially dangerous air pollutant. Although it is universally agreed that the most suitable method of disposal is by landfilling and covering it, only two boards of health out of 351 in the state have been willing to authorize its disposal in a landfill. Why? Because they don't want hazardous waste in their communities, even though it has been removed from their schools or other buildings.

As a regulatory agency, the siting of facilities for disposal of hazardous wastes is beyond our proper jurisdiction. But we know that we shall be frustrated in our efforts to regulate hazardous waste unless, and until, there is public awareness of the need to site such facilities. Since Love Canal, the term "hazardous waste" has evoked only one emotion - fear, and one response - we don't want it in our community. It is going to be difficult to convince the public that it's already in their communities and that it's better to regulate it legally than to cope with it illegally.

All of you have dual interest in the hazardous waste problem. As geologists, engineers and scientists your expertise will be needed to identify and resolve existing hazardous waste problems and to site new facilities, when that day comes. As individuals, you have a personal stake in protecting yourselves and your families from the consequences of irresponsible hazardous waste disposal. This protection, I assure you, can only come about through the establishment of an adequate number of proper disposal alternatives within the state.

# Geochemistry of hazardous waste disposal

O. C. BRAIDS
Geraghty & Miller, Inc.

# 12

# TECTONICS

Session moderator

A. Lacroix
McClelland Engineers, Inc.

# Fluid inclusion studies
# for dating fault movement

## J. H. PECK
## Stone & Webster Engineering Corporation

## ABSTRACT

Faulting is pervasive in New England and records tectonic movements which have occurred in the geologic past. No presently active faults are known. Determination of the age of last movement on old faults is difficult but is required when faulting is found on or near nuclear reactor sites or other facilities licensed by the Nuclear Regulatory Commission. Analyses of fluids trapped within minerals which have crystallized from aqueous solutions circulating in fault planes give specific data on the geologic conditions present at the time of crystallization. Fluid inclusions reveal ranges of temperature, pressure, salinity, composition, and oxidation state of the solutions.

The studies of fluid inclusions in quartz, calcite, sphalerite, and other less common transparent crystalline minerals in fault zones provide clues as to depth of overburden, geothermal conditions, and anomalous fluid sources after initial fault movement. The minerals themselves act as sensitive strain indicators for the detection of movement after various stages of mineral crystallization.

Determination of the temperature range of crystal formation, the approximate formation pressure, and the composition of the fluids has enabled the geologist to put limiting values on the depth and other geologic conditions of formation. Assuming reasonable values for hydrostatic and lithostatic pressures and geothermal gradients, one can calculate qualitatively a depth range for crystallization. Minimum age of last fault movement is approximated by assuming conservative denudation rates and calculating the time necessary to exhume the mineralized fault.

## INTRODUCTION

Fluid inclusions are microscopic samples of liquid, gas, or both, which have been trapped within minerals during or after crystallization. These inclusions are thus very small remnants of the solutions from which the minerals were formed: they are bits of geologic history preserved for study. Where minerals have grown from solution circulating in fault zones, we have an opportunity to recreate part of the history of the zones by study of the fluid inclusions contained within the minerals.

Faults in New England are pervasive. In almost every major rock excavation, road cut, or natural exposure, indications of faulting in the vicinity are common. A trip through even short segments of tunnels in eastern Massachusetts shows that faults are the rule rather than the exception. Many of the faults show some form of mineralization within them, but not all.

Stratigraphic relationships give few clues to the age of fault movement. The rocks involved in fault movements are mostly Paleozoic in age or older, and they are overlain by Wisconsin age glacial deposits or even younger Holocene sediments. In a few places Mesozoic rocks may reduce the time gap significantly but even then a 100-million year (more or less) hiatus still exists.

Much of this interest in fault dating is the direct result of regulations governing the siting and safety analysis of nuclear facilities. The federal regulations require that faults be investigated to determine if they are capable of producing significant earthquakes (USAEC, 1973). Faults are judged capable if they show at least one movement within the last 35,000 years, or more than one in the last 500,000 years. In New England, the stratigraphic hiatus between bed rock and the overlying soil deposits does not allow a positive determination of fault capability by direct geological observation. The critical dates fall within the no-record gap. Several techniques have been utilized in the past decade or two to date fault movement. Radiometric dating of fault gouge, correlation with faults of established tectonic age, and inference based on style of deformation are a few.

The analysis of fluids trapped in the minerals which have grown within fault planes has allowed an indirect means of estimating the minimum age of faulting. The method and rationale are the subject of this brief discussion.

## MINERALS IN FAULT ZONES

Fault zones are mineralized to varying degrees. Gouge minerals formed from faulting itself and exotic minerals derived from wall rocks are not considered here. This report is concerned only with the crystalline secondary minerals formed from circulating solutions. Quartz, calcite, fluorite, sphalerite, and other less common transparent minerals contain fluid inclusions which can be studied under the microscope. Opaque or translucent, or aphanitic, minerals cannot be used for fluid inclusion study but may supply supplementary paragenetic or textural information useful for the analysis. Probably the most common minerals which occur in mineralized faults and provide good material for fluid inclusion analyses are quartz and calcite. It is important for the analyses that the minerals fill the fault zone, or that it can be shown by other geometric relationships that movement since last crystallization cannot have occurred without affecting the crystals.

## FLUID INCLUSIONS

A general description of fluid inclusions and their occurrence and study is given by Roedder (1967; 1972). Primary fluid inclusions are trapped during original growth and consist of the fluids from which the mineral host was precipitating. Secondary fluid inclusions are formed at some time after crystallization of the host when later fluids penetrate along fractures which are slowly healed by recrystallization. In analyzing minerals for fault dating, both primary and secondary inclusions are important sources of information.

The fluids trapped in inclusions may undergo changes after entrapment. Liquids trapped at high temperatures contract on cooling and form a vapor phase. This shows as a small bubble within the inclusion similar to the bubble of a carpenter's level. The cooling liquid may also precipitate mineral matter within the inclusion: these are so-called daughter salts. Some fluid inclusions show associations of liquid and vapor or all vapor in the same setting. These indicate growth in a boiling liquid and are useful in obtaining true temperatures of formation because there is no need for a pressure-correction (see Kelly and Turneaure, 1970).

Fluid inclusions are not as simple as outlined above, and their complex relationships need to be studied in great detail under the microscope from a number of samples. Experts in the field are available to do these detailed studies, and they constitute the source of much of the information given here.

Tests which can be utilized for analysis of fluid inclusions are heating tests, freezing tests, and crushing tests. These are all accomplished under high-power microscopic view.

Heating of the mineral specimen beneath the microscope produces changes in fluid inclusions which contain both liquid and vapor phases. The liquid expands until the vapor phase disappears. At this temperature, the inclusion is entirely liquid, and this temperature (corrected for total pressure) should correspond to the temperature of the original fluid at time of entrapment. Further heating will stretch the inclusion walls or fracture them. Heating of many two-phase fluid inclusions, and noting their relationships within the crystals, yields ranges of temperatures for the various primary and secondary inclusions in the samples.

Freezing tests are run to establish qualitative estimates of the salinity of the inclusion liquids. These tests are described fully by Kelly and Turneaure (1970) and Roedder (1963). The depression of the freezing temperature (or melting temperature) is related to the salinity of the liquid. These tests can also indicate values for internal pressure of $CO_2$, if $CO_2$ is present in the inclusions. Freezing will cause $CO_2$ clathrate compounds to form. The temperature at which these compounds disappear on warming is related to the internal $CO_2$ pressure (Takenouchi and Kennedy, 1965).

Crushing tests allow gas within the inclusions to be released. First, this gives a qualitative indication of whether the gas phase is under high pressure. Secondly, the released gases can be collected and analyzed for chemical content. Thirdly, the internal pressures of inclusions may be determined by measuring the expansion of gas when released.

These three types of tests are carried out on large numbers of inclusions within specimens from carefully collected samples. The megascopic and microscopic observations of texture, fabric, mineral paragenesis, fracturing, solid inclusions, and wall rock relationships are very important to the interpretation of the fluid inclusion tests.

## DATA DERIVED FROM INCLUSION STUDIES

Microscopic study and the various tests which can be made on fluid inclusions yield important information which provides limits for the pressure-temperature history of the mineralization. Texture and fabric observations determine the relationship of the minerals to each other and the fault zone itself. Mineral paragenesis establishes the succession and history of mineralization in the zone. Textural relationships indicate episodes of deformation, solution, and rapid or slow crystallization. The occurrence of solid inclusions or other mineral species may indicate the oxidation state of the mineralizing fluids and proximity to source of detritus. Sulfides, for example, are indicative of reducing environments and are sensitive ductile gages of even slight deformation (Kelly, 1975). The temperature, pressure, salinity, and composition information derived from the three test methods, when combined with the other observations, yields a powerful set of data which must be accommodated by the geologic history proposed for the fault.

## RESULTS APPLIED TO FAULTS

Fluid inclusions studies have been performed on a number of mineralized faults in the last few years with varying degrees of success. In Connecticut, a number of small faults cut Paleozoic metasedimentary rocks and late Paleozoic intrusive pegmatites. The faults are overlain by late Wisconsin till. Last movement was followed by deposition of quartz crystals within the faults. The crystals show no apparent deformation and have filled the fault plane in places. Heating experiments on fluid inclusions in the quartz by Dr. Earl Ingerson of the University of Texas showed a temperature range of 118° to 198°C. Correcting for total pressure, these temperatures were probably in the range 148° to 225°C. These temperatures indicate a period of hydrothermal activity subsequent to the faulting of the zone. There is no hydrothermal activity in the area at present and no known cause of hydrothermal activity since Jurassic to Cretaceous time. Based on the temperature of formation and correlation with known periods of hydrothermal activity in the region, the faulting was considered to be Jurassic or older.

In another fault zone in eastern New York, quartz crystals show inclusions that have liquid and vapor in some and vapor only in other adjacent inclusions. These inclusions were studied by Dr. William Kelly of the University of Michigan. In this particular instance, the inclusions indicated crystallization from a boiling liquid and, therefore, the inclusion temperatures are interpreted as true entrapment temperatures (total pressure equals vapor pressure). Crushing tests and freezing tests show that these crystals were formed under rather high pressures and contain gas which expands greatly on release from the inclusions. Freezing tests show that the liquid components are slightly saline and contain dissolved $CO_2$. The salinity appeared to be equivalent to about 3 1/2 percent NaCl and the $CO_2$ pressure about 44 bars minimum. Temperatures ranged from 193° to 201°C for the boiling type. Temperatures for normal liquid/vapor inclusions in the same crystals ranged from 165° to 180°C.

These temperatures and pressures indicate that the quartz grew under conditions of deep burial, not near the surface. The estimated minimum depth of formation based on minimum pressures is about 500 meters. Based on moderate pressures and allowing for $CO_2$ content within the inclusions, depths of 2 km would be reasonable. Temperatures of 200°C at depths of 2 km would require a geothermal gradient of about 90°C/km, much higher than normal. The rocks which are faulted are Middle Ordovician shales and graywackes which occur near the western edge of the Taconic gravity slides. No hydrothermal activity is now present in the vicinity and no record of extensive hydrothermal alteration is seen in the rocks. Thus, the high temperature is interpreted to be primarily the result of formation at significant depth in the crust, probably greater than 2 km and possibly as great as 6 km. Based on denudation rates similar to those determined for the White Mountains area by Doherty and Lyons (1980) of 1 km per 32 m.y., the minimum age of last movement would be earliest Tertiary. Using denudation rates for the Mississippi drainage basin of about 1 km per 19 m.y. (Pierce, 1979), the minimum age would be upper Eocene. Although the age of faulting is probably Ordovician, the fluid inclusion analysis demonstrates beyond a reasonable doubt that there has been no movement

on the fault for millions of years and the fault cannot be considered capable.

Another investigation of faulting in New York revealed calcite-filled slip planes which had a textural and paragenetic history of crystallization which showed a change from reducing to oxidizing conditions and progressive lowering of temperatures from the wall rock inward. Fluid inclusion analysis was done by Dr. H.L. Barnes of Pennsylvania State University. The crystal history showed minor deformations between episodes of crystallization. The fluid inclusions of the various crystal stages had somewhat overlapping ranges of temperatures but defined a decrease from about 170°C to about 90°C. No known hydrothermal activity in the surrounding area has been identified and the mineralization itself is expectable from normal sedimentary basin fluids. Based on the geologic history of the northern Appalachian basin, and given the high temperature and thermal gradients which can be developed during basin compaction and diagenesis (Jones, 1979), it was concluded that the faulting probably took place initially during diagenesis of the basin and that the last movement occurred when temperatures were near 100°C or above. This would be equivalent to about 3 to 4 km of rock in a normal geothermal gradient or 2 to 3 km in a region of elevated geothermal gradient. Based on Mississippi drainage denudation rates, this would place a minimum age of faulting at 38 to 57 million years--certainly not capable faulting by the definition of the Nuclear Regulatory Commission.

CONCLUSION

The study of fluid inclusions within suitable minerals which have grown in fault zones subsequent to fault movement yields useful geologic data. The data can be obtained relatively rapidly and inexpensively. The data have limitations and cannot be applied without knowledge of the geologic setting and the geometry of the fault system itself. When conditions allow, the use of temperature, pressure, paragenesis, and textural relationships derived from fluid inclusion studies can be used in a qualitative manner to provide estimates of minimum age of last fault movement. The fluid inclusion data should not stand alone but are best utilized to complement other geologic and laboratory studies. Used in a conservative manner, the fluid inclusion studies provide a useful tool in the study of fault history.

REFERENCES

Doherty, J.T., and Lyons, J.B., 1980, Mesozoic erosion rates in northern New England: Geological Society of America Bulletin, Part I, v. 91, n. 1, p. 16-20.

Jones, P.H., 1975, Geothermal and hydrocarbon regimes, northern Gulf of Mexico Basin, in Proceedings of the First Geopressured Geothermal Energy Conference: Dorfman, M.H., and Dellar, R.W., eds., University of Texas, p. 15-89.

Kelly, W.C., 1975, Analysis of fluid inclusions in quartz crystals from Greene County nuclear power plant site: Preliminary Safety Analysis Report, Appendix 2C, Power Authority of the State of New York Docket No. 50549, v. 4, 26 p.

Kelly, W.C., and Turneaure, F.S., 1970, Mineralogy, paragenesis and geothermometry of the tin and tungsten deposits of the eastern Andes, Bolivia: Economic Geology, v. 65, p. 609-680.

Pierce, D.S., 1979, Long term erosion as a factor in siting an underground nuclear waste facility: Geological Society of America, Abstracts with Programs, v. 11, n. 1, p. 48-49.

Roedder, E., 1963, Studies of fluid inclusions

II--freezing data and their interpretation: Economic Geology, v. 58, p. 167-211.

Roedder, E., 1967, Fluid inclusions as samples of ore fluids, in Barnes, H.L., ed., Hydrothermal ore formation: Holt, Rinehart and Winston, p. 515-574.

Roedder, E., 1972, Composition of fluid inclusions, Chapter JJ, Data of Geochemistry, 6th Ed.: U. S. Geological Survey Professional Paper 440JJ, 164 p.

Takenouchi, S., and Kennedy, G.C., 1965, Dissociation pressures of the phase $CO_2 \cdot 5 \, 3/4$ $H_2O$: Journal of Geology, v. 73, p. 383-390.

U.S. Atomic Energy Commission, 1973, Seismic and geologic siting criteria: 10CFR100, Appendix A, Federal Register, v. 38, no. 218, p. 31279-31285.

# New fault and fracture domains of southwestern New England— Hints on localization of the Mesozoic basins

D. U. WISE

Department of Geology and Geography,
University of Massachusetts at Amherst

## ABSTRACT

Fracture and fault data were collected at more than 500 stations throughout southwestern New England. They show a variety of scales and types of domains for the different structural elements. Areas of similarly oriented joint systems can be traced over distances of 20 to 100 kilometers before giving way, locally abruptly, to other systems. Topographic lineament swarms appear to have orientations relatively independent of the local joint or fault patterns with some of their domains extending far beyond southwestern New England. Minor slickensided fault surfaces form a curious domain characterized by strike-slip and oblique-slip motions. This domain, about 50 km wide, projects southeastward into the Newark Basin, is superimposed on the more northward trending grain of the Berkshires, and includes the Pomperaug, Deerfield, and Hartford Mesozoic Basins. The relationship is interpreted as the late Paleozoic and younger Mesozoic core region of the Appalachians, behaving in a slightly ductile fashion beneath brittle surface rocks so as to localize these Mesozoic basins in their present position.

## THE DATA BASE

A long term study of the brittle fracture elements of southwestern New England has been in progress for a number of years at the University of Massachusetts. The data were collected at fracture stations with measurement or notation of orientations and other characteristics of all fault surfaces, joints, joint zones, macrojoints, veins, etc., in large outcrop areas. Depending on the size of the outcrop area, 50 to several hundred measurements were made for each station. All data were computer encoded for easy interpretation and analysis.

These stations are scattered across the Albany and Hartford 1 x 2 degree quadrangles (the north and south halves, respectively, of Fig. 1). Many of the stations are concentrated in six E-W lines evident in Figure 1 as data clusters extending between the Hudson and Connecticut Rivers. The total data base now exceeds 500 stations with more than 25,000 joint observations and 3,000 measurements of motion characteristics of minor slickensided fault surfaces. Wise and students (1979) present a much more complete version of these data than is possible here.

## JOINTING

The dominant orientations of steeply dipping joints as picked off the equal area plots of joints at each station are illustrated in Figure 1. On a regional basis the most common trends are N70°-80°E, N20°-30°E, and N40°-50°E, although other orientations may be strongly developed within restricted domains.

Commonly, over areas 20-50 km across, a set of sub-parallel joints may dominate only to give way gradually or abruptly to other domains. A good example (Fig. 1) is the region of southwesternmost Massachusetts and adjacent New York State. There, almost all stations show a strongly developed, nearly orthogonal joint pattern striking N20°E and N75°W. Eastward along this line of stations in Massachusetts the N20°E set of joints disappears abruptly, and the N75°W set becomes much less prominent. On the lines of stations just north and south of this one, these two joint sets are subdued to absent.

The various joint sets are probably of several different ages. Most of the domains over which individual sets are developed seem to bear little obvious relationship to standard structural divisions of the region. One possible exception may be the N20°-30°E set which is sub-parallel to extensile structures of the Mesozoic Connecticut Valley, locally strongly developed in that area.

It is here suggested that most of the joint sets originated as minor extensile features whose fracture orientations (but not necessarily physical openings) were produced by subtle flexings and foldings of local to regional extent. These flexings were subtle enough to be lost in the intensely deformed rocks upon which they are overprinted. One example might be the N50°E joint set developed in the triangular area bounded by the lowermost Connecticut River and the adjacent coastline (Fig. 1). The trend of this joint set and its localization on the general NE projection of the Connecticut coast suggest an origin of this joint domain by a continuation of the gentle flexure which defines the coastline immediately to the west.

## TOPOGRAPHIC LINEAMENTS

As part of this same study, a variety of types of lineament maps were drawn, using many

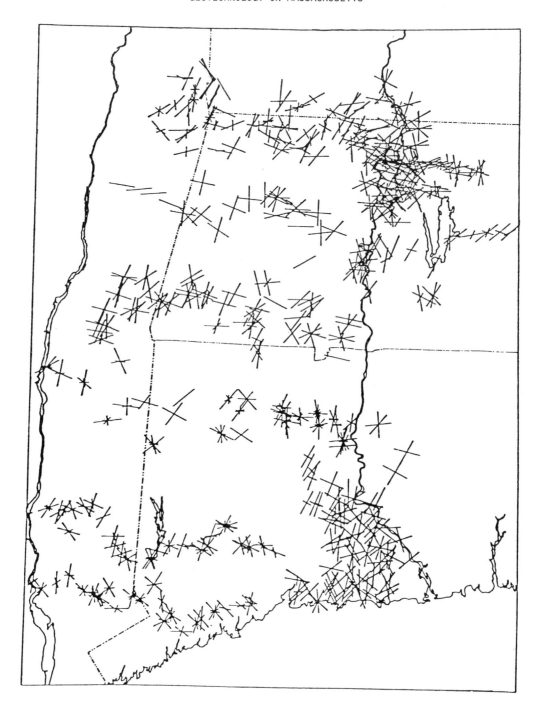

Figure 1.  Trends of steeply dipping major
joint sets derived from plots of data from
individual station locations.

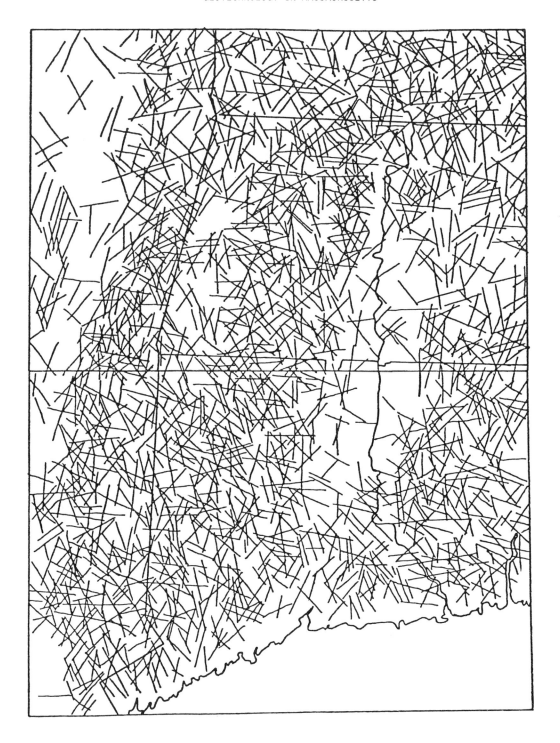

Figure 2. Topographic lineaments derived from
many azimuths of low angle illumination of
raised relief maps. These are considered the
most reliable and reproducible lineaments of
the many sets derived from a variety of types
of imagery. Note the comparative independence
of these lineament swarm domains from most of
the joints for the same areas in Figure 1.

kinds of regional imagery. The problems of variable albedo, shadow directions, man-made clutter, and image distortion (on the radar imagery) all made correlations of the lineament swarms and systems dubious at best. The most reliable lineament maps, in the opinion of the author, are those produced by combining results from images of raised plastic relief maps side-illuminated from a variety of azimuths (Wise, 1968; Wise et al., 1979). The lineament map of Figure 2 was prepared in this way. The north and south halves of the figure were drawn separately at different times. Consequently, the fact that many lineament swarm domains can be traced easily across the E-W centerline of the figure must be ascribed either to chance at an improbably high level or to the reality and validity of at least some of the lineament swarms as drawn.

Several lineament swarm trends of Figure 2 are regional in extent. N20°E, N20°W, and N60°-70°E sets are traceable as major components of the topographic grain of quadrangle after quadrangle of the northern Appalachians (Wise, 1976). Others seem more locally developed as, for example, a pervasive N10°-15°E set on the eastern side of the Hudson River valley. A N45°E set is strongly developed in northwestern Connecticut with some projection along strike into adjacent areas.

The origins of these lineament swarm domains are interpreted in accord with a study of lineament domains of all Italy in relation to other structural features (Wise et al., under review). It is believed they are formed perpendicular to late and post-orogenic regional extensile stresses. In Italy, and probably here, many of them mark the trends and locations of broad regional flexures. Some of the individual lines in the swarms are identifiable as small to large faults, predominantly of normal or vertical displacement. Most appear to be zones of more intense joint development which have been selectively eroded and enhanced. The N60°-70°E set, with the longest average lengths of individual lines, has been interpreted as the trace of the maximum compressive stress in the present day stress field (Wise, 1976).

FAULTING

Probably the most significant finding of this study is that a broad zone of fault types other than typical dip-slip varieties trends NE more or less on the projection of the Newark Basin-Ramapo system (Fig. 3). Black areas on the figure are clusters of stations where strike-slip and oblique-slip slickensides predominate over dip-slip motions. The domain of strike-slip components is bounded to the west or northwest by areas in which outcrop-scale slickensided surfaces are much more difficult to find. This observation of change in fault density was made by individual groups of people along each of the four northern traverses. All noted a slickenside dead spot or "no fault zone" in their line of stations. The zone of less abundant minor faults is thus not a

function of differing observers missing some feature, nor does it seem to be particularly a function of average size of exposure, nor rock type. Instead it appears to be an area which simply did not suffer as much post-metamorphic jostling of minor blocks.

The zone in which outcrop-scale $\sigma_2$ (intermediate stress axis) seems to plunge at steeper than usual angles is about 50 km wide as it crosses the grain of the Berkshires. Its western boundary has been generally defined by this study. A northern terminus or at least a narrowing of the zone is suggested at the head of the Mesozoic Deerfield Basin. The eastern boundary seems to wander near the Connecticut River southward across two-thirds of Connecticut. Unfortunately, the present data base does not extend very far into the Paleozoics of Connecticut east of the Mesozoic border fault. Farther southeast in the Narragansett Pier area of Rhode Island, large numbers of minor left lateral strike-slip faults of severage ages trend E-W (Wise et al., 1975). To the northeast, the eastern two-thirds of the Quabbin tunnel data logs show predominantly ENE striking strike-slip faults (central Massachusetts at the eastern edge of Figure 3). The eastern end of the northern traverse is also a region of predominant strike-slip faults. Any or all of these eastern strike-slip regions could be extensions of the strike-slip domain insofar as it is constrained by the present data base.

Through computerization of all the data, plots of all the azimuths or slickenlines of the various fault classes were produced. Within the Connecticut Valley and adjacent areas, normal and vertical dip-slip faults of N to NE trends seem to be more common. Families of dip-slip faults indicative of a Mesozoic extension oriented about N60°-70°W are present in many areas along the eastern portion of the Connecticut Valley and in the adjacent crystalline rocks.

Evidence of more complicated fault motions appears throughout the area. The Meriden area of Connecticut (large black area in central Connecticut of Figure 3) is almost completely dominated by strike-slip slickenlines, even though the major displacement on the master NE-trending faults of that area must be dip-slip. Later stages of N-S compression and some complicated rotations are suggested to account for these features, as well as anomalous rotation of a major block near the Farmington Reservoir of Connecticut. Complicated patterns of strike-slip motions also appear at the head of the Connecticut Valley in the Montague Basin. Individual plots showing the azimuths of faults for that area have a complicated pattern but reveal one surprising feature: even though NE or NNE quadrangle-scale faults are common throughout this zone on the projection of the Ramapo-Newark Basin disturbed area, the minor outcrop-scale slickensided and slickenlined surfaces are conspicuously lacking in parallel fault orientations! If any pattern can be seen in the minor outcrop scale faults, it is a tendency for high frequencies of NW-trending strikes.

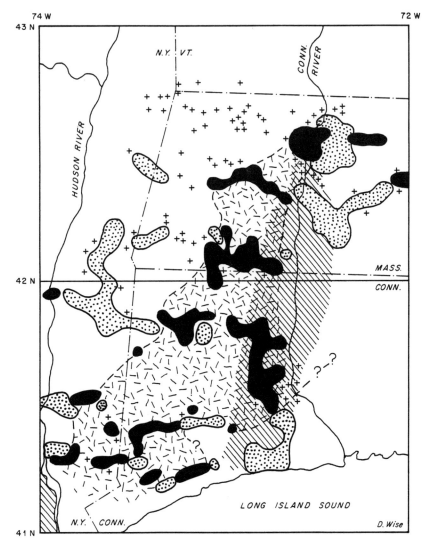

Figure 3. Patterns of dominant motion on
minor slickenlines from clusters of individual
stations. Areas of stations dominated by
oblique or strike-slip motions are blackened.
The NE-trending zone in which these blackened
areas predominate is patterned.

The ages of these fault patterns are for the most part late or post-metamorphic. Relatively few mylonites and related zones were recorded. Breccia zones were not particularly common. Instead, the minor slickensided and slickenlined surfaces are associated mostly with low grade metamorphic minerals. Chlorite, quartz, and calcite are typical associates. The fact that the zone is superimposed on, and cuts transversely across, the grain of the Jurassic rocks of the Mesozoic Basin in the Connecticut Valley indicates that the zone is at least in part Jurassic or younger in age. The high level of tectonic activity in the Jurassic in this region suggests Jurassic as the most probable but by no means the proven age for the domain.

INTERPRETATION

These studies show a complex of overlapping domains of many classes and ages of fractures. Some correlate in location of domain boundaries and orientation, but for the most part they seem semi-independent of each other. They also appear to have little obvious relationship to the traditional structural provinces and divisions of southwestern New England. Two of the classes, joints and topographic lineaments, are suggested as originating largely as extensile features associated with local to broad but subtle flexures of the region. McHone (1978) has described Mesozoic dike swarms of many ages in northern New England with domain sizes and relationship to country rock not unlike some of the swarms described here. There may well be a very complicated late Paleozoic, Mesozoic and Cenozoic brittle fracture history to be gleaned from the Appalachian core region as we come to define and understand these brittle structures more fully.

Most significant of the fracture domains are those marked by outcrop-scale slickensided and slickenlined surfaces. These fall into at least two different types and domains indicative of contrasting stress history.

- One domain, as developed most strongly along the Connecticut Valley and just to the east of it, is characterized by minor Mesozoic normal faults permitting extension perpendicular to and in general accord with the N30°E basaltic Jurassic dike swarms of the area.

- The second domain is a 50 km wide zone across the southern Berkshires on the NE projection of the Newark Basin. It is characterized by steeply plunging sigma 2 (intermediate) stress axes but has a wide variety of strikes of the individual strike-slip faults. The zone must be, at least in part, younger than the Mesozoic Basin fill upon which it is superimposed.

This strike-slip minor fault domain corresponds in a general way to the core region of this portion of the Appalachians, a zone which at depth in later Paleozoic and early Mesozoic time might have remained slightly more ductile than the surrounding regions. As such it could have concentrated a variety of ages and orientations of lateral strains along its length. These were manifested in the brittle near-surface rocks as minor strike-slip motions on both new and pre-existing joint surfaces. With the onset of great rifting stresses of the early Mesozoic, much of the strain was concentrated in this same weakened zone but strongly influenced by older anisotropies of the area. The older Ramapo Fault was reactivated to mark the boundary of the deep ductile zone in the Newark Basin area. The westward dipping flanks of the mantled gneiss domes of the Bronson Hill Anticlinorium were utilized as master faults bounding the Connecticut Valley Basin, even though their N-S strike was not completely in accord with the N60°W extension being superimposed on the region. The result was the family of N30°E normal faults that characterize the area just east of the Connecticut River and contribute to the jagged nature of the border fault zone in that region.

There were probably many small normal faults across the region as the Mesozoic rifting episode began. However, those that had the advantage of passing downward as listric faults into the ductile core region became the master faults of the Mesozoic basins. The ductile core region concentrated the greatest stretching and hence the greatest sinking along it. Thus, it localized the deepest parts of the Connecticut Valley Basin in the vicinity of the Massachusetts-Connecticut State line approximately in the center of the zone. Northward and southward of that area, the Mesozoic fill thins and fails to be preserved at about the northern and southern boundaries of the two States. Some strike-slip motions continued to be concentrated along the zone subsequent to the creation of the Mesozoic basins, superimposing some minor strike-slip fault motions on the basin fill.

ACKNOWLEDGMENTS

Portions of this work were supported by the Nuclear Regulatory Commission, the National Aeronautics and Space Administration, and the Mobil Oil Company. Many of my colleagues on the faculty of the University of Massachusetts gave generous assistance both to me and to many students involved in the various studies. Students who performed much of the data collection were Colleen Barton, Paul Bauer, William Chandler, Farinaz Danesh, Lee Estabrook, Arthur Goldstein, Matthew Golombek, David Haines, Michael Hozik, Joseph Ingari, Polly Knowlton, Thomas Maher, Dimitri Massaras, Christine Peterson, Jeffrey Pferd, Robert Piepul, Imants Reks, Jay Silverman, Gerard Smith, Gerald Williams, and Steven Wrenn.

REFERENCES

McHone, J.G., 1978, Distribution, orientations and ages of mafic dikes in central New England: Geological Society of America Bulletin, v. 89, p. 1645-1655.

Wise, D.U., and students, 1979, Fault, fracture
and lineament data for western Massachusetts
and western Connecticut: Final report to
the Nuclear Regulatory Commission for contract number AT(49-24-0291), 250 p.

Wise, D.U., Hozik, M.J., Goldstein, A.G., and
Piepul, R.G., 1975, Minor fault motions in
relation to Mesozoic tectonics of southern
New England: Transactions, American Geophysical Union, v. 56, p. 451. Abstract.

Wise, D.U., 1976, Sub-continental sized fracture

systems etched into the topography of New
England, in Proceedings of the First International Converence on New Basement Tectonics: Utah Geological Association Publications, v. 5, p. 416-422.

Wise, D.U., Funiciello, R., Parotto, M., and
Salvini, F., Lineament mechanisms and
tectonic settings indicated by fracture
domains of Italy: Unpublished manuscript.

Williams, H., 1978, Tectonic-lithofacies map of
the Appalachian Orogen: Memorial University
of Newfoundland, Map 1.

Hors-texte

The Westfield traprock quarry in Westfield, Massachusetts.  Excavations,
just right of center, run for about two miles north-south along the East
Mountain ridge.  North is to the top.  The Massachusetts turnpike runs
along the north edge of the area photographed, and the Westfield River
crosses the lower part.  On its north bank there are railroad tracks
with a spur line to the quarry.

# Neotectonic events in New England—
# Current status of research on earthquakes

P. J. BAROSH
Weston Observatory
Department of Geology and Geophysics
Boston College

## ABSTRACT

Historical and instrumental earthquake data show New England to have a continuing moderate level of seismicity. The epicentral pattern indicates a wide variation in earthquake activity across the region with the moderate and larger earthquakes concentrated in several areas. Suggestions that earthquakes are related to postglacial rebound or distribution of basic plutons does not appear to explain this pattern. Investigations of the areas of higher seismicity revealed the presence of abundant faults and probable faults, and the epicentral trends appear to parallel the local structural trends. This suggests that the earthquakes are related to faults, although no fault has yet been proven active nor is the location of epicenters sufficiently accurate to locate an earthquake on a particular fault unequivocally.

The pattern of seismicity is only poorly correlated with the dominant Paleozoic tectonic features of the region. Many of the areas of activity occur where high-angle normal faults are present, and many of these faults are Mesozoic or younger in age. Mesozoic intrusive rocks also occur in some of the seismically active areas.

Seismic activity occurs mostly in lowland areas below 300 m in elevation, particularly in bays and major river valleys, except for a few locations in the Adirondack and White Mountains. A few active areas are known to be subsiding at present, and the Adirondack Mountains are rising. Earthquakes, geomorphic features and present vertical movements may all be related to structural control in bed rock. Reactivation of extensional faults due to minor rifting could account for the seismicity of the region.

## INTRODUCTION

Causes of moderate but persistent seismic activity in the northeastern United States and adjacent Canada have been difficult to assess due to lack of sufficient geologic and seismologic data. There is a great need to improve our understanding and to evaluate the hazards of earthquakes in order to provide a better basis for the design of critical structures to withstand the regional seismic activity. The New England Seismotectonic Study was initiated to meet this need. Data generated by this study in conjunction with the improved earthquake location data of the Northeastern United States Seismic Network, stud-

ies by utility companies for power plant sites, studies in New York by the Lamont Doherty Geophysical Survey, and studies in adjacent Canada by the Earth Physics Branch of the Canadian Geological Survey have vastly improved our knowledge of the nature of earthquakes in the region over the past several years. This report identifies the present research activity in New England and summarizes some of the general results.

## NEW ENGLAND SEISMOTECTONIC STUDY

The New England Seismotectonic Study is a six-year multifaceted study which integrates geological, geophysical, and seismological research to investigate earthquake mechanisms and better define earthquake zonation in the northeastern United States.

The study, now in its fourth year, is sponsored by the U.S. Nuclear Regulatory Commission. It is a cooperative study drawing its personnel from various universities and State and Federal geological surveys. It is planned and coordinated from Weston Observatory of Boston College. The study involves about 30 geologists and geophysicists annually plus their assistants and, on occasion, geodesists, historians, and archaeologists. Faculty and research personnel from 19 universities have participated in the program to date. The multi-year nature of the study allows a systematic acquisition of information needed to prepare an earthquake zonation map by mid-1982.

A series of integrated studies, geologic, geophysical, remote sensing, and others, has been planned to investigate the geologic structure and fault history of each of the areas of higher seismic activity in the region. Operation of a portable seismograph array also has been planned for each area for better epicentral control. Paralleling the local studies, regional maps are being prepared such as: epicenter maps (Chiburis, in press), a map showing fault tectonics (Barosh and Johnson, 1978), a gravity map (Hildreth, 1979), a magnetic lineament map (Barosh and others, 1977) and a Landsat lineament map (Isachsen and McKendree, 1977). Both local and regional data are being used to look for any consistent relationship to seismicity. The reports of several of these studies have been completed (see Barosh, 1979, and Appendix A; Wise, 1981); others are in preparation.

The seismograph records for New England have been reviewed to better locate and to search for

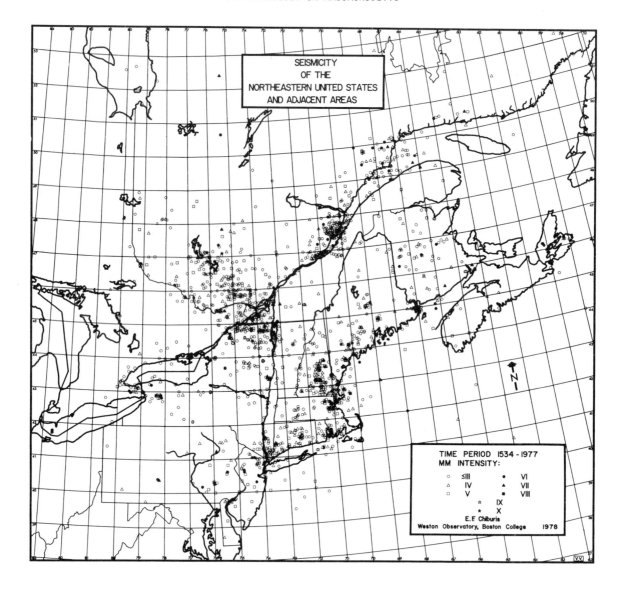

Figure 1. Seismicity of the northeastern
United States and adjacent areas.

additional past seismic events. These revised
seismic data along with historical data have been
used to compile a more consistent earthquake cat-
alogue and epicenter map of the region (Fig. 1)
(Chiburis, in press). These improved data are
now providing the basis for new seismological
studies.

SEISMICITY

Seismic activity over the past 350 years in
New England and its vicinity has been very un-
even in distribution (Fig. 1). It appears to have

been concentrated in only a few areas. The modern
day instrumentally located earthquakes occur mainly in areas noted for earthquakes earlier (Barosh,
1979). Population and seismograph distribution
do not appear to have greatly biased the results.
However, the level of activity within a few areas
of concentration has varied considerably with
time, and western New York does not show up in the
historic records (Paul Pomeroy, pers. comm.).
The largest earthquake in New England was the 1755
earthquake located at sea north of Cape Ann. This
earthquake was of approximately intensity VIII and
caused over 200 chimneys to fall in Boston (Boston
Edison, 1976).

## GEOLOGIC RELATIONSHIPS

Investigations in the areas of higher seismic activity (Fig. 2) have revealed numerous faults and probable faults, some with very large displacements (Barosh, 1979, Table 1). None so far have been proven active, although the results of a detailed seismic survey on Lake Champlain strongly suggest that the Pleistocene deposits have been offset by high-angle faults in bed rock (J.J. Dowling and A.S. Hunt, written comm.). Most faults in the region appear to have originated

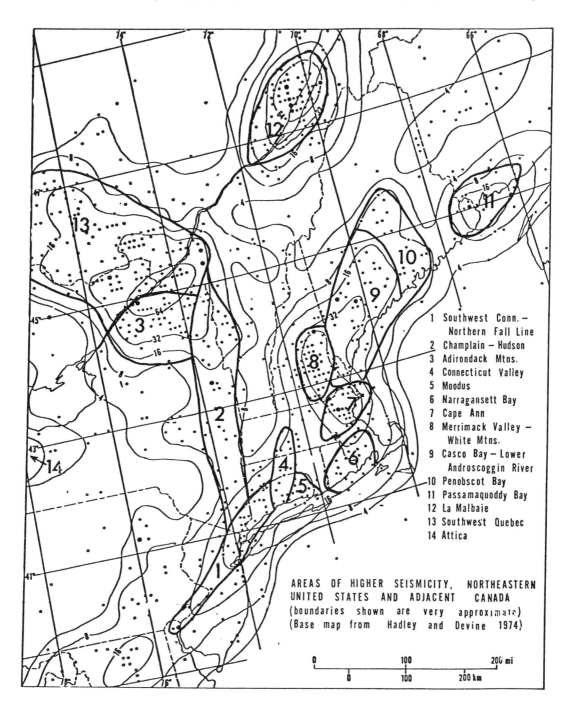

1  Southwest Conn. –
   Northern Fall Line
2  Champlain – Hudson
3  Adirondack Mtns.
4  Connecticut Valley
5  Moodus
6  Narragansett Bay
7  Cape Ann
8  Merrimack Valley –
   White Mtns.
9  Casco Bay – Lower
   Androscoggin River
10 Penobscot Bay
11 Passamaquoddy Bay
12 La Malbaie
13 Southwest Quebec
14 Attica

AREAS OF HIGHER SEISMICITY, NORTHEASTERN
UNITED STATES AND ADJACENT CANADA
(boundaries shown are very approximate)
(Base map from Hadley and Devine 1974)

Figure 2.  Areas of higher seismicity, northeastern
United States and adjacent Canada.

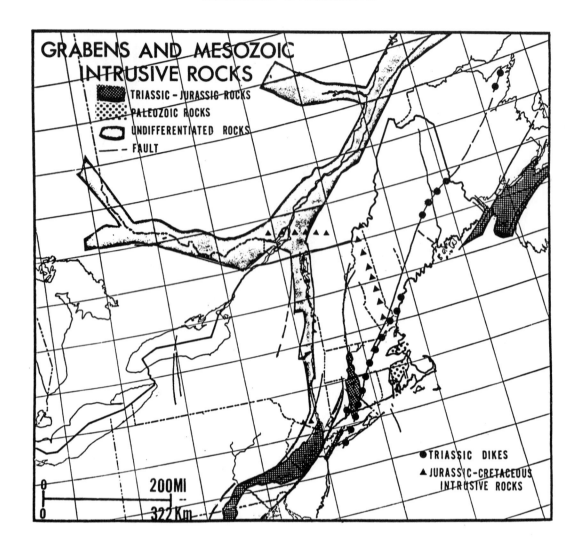

Figure 3. Grabens and Mesozoic intrusive rocks.

during the Paleozoic or latest Precambrian as deep-seated compressive structures, some of which were reactivated under shallower and more brittle tensional conditions during the Mesozoic or since.

A great deal of new information has been learned over the past few years about Paleozoic tectonic features and particularly plate tectonics. Regional tectonic patterns, however, show only spotty correlations with the pattern of modern day seismicity.

Many major Paleozoic structures coincide only locally or not at all with the distribution of seismic activity. The trace of the Paleozoic plate boundary, for example, which is marked in part by the Clinton-Newbury fault zone, passes

through an active area near Cape Ann, but shows no evidence of seismicity elsewhere. Paleozoic structural blocks generally cannot be related to areas of seismic activity, except that areas of very low earthquake activity appear to correspond to the eastern Vermont and Catskill Mountains structural blocks. Nor can seismic activity be correlated with the distribution of mafic plutons.

Onshore areas of Mesozoic high-angle extensional faults and granitic intrusive rocks show, where known, a better correlation with seismic activity than Paleozoic features (Fig. 3). Other areas of high-angle extensional graben-forming faults of unknown age also show a generally good correlation with seismic activity (Fig. 3). These may have formed during the general period of tension that dominated Mesozoic time.

## TOPOGRAPHY AND PRESENT SURFACE MOVEMENTS

Vertical uplift is known to have occurred in the region since the end of the Pleistocene about 13,000 years ago. Glacial rebound that resulted from melting of the east continental ice sheet caused a progressive rise in the land surface from south to north across New England of about 1 m per kilometer. This general rise shows little correspondence to the pattern of seismic activity.

Earthquakes in New England and adjacent areas are mainly confined to lowland areas below 300 m, except for a few in the Adirondack and White Mountains. They are particularly abundant in bays and major river valleys. Most indentations in the New England coastline appear to be active.

By the use of various releveling methods, six areas of seismic activity have been found to be undergoing vertical movement at present (Fig. 4). The Adirondacks are rising (Isachsen, 1975), but the other areas are subsiding. The relative rate of subsidence in the Passamaquoddy Bay area of Maine is 9 mm per year (Tyler, Ladd and Borns, 1979). This subsidence of the lowlands, which is the reverse of glacial rebound, is possibly caused by some other tectonic force and may be responsible for generating earthquakes.

## CONCLUSIONS

The irregular distribution pattern of historic and instrumentally located earthquakes

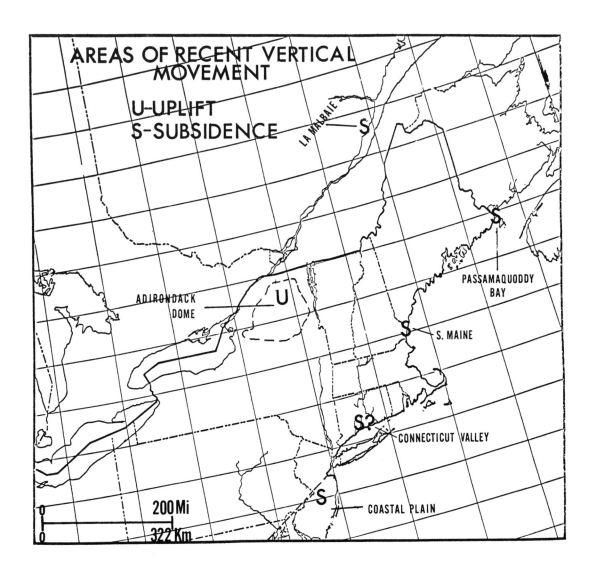

Figure 4. Areas of recent vertical movement.

appears to represent a good approximation of the seismically active areas. Faults are present in these areas, and the general trend of epicenters parallels the general trend of geologic structures. No fault has yet been proven active, however, nor are epicenters located sufficiently accurately to assign an epicenter convincingly to a particular fault.

The nearly aseismic areas of eastern Vermont and the Catskill Mountains correspond with Paleozoic structural blocks, but in general the overall correspondence of Paleozoic tectonic features with seismicity is poor. The distribution of high-angle extensional faults and grabens, some of known Mesozoic age, and Mesozoic intrusive rocks shows a fair correspondence with areas of seismic activity.

Earthquakes generally occur in lowlands below 300 m elevation, except for some in the Adirondack and White Mountains. Several lowland active areas are known to be subsiding at present, and the Adirondacks are rising. Both the distribution of earthquakes in lowlands and present subsidence may be related to structural control in bed rock. Reactivation of graben-forming extensional faults, due to present day minor rifting across the region, could account for the earthquake activity and subsidence.

## REFERENCES

Barosh, P.J., 1979, New England seismotectonic study activities during fiscal year 1978: U.S. Nuclear Regulatory Commission Report NUREG/CR-0939, 178 p., appendices.

Barosh, P.J., and Johnson, C.K., 1978, Fault map of onshore-offshore northeast United States and southeast Canada from published sources: New England Seismotectonic Study Report, Weston Observatory, Boston College, scale 1:1,000,000.

Barosh, P.J., Pease, M.H., Jr., Schnabel, R.W., Bell, K.G., and Peper, J.P., 1977, Aeromagnetic lineament map of southern New England showing relation of lineaments to bedrock geology: U.S. Geological Survey Miscellaneous Field Studies Map MF-885, scale 1:250,000.

Boston Edison Company, 1976, History of seismicity in New England: Boston Edison Company, Pilgrim Unit No. 2.

Chiburis, E.F., Earthquake epicenter map of the northeastern United States and adjacent areas, 1534-1977: New York State Museum Map and Chart Series, scale 1:1,000,000. In press.

Hadley, J.B., and Devine, J.F., 1974, Seismotectonic map of the eastern United States: U.S. Geological Survey Miscellaneous Field Studies Map MF-620.

Hildreth, C.T., 1979, Bouguer gravity map of northeastern United States and southeastern Canada onshore and offshore: New York State Museum Map and Chart Series No. 32, scale 1:1,000,000.

Isachsen, Y.W., 1975, Possible evidence for contemporary doming of the Adirondack Mountains, New York, and suggested implications for regional tectonics and seismicity: Tectonophysics, v. 29, p. 169-181.

Isachsen, Y.W., and McKendree, W.G., 1977, Preliminary brittle structures map of New York, and generalized map of recorded joint systems in New York: New York State Museum Map and Chart Series 31, 7 maps.

Tyler, D.A., Ladd, J., and Borns, H.W., 1979, Crustal subsidence in eastern Maine: U.S. Nuclear Regulatory Commission Report NUREG/CR-0887, 7 p.

Wise, D.U., 1981, New fault and fracture domains of southwestern New England--hints on localization of the Mesozoic basins: Geotechnology in Massachusetts (this volume).

# Tectonics and earthquakes of Massachusetts from a regional context

## J. R. RAND
### Cundy's Harbor, Maine

## R. J. HOLT
### Weston Geophysical Corporation

## ABSTRACT

The tectonic history of the northeastern region which includes Massachusetts is characterized by a series of dynamic compressional and extensional deformations which began in Late Precambrian time and continued until late in the Mesozoic Era. The earlier compressional orogenic episodes successively created and joined distinctive blocks of crystalline basement, ultimately to form the present continental crust of the region. Following the development of these primary blocks, Late Paleozoic oblique continent-continent collisions and Mesozoic rifting and volcanic-plutonic activity locally superimposed younger tectonic structures on the earlier-consolidated crustal blocks.

The region's historical earthquakes greater than intensity VI(MM), in an estimated magnitude range of 5.2 to 7.0, occurred near La Malbaie, Montréal and Cornwall-Massena on the St. Lawrence River; off Cape Ann, Massachusetts; near the Ossipee Mountains in New Hampshire; and in northeastern and southwestern New Jersey. Most historical events of lesser intensity, plus very small instrumentally-detected modern earthquakes, tend to cluster in the areas of the larger events. These seismicity patterns also generally conform with distinctive, geologically-younger tectonic domains exhibiting discontinuities in bedrock rigidity, density, or structural geometry. Most of Massachusetts is historically aseismic. The larger earthquakes have occurred in the northeast corner, where a major post-metamorphic fault system has been intruded by a cylindrical mafic pluton.

## INTRODUCTION

The New England region can be subdivided into five basic blocks of crystalline basement that were created by pre-Carboniferous orogenic forces, and were joined to form the present continental crust of the land area. These blocks are designated A, B, C, D and E in Figure 1. Subsequent to their creation, and to their joining under conditions variously of orogenic compression or continent-to-continent collision, the blocks were deformed by faulting and locally disrupted by volcanic and plutonic activity under conditions of crustal extension, intermittently during the interval from Late Paleozoic to Middle Cretaceous time. The major areas of Mesozoic rift faulting and plutonic invasion are designated "F" on Figure 1 (rifts = dots and horizontal lines; plutons

= solid black). The region is not known to have experienced dynamic tectonism for the past 100 million years, although it has undergone broad epeirogenic warping and, in the past million-or-so years, intermittent crustal depression and rebound associated with the passage of continental glaciations.

## TECTONIC PROVINCES

To characterize briefly what we see as the five basic crustal blocks of the region, as defined on Figure 1:

● Block A is comprised of Upper Precambrian geosynclinal formations that were consolidated to a regionally-extensive crustal block during the Grenvillian orogeny, about 1100 million years ago. The closely-spaced stipple pattern on Figure 1 defines the area where Grenvillian rocks crop out in the Adirondack uplift.

● Block B is comprised largely of Late Precambrian basement rocks that were consolidated and widely intruded during the Avalonian orogeny, about 600 million years ago. The Avalonian basement also encloses intrusive masses whose radiometric ages fall between 400 to 450 million years, plus several supracrustal basins containing Early to Late Paleozoic sedimentary and volcanic continental assemblages.

● Block C is made up of Early Paleozoic geosynclinal and volcaniclastic rocks having island arc affinities, for which radiometric dating suggests consolidation as a crustal block by orogenic forces about 480 to 500 million years ago. In common with Block B, Block C also contains intrusive masses dating from 400 to 450 million years in northeastern Massachusetts and southeastern New Hampshire. In the Penobscot Bay area, Maine, Block C contains Late Precambrian rocks dated at 600 million years; in eastern Connecticut, a thin-skinned slice of Block C has over-ridden Block B along the Lake Char and Honey Hill faults.

● Block D is essentially comprised of Cambrian and Early Ordovician geosynclinal formations with remobilized imbricate thrust sheets of Grenvillian basement in the western part (stippled areas on Figure 1), and an Ordovician island arc sequence along the eastern edge, all consolidated and annexed to the Grenvillian craton by westerly-directed compression during the Taconic orogeny, culminating about 450 million years ago. The block also contains a synform of Silurian and Devonian mio- and eugeosynclinal rocks (widely-spaced rulings on Figure 1), and rift basins of Triassic-to-Jurassic age (dots and rulings on Figure 1).

● Block E is comprised of Silurian and Devonian eugeosynclinal deposits that were compressed and uplifted between the Taconic Block D to the west and an undetermined northwesterly-advancing continental mass to the east, complexly folded, metamorphosed, faulted, intruded and consolidated to form the final crustal block of the region, during the Acadian orogeny which culminated about 360 million years ago. Block E is commonly known as the Merrimack Synclinorium.

## PROVINCE SEISMICITY

Well, that's all very nice. But our interest here is in seismicity, and the question is, "What have ancient tectonic provinces got to do with modern earthquakes?" As depicted in Figure 2, the answer seems to be "Nothing specific." Block E, the Merrimack Synclinorium, does seem to contain a disproportionate number of epicenters, but they are distinctly clustered and, in 250 years of population history, have not wandered south within the province from New Hampshire into central Massachusetts. Conversely, Block D, the fold belt containing the Green Mountain and Bronson Hill Anticlinoria and the Middlebury and Connecticut Valley Synclinoria, is largely characterized by its lack of seismicity, except to the south in Connecticut, southeasternmost New York and New Jersey. The greatest historical seismic energy release in new England has occurred in northeastern Massachusetts toward Cape Ann, indiscriminately overlapping the boundary of two ancient provinces. It seems fair to conclude that something other than ancient tectonic provinces per se controls the accumulation and sudden release of crustal stress.

## POST-METAMORPHIC DEFORMATIONS

Consider now what has happened to New England subsequent to the orogenic development of the five basic crustal blocks. Following the Acadian orogeny the region was subjected first to a sequence of continent-to-continent glancing collisions in Late Paleozoic time, and then to episodes of crustal extension, rifting and volcanic-plutonic invasions, during much of the Mesozoic Era. These post-metamorphic events variously superimposed or reactivated deep-seated fault systems in the basement blocks (Fig. 3), both in eastern and southern New England and in the ancient failed arm of the Grenvillian craton northwesterly from Montréal.

During the upper Paleozoic Variscan and Allegheny continent-to-continent collisions, a strike-slip fault system sliced along the general boundary zone of Blocks C and E in southern Maine. The Avalonian Block B was transported into place in southeastern New England along a major trans-current fault system of which the Bloody Bluff

fault in northeastern Massachusetts is a primary feature. This transverse shifting of coastal blocks was followed at the end of the Paleozoic by complex thrust faulting in a broad zone of deformation in northeastern Massachusetts, bounded by the Clinton-Newbury fault and the North Border fault of the Boston Basin. Carboniferous rocks of the Boston and Narragansett Basins were folded and deformed by relatively thin-skinned thrust faulting. The Ramapo fault system in northern New Jersey was reactivated. Eastern Pennsylvania experienced widespread folding, thrust faulting and Grenvillian basement remobilization.

During the Mesozoic Era, up to about 100 million years ago, crustal extension attendant upon the departure of the continental mass or masses responsible for the Variscan and Allegheny collisions led to rifting in the Gulf of Maine, in the southern Connecticut Valley, and along the east edge of the Appalachian chain from New Jersey into Alabama. Volcanic-plutonic complexes were emplaced in central New England at discrete time intervals in Triassic, Jurassic and, finally, in company with the birth of the Monteregian plutonic belt in southern Québec, in Middle Cretaceous times. These post-metamorphic deformations produced a pattern of regional faults (Fig. 3) which contemporary field mapping is still in the process of defining.

## TECTONIC-STRUCTURE SEISMICITY

Unlike the apparent non-correlation of ancient tectonic provinces with seismicity, the distribution of post-metamorphic faults does seem to coincide well with the historic distribution of earthquakes in the region, as shown on Figure 4. Furthermore, an apparently higher frequency of seismic activity is spatially associated with areas having a greater frequency of mapped brittle-fracture deformation. Conversely, the broad areas in the region that are characterized by their infrequent, widely-spaced and low-intensity historical seismicity are also characterized by the apparent absence of deep-crustal, post-metamorphic brittle-fracture deformations.

## TECHNICAL CONTROLS

We must offer here three caveats.

First, although the larger earthquakes shown here are well documented, some of the historically "felt" events may not have been earthquakes at all, but may have originated as quarry or highway blasts, or as frost-cracking phenomena ("cryoseisms"). J. R. Rand's compilation of earthquake epicenters shown on Figures 2 and 4 is informal, gleaned from Preliminary Safety Analysis Reports and other special reports for nuclear power plant studies at Seabrook Station, Pilgrim Unit II, New England Power 1 & 2 and Yankee Rowe Nuclear Power Plant (all Weston Geophysical Corporation basic data), augmented with modern data from the Northeastern U. S. Seismic Network of Weston Observatory. Almost all epicentral plots have inherent

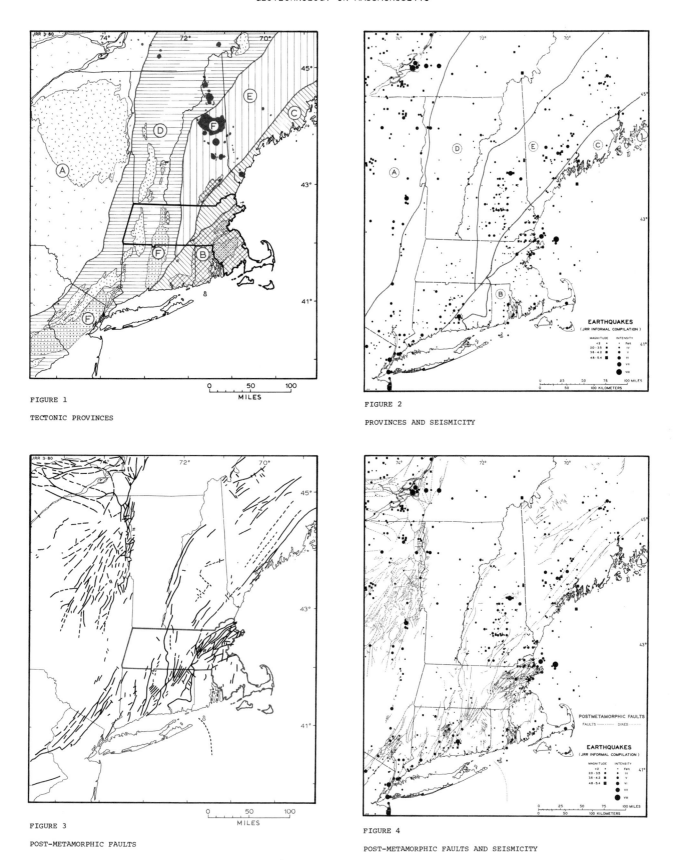

FIGURE 1

TECTONIC PROVINCES

FIGURE 2

PROVINCES AND SEISMICITY

FIGURE 3

POST-METAMORPHIC FAULTS

FIGURE 4

POST-METAMORPHIC FAULTS AND SEISMICITY

possible location inaccuracies of somewhere between 3 and 15-or-more miles. The numerous low-magnitude events detected by the Northeastern Seismic Network since 1975 conform well with seismicity patterns of the historical record.

Second, focal depths of New England earthquakes have not been accurately measured, but are generally considered to be on the order of 5 to 15 kilometers. Some events in south-central Connecticut may have originated at shallower depths. All that our geologic maps show us is structure and lithology at ground surface, and it may be unjustifiably simplistic in every case to "correlate" a ground-surface geologic feature with an at-depth seismological circumstance.

And third, published geologic reports are not of uniform quality and detail from place to place throughout the region. Until a few years ago, much historical mapping of the crystalline rocks in New England paid relatively little attention to post-metamorphic deformations. The historical sequence of development, and the age and style of final motion on many of the post-metamorphic faults shown on Figure 3 have not been clearly defined. A few fault traces depicted here may actually be on metamorphic faults. Thanks to our extensive glacial cover, there is undoubtedly a substantial number of post-metamorphic faults which have not yet been detected.

## LOCALIZATION OF SEISMICITY

Notwithstanding the problems, it would seem that there may be a reasonable degree of truth in the apparent mutual clusterings of post-metamorphic fault systems with historical seismicity and that future field revelations should enhance, rather than confuse, the apparent relationship between regional brittle-fracture deformations and crustal stress accumulations.

It is our thesis that seismicity in the region results from modern stress regimes which accumulate strain in distinct zones of rock weakness, or at specific locations where there is a marked discontinuity in rock rigidity, geometry or density (reflecting lithologic change). The orientation of the contemporary crustal stress relative to the orientation of zones of weakness or discontinuity influences the degree of seismicity and the type of earthquake mechanism at those locations. There is no reason to assume that seismic activity which has occurred in the past on anomalous tectonic structures in one part of a broad, ancient tectonic province might, in the future, occur in some other part of that regional province where no comparable structural features exist.

The larger New England-area earthquakes include an intensity VIII(MM) event and an intensity VII(MM) event in 1755 and 1727, respectively, just offshore from Cape Ann, northeastern Massachusetts; two intensity VII(MM) events in 1940, plotted near South Tamworth, New Hampshire; an intensity VI-VII(MM) event in 1791 near Moodus,

Connecticut; and three intensity VII(MM) events in 1737, 1884 and 1927 between New York City and Sandy Hook, New Jersey. As discussed elsewhere at this conference in papers by V. J. Murphy and others, and by G. Leblanc and others, the larger Cape Ann events occurred in a terrain characterized by intense post-metamorphic fault deformation, near the location of a buried cylindrical mafic pluton; and the South Tamworth events are plotted at the location where a post-metamorphic fault system passes tangent to the cylindrical mafic pluton of the Ossipee Complex. Continuing microseismic activity in this latter area coincides with linear magnetic anomalies which appear to reflect border and internal faults of a collapsed volcanic caldera. A smaller intensity VI(MM), magnitude 4.9, earthquake occurred in 1973 in southeastern Québec, where post-metamorphic normal faults similarly occur in the area of the cylindrical Cretaceous pluton of the Megantic Complex.

In south-central Connecticut, the relatively shallow seismicity occurs in a discrete area of anomalous structure, where northwest-trending magnetic, gravity and bedrock fabric is intersected by clustered northeast-striking post-metamorphic faults and a prominent northeast-trending Mesozoic dike swarm. The bedrock structure is hidden in the New York City-to-Sandy Hook area, but geophysical data show the higher-intensity seismicity to coincide closely with a site of extreme gravity differential transected by a northeast-trending linear magnetic anomaly. A short distance to the north of this area, the Ramapo fault system, which has been intermittently active since Late Precambrian time, exhibits continued modern microseismic activity.

## SUMMARY

The evidence that we see suggests that the western two-thirds of Massachusetts has been and should continue to be almost aseismic. Also, the thrust fault complex in the northeastern part of the state has been and should continue to be the locus of substantial seismic energy release, with the potential for causing significant damage to poorly-built structures or to those resting on unstable foundations. It should be emphasized that major architectural projects should always be designed and founded with an awareness of earthquake potential in northeastern Massachusetts.

Although residents of western Massachusetts may rarely be awakened by home-grown earthquakes, the attenuation of seismic-wave propagation in the crystalline crust of New England and adjacent cratonic regions is so low that even those residents may occasionally find some dishes broken and a pendulum clock or two stopped, not only by a large event at Cape Ann, but also by energy released from discrete tectonic structures in such foreign locations as Lake George, New York; La Malbaie, Québec; or even possibly New Madrid, Missouri. They and their fellow citizens to the northeast in Essex County may gain some consolation, however, in the knowledge that no evidence has been found to date of surface faulting of the crystalline bedrock due to historical earthquakes in the New England region.

GENERAL REFERENCES

Boston Edison Company, 1976, Pilgrim Unit II, Pre-liminary safety analysis report: Docket No. 50-471, Nuclear Regulatory Commission.

New England Power Company, 1978, NEP 1 & 2, Preliminary safety analysis report: Docket Nos. 50-568, 50-569, Nuclear Regulatory Commission.

Public Service Co. of New Hampshire, 1974, Seabrook Station, Preliminary safety analysis report: Nuclear Regulatory Commission.

Weston Geophysical Corporation, 1979, Geology and seismology, Yankee Rowe Nuclear Power Plant: prepared for Yankee Atomic Electric Company, Westborough, Massachusetts.

Hors-texte

Cape Ann, Gloucester, and the Parker River estuary, Massachusetts,
looking west.  (Courtesy, Aerial Photos of New England.)

Old Man of the Mountain, Franconia Notch, New Hampshire. Upper left, looking forward down on the rock mass comprising the Old Man's profile. Upper right, looking N 35° W, showing the south face of the profile and the precarious "upper lip" and "chin," blocks 4 and 5 in the paper. Lower left, showing a prominent fault (set 7) in the center, also blocks 1-5 and the south face. (Fowler.)

Lower right, typical surface of sound bed rock in Sweden. (Söderberg and Bjork, Figure 1.)

Above, the motor ship R. L. Perkins, used for drilling in the Gulf of Mexico by McClelland Engineers, Inc. (Focht, Figure 1.)

Below, a Parade of Tall Ships was one of the events that marked the 350th Anniversary of the City of Boston in 1980. Shown here is the painting "Operation Sail — Boston 1980," reproduced by permission of the artist, Kipp Soldwedel, and of Ship Lore, 470 Park Avenue, New York, NY 10022. The USS Constitution appears in the center, flanked by the USCG Eagle (left) and the Danmark. The general area in 1775 is compared with the city of today in end paper maps with this volume on geotechnology.

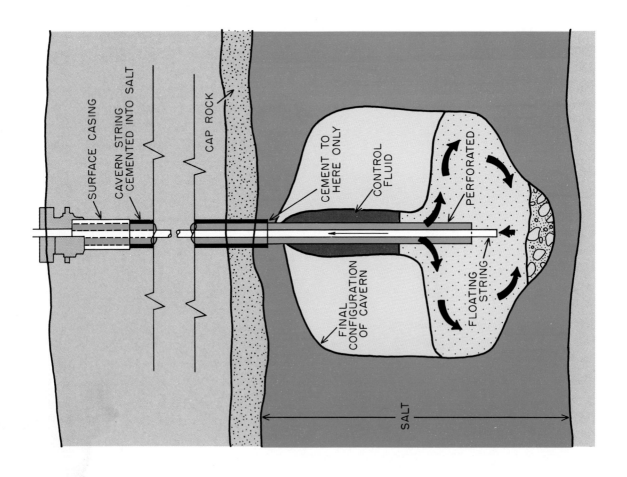

Left, method for solution mining of salt to provide storage facilities for crude oil in the Strait of Canso area, Nova Scotia. Right, model of an underground storage cavern in salt at Hardisty, Alberta. (Petranik and Lane.)

4530

4600

4700

SURFACE CASING

CAVERN STRING
CEMENTED INTO SALT

CAP ROCK

CEMENT TO
HERE ONLY

CONTROL
FLUID

FINAL
CONFIGURATION
OF CAVERN

PERFORATED.

FLOATING
STRING

SALT

# Earthquakes and mafic plutons—
# Some instrumental data

G. LEBLANC
R. J. HOLT
G. KLIMKIEWICZ
J. C. JOHNSTON
Weston Geophysical Corporation

## ABSTRACT

Intraplate earthquakes are still hard to explain, thus making prediction subject to skepticism. The concept of stress concentration around some structural inhomogeneities has been proposed. These inhomogeneities need not be apparent at the surface to be active at depth. Mafic intrusives are among those structures with surface expression that have been considered as potential stress concentrators.

A 2-1/2 year seismic monitoring survey around large intrusives in the Ossipee region, New Hampshire, has revealed some microseismic activity. The epicenters form a lineament which is spatially correlated to geological and aeromagnetic features. The rate of microactivity is steady, about one event per month. Considering that the Ossipee events of December 1940 were in the 5.4 to 5.8 magnitude range, this rate of microactivity is relatively compatible with the rate observed around the La Malbaie, Québec, structure (about 15 events per month), where the larger March 1925 event with a magnitude of 6.6 to 7.0 occurred. The identification of such active structures is helpful in assessing seismic potential, because they may enable us to predict the locations of some future large events.

## INTRODUCTION

More than 85 percent of the world seismicity is well explained by the theory of plate tectonics. Earthquakes are controlled by the boundary interaction of the moving plates. Various stress regimes have been identified: spreading ridges; transform faults; subduction zones; and specific types of earthquake mechanism that have been associated with each regime. Gradually, this knowledge of the causative factors of earthquakes has permitted more and more generalizations to be made and, in some cases, has supported some degree of prediction.

Unfortunately, the rest of the world seismicity occurring within the confines of continental plates is not so well understood. To a large

extent, this is due to the fact that significant intraplate earthquakes are much more infrequent than those occurring on plate boundaries, and that modern seismic instrumentation is relatively recent with respect to our intraplate earthquakes. Most of the large intraplate events--such as the 1812 New Madrid, Missouri, event; the Anna, Ohio, events; the Attica, New York, event; the La Malbaie, Québec, events of 1638, 1663, 1925; and, closer to New England, the Cape Ann events of 1727, 1755, and the Ossipee events of 1940 (Fig. 1)--are all historical events for which little, if any, instrumental information has been obtained, such as reliable location, fault plane solution, and focal depth estimates.

There are other possible reasons why our understanding of eastern intraplate events progresses slowly. First, seismologists and geologists are unconsciously influenced by western United States tectonics, where spatial correlation between epicenters and well mapped faults or major geological boundaries is possible and readily made. In northeastern North America, these correlations with surface faulting are not as easy. Second, seismologists, and geologists as well, have been externally compelled to devote much of their attention and research to the acceptance or rejection of "tectonic provinces," or "seismic risk zones," often used in building codes and licensing regulations.

Eastern earthquakes are known to have no surface expressions, while western events sometimes do break ground surface. Eastern events occur in the upper half of the crust, seldom near the surface. For this reason, geophysical methods, which aid subsurface interpretation, should definitely be used more widely, in parallel with geological mapping, in the search for causative structures.

## ZONES OF SEISMIC ACTIVITY

At the starting point, one should let the epicentral distribution of those events, considered well located, suggest the general areas where intensive geophysical and geological studies should be conducted.

It should be noted that on Figure 1 many of the smaller events, which have been instrumentally located, cluster around some of the larger historical events, e.g., near Ossipee, New Hampshire, Cape Ann, Massachusetts, and Haddam, Connecticut. Clearly, these zones are the most important for seismic risk considerations, and deserve prime

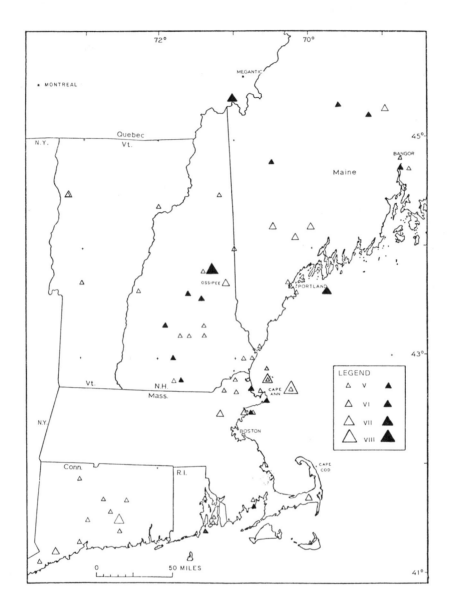

Figure 1. Locations of more important earthquakes in New England (up to 1977). Size of
the symbol indicates intensity of the earthquake. An open symbol indicates that the
location was based on historical data. A
solid symbol indicates that the location was
determined instrumentally. (Source: Our New
England Earthquakes, Weston Geophysical
Corporation, 1977).

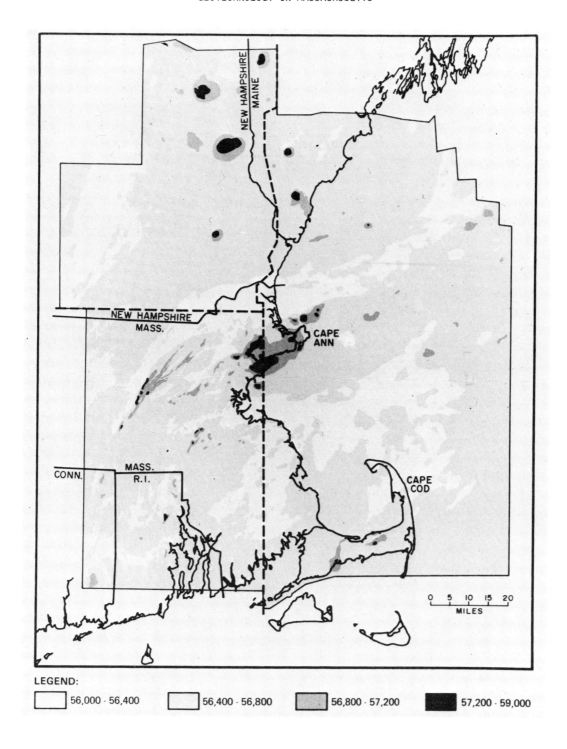

LEGEND:

| | | | |
|---|---|---|---|
| ☐ 56,000 - 56,400 | ☐ 56,400 - 56,800 | ▦ 56,800 - 57,200 | ■ 57,200 - 59,000 |

Figure 2. Aeromagnetic map of New England showing most important anomalies. (Units are gammas.) (Source: Our New England Earthquakes, Weston Geophysical Corporation, 1977).

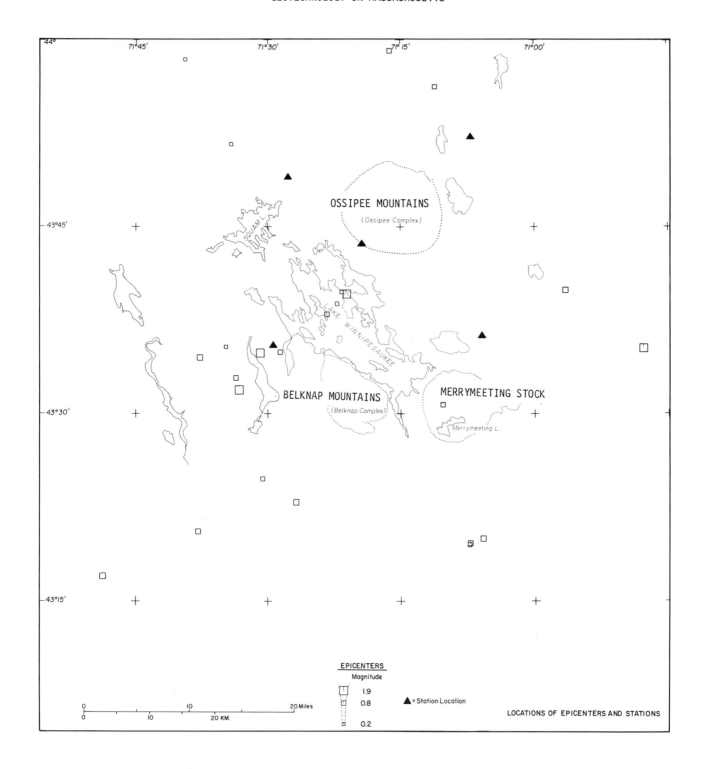

Figure 3. Locations of microearthquake epicenters and seismograph stations of the Ossipee
region seismic monitoring experiment.

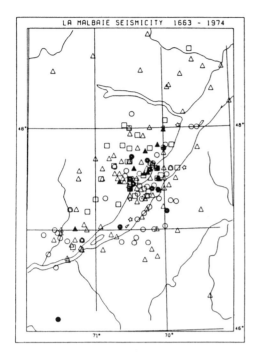

Figure 4A. Seismicity of the St. Lawrence River Valley in the vicinity of the La Malbaie region. Symbols represent magnitude ranges: circle < 3, 3 ≤ triangle < 4, 4 ≤ square < 5, 5 ≤ star < 6, 6 ≤ circled star. Filled symbols represent more reliable positions. Microearthquakes are not plotted.

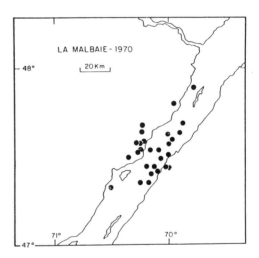

Figure 4B. Epicenters of 1970 experiment.

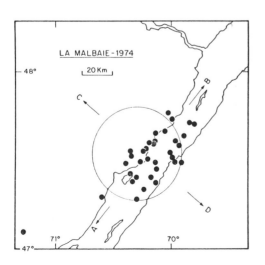

Figure 4C. Epicenters of 1974 experiment. Circle represents outer boundary of Charlevoix structure. (Source: Leblanc and Buchbinder, 1977).

attention. The historical occurrence of some large events in a certain area, whether or not a lower level of seismicity has also been recorded, is the unequivocal sign that a major structure exists there, concentrating the regional stresses that were once released and most likely will be released again.

The concept of stress concentrators has been evoked recently by various researchers in an effort to explain the occurrence of significant earthquakes. Within this context, any structural and/or lithological inhomogeneity that exists at some depth in the crust qualifies as a potential stress concentrator. We know, from college physics experiments, the effect of a conductor within an electrical field, or iron filings in a magnetic field. Mafic plutons constitute one important type of crustal inhomogeneities that can disturb the elastic field within the crustal rocks. Their physical properties, such as density and rigidity, can be substantially different from those of the surrounding rock. Also, their dimensions can be large enough to constitute important crustal inhomogeneities.

In New England, the Cape Ann events and the Ossipee events are at the top of the list of historical events in terms of size (intensity VII and VIII and magnitude 5.4 to 5.7). At an early stage, the Ossipee epicenters had been spatially correlated with the Ossipee Mountains, which show a large magnetic anomaly, a fact that is indicative of their mafic plutonic nature. But it took special aeromagnetic surveys in 1976 (Fig. 2) to detect the presence of another pluton near the estimated Cape Ann epicenters. The time had thus come to assess experimentally the theory that such large intrusives are indeed stress concentrators. For reasons of accessibility, the Ossipee region was selected for the deployment of a high gain seismic network. If indeed stresses are now concentrated around the structure, they should reveal themselves, as in other known cases, by a steady rate of microearthquake activity.

## THE OSSIPEE PLUTONS

Five short period vertical instruments, as shown in Figure 3, were installed in Madison, Center Sandwich, Moultonboro, Laconia, and East Wolfeboro, New Hampshire. The signals were telemetered by phone to Westboro, Massachusetts. The experiment lasted from the fall of 1976 to December 1978. A total of 24 microearthquakes with magnitudes ranging from 0 to 2 and calculated focal depths from 0 to 16 km were recorded over 26 months, yielding an average rate of 1 event per month. This relatively steady microactivity can be compared with the steady rate of activity observed near the well known structure of the Charlevoix Crater, at La Malbaie, Québec, where larger historical earthquakes (intensity IX and magnitude 7+) have occurred.

Figure 4a shows a zone of historical events, many of which have been clearly mislocated by 50 km+. The results of two microearthquake surveys

in 1970 and 1974 in the La Malbaie region (Figs. 4b and 4c) have shown an almost identical distribution of epicenters in time and space. During these two summer experiments, the same rate of 1 event per 2 days was observed. The detection threshold was roughly similar to that of the Ossipee net. Considering that La Malbaie has had magnitude 7 events, and Ossipee only magnitude 5.4, the rates of observed microseismicity are compatible, and could reflect either the regional stress field and/or the structure dimensions.

Returning to the Ossipee structure, we find that the recorded seismic activity is reasonably well confined to the Ossipee region (Fig. 3). It is mostly distributed along three linear patterns. The first trends northeast, cutting across Lake Winnipesaukee and ending near the Ossipee complex. This trend is almost radial to the Ossipee Mountains. The second one runs southeast, almost tangential to the Belknap complex. The last one trends also northeast, radially to the Belknap complex.

An examination of some small scale aeromagnetic data (proprietary to Boston Edison) suggests that these three seismic lineaments coincide with three linear zones where the magnetic field is visibly disturbed. It should be noted that the first segment coincides very well with the contact between the Meredith porphyritic granite and the Littleton formation.

The original epicenters of the December 1940 events were located to the north of the Ossipee Mountains where the largest felt intensity had been reported. Taking into account the epicentral location uncertainty based on such an intensity report and the very few instrumental readings available at the time, as listed in the North Eastern Seismicity Association Bulletin, the events could well have occurred along the present distribution of the microactivity.

Recent relocations of instrumental earthquakes near La Malbaie have shown a good correlation with the present microearthquake activity (Stevens, 1980) and the relocated epicenters. The same correlation may well exist for the Ossipee case.

## CONCLUSION

In conclusion, the Ossipee experiment has indeed confirmed that a large pluton can concentrate stresses in its immediate vicinity. The steady rate of activity, even if low, as well as the spatial correlation of the microevents with structures that have a geological and geophysical expression suggest that a structure causative of moderate earthquakes has indeed been identified.

It would be an advantage to monitor other crustal structures to see if they also manifest steady microseismic activity. If so, they might well be the sites of future significant earthquakes.

## REFERENCES

Leblanc, G., and Buchbinder, G., 1977, Second microearthquake survey of the St. Lawrence Valley near La Malbaie, Québec: Canadian Journal of Earth Sciences, v. 14, p. 2778-2789.

Stevens, A. E., 1980, Reexamination of some larger La Malbaie, Québec, earthquakes (1924-1978): Bulletin of the Seismological Society of America, v. 70, p. 529-557.  □

Hors-texte

A twin-engine Piper Navajo, as used in an aeromagnetic survey of southeastern New England and the
western part of the Gulf of Maine in 1976.  The
aircraft was equipped with ANA (Aircraft Navigation
System with Atomic-Frequency-Standards) for accurate positioning.  (Courtesy:  Prakla-Seismos; Aero
Service Division, Western Geophysical Company of
America; Weston Geophysical Research, Inc.; and
the Boston Edison Company, Docket No. 50-471.)

# 13

# NEARSHORE ZONES

Session moderator

S. S. Quarrier
Connecticut Geological and Natural History Survey

# The Cape Cod environmental atlas— What do we tell the planners, and how?

## A. H. BROWNLOW
### Department of Geology
### Boston University

ABSTRACT

Geologists have to become more involved in land-use planning. Major reasons for even greater involvement are as follows: (1) Geology is seriously underutilized in planning for development and management of the land; (2) The general public, and even some land-use planners, are unaware of what geology has to offer; (3) Geologic contributions can provide economic and cultural benefits, and can save human lives as well; and (4) Active participation in land-use planning will benefit the profession by providing jobs for geologists and public support for geologic research.

This paper describes the history of an interdisciplinary project that attempts to inform the general public of the relationship between the natural materials and processes of Cape Cod and land-use planning. Cape Cod represents a prime example of land-use problems that must be faced in coming years. Here a rapidly growing population is meeting head-on with a particularly fragile environment. If land-use planning is needed anywhere, it is needed on Cape Cod.

## DISCUSSION

The recently published Cape Cod environmental atlas (Brownlow, ed., 1979) brings together, in one publication, a summary of the wide variety of environmental information that is now scattered throughout many published and unpublished sources. The atlas consists of six articles and ten maps that summarize our present knowledge of the topography, geology, soils, vegetation, ground water, shoreline processes, archaeology, and current land use of Cape Cod. The material is written for the general public, particularly for planners and decision-makers.

## CONCLUSIONS

Certain conclusions resulting from this project are relevant for geologists planning to participate in similar efforts.

- Despite the many governmental and private agencies that support environmental activities, it is just as hard to get support for this type of project as it is for "pure" science projects.

- Supervising an interdisciplinary project is not easy. Scientists in other fields and social scientists bring different perspectives and different values to a project, which makes it difficult to produce a coherent result.

- The relevant literature is so scattered and so variable in quality and nature that it is very difficult to find all of it and to properly summarize it.

- Probably the toughest part of preparing a publication for the general public is selecting the types of maps to use. The maps should provide relevant, useful, and understandable information, yet they should not be overly technical and overly detailed.

- Geologists who are planning to help the planners should not expect to be welcomed enthusiastically. In addition, it is sometimes difficult to determine exactly who the planners are that require help.

- Once the project is finished, do not expect the planners and others to be overwhelmingly grateful. As mentioned earlier, the general public, and even some land-use planners, are unaware of what geologists and other scientists have to offer. Also, some do not have a great deal of faith in the scientific method.

- The only way geologists can have a significant impact on land-use planning is by active selling of their product. They have to continually advertise what they can do and, even when a project is finished, the job is not done, for then it must be sold to the planners and to the public.

Many geologists are doing research and producing technical publications on environmental problems. In most cases, their audience consists of other technically trained personnel. This work, while vitally necessary, must be accompanied by efforts to inform planners and the general public, clearly and in mainly non-technical language, of data and interpretations necessary for making informed decisions on land-use planning.  The Cape Cod environmental atlas is an example of what can be done in this regard.

REFERENCE

Brownlow, A.H., editor, 1979, Cape Cod environmental atlas:  Boston University, Department of Geology, 62 p.                   □

Hors-texte

Bicentennial medals.  To commemorate the U.S. Bicentennial in 1976, the Franklin Mint of Pennsylvania issued a series of 50 medals, one for each of the states.  The photographs reproduced here, by permission, show both the front and the reverse sides.

(f) SBS-6

**The Fifty-State Bicentennial Medal Collection**
Massachusetts
Struck in Sterling Silver
Size: 39mm

The collection serves as a reminder that most of the metals used in coinage have been included in the search for minerals throughout New England.  Copper, gold, nickel, silver, and zinc are among them.  Because of mines and prospects for these and other natural resources, the subsurface has been revealed in numerous places.  The resulting maps and reports on the geology of New England assist in interpretations of the underground, for which other uses besides mineral extraction, water supply, and transportation are becoming feasible.  Storage of compressed air in deep caverns is among the proposals now being actively considered.

# Erosion and shingle movement at Mann Hill Beach, Scituate, Massachusetts, during the blizzard of February 1978

B. M. BRENNINKMEYER, S. J.

Coastal Research Unit
Department of Geology and Geophysics
Boston College

## ABSTRACT

Mann Hill Beach in Scituate, Massachusetts, is a slightly arcuate, 1 km long, baymouth shingle bar oriented almost N45°W so that it is fully exposed to nor'easters. During the blizzard of February 6 and 7, 1978, with a tidal elevation of 2.0 m above mean low water and waves calculated to have been between 3.4 and 6.7 m in height on top of a storm surge of 1.3 m, 150,000 m³ of shingle was eroded from the beach. This erosion lowered the elevation of the beach 1.7 m. Thirty percent of this shingle was deposited landward of the barrier in a 1.5 m deep, 30 m wide apron with steep (15°) foreset beds. The remaining 70 percent of the shingle was deposited offshore and is slowly returning at the rate of 2000 m³/month. The net effect of the storm was to move the mean high tide line 15 m landward.

The average size of the shingle on Mann Hill Beach is 4.2 cm. It increases gradually to the southeast. The shingle consists of 24 percent granite and granodiorite, 28 percent rhyolite and andesite, 15 percent basalt, 13 percent diorite, 11 percent quartzite and 9 percent siltstone. The lithologies are not admixed uniformly across the beach. There is more rhyolite and quartzite on the lower fringes of the shingle and more siltstone and andesite on top of the berm. This is because of the differences in their shape. During the blizzard, pebbles of all shapes were brought in by storm waves. Disks, being lighter than spheres of the same diameter, possess a lower settling velocity and are thrown up higher on the beach. Pebbles that roll more readily (spheres and rollers) are transported farther seaward by the backwash. Thus, at the seaward edge of the shingle there are relatively more spheres and rollers while disks and blades are more common on the berm.

## INTRODUCTION

Mann Hill Beach is a 1 km long baymouth shingle bar located in Scituate, Massachusetts, 48 km south of Boston (Fig. 1). The beach blocks Musquashcut Pond from the ocean. The beach was named after one of Scituate's original settlers, Richard Mann, who came from the Plymouth Plantation in the mid 1640's to settle on Mann Hill, 400 m landward of the beach at an elevation of 19.8 m.

One of the earliest mentions of Mann Hill Beach refers to April 16, 1851, when a storm ac-

tually formed a 12 m wide tidal inlet between the ocean and Musquashcut Pond. For a time the inlet was so deep that fishermen used to go through the "gully" with their boats. The opening gradually filled in, but a large volume of sand had been carried into the pond to form tidal flats, acres in extent, on which beach grass grows today (Spayne, 1977). By 1892 the opening had closed completely. It is believed that the storm of November 27, 1898, actually formed the large shingle berm. The shingle was deposited by the storm to a height of seven meters above mean low water. In February 1972 the southern end of the barrier was breached. During the blizzard of February 6 and 7, 1978, the whole barrier was overtopped by waves.

## BLIZZARD OF '78

Several factors must operate simultaneously to produce a large storm system. First, there must be an area of strong temperature gradients at low elevations. Secondly, a wind flow and temperature change that cuts across latitude must exist in the upper atmosphere to enhance the low level surface front. If the upper and lower fronts come into phase, both systems mesh and feed each other. The rising low level air will flow into an upper air void, and sinking upper air will find a deficit of air or slight vacuum in the lower levels.

On February 5, 1978, a significant upper level trough from Hudson Bay south to Minnesota was moving eastward. At the same time, on the surface, a well developed low pressure system was beginning to form along the Carolinas and move northeast. On February 6, the surface low was joined by another one coming from the Ohio valley. A strong cyclonic circulation started to form. Ships from Bermuda to New York reported gusts of wind up to 93 km/hr and heavy seas (Blackford, 1979). During the first 24 hours of life of this surface storm, its track was northeast, parallel to the coast. As is seen in Figure 2, the track was parallel to the upper level wind flow. The upper level winds actually steered the storm. By the evening of February 6, the upper and lower level air masses began to join. With the merging of the two levels, the steering effect of the upper level winds on the storm was lost. The rate of advancement slowed, and the storm track became less predictable. In this case, the storm stalled off Long Island and looped westward.

All through February 6 and 7, the massive

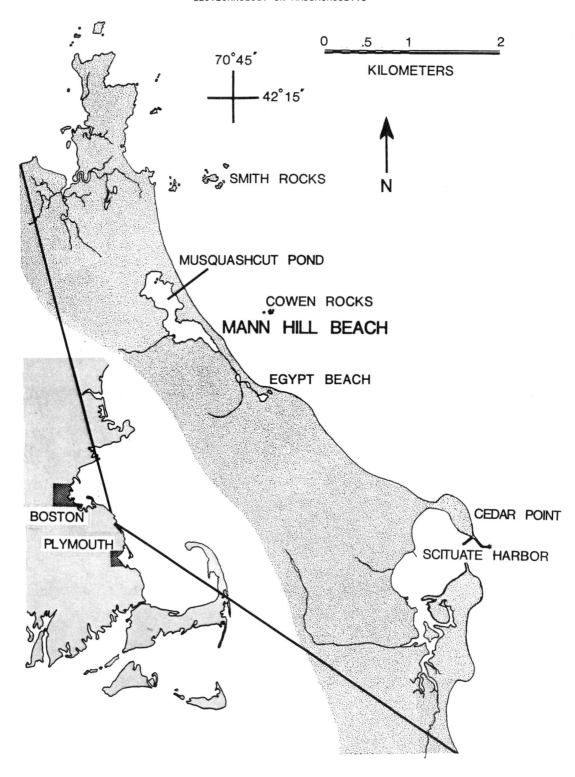

Figure 1. Location and vicinity map of
Mann Hill Beach at Scituate, Massachusetts.

TABLE 1. HISTORICAL FLOOD DATA IN MASSACHUSETTS: MAXIMUM STILL WATER
TIDE HEIGHTS AT BOSTON AND SCITUATE  (m)

| Date | | Boston observed[1] | adjusted[2] | Boston observed[3] | Scituate observed[4] | adjusted[5] |
|---|---|---|---|---|---|---|
| February 7 | 1978 | 3.14 | 3.14 | 3.11 | 3.33 | 3.33 |
| April 16 | 1851 | 3.07 | 3.16 | 3.05 | 2.69 | 2.79 |
| December 26 | 1909 | 3.02 | 3.20 | 3.05 | | |
| November 27 | 1898 | | | 2.89 | 2.93 | 3.12 |
| | 1954 | | | | 2.95 | 3.05 |
| December 29 | 1959 | 2.83 | 2.89 | 2.87 | | |
| April 18 | 1852 | | | 2.83 | | |
| December 27 | 1839 | 2.80 | | 2.77 | | |
| December 15 | 1839 | 2.80 | | | | |
| February 19 | 1972 | 2.77 | 2.77 | 2.77 | | |
| February 24 | 1723 | 2.77 | | 3.20 | | |
| | 1938 | | | | 2.77 | 2.89 |
| March 26 | 1830 | 2.74 | | | | |
| May 26 | 1967 | 2.71 | 2.74 | | | |
| April 21 | 1940 | 2.71 | 2.83 | 2.74 | | |
| December 29 | 1853 | 2.71 | 2.80 | | | |
| December 4 | 1786 | 2.71 | | | | |
| January 20 | 1961 | 2.68 | 2.71 | 2.68 | | |
| November 30 | 1944 | 2.68 | 2.77 | 2.68 | | |
| March 4 | 1931 | 2.68 | 2.80 | 2.68 | 2.55 | 2.71 |
| December 3 | 1854 | 2.68 | 2.77 | | | |
| November 3 | 1861 | 2.65 | 2.77 | | | |
| January 9 | 1978 | 2.62 | 2.62 | | | |
| March 16 | 1976 | 2.62 | 2.62 | | | |
| March 17 | 1956 | 2.62 | 2.68 | 2.62 | 2.88 | 2.94 |
| April 7 | 1958 | 2.59 | 2.65 | 2.59 | | |
| November 15 | 1871 | 2.59 | 2.65 | | | |
| November 23 | 1858 | 2.59 | 2.71 | 2.53 | | |
| December 2 | 1974 | 2.56 | 2.56 | 2.56 | | |
| March 7 | 1962 | 2.56 | 2.59 | 2.50 | | |
| April 4 | 1973 | 2.52 | 2.53 | 2.56 | | |
| December 12 | 1972 | 2.52 | 2.53 | | | |
| January 28 | 1933 | 2.52 | 2.65 | 2.53 | | |
| December 31 | 1857 | 2.52 | 2.65 | | | |
| November 10 | 1947 | | | 2.50 | | |
| | 1945 | | | | 2.44 | 2.57 |
| February 28 | 1958 | | | 2.50 | | |

[1] Records have been collected in Boston since 1723.  Elevations from 1723 to 1850 are of questionable reliability.  Yearly records collected by several federal agencies since 1851 are believed to be accurate. Data from Gadoury (1979).

[2] Observed values after adjustment for rising sea level; adjustments made to 1970 sea levels, based on Hicks (1978).

[3] Observed values reported by U.S. Army Corps of Engineers 1964, 1977 and 1979.

[4] A board attached to "Old Ice House" at Hugo's Lighthouse restaurant, in Cohasset, has been marked with several flood events since 1851.  It is not known what floods, if any, were not marked.  Only the years are given; dates assigned here are those considered most probable.  (Cohasset is adjacent to North Scituate.)

[5] Observed values after adjustment for rising sea level; adjustments made to 1980 sea levels, based on Hicks (1978).

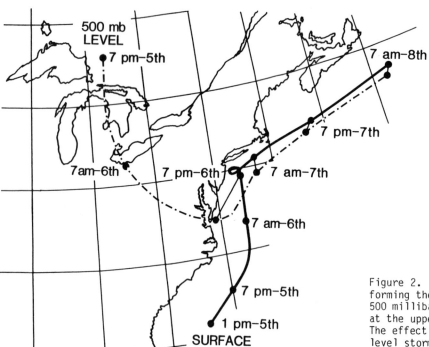

Figure 2. Storm tracks from February 5-8, 1978, forming the blizzard on February 6 and 7. The 500 millibar track shows the center of the storm at the upper level of the atmosphere (± 5500 m). The effect of the merging of the upper and lower level storm centers on the night of February 6 can readily be seen. (Source: U.S. Department of Commerce, NOAA Daily Weather Maps).

TABLE 2. OBSERVED WIND AND WAVE DATA (MODIFIED FROM MARINE COASTAL WEATHER LOG)

| BOSTON LIGHT STATION | (42 | 19.7'N - 70 | 53.4'W) | | |
|---|---|---|---|---|---|
| Date | Time | Wind direction | Wind velocity (km/hr) | Wave height (m) | Wave period (sec) |
| 2/6/78 | 10:00 | NW | -- | .3 | 5 |
| | 19:00 | -- | -- | 1.2 | 7 |
| | 22:00 | NE | -- | 1.8 | 5 |
| 2/7/78 | 1:00 | NE | -- | 2.7 | 7 |
| | 4:00 | NE | -- | 2.7 | 7 |
| | 7:00 | ENE | -- | 1.2 | 6 |
| | 10:00 | -- | -- | 2.7 | 10 |

| GLOUCESTER | (42 | 34.8'N - 70 | 39.8'W) | | |
|---|---|---|---|---|---|
| Date | Time | Wind direction | Wind velocity (km/hr) | Wave height (m) | Wave period (sec) |
| 2/6/78 | 10:00 | NE | 40.7 | .3 | 5 |
| | 19:00 | ENE | 74.1 | 1.2 | 6 |
| | 22:00 | ENE | 83.3 | 1.2 | 6 |
| 2/7/78 | 1:00 | NE | 74.7 | 1.5 | 8 |
| | 4:00 | NE | 64.8 | 2.4 | 8 |
| | 7:00 | NE | 64.8 | 2.4 | 8 |
| | 10:00 | NE | 64.8 | 2.4 | 8 |
| | 13:00 | N | 46.3 | 3.0 | 10 |
| | 16:00 | NNE | 51.8 | 3.0 | 10 |
| | 22:00 | N | 37.0 | 2.7 | 7 |

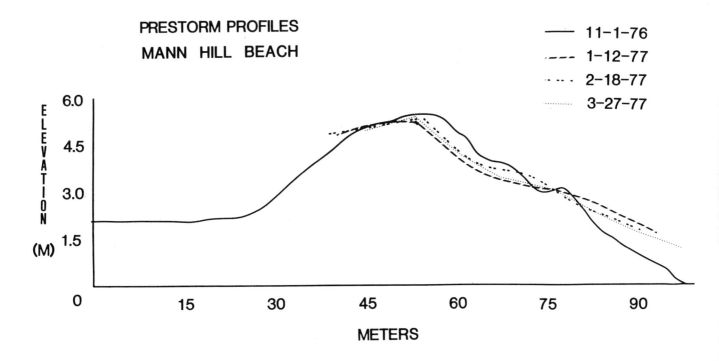

Figure 3. Representative pre-blizzard profiles along the center of Mann Hill Beach. The elevations are relative to mean low water. (Data recalculated from Rust, 1977).

Figure 4. Comparative profiles showing the erosion and deposition due to the blizzard of 1978. The profiles were taken along the same line as those in Figure 3. The elevations are relative to mean low water. (Data recalculated from Rust, 1977, and Schultz, 1979).

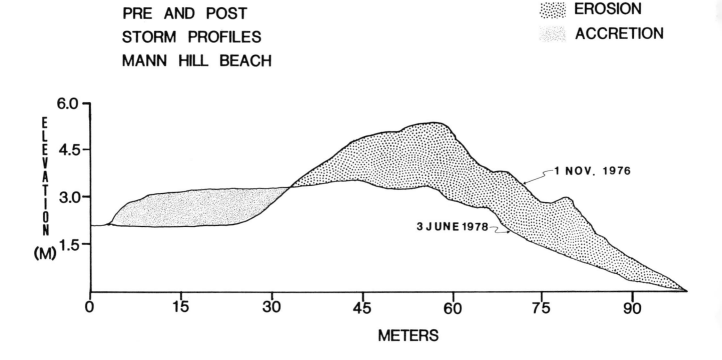

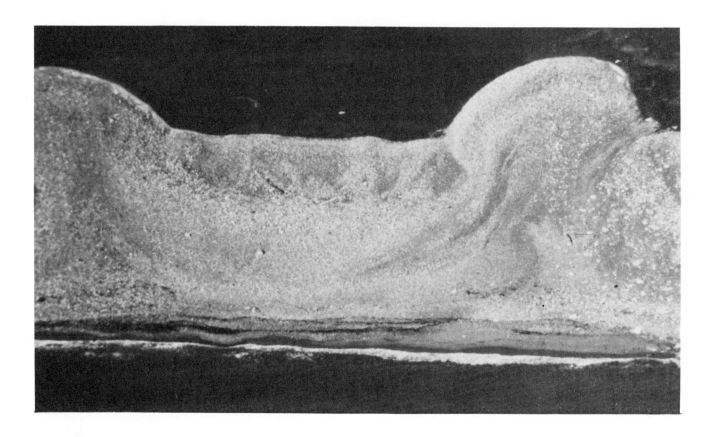

Figure 5. Upper left: Overwash deposits of cobbles into Musquashcut Pond. Photograph taken two weeks after the blizzard. Lower left: Depth of overwash on Mann Hill Beach during the blizzard. The car was lifted 50 cm above the pavement.
Above: Overwash channel.
Below: Foreset deltaic lobes landward of the overwash channel.

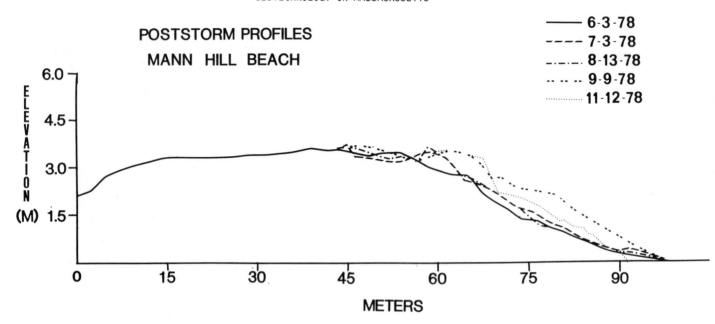

Figure 6. Post storm profile development along the same line as Figure 3. The elevations are relative to mean low water. (Data recalculated from Schultz, 1979, and Siminitz and Pfeiffer, 1978).

Figure 7. Changes in profiles along the same line as Figure 3 after the beach had been bulldozed in the spring of 1979. The elevations are relative to mean low water. (Data recalculated from Scituate Department of Public Works, February 28, 1979, and Maher and McMahon, 1979).

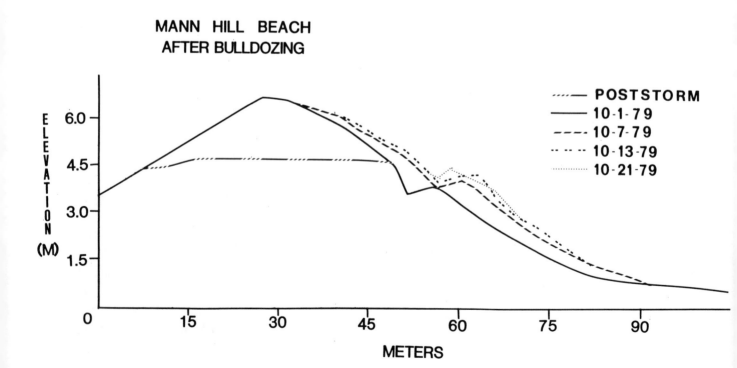

system pumped moist hot air to the highest reaches of the atmosphere (12-15000 m) only to crystallize and fall as snow. At the same time, surface winds moving counterclockwise around the low reached sustained velocities of 98 km/hr and peak velocities of 146 km/hr at Boston's Logan Airport and 170 km/hr at Chatham.

The winds produced a storm combined with the snow and formed a blizzard. The terms storm and blizzard will be used interchangeably. These winds came into Massachusetts Bay, producing a storm surge which raised the water level a maximum of 1.34 m above the predicted water elevations. The predicted tidal elevations for February 6 and 7 were already high due to the full moon spring tides and the closeness of the moon and earth to a perigean position. Table 1 shows the maximum still water tide heights of February 7, 1978, in relation to tide heights of other historic storms.

The history of severe storms in Massachusetts dates back to August, 1635. Only the storms with a mean water elevation greater than 2.5 m are listed in Table 1. Since 1931 these high tides have hit the Massachusetts coast approximately every 23 months and seem to be increasing in frequency.

Since 1962, several major storms, not necessarily accompanied by abnormal high tides, have caused severe beach and cliff erosion in Massachusetts. Apart from the February blizzard, the most severe was that of February 19-20, 1972. According to Richardson's (1977) research, damage was caused by storms of November 11-13, 1968; March 2-3, 1969; March 3-5, 1971; January 28-29, 1973; March 17, 1976; and January 20-21, 1978. Other periods with lesser storm damage have been November 29-30, 1963; December 29, 1966; December 16-17, 1970; and February 24-25, 1977.

Superimposed upon the water elevations of the tides and storm surge are the waves formed by the wind. The waves during the blizzard were extraordinarily large not only because of the strength of the wind but also the quasi-stationary nature of the storm system during the night of the sixth, as the upper and lower storms merged. In semi-sheltered stations with observations made in poor visibility, the sea state was as shown in Table 2. In open ocean deep water, wave heights of 6.1-7.6

m were reported during the night of the sixth by an officer aboard the Coast Guard vessel Cape Cross (Fitzgerald, 1978). Personnel aboard the Jay Robertson, a jackup drill rig 1.8 km offshore from Hampton Beach, NH, observed 7.9 m high waves actually scraping the bottom of the drilling barge which was jacked up 13.7 m above mean low water (Hartwell, 1978).

Wave heights and periods predicted by the Sverdrup-Munk-Bretschneider method (U.S. Army CERC, 1973), using minimum and maximum conditions, give estimates of 3.4 m high waves with a 7 second period and 6.7 m waves with a 10 second period respectively (Table 3).

BEACH CHANGES

Prestorm

Prior to the February blizzard, the crest of the beach at Mann Hill reached 5.5 m above mean low water. The average seaward slope was between 7° and 8° and the landward slope was 9°. Monthly profiles show an average of 50 $m^3$/m/month change in the topography of the foreshore (Rust, 1977, an example of one set, is shown in Figure 3). These changes were due primarily to the building up of a series of berms during spring tides and erosion after minor storms.

Blizzard of '78

During the blizzard, approximately 150,000 $m^3$ of the shingle was lost from the foreshore of Mann Hill Beach, lowering the apex of the berm from 5.5 m to 3.8 m (Fig. 4). Roughly 30 percent of the shingle lost from the foreshore was deposited landward of the barrier in Musquashcut Pond and Sheep Ponds, and the marsh between them. Forty-five $m^3$/m was deposited to a depth of 1.5 m in a 30 m wide apron. The remaining 70 percent was deposited offshore, presumably in longshore bars.

The appearance of the barrier changed drastically. Before the storm, the cross section of Mann Hill was roughly an isosceles triangle. After the storm, the apex was flattened and widened so that there was a large flat expanse of shingle. The front edge of the slope had decreased to 6° while the backslope had increased to 15 degrees, yet spanned only 2.2 m. The backslope showed all the characteristics of a classic Gilbert delta with topset and pronounced foreset beds (Fig. 5). Channels were excavated in the topset beds by local concentrations of water velocity maxima. At the base of these channels, lobate fans of gravel accumulated.

Recovery

In the spring of 1978, in order to enhance the water storage capability of Musquashcut Pond and to prevent overtopping of the barrier by storm waves and storm surge, the town of Scituate bull-

TABLE 3. WAVE PREDICTION FOR THE BLIZZARD OF '78 USING THE SVERDRUP-MUNK-BRETSCHNEIDER METHOD (U.S. ARMY CERC, 1973)

|  | Minimum | Maximum |
|---|---|---|
| Fetch | 185 km | 555 km |
| Duration | 12 hrs | 24 hrs |
| Wind velocity | 55 km/hr | 74 km/hr |
| Predicted wave height | 3.4 m | 6.7 m |
| Predicted wave period | 7 sec | 10 sec |

dozed the beach back into an isosceles triangle with the apex 6.7 m above mean low water. In the process they moved 140,000 m³, almost as much as the blizzard had moved (Fig. 6).

Since then, the foreshore has regained about 40 m³/m as the bars deposited offshore during the blizzard become welded on to the barrier. The deposition goes to the top of the berm (Fig. 7).

## CUSPS

Diffraction and refraction of waves around Cowen Rocks 0.7 km offshore may set up an interference pattern between these waves and unaffected incoming waves, such that up to three sets of cusps are usually well developed on Mann Hill Beach. Cusps are crescent shaped mounds of coarser material (Fig. 8). Cusps may also be formed by the interaction of transversal waves (edge waves) which are excited by incident waves. Edge waves are surface waves trapped by refraction at an angle to the shore. They have a maximum amplitude at the shore line. The interaction between these edge waves and incident waves affects the breaker height along the shore. This may set up a circulation pattern in the nearshore zone consisting of an onshore flow towards the breakers, a longshore current and an offshore flow in a strong, narrow rip current. These rip currents are located at the antinodes of the edge waves (Bowen; 1969, 1973).

Cusps develop once this circulation pattern is set up. Cusps on a sandy beach are noticeable first as patches of gravel, shells or other coarse material a few centimeters thick. The backwash moves away from the patches and returns in a channel, rather than returning in dispersed flow. This process is repeated and intensified until the backwash flow attains such momentum that the next swash cannot proceed against it and is projected onto the apices of the developing cusp. There the coarsest particles are deposited while the finer grains stay entrained as the water swings into the adjacent bays without stopping (Bagnold, 1940). These apices become more and more imbricated with each passing high tide. The cusps will change in size and become reoriented or even eradicated by

a change in the sea state.

Table 4 illustrates the difference in cusp spacing both before and after the blizzard. Quite frequently, as in November 1976, there were two sets of cusps; the higher up the beach, the larger the cusp spacing. Three sets of cusps have been observed (Brenninkmeyer, 1976). During the storm cusps reached an average size of more than 35 m from front to back and more than 12 m from apex to apex along the beach (Spayne, 1978). After the blizzard cusp spacing reverted back to between 4-8 m in size (Scully and Nwankwo, 1979). The orientation of the cusps and horns was usually not normal to the beach. Often they were oriented to the northeast, the direction of the incoming waves.

## SEDIMENT SIZE

A sand beach is composed of particles of 0.0625 to 2.00 mm sand size, while gravel deposits have particle sizes coarser than sand. In the literature there is some ambiguity concerning the use of the terms "pebble" and "gravel." Many workers use the word "gravel" to refer to pebble-sized particles. The problem stems from usage of different particle size scales. Some researchers utilize the U.S. Department of Agriculture and Soil Science Society of America scale which classifies particles ranging in size from 2-80 mm as gravel. Others, including the U.S. Army Corps of Engineers and the Water and Power Resources Service, use the term "gravel" to designate sediment between 4.76 and 76.2 mm. Europeans, by and large, follow Atterberg (1905) who does not use the term "gravel." Rather he uses "pebble" to designate sizes between 2 and 19 mm. Most American researchers follow the size scale proposed by Udden (1914) or Wentworth (1922, 1933) as modified by Lane and others (1957) in which "pebbles" refers to particles between 2 and 64 mm and "cobbles" refers to those between 64 and 256 mm, while the term "boulders" refers to larger sized particles. The Wentworth scale will be followed in this paper. The term "gravel" will be used if no particular size designation is intended except that it is coarser than sand. However, gravels are usually admixed with sand.

The term "shingle" is commonly used by the British (Wood, 1971; Carr, 1975) to designate coarse, loose, well-rounded and water-worn detritus, greater than 4 mm in size but no larger than 256 mm, occurring typically on the higher parts of a beach and therefore relatively free from finer material.

## SEDIMENT SIZE DISTRIBUTION

The sediment size at Mann Hill Beach ranges from fine sand to boulders over 30 cm in size. On the lower foreshore, fine sand is dominant. On the middle foreshore, halfway between low and high tide, pebbles start to make their appearance. On the upper foreshore, shingle is found. The average of all the shingle sizes, based on 15,000

TABLE 4. CUSP DIMENSIONS BEFORE AND AFTER THE BLIZZARD OF '78 AT MANN HILL BEACH. (DATA RECALCULATED FROM SPAYNE, 1978, RUST, 1977, SCULLY AND NWANKWO, 1979)

| Date | Cusp dimensions | |
|---|---|---|
| | Length (m) | Width (m) |
| 11-28-76, set 1 | 2.97 | 2.59 |
| 11-28-76, set 2 | 8.94 | 3.69 |
| 1-22-77 | 13.32 | --- |
| 2-22-78 | 35.20 | 12.00 |
| 10-01-79 | 6.44 | 4.01 |
| 11-18-79 | 7.76 | 6.97 |

Figure 8. Two sets of well developed cusps at
Mann Hill Beach in January 1976. Top photograph shows the size distribution of shingle
within a set of northeast-oriented cusp series.
In the bottom photograph the small box just
off center of the picture is 15 cm in length.

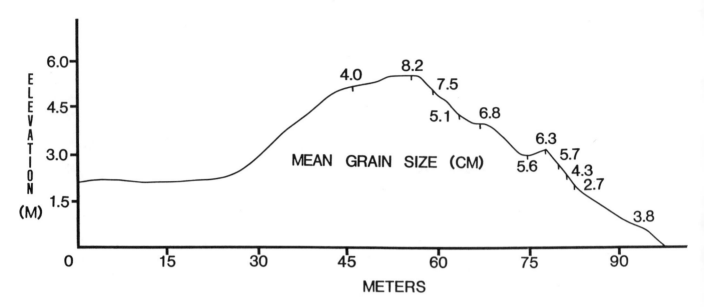

Figure 9. Upper diagram. Prestorm sediment
size distribution along the profile line in
Figure 3. Lower diagram. Sediment shape distribution along this profile line. The numbers
above the shape histograms refer to the number
of meters from the arbitrary starting point of
the profile. (Data from Rust, 1977).

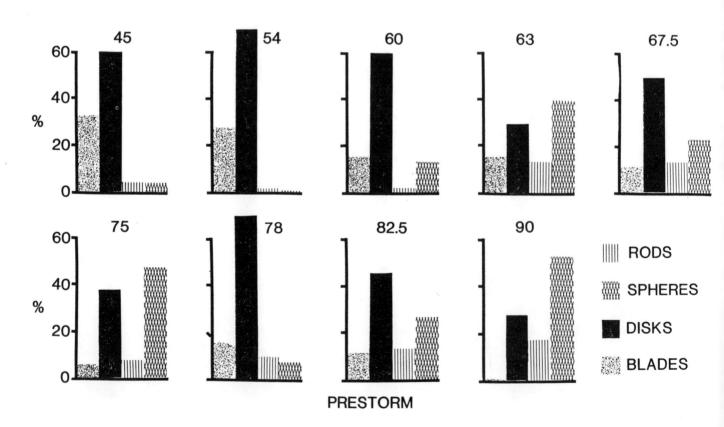

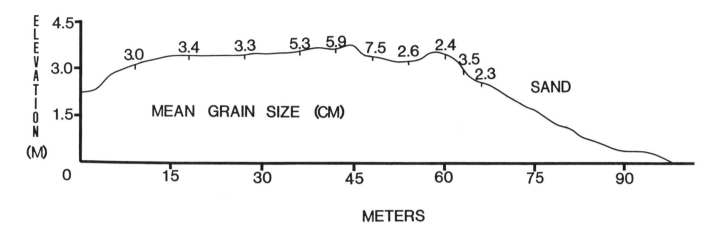

Figure 10. Upper diagram. Poststorm sediment size distribution along the profile line in Figure 3. Lower diagram. Sediment shape distribution along this profile line. The numbers above the shape histograms refer to the number of meters from the arbitrary starting point of the profile. (Data from Siminitz and Pfeiffer, 1978; Nachlas and McGlew, 1979; and Schultz, 1979).

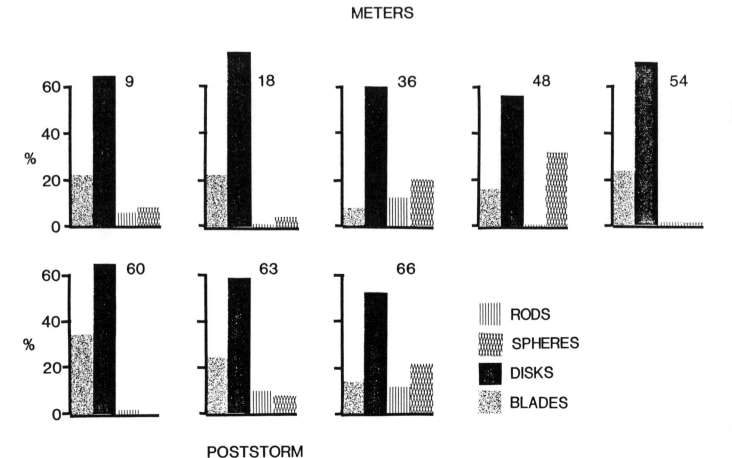

measurements of the largest diameter, is 4.2 cm (Rust, 1977; Siminitz and Pfeiffer, 1978; Schultz, 1979). The distribution of shingle sizes before and after the storm is shown in Figures 9 and 10.

There is a gradual increase in size from the upper foreshore to the berm. The largest sizes are found at the berm. Generally, a decrease in size is found landward of the berm. If more than one berm is present, as is often the case, there is a small decrease in size just landward of the berm in the swale. As can be seen in Figures 9 and 10, there was little change in the average grain size before and after the storm. If anything, the post storm sizes were finer. The sizes before and after the blizzard are not statistically different; however, distribution of sizes was different. After the storm, the shingle became present a lot higher up on the beach. The backwash had not yet had sufficient time to roll the rounder pebbles down from the upper foreshore.

Along the beach there is a gradual increase of shingle grain size from north to south. In the north, the average size is 3.1 cm while in the south it is 5.3 cm. The only places where there is a local variation in this along-the-beach increase in sediment size are within the cusps. Inside the cusp bays, the coarsest sediment is found in the landward end and on the north side (Table 5).

TABLE 5. CUSP SEDIMENT SIZE DISTRIBUTION

| Location | Distribution (cm) | | |
|----------|------|------|------|
| Back of bay | 12.9 | 6.3 | 3.9 |
| Middle of bay | 4.0 | 4.1 | 3.9 |
| Front of bay | 3.4 | 3.0 | 3.4 |
| North edge of bay | 15.4 | 5.5 | 6.5 |
| South edge of bay | 5.5 | 4.7 | 2.5 |

SHINGLE LITHOLOGY

There are seven common rock types found in the pebbles on Mann Hill Beach. As can be seen in Table 6, the most frequent rock types are granite and granodiorite. The most common is the foliated, light pinkish-gray, medium-grained Dedham Granodiorite which has 25 percent quartz and 10 percent altered biotite, with the remainder composed of saussuritized plagioclase and orthoclase. In the Dedham clasts at Mann Hill Beach there are many xenoliths of two types of diorite and a fine grained ampibolite. Less common at Mann Hill are clasts of the Westwood granite. This granite is pinkish-gray, fine- to medium-grained with 25-35 percent quartz, 10 percent microperthite and accessory apatite, sphene and magnetite (Chute, 1965). Even rarer in the shingle is an unnamed medium gray, foliated biotite

granite composed of 30-60 percent plagioclase which is almost completely altered to sericite, epidote and albite, 10-35 percent orthoclase and microcline and 5 percent olivine green biotite and large sodic plagioclase phenocrysts (Chute, 1965).

The siltstone clasts are a greenish to brownish-gray, fine-grained, thin-bedded argillite which contains quartz, sericite and opaque minerals (probably graphite) in a finer matrix too small to be identifiable. The siltstone probably belongs to the Boston Bay Group, specifically the Cambridge Argillite or possibly the Braintree Argillite (Chute, 1969).

Both the rhyolite and andesite rock types are part of the Mattapan Volcanic Complex. The rhyolite is predominantly red and purple but may be brown tuffs and flows, usually with small phenocrysts of quartz and microperthite. Most of the "rhyolite" is so fine grained that it is taken to be a divitrified tuff. The andesite is bluish- to greenish-gray with small phenocrysts of sericitized plagioclase, quartz and chlorite in a groundmass of very fine plagioclase laths. Secondary epidote is common, giving the rock a greenish tinge.

The basalt is medium to dark grayish-green, fine-grained massive rock. It frequently has a subophitic texture. The basalt probably represents the diabase dikes so prevalent throughout the neighboring quadrangles.

The diorite is fine- to medium-grained, massive, and dark greenish-gray in color. It consists predominantly of plagioclase (which is almost completely altered to epidote), albite and sericite, with lesser amounts of hornblende, a light pyroxene and olive green biotite.

The quartzite is light gray to white massive quartzite with minor quantities of biotite. It is probably Westboro Quartzite (Nelson, 1975).

The least common rock is the grayish-green amphibolite in which the layers have fine alterations of felsic and mafic minerals producing a striped appearance. Hornblende and plagioclase are the principal components with minor amounts of chlorite, quartz, epidote, sphene and calcite. The amphibolite is common only as xenoliths in the Dedham Granodiorite.

On Mann Hill Beach not all of the lithologies are admixed equally. There is more rhyolite and quartzite on the lower fringes of the shingle, and more siltstone and andesite on top of the berm. There was also a change in the quantities of different lithologies before and after the blizzard (Table 7). There was more granite, diorite, andesite, and quartzite and less rhyolite and basalt after the storm.

SHINGLE SHAPE

Anyone who has visited a shingle beach has

seen the difference in the shape of the pebbles at mid-tide and those at the top of the berm. A description of shape or geometric forms involves several different but related concepts. On the one hand are the shape factors which depend on the relative lengths of the particle with respect to standard Cartesian coordinates. On the other hand is the angularity or roundness of the sediment particles.

In 1935 Zingg demonstrated that if the ratio of the intermediate to the maximum lengths (B/A) of a pebble is plotted against the ratio of the shortest to the intermediate lengths (C/B), the particle may be classified according to its shape. Zingg utilized four shape classes (Figure 11).

The proportion of disks and blades, 83.8 percent (Table 6), at Mann Hill Beach is surprising, especially in view of the large proportion of non-layered rocks composed of equidimensional grains (granite, diorite, and quartzite). However, the Boston Basin and surrounding areas are characterized by thrust faults, tear faults and normal faults. Especially in the southern part of the basin, the structure consists of numerous thrusted anticlines which constitute an imbricate block structure with minor thrusts and rock slices (Billings, 1929). Locally, numerous shears are present that are spaced at intervals of between 1 and 100 cm. Moreover, two types of cleavage are prevalent. These ruptures are uniformly perpendicular to the bedding and to the imbricate blocks. Also nearly ubiquitous is a set of remarkably parallel joints spaced at intervals of 1 cm to 15 m. When two or three sets of joints are closely spaced, the rocks break into parallellopipeda 5-50 cm on a side (Billings, 1976). These, after being eroded by glacial ice and deposited in drumlins or moraines, are rounded by wave-induced transportation to form the disks and blades.

The original concept of sphericity or the degree to which the particle approaches the form of a sphere was defined by Wadell (1932) as the surface of a sphere of the same volume. Since the measurement of the surface area of an irregular pebble is difficult, Wadell (1933) proposed a practical or operational definition of sphericity: the cube root of the volume of the particle divided by the volume of a circumscribing sphere.

The lines of equal operational sphericity swing across the Zingg chart as hyperboloid curves (Fig. 12), indicating that particles of decidedly different appearance such as disks and rollers may have the same dynamic behavior in water provided they have the same density. For a given volume, a sphere has less surface area than particles of any other shape. As the shape departs from spheroid, the ratio of surface area to volume increases. This relation affects the resistance of the pebble to movement by water.

There is another factor that influences transportation by traction, namely the pivotability. Pivotability is the tendency to start rolling on a slope (Kuenen, 1964). It is a shape characteristic unrelated to weight, size or density. However, it is not an independent property for it is related to both roundness and general shape. For instance, a disk is less pivotable than a cube. But an angular cube is less pivotable (more stable) than a rounded one. On the other hand a rounded disk can have the same pivotability as an angular cube (Fig. 13). Pivotability can be measured by introducing shingle clasts down a rotating inclined drum and measuring the time it takes for the pebble to emerge. The more pivotable a particle, the shorter the time necessary to roll down the length of a drum (Winkelmolen, 1971).

## SHINGLE MOVEMENT

Net landward motion of shingle during normal sea conditions is small. During storms, pebbles of all shapes are brought in by waves from the offshore tills and ground moraine. Since disks are lighter than spheroids of the same diameter and have a lower settling velocity than pebbles of any other shape, they are thrown up higher on the beach (Krumbein, 1942; McNown and Malaika, 1950). This can be seen in Figure 9 at stations 45, 54 and 60 meters on the higher berm and station 78 meters on the lower berm. On the post blizzard profile (Fig. 10) stations at 54, 60 and 63 meters show a preponderance of disks.

Once gravel is high up on the berm, a sorting mechanism takes place. Backwash moving through the gravel moves the finer sizes seaward (Bluck, 1967). The size and shape of grains in this seaward moving gravel is dependent on the size and geometry of the pore spaces. Usually a fringe of spherical pebbles is found at the seaward edge of the shingle. These probably have moved through the pore spaces. Rods, however, are caught in the interstices, for they orient themselves with the long axis parallel to the beach.

Seaward movement of the surface particles from the berm scarp takes place under normal conditions. In the backwash, because it moves particles along the bottom, pivotability becomes important. Figure 14 shows the increase in relative pivotability of the gravel seaward of the post bulldozed berm (Fig. 7). In general, spherical and roller shaped particles move faster than disks. Spheres and rollers will be transported farther seaward by the backwash. Thus, at the seaward edge of the shingle there is an area with relatively large numbers of spheres and rollers (Fig. 9, stations 63 and 75). Note the relationship between stations 78, 82.5 and 90 m on the seaward side of the lower berm. Even after the blizzard there was time for the backwash to redistribute the rollers and spheres from the edge of the overwash (Fig. 10, stations 36 and 48 m). The backwash, since the blizzard, had redistributed these shapes seaward of the small berm (Fig. 10, stations 60, 63 and 66).

Although the disks lag behind, they are not stationary. They become imbricated. Percolation by the backwash produces an imbrication of the shingle, so that the gravel dips seaward. By

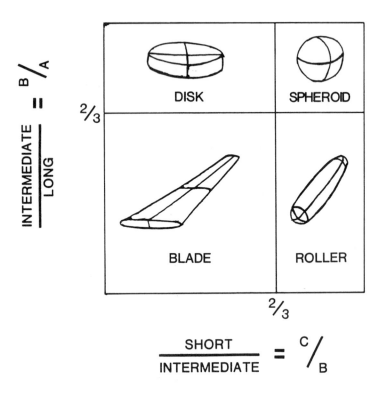

Figure 11. Zingg classification of pebble shape. A is the length of the long axis of the pebble, B the length of the intermediate, and C the short axis (Zingg, 1935).

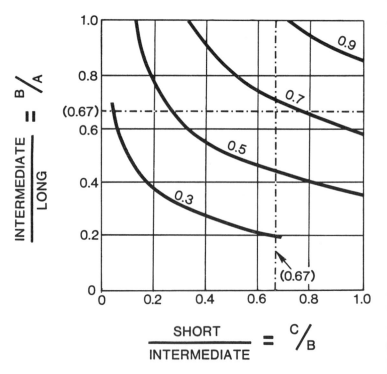

Figure 12. Relationship of Wadell's (1933) operational sphericity and Zingg's (1935) shape classification. Because the sphericity lines cut across different shapes, diverse shapes may have the same hydrodynamic characteristics.

TABLE 6.  LITHOLOGY AND SHAPES OF THE SHINGLE ON MANN HILL BEACH IN PERCENTAGE OF 15,000 MEASUREMENTS

| Lithology | Disks | Blades | Spheroids | Rollers | Total (percent) |
|---|---|---|---|---|---|
| Granite/Granodiorite | 51.1 | 24.1 | 18.8 | 6.0 | 24.1 |
| Rhyolite | 61.3 | 19.9 | 11.4 | 7.4 | 18.0 |
| Basalt | 62.6 | 28.5 | 4.5 | 4.4 | 14.6 |
| Diorite | 65.0 | 24.2 | 5.4 | 5.4 | 13.1 |
| Andesite | 57.7 | 30.5 | 4.7 | 7.1 | 10.9 |
| Quartzite | 62.7 | 14.1 | 15.5 | 7.7 | 10.6 |
| Siltstone | 55.9 | 40.1 | 1.9 | 2.1 | 8.6 |
| Others (Amphibolite) | .1 | | | | |
| Total or weighted average | 58.8 | 25.0 | 10.3 | 5.9 | 100.0 |

TABLE 7.  COMPARISON OF PRE- AND POST-BLIZZARD OF '78 LITHOLOGICAL DISTRIBUTION AND SHAPES OF THE SHINGLE AT MANN HILL BEACH

| | Prestorm shapes | | | | |
|---|---|---|---|---|---|
| Lithology | Disks | Blades | Spheroids | Rollers | Total (percent) |
| Granite/Granodiorite | 10.5 | 1.9 | 6.5 | 2.3 | 21.2 |
| Rhyolite | 13.8 | 3.7 | 3.0 | 2.3 | 22.8 |
| Basalt | 10.0 | 5.5 | 1.5 | 0.8 | 17.8 |
| Diorite | 7.2 | 2.1 | 0.8 | 0.7 | 10.8 |
| Andesite | 5.9 | 2.3 | 0.6 | 1.0 | 9.8 |
| Quartzite | 3.4 | 1.3 | 2.2 | 1.0 | 7.9 |
| Siltstone | 5.8 | 3.6 | 0.2 | 0.1 | 9.7 |
| Total | 56.6 | 20.4 | 14.8 | 8.2 | 100.0 |

| | Poststorm shapes | | | | |
|---|---|---|---|---|---|
| Lithology | Disks | Blades | Spheroids | Rollers | Total (percent) |
| Granite/Granodiorite | 13.3 | 3.4 | 6.0 | 1.3 | 24.0 |
| Rhyolite | 10.9 | 3.8 | 2.1 | 1.4 | 18.2 |
| Basalt | 6.4 | 4.2 | 0.6 | 0.4 | 11.6 |
| Diorite | 8.7 | 2.5 | 0.3 | 0.3 | 11.8 |
| Andesite | 7.8 | 4.0 | 0.2 | 0.9 | 12.9 |
| Quartzite | 7.6 | 1.2 | 1.6 | 1.2 | 11.6 |
| Siltstone | 5.0 | 2.8 | 1.7 | 0.4 | 9.9 |
| Total | 59.7 | 21.9 | 12.5 | 5.9 | 100.0 |

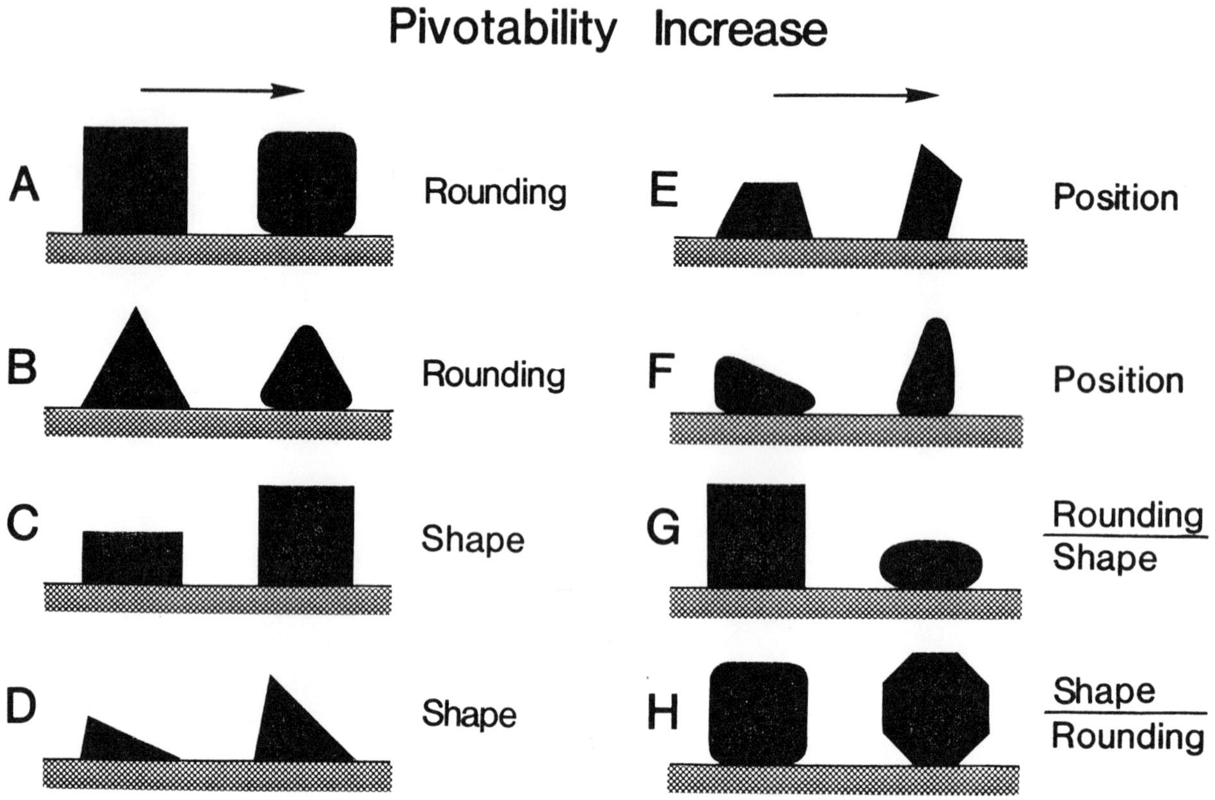

# Pivotability Increase

Figure 13. The increase in pivotability (more readily moved) due to shape, rounding, or position of similar particles. The more pivotable pebble is on the right. A and B, the rounding has increased pivotability; C and D, the flatter the shape, the less pivotable is the particle; E and F, identical shapes in which position of deposition makes the right hand more pivotable; G, rounding predominates over shape in causing higher pivotability; H, shape predominates over rounding in causing higher pivotability. (After Kuenen, 1964).

Figure 14. Increase in pivotability of four samples of 50 pebbles with increasing distance seaward of the apex of the berm in Figure 7. (Data from Bresnahan, 1979). The longer it takes for the pebbles to traverse through the rotating cylinder, the lower their pivotability and the less likely they are going to be transported down the beach face by the backwash. The pivotability scale on the right of the diagram is arbitrary.

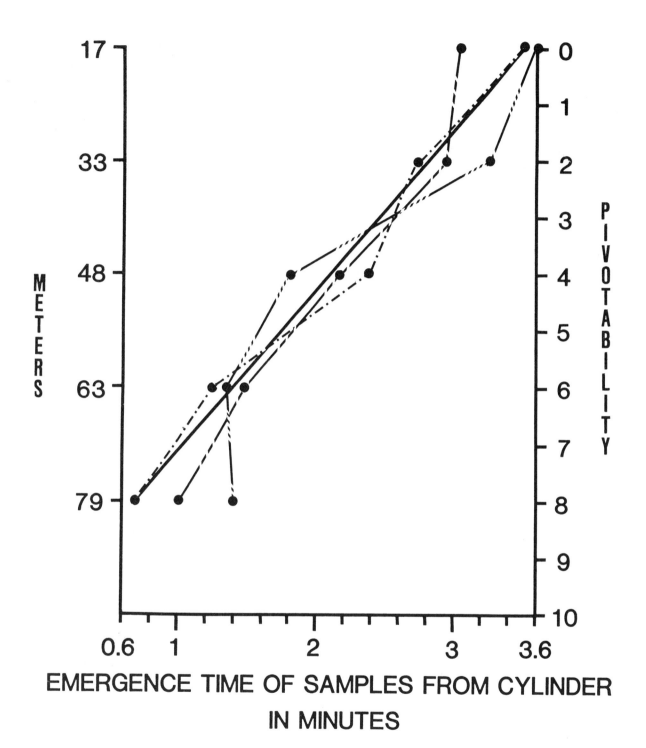

EMERGENCE TIME OF SAMPLES FROM CYLINDER
IN MINUTES

means of a caterpillar type action, the disks are slowly moved seaward. This movement is irregular, resulting in a wide range of dip values, from 0° to 85°, but averaging 39°.

## CONCLUSIONS

During the blizzard of February 6 and 7, 1978, with still water reaching 3.3 m above mean low water and with waves between 3.4 and 6.7 m high, 150,000 m$^3$ was eroded from the shingled, 1100 m long foreshore at Mann Hill Beach, Scituate, Massachusetts. Roughly 30 percent of this shingle was deposited in a 1.5 m high, 30 m wide overwash apron. The rest was lost offshore.

The grain size of the shingle, averaging 4.2 cm, did not change during the blizzard. The shingle shapes, however, were rearranged. Most common are disks and blades. They are the dominant shingle shapes on the highest parts of the beach. Rods and especially spheres, on the other hand, are found on the middle foreshore and in swales. They were rolled there by the backwash.

## ACKNOWLEDGMENTS

Any investigation requiring the gathering of field data is the work of many individuals. Thanks are due to all who assisted in many ways, including the members of the Modern Sedimentary Environments class at Boston College--Claire Bresnahan, Kevin Maher, Sue McGlew, Tom McMahon, Paul Nachlas, Adam Nwankwo, and Marguerite Scully; Lee Rust and Heidi Schultz of Wellesley College; and Robert Spayne and his students at Boston State College. I would also like to acknowledge gratefully the help of Bill Girolamo, Pablo Huidobro, Michelle Pfeiffer, Pam Siminitz and Carroll Stewart, and especially Becky Buxton and David Roy.

## REFERENCES

Atterberg, A., 1905, Die rationalle Klassifikation der Sande und Kiese: Chemischer Zeitung, v. 29, p. 195-198.

Bagnold, R.A., 1940, Beach formation by waves--some model experiments in a wave table: Journal of Institute of Civil Engineers, v. 15, p. 27-52.

Billings, M.P., 1929, Structural geology of the eastern part of the Boston Basin: American Journal of Science, 5th series, v. 18, p. 97-137.

Billings, M.P., 1976, Geology of the Boston Basin: Geological Society of America Memoir, 146, p. 5-30.

Blackford, P.A., 1979, The anatomy of the February '78 blizzard: in Stewart, R.F., ed., Blizzard of '78: Conference Proceedings, Bridgewater State College, p. 6-13.

Bluck, A.J., 1967, Sedimentation of beach gravels--examples from South Wales: Journal of Sedimentary Petrology, v. 37, p. 128-156.

Bowen, A.J., 1969, Rip currents: Journal of Geophysical Research, v. 74, p. 5467-5478.

Bowen, A.J., 1973, Edge waves and the littoral environment: Proceedings, Thirteenth Conference on Coastal Engineering, American Society of Civil Engineers, p. 1313-1320.

Brenninkmeyer, S.J., B.M., 1976, Dynamics of sedimentation and coastal geology from Boston to Plymouth: in Cameron, B., ed., Geology of southeastern New England: Sixty-eighth Annual Meeting, New England Intercollegiate Geological Conference, p. 205-223.

Bresnahan, C.M., 1979, Pivotability of Mann Hill Beach shingle: Unpub. paper in Modern Sedimentary Environments, Boston College, 4 p.

Carr, A.P., 1975, Differential movement of coarse sediment particles: Proceedings of Fourteenth Conference on Coastal Engineering, American Society of Civil Engineers, p. 851-870.

Chute, N.E., 1965, Geological map of the Scituate Quadrangle, Plymouth County, Massachusetts: U.S. Geological Survey Map GQ 467.

Chute, N.E., 1969, Bedrock geologic map of the Blue Hill Quadrangle, Norfolk and Suffolk Counties, Massachusetts: U.S. Geological Survey Map GQ 796.

Fitzgerald, D.M., 1978, The effects of the 6-7 February 1978 storm on Winthrop Beach, in Jones, J.R., ed., The blizzard of 1978: Boston State College, p. 65-79.

Gadoury, R.A., 1979, Coastal flood of February 7, 1978, in Maine, Massachusetts and New Hampshire: U.S. Geological Survey Water Resource Investigation 79-61, 57 p.

Hartwell, A.D., 1978, Northeasterly storm effects in the western Gulf of Maine and the February 1978 "storm of the century": in Jones, J.R., ed., The blizzard of 1978: Boston State College, p. 37-54.

Hicks, S.D., 1978, An average geopotential sea level series for the United States: Journal of Geophysical Research, v. 83, p. 1377-1380.

Krumbein, W.C., 1942, Settling velocity and flume behavior of nonspherical particles: American Geophysical Union Transactions, v. 13, p. 621-633.

Kuenen, P.H., 1964, Experimental abrasion--6 surf action: Sedimentology, v. 3, p. 29-34.

Lane, E.W., and others, 1957, Report of the subcommittee on sedimentation terminology: American Geophysical Union Transactions, v.

28, p. 936-938.

Maher, K., and McMahon, T., 1979, Mann Hill Beach profiles: Unpub. paper in Modern Sedimentary Environments, Boston College, 79 p.

McNown, A., and Malaika, J., 1950, The effect of particle shape on the settling velocity at low Reynolds numbers: American Geophysical Union Transactions, v. 31, p. 74-82.

Nachlas, P., and McGlew, S., 1979, Grain size analysis of Mann Hill Beach: Unpub. paper in Modern Sedimentary Environments, Boston College, 7 p.

Nelson, A.E., 1975, Bedrock geologic map of the Natick Quadrangle, Middlesex and Norfolk Counties, Massachusetts: U.S. Geological Survey Map GQ 1208.

Richardson, W.S., 1977, Forecasting beach erosion along the oceanic coastline of the northeast and Mid-Atlantic states: Unpub. M.A. thesis, College of William and Mary, Williamsburg VA, 121 p.

Rust, L.D., 1977, Non-storm, storm and recovery stages of beach development for a pebble baymouth bar: Mann Hill Beach, Scituate, Massachusetts: Unpub. Geology Honors Thesis, Wellesley College, Wellesley, MA, 106 p.

Schultz, H.A., 1979, The blizzard of 1978, the erosion and sediment transport at Mann Hill pebble beach, Scituate, Massachusetts: Unpub. Geology Honors Thesis, Wellesley College, Wellesley, MA, 52 p.

Scully, M., and Nwankwo, A., 1979, Bedforms at Mann Hill Beach: Unpub. paper in Modern Sedimentary Environments, Boston College, 15 p.

Siminitz, P., and Pfeiffer, M., 1978, Shape and size distribution of cobbles on Mann Hill Beach, North Scituate, Massachusetts: Unpub. paper in Coastal Geology, Boston College, 35 p.

Spayne, R.W., 1977, Shingle beach, North Scituate, Massachusetts--a geomorphological study: Boston College, 100 p.

Spayne, R.W., 1978, Prestorm and post-storm conditions at selected beaches in Scituate: in Jones, J.R., ed., The blizzard of 1978: Boston State College, p. 91-98.

Udden, J.A., 1914, Mechanical composition of clastic sediments: Geological Society of America Bulletin, v. 25, p. 655-714.

U.S. Army Corps of Engineers, 1964, Hurricane survey--Interim Report, Massachusetts coastal and tidal areas: Waltham, MA, 12 p.

U.S. Army Corps of Engineers, 1977, Beach erosion control study for Cape Cod, Massachusetts, Waltham, MA, 36 p.

U.S. Army Corps of Engineers, 1979, Blizzard of 1978 coastal storm damage study: Waltham, MA, 48 p.

U.S. Army Corps of Engineers, Coastal Engineering Research Center, 1973, Shore protection manual, 3 volumes.

Wadell, H.A., 1932, Volume, shape and roundness of rock particles: Journal of Geology, v. 40, p. 443-451.

Wadell, H.A., 1933, Sphericity and roundness of rock particles: Journal of Geology, v. 41, p. 310-331.

Wentworth, C.K., 1922, The shapes of beach pebbles: U.S. Geological Survey, Professional Paper 131C, p. 75-83.

Wentworth, C.K., 1933, Fundamental limits to the sizes of clastic grains: Science, v. 77, p. 633-634.

Winkelmolen, A.N., 1971, Rollability, a functional shape property of sand grains: Journal of Sedimentary Petrology, v. 41, p. 703-714.

Wood, A.M., 1971, Characteristics of shingle beaches: the solution to some practical problems: Proceedings of Twelfth Conference on Coastal Engineering, American Society of Civil Engineers, p. 1059-1076.

Zingg, T., 1935, Beitrag zur Schotteranalyse: Schweizerische Mineralogische und Petrographische Mitteilungen, v. 15, p. 39-140.

Hors-texte    Part of a relief diagram of the continental margin of eastern North America, by D. Monahan (Canadian Hydrographic Service, Chart 810, 1971.) Massachusetts is in the center, Nantucket Shoals marking the offshore zone.

# Mapping techniques and historical shoreline analysis— Nauset Spit, Massachusetts

F. J. ANDERS National Park Service Cooperative Research Unit
S. P. LEATHERMAN University of Massachusetts at Amherst

## ABSTRACT

Barrier evolution and migrational processes are currently being studied on Nauset Spit, Cape Cod, utilizing a new mapping methodology. Manually rectified historical aerial photographs and NOS shoreline manuscripts were digitally compiled to yield accurate computer-plotted maps of the study area. The NOS data allowed for an examination of net changes and delineation of trends characteristic of the barrier over a longer period of record (1850s to the present).

Since 1938 Nauset Harbor Inlet has been migrating northward, shortening Coast Guard Beach (CGB) spit. During this same time interval, the spit has retreated landward an average of 3 ft/yr. This erosion has resulted in a relative change of barrier environments, especially the proportion of dune to washover areas. Despite intermittent overwash activity, the northern spit (CGB) has continued to narrow in width during this time period. Therefore, Coast Guard Beach is progressively becoming narrower and relatively lower through time with loss of the formerly substantial foredune.

## INTRODUCTION

Changes occurring in the configuration of shorelines have always been of special interest to coastal scientists, managers, and navigators. Ground-constructed maps and charts have historically played an important role in monitoring the actual position of the boundary between land and water. Since the late 1930s, delineation of the rapidly changing land-sea interface has been enhanced by the use of vertical aerial photographs.

The National Ocean Survey (NOS) "T" sheets are the most accurate maps commonly available for the coastal zone. Stable points located on these maps are accurate to within 0.3 mm of their actual positions at the scale of the map (1:10,000). This accuracy makes them quite useful in delineating the land-water boundary, particularly net changes over the long term. However, when detailed monitoring of processes resulting in barrier island migration is desired, these maps have two limitations. First, NOS maps are not sufficiently detailed to allow for a thorough analysis of changes in various barrier environments. Since the nearshore bathymetry is of paramount importance for navigation, delineation of barrier topography and vegetative communities receives much less attention. Second, only longer term trends can be determined since the maps are not produced at frequent intervals, which precludes a detailed understanding and interpretation of the

short term physical processes and morphological responses. The long term rate and nature of barrier migration is the integration of many episodic events.

The U.S. Geological Survey topographic maps can provide some additional detail in comparison to NOS shoreline manuscripts. However, as with the "T" sheets, these maps are updated at infrequent intervals. Also, their accuracy could be a problem since the topographic maps are produced just within the guidelines of National Map Accuracy Standards, which allows for no more than 10 percent of the stable points tested to be in error by more than 1/30 of an inch at the scale of the map. On the standard 7.5 minute quadrangles (1:24,000), 1/30 of an inch would mean an error of 65 feet in the actual location of a stable point. Other points, such as shoreline positions, are located with an even larger potential error.

One additional problem with using a 1:24,000 or smaller scale map is that the smallest field distance that can be consistently measured with the unaided eye at a 1:24,000 scale is between 16 and 39 feet. On the 1:10,000 scale "T" sheets, the smallest field distance measurable is between 7 and 16 feet.

Aerial photographs can be used to provide the necessary detail and short-time interval required for detecting and evaluating the processes shaping the coastline. The use of vertical photographs for determining the rates of shoreline change at selected points was well documented by Stafford (1971). Since then a number of coastal scientists have used air photos to monitor shoreline recession (Dolan et al., 1978; Fisher, 1977; Leatherman, 1979) and qualitative changes in barrier environments (Boc and Langfelder, 1977; Hosier and Cleary, 1977).

In most cases, final maps are produced by transferring the air photo data to an appropriate base map, and the readily available U.S.G.S. topographic maps have often been selected for this purpose. As previously discussed, these maps already have a 65-feet potential error to which errors associated with air photo mapping would be added. The product is a map of low accuracy, upon which only major changes in the shoreline can be meaningfully measured.

Many coastal scientists (e.g., Dolan et al., 1978) have ignored the problem of point displacement due to tilt in imagery. However, photogrammetrists have long been concerned with this problem since few photos are truly vertical and tilts of up to three degrees are not unusual. Some correction for tilt distortion must be made on almost every photograph prior to mapping.

The relationship between a vertical photograph and a tilted photo is illustrated in Figure 1. The amount of displacement of any point on a photo due to tilt ($D_t$) can be calculated with the following relationship:

$$D_t = \frac{Y^2 (\sin T)(\cos P)}{F - (Y \sin T)(\cos P)}$$

where  Y = distance from the point to the isocenter
F = focal length of the lens
T = angle of tilt of the photograph
P = angle between principal line and radial line from the isocenter to the point (within the plane of the photograph).

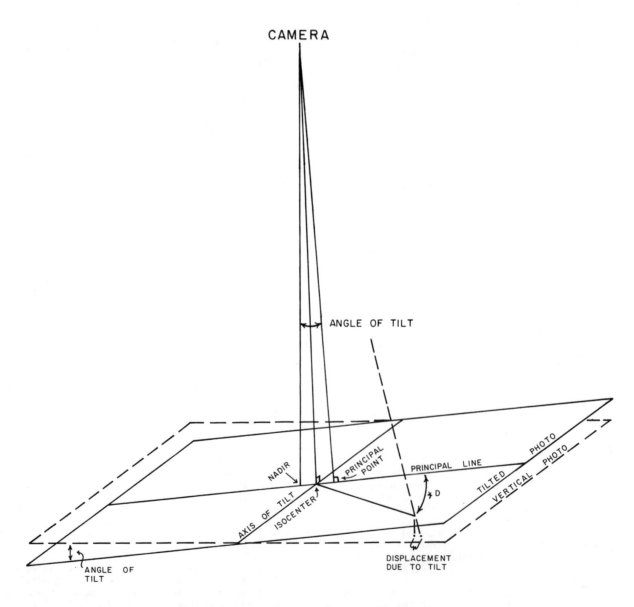

Figure 1. The relationship between a tilted aerial photograph and an exactly vertical photograph.

As apparent from this equation, the amount of displacement increases with distance from the iso-center and with increasing tilt. For example, a point 4.2 mm from the isocenter and 40 degrees from the principal line on a 1:20,000 photo, tilted only 1 degree, would have an error of 65 feet in its true ground location. A photo with a 3 degree tilt would yield an error of almost 200 feet in its ground location (the shoreline could be displaced horizontally by this amount from its actual position).

Photo mapping techniques, which fail to correct for tilt (and elevation distortion in some cases) and which use USGS topographic maps as a base, could have errors ranging from 65 feet to over 265 feet. This amount of error is quite alarming when most shorelines along the U.S. are experiencing changes which average less than 3 ft per year (U.S. Army Corps of Engineers, 1971). Therefore, 120 feet of erosion, during the 40 years for which aerial photography of the coastline is available, is well within the error margin of many maps. As a result, aerial photographs cannot be used directly as maps if accuracy is a requirement; meaningful shoreline change data require rectified imagery. However, limited quali-tative information on vegetative communities and morphological features can be obtained directly from air photos.

MAPPING PROCEDURE

In order to avoid the aforementioned problems in mapping historical changes along Nauset Spit, a new technique of map construction was devised with assistance from the National Ocean Survey. The first step in the procedure is to locate stable control points on each photograph. The same points should be accurately marked on the appropriate NOS "T" sheet. Road intersections and buildings are the best points; however, they are not always present on barriers or the mainland shoreline. Natural fea-tures, which have remained stable over the duration of the mapping interval, can be used to supplement the cultural control points. A minimum of four con-trol points were located and accurately plotted on each photograph of Nauset Spit for each date of photography and on the corresponding "T" sheet.

The next step was production of a base map onto which the photographic data could be transferred.

The State Plane coordinate system intersections on the "T" sheets served as a set of primary control points. The previously located cultural and natural points became secondary controls. The relative position of every control point was then determined with an X-Y digitizer. Since the State Plane coordinates were already known for the primary con-trol points, the CONVERT program developed by the National Ocean Survey was used to transform all the digitized secondary control points into State Plane format. These points were then plotted on a mylar base at a 1:10,000 scale via a second computer program (P2NDPT) and a Calcomp plotter. The mylar sheet became the base map onto which the shoreline data was transferred.

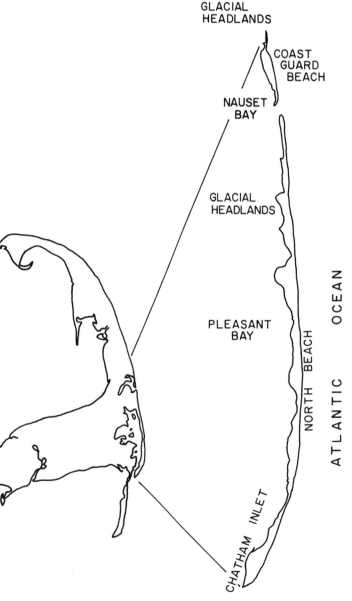

Figure 2. Nauset Spit System, consisting of Coast Guard Beach and North Beach.

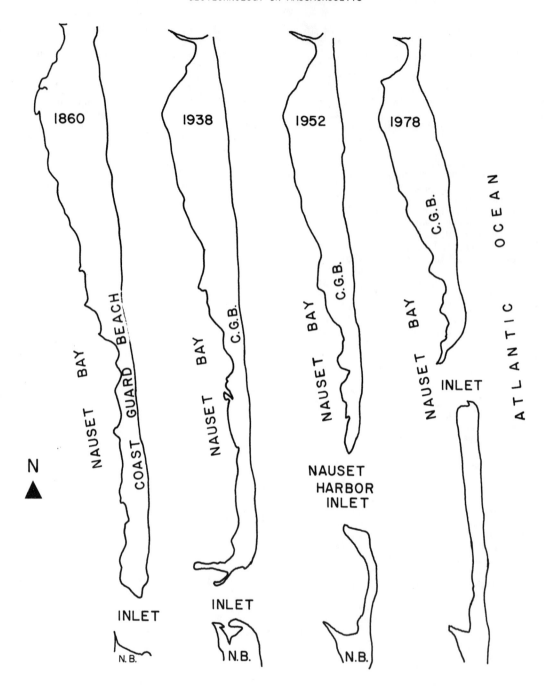

Figure 3. From 1860 to 1978 Nauset Inlet migrated
northward, shortening Coast Guard Beach.

Concurrent with the production of the base maps, air photographs from 1938, 1952, and 1978 were stereoscopically annotated to highlight the features to be mapped. Ocean and bay shorelines, dunes, shrub communities, marsh, and washovers were carefully delineated on each photo.

The photographic data were transferred to the base maps with the aid of a Bausch & Lomb Zoom Transfer Scope (ZTS). Individual photographs were optically overlaid onto the base maps. Scale and stretch adjustments were made until a best fit between the control points on the photograph and base map was achieved. Perfect alignment of all control points was not possible because of the inability of the ZTS to correct for tilt. However, once the best possible fit was achieved, most of the distortion was removed, and the photographic data was directly traced onto the base map. This procedure was repeated for each set of historical photographs.

After the base maps were completed, pertinent information, such as shorelines and vegetative community boundaries, was digitized. In addition, "T" sheets from 1851-1868, 1886, 1941, and 1965 were digitized to supplement and greatly lengthen the historic record of changes along Nauset Spit. This digital information was then transferred to magnetic tapes for computational purposes. Utilizing several plotting programs developed by our research team, it was then possible to have the computer quickly and accurately produce any desired map. Scale changes, various levels of detail, overlays, and different line types are all possible with these programs, which give the operator a wide range of options for graphical display.

HISTORICAL SHORELINE CHANGES

The Nauset Spit system lies along the southeastern edge of outer Cape Cod. This barrier beach is divisible into two distinct parts: Coast Guard Beach to the north and North Beach to the south (Fig. 2). North Beach has undergone dramatic changes since the mid-1800s, when it was divided into two sections by an inlet. The sand-starved island, south of the inlet, migrated rapidly landward (146 ft/yr) and was welded onto the mainland shoreline of Chatham. Since formation of the inlet in 1846, the north spit (North Beach) has grown south at an average rate of 240 ft per year. At the present time, North Beach is only one mile short of its length in 1845.

The earliest map of Coast Guard Beach dates back to the time of North American explorers. The 1605 map, compiled by Samuel de Champlain, shows Nauset Harbor Inlet to be dividing the spit at the approximate center of the embayment. The coastline was also considerably more seaward of its present position, as pictorially demonstrated by overlaying a recent USGS map and Champlain's map (Leatherman, 1979).

The 1860 map of Coast Guard Beach shows the spit to be quite long and the inlet to be at the southernmost portion of Nauset Harbor against the glacial headlands (Fig. 3). At this time the spit

was 2.8 miles long, having migrated southward since Champlain's time. In 1938 the inlet was located at approximately the same position. However, the inlet had begun to move northward by 1941, shortening Coast Guard Beach spit and developing a smaller spit extending north from the glacial headlands. By 1952

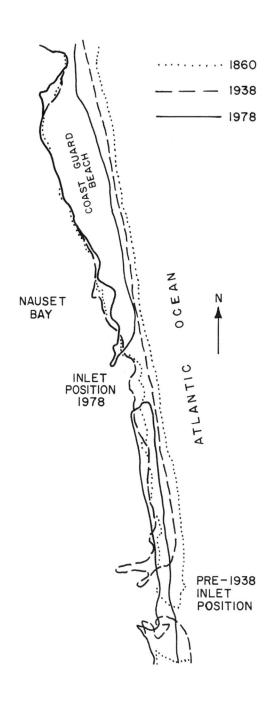

Figure 4. Historical shoreline erosion and inlet movement over 120 year period.

the northward movement of the inlet was quite pronounced (Fig. 3), and over 3400 ft of spit had been
removed from the southern terminus of Coast Guard
Beach. Between 1952 and 1978 an additional 2300 ft
was eroded from the tip of Coast Guard Beach as the
inlet continued to migrate north. Spit growth or
retreat is dependent upon the direction of the net
littoral drift, which seems to be quite variable
through time. Several coastal scientists have
suggested that the northward migration of the inlet
is due to a southerly shift in the nodal point to
the vicinity of North Beach (N.B.), and a resultant
northward net movement of material along Coast Guard
Beach.

During the 1938 to 1978 period, the width of
Nauset Harbor Inlet also changed, reflecting its
lateral migrational tendencies. The maximum throat
width measured was 2000 ft in 1952, but the inlet
shrank to 900 ft in width by 1978. Since the flow
of water through the inlet was essentially unchanged
and the cross-sectional area presumably remained
constant, the inlet must have been deeper in 1978.
Likewise, in 1938 when the inlet was against the
glacial headlands its width was only 775 ft. However, its width increased to 1300 ft and depth decreased in 1941 as it began to move northward. These
data suggest that during times of relative stability
or slow migration, the inlet naturally maintains itself in a narrow, deep configuration. In times of
rapid inlet migration, the inlet channel widens and
becomes more shallow.

Concurrent with its shortening in length, Coast
Guard Beach has also experienced shoreline erosion,
averaging 3 ft/yr between 1938 and 1978 (Fig. 4).
These measurements were made from maps at a 200 ft
interval along the entire length of the spit. The
most rapid rate of ocean shore erosion occurred
between 1941 and 1952 when an average of 11 ft/yr of
beach was lost. Between 1952 and 1978 the rate
slowed to 1.7 ft/yr. The overall rate of 3 ft/yr
agrees with field data collected by Zeigler et al.
(1964) for the long term rate of erosion along outer
Cape Cod. Despite loss of sediment from the ocean
side, there was little growth of the spit on its bay
side. Sediment deposition by overwash into the bay
or on top of the salt marsh was of a localized
nature (Fig. 5). The net result is a narrowing of
the spit in general and the dune line in particular between 1860 and 1978.

Coast Guard Beach is composed of four primary
barrier environments - beach, dune, washover, and
marsh; their distribution is shown in Figure 6.
During 1938 and 1978, when the spit was growing
aerially smaller, the relative percentage of these
four environments changed. In 1938, 39 percent of
the spit was marsh, 37 percent was dune, 8 percent
was washover, and 16 percent was beach. By 1952
the percentages had changed to 46 percent marsh,
32 percent dune, 9 percent washover and 13 percent
beach. After the severe storm of February 1978,
the dune decreased to only 18 percent of the total
area and washover increased to 17 percent (Fig. 7).
The beach area remained relatively unchanged, and
the relative percentage of marsh increased to 50
percent by 1978. This increase in marsh area is

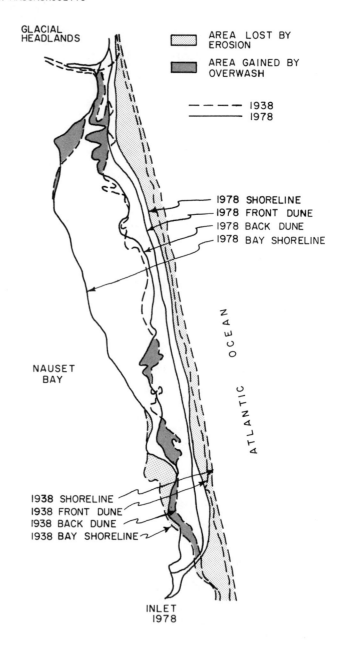

AREA LOST BY EROSION

AREA GAINED BY OVERWASH

– – – – 1938
———— 1978

GLACIAL HEADLANDS

1978 SHORELINE
1978 FRONT DUNE
1978 BACK DUNE
1978 BAY SHORELINE

NAUSET BAY

ATLANTIC OCEAN

1938 SHORELINE
1938 FRONT DUNE
1938 BACK DUNE
1938 BAY SHORELINE

INLET 1978

Figure 5. Overlay of Coast Guard Beach, showing
shoreline erosion and overwash deposition.

apparent only because most of the marsh on Coast
Guard Beach is located in a protected position.
Therefore, as the spit decreased in length and
width, little marsh was lost so that its area relative to the area of the entire spit actually
increased. Total area of marsh actually decreased
from 0.19 mi$^2$ in 1938 to 0.15 mi$^2$ in 1978, while
the entire spit was reduced from 0.5 mi$^2$ to 0.3 mi$^2$
during this same time interval.

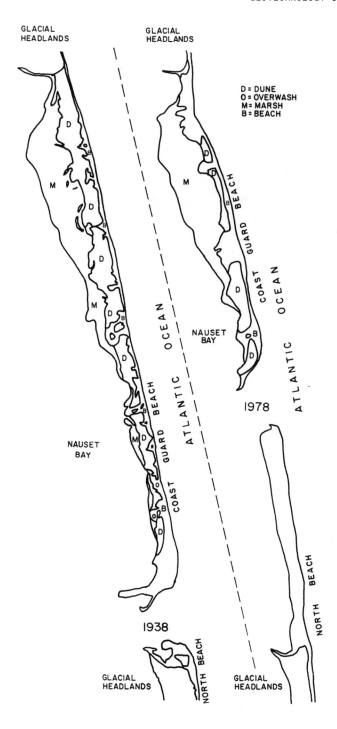

Figure 6. Distribution of barrier environments on Coast Guard Beach.

Littoral drift, inlet migration, overwash, and dune migration are the processes responsible for barrier dynamics. From the map data, it is apparent that littoral drift and inlet migration are principally responsible for the evolution of Coast Guard Beach. Overwash, which is generally viewed as a major process in barrier maintenance, did not prevent Coast Guard Beach from becoming narrower between 1860 and 1978. As previously shown (Fig. 5), overwash was only locally important over the 120-year span. Leatherman (1979) suggested that overwash becomes significant in landward migration only when a critical barrier width is reached. These data suggest that Coast Guard Beach still exceeds that critical width and thus will continue to narrow through time. Inlet migration seems to be the principal mechanism for horizontal displacement of this northern barrier beach.

SUMMARY AND CONCLUSIONS

This research has yielded an improved technique for mapping coastal environments and provided some new data and insights into the dynamics of Nauset Spit. Our air photo mapping procedure is still in the innovative stage as new techniques are being experimentally tested. Presently, we are using a manual radial plotting technique to produce the base maps. Data transfer is accomplished with a Zeiss Aerosketchmaster; this new procedure allows for complete removal of tilt distortion and hence greater accuracy than with the Zoom Transfer Scope. Our ultimate goal is to eliminate the manual steps and digitize the aerial photographs directly, using a computer program to mathematically rectify the imagery for machine plotting.

Historical shoreline analysis has indicated that inlet dynamics is the principal process shaping Coast Guard Beach; overwash is important only locally. There has been a net decrease in the sub-aerial barrier area since 1860 as a result of shoreline erosion. Sufficient washover sediments have not reached the bay shore of Coast Guard Beach to prevent this significant narrowing. It appears that the contribution of overwash in barrier maintenance is limited since Coast Guard Beach still exceeds the critical width for overwash to be an effective agent of lateral migration. The exact value for Coast Guard Beach has not been determined; until that width is approached, the barrier will continue to narrow through time. The effectiveness of overwash as an agent of barrier migration will increase as the spit continues to narrow and as the dunes are destroyed.

The rapid erosion rate along the ocean side of Coast Guard Beach may be linked to the southerly shift in the nodal point. A change in the littoral drift direction northward would reduce the sediment source area supplying Coast Guard Beach. Also, sediment would have to bypass Nauset Inlet in order to nourish Coast Guard Beach, with possible losses to the ebb and flood tidal deltas. The result would be a reduction in sediment supply to Coast Guard Beach and hence increased shoreline erosion.

Figure 7.  Extensive washovers were generated by the February 6-7,
1978, blizzard on Coast Guard Beach (view is southward).

Coast Guard Beach can also be expected to shorten through time as the inlet continues to migrate north. Since 1938 Nauset Harbor Inlet has been migrating northward, most likely due to a southerly shift in the nodal point. If the point of littoral drift divergence remains south of the inlet, it will drive the inlet northward and thus result in the demise of Coast Guard Beach as presently mapped.

## ACKNOWLEDGMENTS

We appreciate the assistance of Robert Fisher, NOAA-National Ocean Survey, and Robert Gonter and Tung Hsu, University of Massachusetts Computer Center, for helping us establish the air photo mapping technique. Marie Ferland assisted with the data collection and analysis. This research was supported by the North Atlantic Regional Office of the National Park Service with supplemental assistance from the National Ocean Survey.

## REFERENCES AND BIBLIOGRAPHY

Boc, S.J., and Langfelder, J., 1977, An analysis of beach overwash along North Carolina's coast: North Carolina State University at Raleigh, Report 77-9, 17 p.

Dolan, R., Hayden, B., and Heywood, J., 1978, A new photogrammetric method for determining shoreline erosion: Coastal Engineering, v. 2, p. 21-39.

Ellis, M.Y., ed., 1978, Coastal mapping handbook: U.S. Department of Interior - Geological Survey, and U.S. Department of Commerce - National Oceanic and Atmospheric Administration. Washington, D.C., Government Printing Office, 197 p.

Fisher, J.J., 1977, Teaching geologic/earth science remote sensing at collegiate and secondary school level: Journal of Geological Education, v. 25, p. 1-13.

Fisher, J.J., and Simpson, E.J., 1979, Washover and tidal sedimentation rates as environmental factors in development of a transgressive barrier shoreline, in Leatherman, S.P., ed., Barrier islands: New York, N.Y., Academic Press, p. 127-148.

Gatto, L.W., 1979, Historical shoreline changes along the outer coast of Cape Cod, in Leatherman, S.P., ed., Environmental geologic guide to Cape Cod National Seashore: Society of Economic Paleontologists and Mineralogists, p. 69-90.

Goldsmith, V., 1972, Coastal processes of a barrier island complex and adjacent ocean floor: Monomoy Island - Nauset Spit, Cape Cod, Massachusetts, Ph.D. dissertation, Geology Department, University of Massachusetts, 469 p.

Hennigar, H.F., 1979, Historical evolution of coastal sand dunes on Currituck Spit, Virginia (North Carolina): M.A. in Marine Sciences, William and Mary College, Virginia, 121 p.

Hosier, P.E., and Cleary, W.J., 1977, Cyclic geomorphic patterns of washover on a barrier island in southeastern North Carolina: Environmental Geology, v. 2, p. 23-31.

Langfelder, J., Stafford, D., and Amein, M., 1968, A reconnaissance of coastal erosion in North Carolina: North Carolina State University, Department of Civil Engineering, 127 p.

Leatherman, S.P., 1979, Overwash processes on Nauset Spit, in Leatherman, S.P., ed., Environmental geologic guide to Cape Cod National Seashore: Society of Economic Paleontologists and Mineralogists, p. 171-172.

Leatherman, S.P., 1979a, Migration of Assateague Island, Maryland, by inlet and overwash processes: Geology, v. 7, p. 104-107.

Leatherman, S.P., and Zaremba, R., 1980, Overwash processes and foredune ecology, Nauset Spit, Cape Cod: Report in preparation.

Stafford, D.B., 1971, An aerial photographic technique for beach erosion surveys in North Carolina: U.S. Army Coastal Engineering Research Center Technical Memorandum no. 36, 115 p.

Stafford, D.B., and Langfelder, J., 1971, Air photo survey of coastal erosion: Photogrammetric Engineering, v. 37, no. 6, p. 565-575.

Tanner, W.F., 1978, Standards for measuring shoreline changes: Proceedings of Workshop, Florida State University, 88 p.

Thompson, M.M., 1965, Manual of photogrammetry: v. 1., Falls Church, Virginia, American Society of Photogrammetry, 536 p.

U.S. Army Corps of Engineers, 1971, National shoreline study: Washington, D.C., U.S. Government Printing Office, several volumes.

Wolf, P.R., 1974, Elements of photogrammetry: New York, McGraw-Hill, 562 p.

Wright, A.E., and Brenninkmeyer, S.J., B.M., 1979, Sedimentation patterns at Nauset Inlet, Cape Cod, Massachusetts, in Leatherman, S.P., ed., Environmental geologic guide to Cape Cod National Seashore: Society of Economic Paleontologists and Mineralogists, p. 119-140.

Zeigler, J.M., Tuttle, S.D., Giese, G.S., and Tasha, H.J., 1964, Residence time of sand composing the beaches and bars of outer Cape Cod: American Society of Civil Engineers, Proceedings of Ninth Conference in Coastal Engineering, p. 403-416.

Part of a physiographic diagram of the Atlantic coastal plain and continental shelf of North America, by T.R. Alpha and J.C. Maher (1964). This part, south to north, is from Cape Hatteras to the Gulf of St. Lawrence. The Appalachian Highlands are shown, and beyond them the Great Lakes and Hudson Bay. In this arrangement Massachusetts occupies the center. (Courtesy, American Association of Petroleum Geologists.)

Hors-texte

# Origin and development of a cuspate foreland at Grape Island, Boston Harbor, Massachusetts

J. J. FISHER
Department of Geology
University of Rhode Island

J. R. JONES
Department of Geography
University of Texas at Austin

ABSTRACT

The Boston Harbor coastal environment is unique to the United States. It largely consists of drumlin and rock core islands, complex spit-tombolo systems, drowned estuaries, and drumlin headlands. Unconsolidated glacial till is the source of the beach sediment for many of the Harbor Islands. The present shoreline has been greatly altered during the last three hundred years by both natural and man-induced factors. One Boston Harbor island which well exemplifies shoreline change is Grape Island. Although the geomorphic history of Grape Island is generally similar to that of other Harbor Islands, a cuspate foreland has developed on the island's southeastern segment. The cuspate foreland is roughly triangular in shape and is formed by three main relict beach ridges with associated swales. Subsurface sediments indicate an alternating pattern of coarser sediment in the ridges while the swales are composed of finer sands, silts, and clays. Dates for the development of this feature are suggested by Carbon-14 dating of charcoal and shell material from midden sites. The development of this foreland was due to a combination of factors including sea level rise, sediment supply, longshore transportation processes, and storm activity.

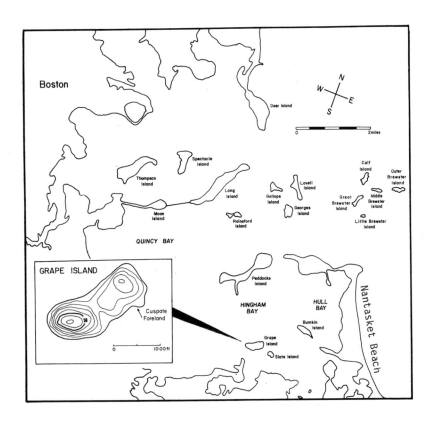

Figure 1. Islands in Boston Harbor. The insert shows the Grape Island study area.

## INTRODUCTION

Boston Harbor consists of drumlin and rock core islands, complex-spit tombolo systems, drowned estuaries, and drumlin headlands (Fig. 1).

Many of the Harbor Islands and drumlin headlands are aligned with the movement of Pleistocene ice flow. Kaye (1961) discovered the resultant stratigraphy of the adjacent Boston area to consist of four glacial drifts interbedded with three layers of marine clay. This appears to indicate at least four major ice advances followed by four ice retreats. The till fabric of these drumlins is generally poorly sorted with few clasts exceeding two feet in diameter.

The materials that now form the Harbor Islands were originally deposited on the land surface as a result of Pleistocene glaciation within the Boston Basin 10,000 to 18,000 years B.P. As the sea level rose to its present stand about 3,000 B.P. (Kaye and Barghoorn, 1964), the lower and middle sections of the drumlins were drowned by the encroaching water, thereby forming islands. The unconsolidated drumlin till provides a source for beach sediment on many of the islands. Some of the Harbor Island beaches do not display a till-fabric material beach, but shingle and cold water carbonate sediments comprise the beaches.

The shoreline configuration of the harbor as it relates to the islands has greatly changed during the last 300 years. These changes were in part induced by man's activities (Snow, 1971), while others were directly related to natural phenomena. For example, agriculture and building of structures upset sedimentation patterns on many of the islands, and high-energy storm events led to increased erosional rates along the beaches and drumlin cliff faces, particularly on northeast, exposed portions of the Harbor Islands.

## PHYSIOGRAPHY OF GRAPE ISLAND

One island within the Boston Harbor system which exemplifies active natural shoreline change is Grape Island (Fig. 1). Grape Island is located near the mouth of the Weymouth Back River in Hull Bay. It was originally granted to the Town of Weymouth in 1636 and is presently maintained by the Massachusetts Division of Environmental Management. It was first used by native Americans for clamming, as is evidenced by the numerous middens and artifacts which have been dug up through the last 300 years.

In Colonial times it was primarily used for farming. The geomorphic history of Grape Island is similar to that of other drumlin islands in the harbor. The island consists of two drumlins with occasional outcrops of bed rock. However, on the southeastern segment of the island a cuspate foreland has developed. The cuspate foreland is unique because it is the only foreland feature in the Boston Harbor island system to contain relict beach/berm ridges. The foreland was deposited against a glacial till upland surface formed on the drumlin.

The cuspate foreland proper is roughly the shape of a triangle with the base, 450 feet long, against the foot of the drumloid hill on Grape Island (Fig. 2). The remaining two shoreline sides are 300 feet (south beach) and 250 feet (east beach) in length. Topography of the foreland consists exclusively of three main relict beach ridges with associated swales that extend the entire length of the foreland.

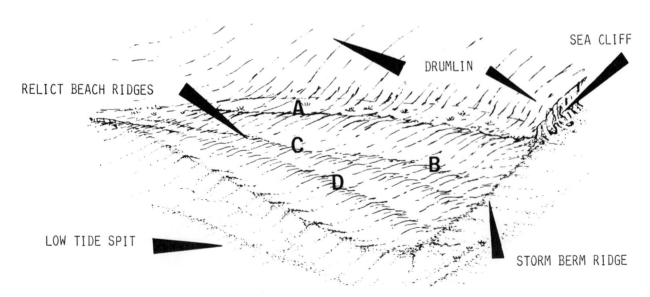

Figure 2. Physiographic diagram of the Grape Island cuspate foreland.

Ridge A, closest to the hill, is the highest at 2.5 feet over the neighboring swale, while the remaining ridges (C and D) are 1.5 and 1.0 feet above their swales. A minor beach ridge (B) branches from the second ridge near its eastern end while the wider swale exists between the innermost beach ridge and the base of the drumloid hill. Bordering the foreland along its shoreline is a prominent storm berm (ridge) above the high tide line. Between the high tide and low tide shorelines, a sandy spit runs parallel to the foreland along the south beach, while a similar small spit is parallel to the east beach.

The present storm berm is also 2.5 feet above its landward swale, but its crest is 1.0 foot higher in elevation than the highest relict beach ridge, ridge A. The lowest swale, however, is the first one at the base of the hill and is from 0.5 to 1.0 foot below the base of other swales farther seaward. Vegetational variations mark these different morphologic units of the foreland. Sumac trees are common on the drumlins, giving way to low shrub growth in the first wider swale, with grass present in the other swales. The ridges usually have less vegetation and show numerous fine sandy areas. The landward side of the storm berm ridge has extensive shrub vegetation, while its seaward side is composed entirely of shell.

## SEDIMENT SAMPLING PROCEDURES

An investigation of the subsurface sediments and sedimentation patterns was necessary to understand the processes that led to development of the cuspate foreland.

Forty cores were taken within the cuspate foreland in order to map the subsurface distribution of sediments (Fig. 3). The core samples were obtained at the depth corresponding to the marine clay layer with a hand auger. Care was taken to collect only the sediment at the interface with the clay layer 3 to 10 feet in depth from the surface. The sediment samples were dried, split and sieved at 1/4 Ø intervals (Folk, 1974). Each sieved sample was divided into sub-classes on the basis of its size: gravel (< -2Ø); sand (-2Ø to 4Ø); silt and clay (> 4Ø). Two sample sites yielding organic materials were Carbon-14 dated. The two sediment classes of gravel and sand were mapped with the SYMAP computer program package at 10 percent contour intervals.

## INTERPRETATION OF SEDIMENTS

The percentage of gravel (Fig. 4) indicates a general coarsening of sediment from south to north. A linear trend can also be identified toward the top of Figure 4. The pattern is interpreted as representing a former sedimentation ridge. Below the southern margin of this linear ridge there are subsurface areas composed of a less coarse gravel deposit. This area probably represents a subsurface depression or subsurface lagoon. Although the sedimentation pattern is not continuous, it is somewhat parallel to the

most northerly ridge. An explanation for the discontinuous pattern is that the lagoonal area was overwashed during high energy events. The subsurface fan-like features located along the southern boundary of the cuspate foreland also resemble washover fans. Given the coarse nature of these deposits, it would seem likely that a past high energy event deposited the high percentage (50 percent to 80 percent) of gravel by breeching the then existing beach ridge. The coarse gravel deposit would thus remain as a lag, within the lagoon.

Figure 5 represents the contoured percentage of the sand-size class. The northern linear ridge is present, although the general percentage of sand is less in proportion than the gravel percentage from Figure 4. The discontinuous lagoonal depression is also present in Figure 5. The sand percentage within the lagoon is relatively high (20 percent to 50 percent). This is also attributed to coarser lag deposits transported during higher energy events. Fan-like deposits are present along the southern margin of the cuspate headland. These are probably the result of storm overwashes.

The source of material which comprises these series of cuspate surface swales is reworked glacial sediment from the eroding drumlin. As sea level rose during the early formation of Boston Harbor, the size of the Grape Island drumlin was reduced, with much of the sediment being carried from the northeast toward the southeast along the Early Holocene shoreline by longshore currents. Storm activity has further eroded the drumlin and increased the amount of sediment available for the cuspate foreland formation. The composition of the transported glacial sediment varies from Cambridge Argillite shingle fragments to a finer-sized silt and clay fraction. The larger till clasts of Roxbury Conglomerate, local igneous rocks and metamorphic rocks, remain as a lag deposit on the shoreline.

## SEA LEVEL CHANGES

Absolute dates of the development of these relict ridges and their associated shorelines are suggested by Carbon-14 dating of charcoal and shell material from two subsurface shell midden sites. While marine shell material can be reworked from previous sites, the shell material in archaeological middens is in situ, providing a more accurate date of deposition than marine shell material in general.

Carbon-14 dating of subsurface shell midden material at a depth of 20 cm, just above the base of the drumloid hill behind the lagoon swale, gave a date of 1260 + 120 years B.P. This indicates that the sea had reached this area at least by this date. However, another sample area encountered a series of subsurface shell middens and charcoal material on the crest of ridge A. Charcoal at a depth of 25 cm gave a date of 890 + 140 years B.P., and charcoal at a depth of 26 cm gave a date of 1015 + 140 years B.P., while shells at

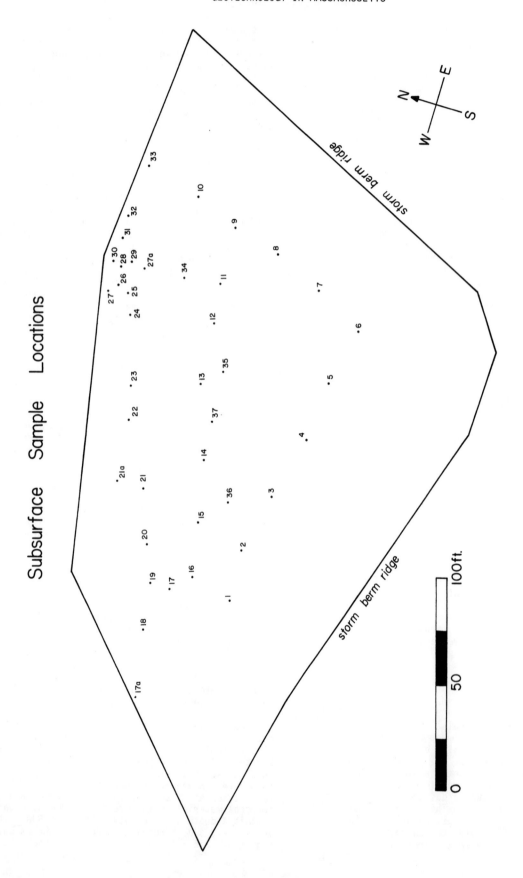

Subsurface Sample Locations

Figure 3. Core sample locations.
Carbon 14 dates are from 27 and 27a.

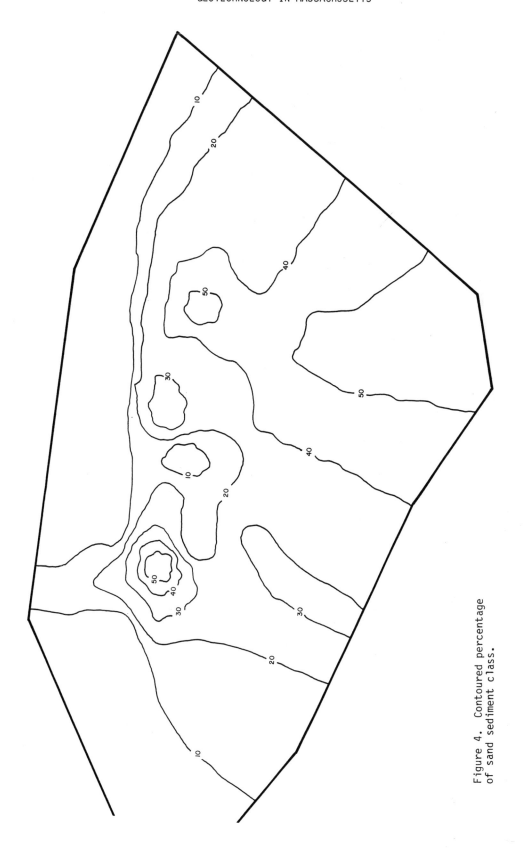

Figure 4. Contoured percentage of sand sediment class.

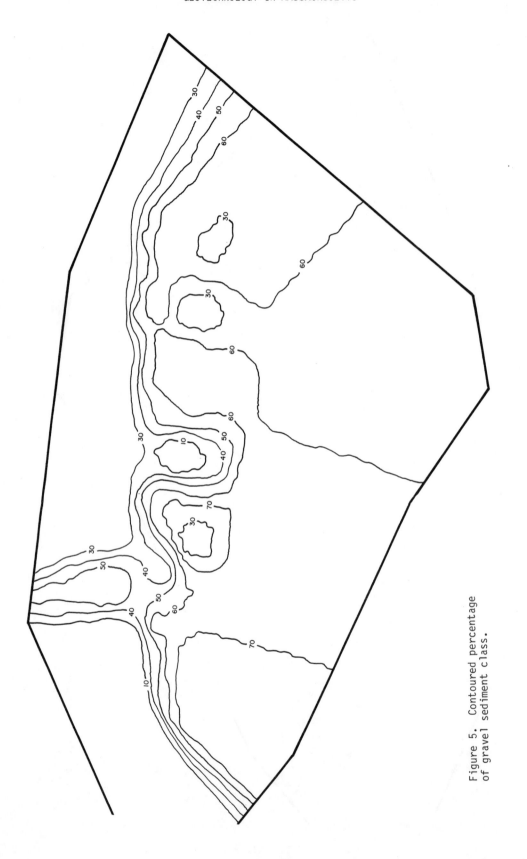

Figure 5. Contoured percentage of gravel sediment class.

30 cm gave the oldest date of 1523 ± 130 years B.P. None of the auger holes to depths of 5 to 10 feet encountered any charcoal or shell midden.

This dating suggests that the drumlin was submerged prior to 1525 years B.P. and that perhaps until 890 years B.P. only ridge A existed. During this period, the site at the base of the hill dated 1260 years B.P. was also occupied. Lack of shell on the later ridges suggests that after 890 years B.P. environmental and coastal geologic conditions changed, so that this area was no longer suitable for shell fish harvesting. Complex closure of the open sea by Nantasket Beach tombolos to the east could perhaps affect the production of shell fish and could also limit the size of subsequent beach ridges. That these later ridges are both smaller and lack shell midden suggests that they may be related to and are a factor in the closing of Hull Bay from the open sea. Unfortunately, conditions of absolute sea level during this time cannot be determined from these dated deposits because the Indians could place their middens at any height above sea level.

CONCLUSIONS

The source of the sand, gravel and shingle material which make up the surface and subsurface sediments of the cuspate foreland is from the northeast end of Grape Island. At least some 2000 feet of drumlin till material has been eroded from this end of the island, and a sea cliff 10 to 20 feet high now fronts this eroded shoreline. Cobble to boulder size material covers a shore platform 2000 feet wide at low tide along this cliffed shoreline and is the lag material from erosion of the glacial till.

Present maximum wave fetch across Hull Bay for this cliffed shoreline is two miles. However, during the initial submergence of the drumlin field of Boston Harbor, the oceanic barrier shoreline along Nantasket Beach may not have been present to limit wave fetch. In his study of the development of neighboring Nantasket Beach tombolo, Johnson (1925, Fig. 2.30, p. 467) presents a model of an open bay with widely separated islands. It is not until the third stage in the development of Nantasket Beach that the tombolo spits begin to enclose Hull Bay. Interestingly, although Grape Island lies within the Nantasket study area of Johnson, he did not include any aspect of the development of this drumloid island, although he studies the erosion of more than twelve drumloid islands into tombolos, spits and barrier beaches.

For Grape Island, as sea level rose, wave erosion along the exposed northeast shoreline supplied sediment to longshore transport in what is an exclusively southerly direction. Any wave fetch from the southeast is effectively blocked by Slate Island, just 1000 feet southeast of the eastern end of Grape Island. From the north, maximum fetch distance across Hull Bay would be a minimum of 2.0 miles or, if Johnson's model is correct, initially it would be an unlimited dis-

tance as an open sea. Thus, winds from the north would develop an exclusive southerly drift. Many of the other drumloid islands in Boston Harbor often exhibit a "winged headland" (sea cliff with flanking spits) type of coastal landform in their pattern of development, where wave action can act equally from opposite directions.

Because of the southerly longshore sediment transport, a spit formed in a westerly direction from the northeastern end of the island. It enclosed a shallow lagoon at the base of the drumloid hill (Fig. 2). Evidence of this spit remains in part, as relict beach ridge A. As erosion of the sea cliff continued, subsequent beaches developed by westerly longshore transport against this spit ridge. These later beaches and their relict ridges are not as prominent as ridge A, either in height or width, because during the time they were developing, the Nantasket Beach tombolos were forming to the east. This activity produced barrier beaches that reduced effective wave action.

As the later ridges developed, wave action not only eroded the sea cliff but also truncated the eastern head of the earlier spit. Truncation by wave erosion of the eastern ends of these relict beach ridges continues to the present day. Relict beach ridge B, which is now a small spur ridge off ridge C, represents a beach which at one time probably extended farther west than evidence presently indicates. The beach and its berm ridge probably extended seaward of ridges C and D south of the present intersection of ridges B and C. Subsequent development of the beach associated with ridge C eroded this southern segment of ridge B. All that now remains of this former, more extensive, shoreline is the small spur ridge B.

The development of low spits of sand between the high and low tide mark along the eastern and southern shorelines indicates that the suggested unidirectional longshore processes described above could produce the relict beach ridges, the "present being a key to the past." In addition, these spits indicate that the processes that developed this foreland continue in action at the present time.

ACKNOWLEDGMENTS

Field work for this project was undertaken by EARTHWATCH volunteers during the summer of 1978. Data analysis was supported in part by the Petroleum Research Fund, administered by the American Chemical Society. Special thanks are due to Paul Reigler who served as field assistant for the project.

REFERENCES

Folk, R.L., 1974, Petrology of sedimentary rocks: Hemphill Publishing Company, Austin, Texas, 182 p.

Johnson, D.W., 1925, New England Acadian shoreline: John Wiley and Sons, Inc., New York, 584 p.

Kaye, C.A., 1961, Pleistocene stratigraphy of Boston, Massachusetts: Short papers in the Geological and Hydrological Sciences, Article 24, U.S. Geological Survey Professional Paper 424-B.

Kaye, C.A., and Barghoorn, E.S., 1964, Late Quaternary sea level change and crustal rise at Boston, Massachusetts, with notes on the autocompaction of peat: Geological Society of America Bulletin, v. 75, p. 63-80.

Snow, E.R., 1971, The islands of Boston Harbor: Dodd, Mead and Company, New York.

# 14

# THE MARINE BOUNDARY

Session moderators

J. S. Schlee
U.S. Geological Survey
Woods Hole, Massachusetts

L. B. Smith, Jr.
Massachusetts Coastal Zone Management Office

# U.S. Geological Survey environmental studies on the continental shelf and slope off New England

J. M. AARON
B. BUTMAN
M. H. BOTHNER

J. C. HAMPSON, JR.
U.S. Geological Survey
Woods Hole, Massachusetts

## ABSTRACT

The U.S. Geological Survey (USGS), in cooperation with the Bureau of Land Management (BLM), is conducting a series of environmental studies aimed at assessing potential geologic hazards and impacts related to development of offshore petroleum resources under the Continental Shelf and Slope of the Georges Bank area off New England (Fig. 1). Particular interest is focused on those potential hazards that might cause oil or other pollutants to be spilled or distributed during exploration, development, production, or transportation activities.

USGS studies include: (1) systematic high-resolution seismic-reflection profiling to determine the shallow stratigraphy and structure of the Continental Shelf and Slope; (2) direct study of the sea floor using manned submersibles; (3) observations of the composition, concentration, distribution, and flux of suspended particulate matter in the water column; (4) bottom sampling and coring for studies of the composition, texture, structure, age, trace-metal content, and geotechnical properties of sediments and rocks that make up the sea floor; and (5) long-term in situ observations of the sea floor and parts of the overlying water column by means of moored instrument packages that take time-lapse photographs of the sea bottom and measure and record hydrographic data (current speed and direction, pressure, temperature, and light transmission).

## GEOLOGIC SETTING

Geologically, Georges Bank and adjacent parts of the Continental Shelf and Slope are seaward extensions of the Atlantic Coastal Plain. The subsurface structure is a broad trough floored by complexly block-faulted Proterozoic and Paleozoic rocks and filled to a thickness of more than 10 km by gently seaward-dipping Mesozoic and Cenozoic sedimentary rocks (Schlee and others, 1979). Compactional draping of these younger strata over relatively uplifted basement blocks has created structures that could trap oil and gas, and therefore present attractive exploration targets.

A surficial veneer of Pleistocene and Holocene sand, silt, and gravel to a maximum thickness of 80 m covers the Georges Bank area of the Continental Shelf and upper Continental Slope (Knott and Hoskins, 1968; Lewis and others, 1980). Most of these sediments are glacial till and outwash deposited in Pleistocene time during periods of lowered sea level.

Potential environmental problems are related to the history and the geologic characteristics of the surficial veneer of Pleistocene and Holocene sediments, to the strength and the circulation dynamics of the vigorous current and wave regime, and to the depositional history and the relatively steep inclination of the Continental Slope. These problems include: (1) scour and mobile bed forms; (2) questionable load-bearing characteristics of the surficial sediments; (3) a probable modern-sediment sink on the Continental Shelf south of Cape Cod, Massachusetts; and (4) possible bottom instability due to slumping and other mass movement of material on the Continental Slope.

## SEDIMENT TRANSPORT

The current and wave regime on Georges Bank is vigorous. Data gathered since 1976 on velocities and directions of tidal currents and mean currents are summarized in Figures 2 and 3, respectively.

Our studies show that tidal currents, which typically are strongest on top of the bank and diminish in strength in the deeper water on the flanks, are competent to rework surficial bottom sediment over much of Georges Bank. Near-surface tidal-current velocities measured near the crest of the bank typically were 35 cm/sec (0.7 knots). Maximum current velocities measured were 100 cm/sec (2 knots) (Folger and others, 1978). The threshold near-bottom current speed required to transport fine sand is about 25 cm/sec. Clearly, surficial bottom sediments on Georges Bank frequently are in motion. During storms, which are common in winter, tidal currents are augmented by wave-driven flow that increases bottom stress and causes increased sediment resuspension and transport. During summer, when seasonal thermoclines are formed, some resuspension by internal waves was observed at 85-m water depth on the south side of the bank.

The orientation of the mean current vectors (Fig. 3) shows a residual clockwise circulation pattern around Georges Bank, as was suggested by Bumpus (1973); the mean flow is southwestward on the south side of the bank and northeastward on the north side. This circulation pattern could influence the trajectory and distribution pattern of spilled oil and other pollutants that may be introduced to the Georges Bank area, and also

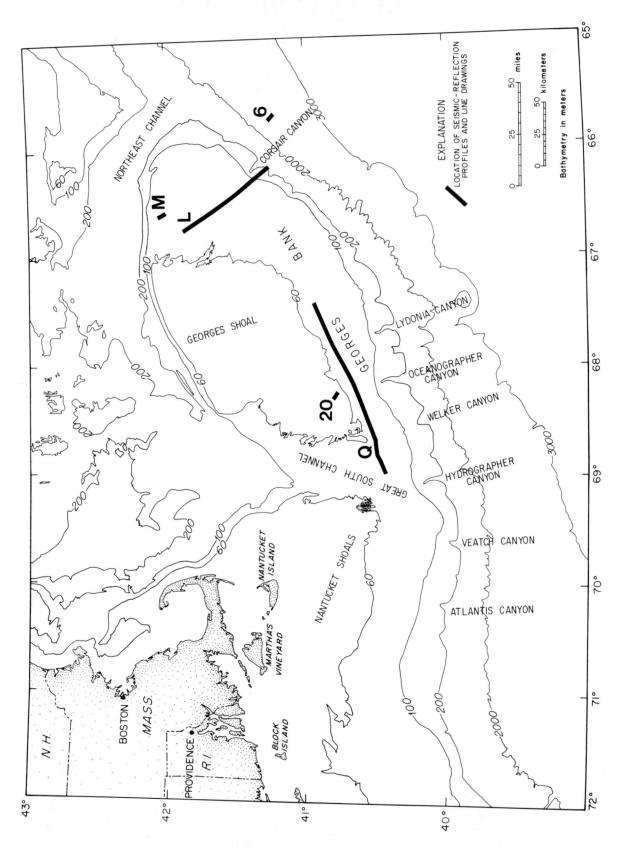

Figure 1. Area of USGS environmental studies showing location of seismic-reflection profiles and line drawings
discussed in this paper.

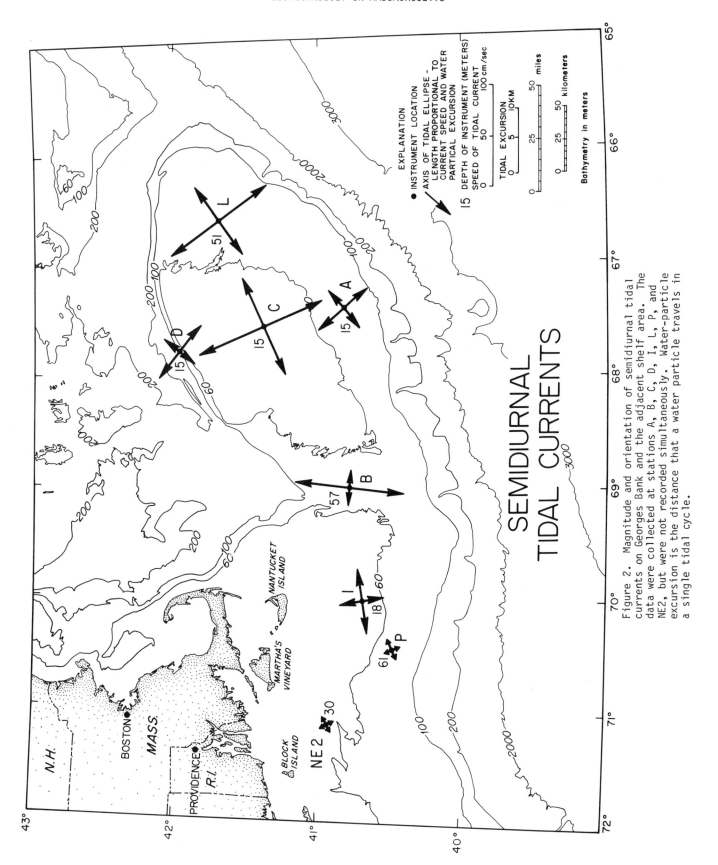

## SEMIDIURNAL TIDAL CURRENTS

**EXPLANATION**

● INSTRUMENT LOCATION

AXIS OF TIDAL ELLIPSE -
LENGTH PROPORTIONAL TO
CURRENT SPEED AND WATER
PARTICAL EXCURSION

15 DEPTH OF INSTRUMENT (METERS)
SPEED OF TIDAL CURRENT

0        50        100 cm/sec

TIDAL EXCURSION
0        5        10KM

0        25        50 miles

0    25    50 kilometers

**Bathymetry in meters**

Figure 2. Magnitude and orientation of semidiurnal tidal
currents on Georges Bank and the adjacent shelf area. The
data were collected at stations A, B, C, D, I, L, P, and
NE2, but were not recorded simultaneously. Water-particle
excursion is the distance that a water particle travels in
a single tidal cycle.

- 523 -

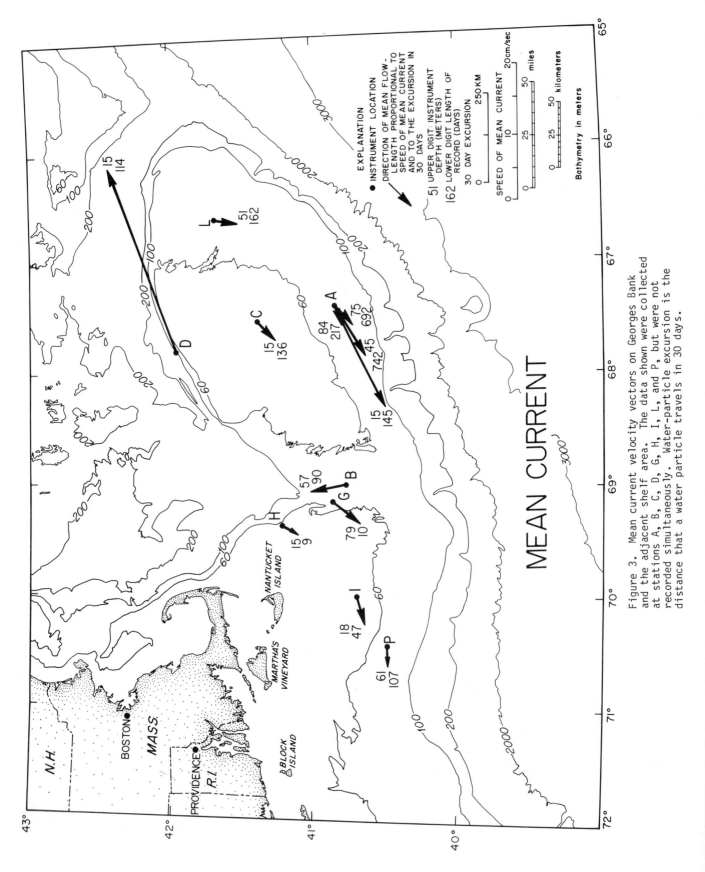

## MEAN CURRENT

EXPLANATION

● INSTRUMENT LOCATION

DIRECTION OF MEAN FLOW-
LENGTH PROPORTIONAL TO
SPEED OF MEAN CURRENT
AND TO THE EXCURSION IN
30 DAYS

51 UPPER DIGIT: INSTRUMENT
DEPTH (METERS)

162 LOWER DIGIT LENGTH OF
RECORD (DAYS)

30 DAY EXCURSION

|—————————————————|
0                250KM

SPEED OF MEAN CURRENT
20cm/sec

0        10        20cm/sec

0      25       50  miles

0      25    50 kilometers

Bathymetry in meters

Figure 3. Mean current velocity vectors on Georges Bank
and the adjacent shelf area. The data shown were collected
at stations A, B, C, D, G, H, I, L, and P, but were not
recorded simultaneously. Water-particle excursion is the
distance that a water particle travels in 30 days.

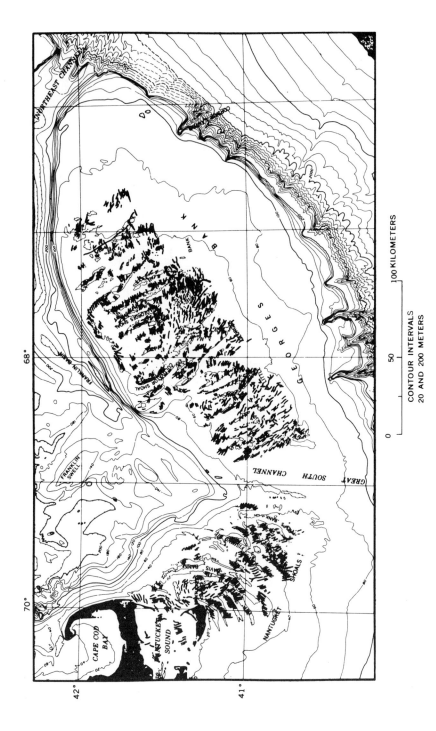

Figure 4. Distribution of sand waves on Georges Bank and Nantucket Shoals. Heavy lines represent crests of sand waves. From Uchupi (1970).

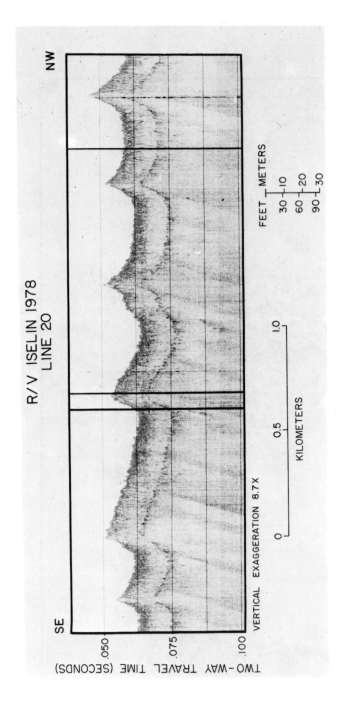

Figure 5. High-resolution seismic-reflection profile line 20 showing sand waves on Georges Bank. See Figure 1 for location of profile.

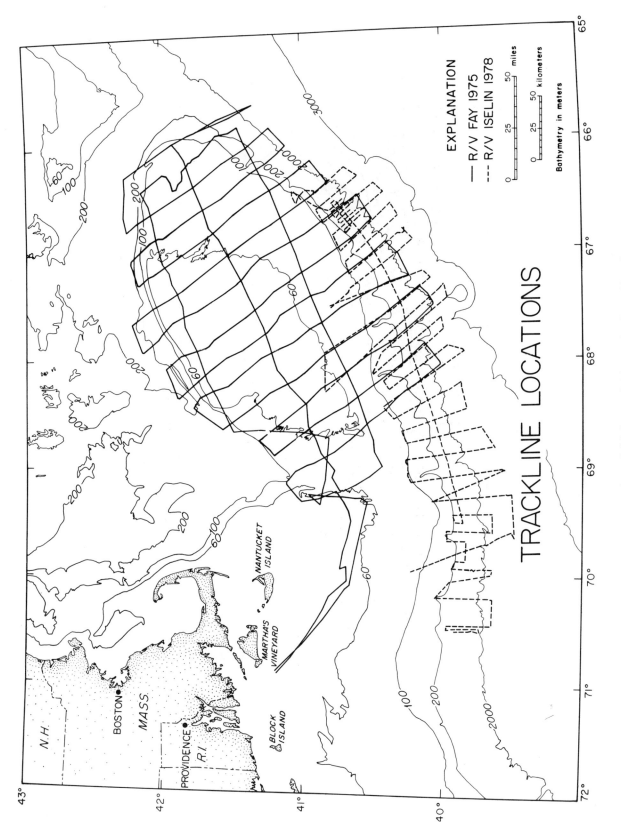

Figure 6. Location of high-resolution seismic-reflection tracklines on Georges Bank and adjacent areas of the Continental Shelf and Slope.

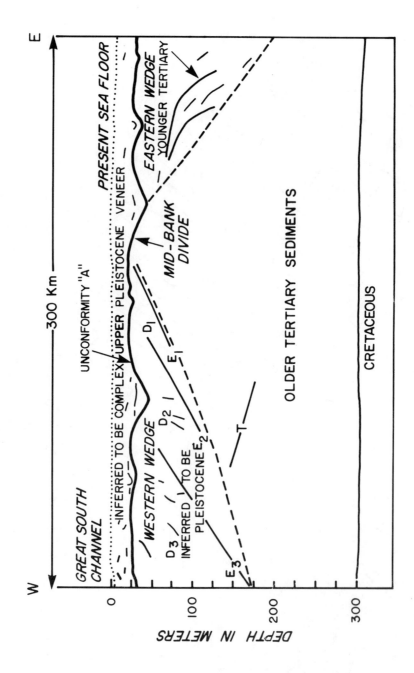

Figure 7. Idealized east-west cross section of Georges Bank showing principal stratigraphic relationships inferred from seismic-reflection data. Lines $E_1$, $E_2$, and $E_3$ designate erosional events (unconformities); intervals $D_1$, $D_2$, and $D_3$ represent periods of deposition and contain irregular, discontinuous acoustic reflectors. Dashed lines bounding older Tertiary sediments are major unconformities. Relative attitude of older Tertiary strata is shown by the line labeled T. Not to scale. From Aaron and others, 1980.

Figure 8. Interpretative drawings showing the shallow structure of Georges Bank made on the basis of reflectors observed in seismic-reflection profiles L and Q (see Fig. 1 for location). Unconformity "A" is dotted where inferred. The letters above the kilometer scale in each drawing show where other seismic tracklines intersect lines L and Q. Breaks in the drawings indicate intervals where no data were collected. Drawings adapted from Lewis and others (1980).

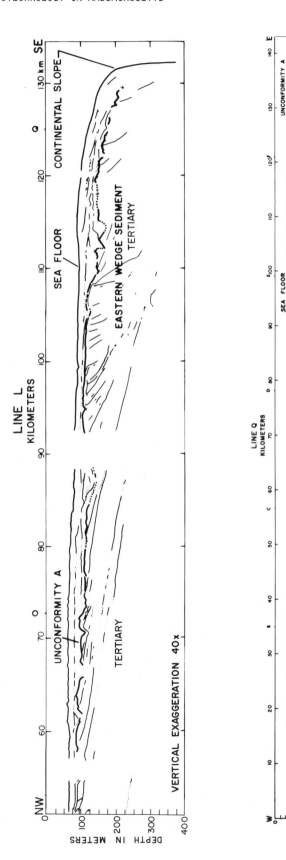

could affect the period of time that such pollutants may remain entrained in the area.

Two potential hazards may result from the strong currents and vigorous motion of surficial bottom sediments on Georges Bank. Scour, which is erosion by the action of flowing water, could remove sediment from the base of support structures (footings, legs, pipelines, etc.) and cause differential settlement of the structure. The structure itself is an obstruction that tends to enhance scour by causing increased local current speeds and shear stress at the bottom. An example of the destructive effect of scour on a support structure on the Nova Scotian shelf was documented by Wilson and Abel (1973). There, a rig installed with scour-protective matting was badly damaged and prematurely abandoned because of erosion and differential settlement after two severe storms.

Mobile bed forms (sand waves), the second potential hazard, are a morphologic result of vigorous sediment transport. These wavelike configurations of the water-sediment interface are migratory features; their size, shape, speed, and direction of movement are related to flow conditions such as water depth and current speed, and to the grain size of sea-floor sediments. Sand waves abound on the New England Continental Shelf, especially on Georges Bank and Nantucket Shoals, in water depths of less than 60 m (Fig. 4). Figure 5 shows sand waves in a high-resolution seismic-reflection profile. Sand waves on Georges Bank typically range in height from 5 to 15 m and in wavelength from 150 to 750 m (Jordan, 1962). The sharp asymmetry of many sand waves on Georges Bank suggests that they are active, although little is known about their migration rate. Stewart and Jordan (1964) showed that, over a 25- to 28-year period, sand waves on Georges Shoal migrated at an average rate of 12 m/yr in an area where tidal current speeds of as much as 2 knots were measured. Further study of such features was begun by the USGS in 1979, but results are not yet available.

Large mobile bed forms are possible hazards to bottom-supported offshore structures. The movement of excessive sand against or around a support structure could weaken the structure either by changing resonant frequency (Garrison and Bea, 1977) or by placing excessive lateral stress on it. Such was the fate of Texas Tower radar stations that were built on Georges Bank in the late 1950's and abandoned a few years later because sand levels around the legs had risen enough to weaken the structures (Emery and Uchupi, 1972).

SHALLOW SUBSURFACE STRUCTURE

Data acquired in systematic high-resolution seismic-reflection surveys (Fig. 6) show that the Georges Bank area is underlain by southeast-dipping Tertiary Coastal Plain strata that have been truncated by erosion on the eastern and western sides of the bank. Younger Tertiary sediments were deposited on the eroded eastern flank, where-

as the western flank was covered by a wedge of prograded Pleistocene sediments (Figs. 7 and 8) (Lewis and others, 1980).

After an interglacial period of marine planation (unconformity "A" in Figs. 7 and 8), the eroded bank surface was covered by as much as 80 m of upper Pleistocene sediments, mostly glacial outwash. The Pleistocene sediments are acoustically complex; they are characterized by acoustically transparent zones and major changes of acoustic character over short distances. Several episodes of channel cutting and filling are inferred (Fig. 9). Although no consistent relationship exists between acoustic and geotechnical properties of a sediment body, the seismic data suggest that the physical properties of these sediments are highly variable. Drilling information from the area (U.S. Department of the Navy, 1954; Hathaway and others, 1979) corroborates this inference and shows that organically-rich clays and silts, which may contain gas (especially methane), are common in the shallow subsurface sediments. When loaded, sediments that have such extreme vertical and horizontal lithologic variability could settle differentially and, therefore, could threaten the stability of man-made structures erected upon them. Such conditions must be considered in the design of the structures and be adequately explored in site surveys.

TEXTURE AND COMPOSITION OF SURFACE SEDIMENTS

Numerous cores and grab samples of bottom sediments have been collected from the Continental Shelf off New England (Figs. 10 and 11) and analyzed by the USGS (Schlee, 1973; Bothner and others, 1980). Sand is the dominant particle size of shelf surface sediments throughout the area. A conspicuous exception, however, is a 4,000 $km^2$ area of the shelf south of Cape Cod, Massachusetts (Fig. 10), where silt and clay may be the dominant size fractions.

Analysis of major clay-mineral groups in core samples indicates that illite is predominant. Moderate amounts of chlorite and small concentrations of kaolinite are also present. Montmorillonite is present only in trace amounts or is absent.

The origin and significance of the abundant silt and clay fraction south of Cape Cod are matters of considerable environmental concern. Some previous studies (Garrison and McMaster, 1966; Schlee, 1973) indicated that these fine-grained sediments are relict, i.e., deposited during an earlier epoch of shelf sedimentation, as were most other shelf sediments, either before or during the Holocene rise in sea level. However, recent USGS studies of carbon-14 ages and determinations of lead-210 profiles (Bothner and others, in press) suggest that these sediments are of modern origin and may be actively accumulating at present.

The source of the fine sediment is not known. A likely possibility is that strong tidal currents and storm waves winnow silt and clay from relict

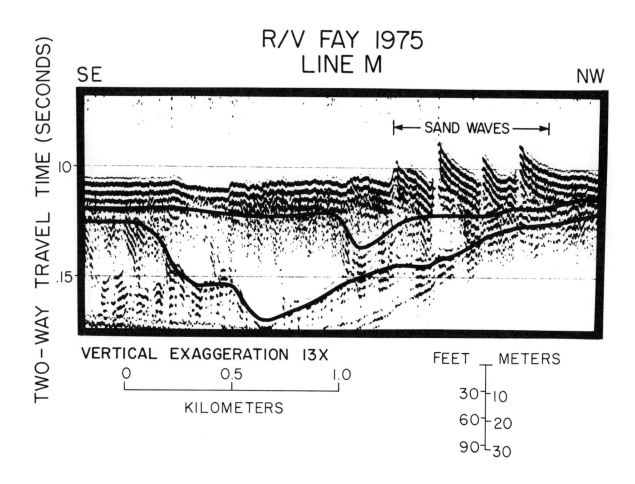

Figure 9. High-resolution seismic-reflection profile line M (see Fig. 1 for location) showing Pleistocene sediments overlying Georges Bank. The heavy lines illustrate episodes of channel cutting and filling.

surficial sediments in the shallower waters of Georges Bank and Nantucket Shoals and transport them westward. Support for this hypothesis is provided by Georges Bank current data (Fig. 2) which show that currents are sufficiently strong to resuspend and transport surficial bottom sediments, and abundant hydrographic evidence (Fig. 3; Bumpus, 1973; Butman and Noble, 1978) of net current drift from Georges Bank westward along the shelf. Moreover, the current data (Fig. 2) show that tidal currents on the shelf south of Cape Cod are significantly weaker than those on Georges Bank and are not sufficient to maintain fine sediment in suspension. Consequently, sediments transported westward from Georges Bank and Nantucket Shoals are deposited south of Cape Cod.

Hydrocarbons, trace metals, and other potential chemical pollutants have a strong affinity to fine-grained sediments. If the fine-grained sediments on the Continental Shelf south of Cape Cod are indeed of modern origin, as is indicated by geochemical data, and derived from relict sediments on Georges Bank and Nantucket Shoals, as is suggested by current data, this area may also be a sink for fine material such as cuttings, drilling muds, and sediment-related pollutants that may be introduced by resource development activities in the Georges Bank area.

SLUMPING ON THE CONTINENTAL SLOPE

Sea-floor instabilities related to mass slumping and sliding of sediment are considered to be one of the most serious potential hazards to development of offshore oil and gas resources. Slumping takes place where the shear stress along a potential surface of failure exceeds the shear resistance along that surface. Submarine slumps may take place on any slope, even of less than 0.5° (Carlson, 1978), in any water depth, and in

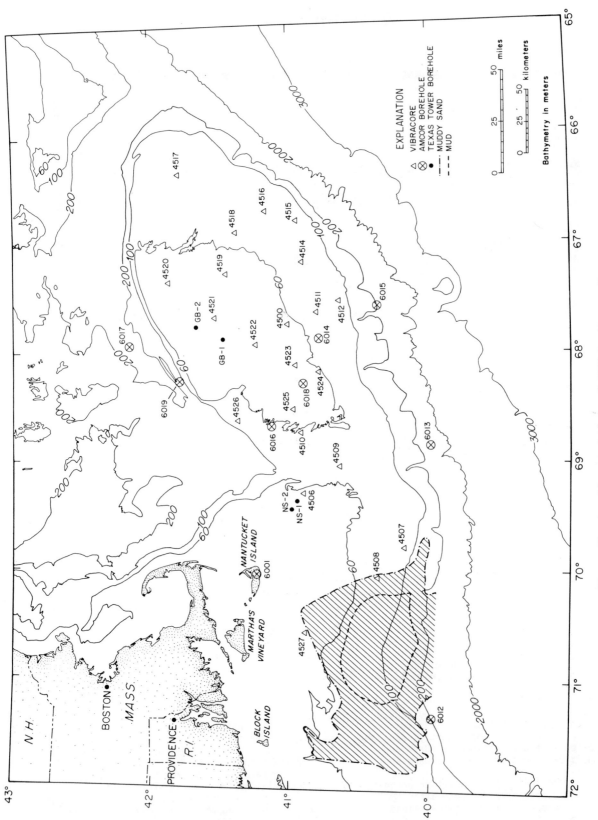

Figure 10. Locations and types of USGS borings on Georges Bank and adjacent shelf area. Locations of Texas tower boreholes are also shown. That part of the shelf underlain by predominantly fine-grained surficial sediments (as determined by Schlee, 1973) is indicated by the lined area; other surficial sediments are predominantly sand.

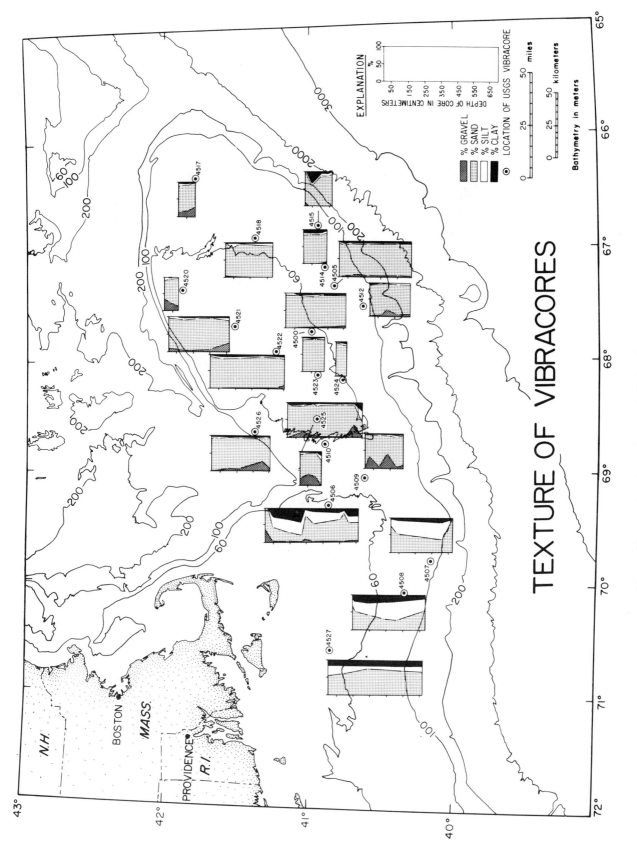

TEXTURE OF VIBRACORES

Figure 11. Textural analyses of USGS vibracores in the Georges Bank area.

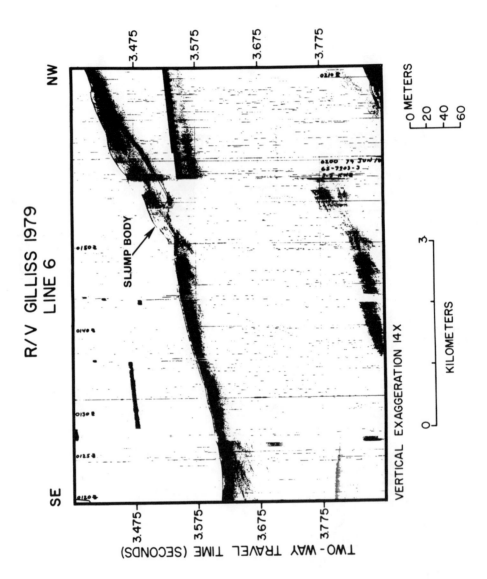

Figure 12. High-resolution seismic-reflection profile line 6 (see Fig. 1 for location) showing a slump body near the base of the Continental Slope off Georges Bank.

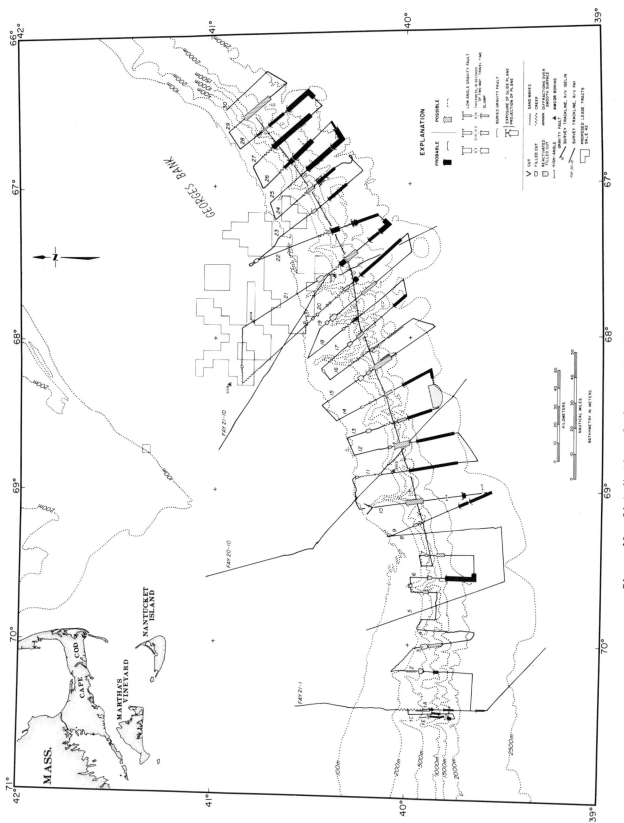

Figure 13. Distribution of slumps and related features on the Continental Slope in the Georges Bank area, based on preliminary interpretation of high-resolution seismic-reflection data.

any sediment lithology. Movement is driven by gravitational forces and may be rapid or slow, continuous or sporadic, and of great or small displacement. Among the processes believed to initiate slumps are: (1) cyclic loading by storm waves or internal waves; (2) dynamic loading by ground acceleration in earthquakes; (3) overloading or oversteepening of slopes by sediment deposition; and (4) oversteepening of slopes by erosion. Resistance to slumping (shear strength) is a function of many factors, chief of which are the size, shape, orientation and packing of the constituent grains, the structure and degree of consolidation of the sediment mass, the distribution and pressure of pore fluids, and the amount of overburden and rate of sediment deposition on a sediment mass.

Large slumps have been inferred from seismic-reflection data on the Continental Slope off New England (Roberson, 1964; Uchupi, 1967; McIlvaine, 1973; J.M. Aaron, unpublished data). Figure 12 illustrates one such slump near the base of the Continental Slope (see Fig. 1 for location).

Preliminary interpretation of USGS high-resolution seismic-reflection data (Fig. 13) indicates that features apparently related to slumping or other forms of mass movement may underlie more than 30 percent of the Continental Slope. However, an important limitation of this interpretation is that slump features are very difficult to identify unequivocally in such widely spaced (about 10 km) seismic-reflection profiles oriented almost perpendicular to the bathymetric contours. The slope is relatively steep (5°-10°) and along much of its length is strongly dissected by large canyons and countless smaller channels and gullies. In seismic-reflection profiles, this rough ("badlands") topography produces profuse diffractions and side-echoes that tend to obscure relationships among subbottom reflecting horizons. Accurate interpretations are further hindered by the lack of adequate bathymetry, which is required to distinguish properly the real slump features from artifacts related to the manner in which the plane of the seismic profile (ship's track) intersected bottom topography. Nevertheless, the interpretations shown in Figure 13 raise serious questions about the nature and extent of slumping and other mass movements of material on the Continental Slope, and the degree to which such instability is potentially hazardous to offshore development.

The age of inferred slumping is a critical concern but is very poorly known. Stanley and Silverberg (1969) described slumping on the Continental Slope off southeastern Canada and, significantly, found evidence that some slumping has taken place in recent time. Elsewhere, the age of slumping is conjectural. Conceivably, most slumping could have taken place during the Pleistocene when large volumes of sediment were carried to the edge of the Continental Shelf as glacial outwash. Even if this were true, however, a corollary question concerns the extent to which conditions of unrelieved metastability dating from periods of substantially higher sedimentation

rates are now present in sediments on the Continental Slope. Ongoing USGS seismic, side-scan sonar, heat flow, and geotechnical studies are designed to provide a better understanding of the extent, age, and stability of slump deposits and to assess the potential for initiation of new slumps and other forms of rapid mass wasting that could be hazardous to offshore resource development.

CONCLUSIONS

The principal conclusions resulting from USGS environmental studies on the Continental Shelf and Slope in the Georges Bank area, and the potential geologic hazards to development of oil and gas resources in the area that are suggested by these conclusions, include:

1. The vigorous current and wave regime causes considerable resuspension and transportation of surficial bottom sediments. Resulting scour and large mobile bed forms could act on support structures to induce instability.

2. The Pleistocene subsurface sediments are characterized by extreme vertical and horizontal variability over short distances. When loaded by support structures, the differential response of such sediments could cause instability of the structures.

3. A 4,000 $km^2$ area of the sea floor south of Cape Cod is covered by as much as 6 m of mud. In contrast to the relict sands that cover the rest of the New England Continental Shelf, this mud deposit appears to have accumulated in modern time, and sedimentation still may be active. The strength and circulation pattern of tidal and mean currents on the Continental Shelf suggest that the mud was derived by winnowing and transporting sediments from Georges Bank and Nantucket Shoals. Consequently, the area of muddy sediments may be a sink for sediment-related pollutants, such as hydrocarbons, trace metals, and drilling fluids that may be introduced to Georges Bank during exploration and development activities.

4. The Continental Slope is characterized by rough topography and steep slopes; and periods of rapid sediment deposition took place during the Pleistocene. Evidence indicates that mass down-slope slumping and sliding of sediments have taken place in the past. If slumping and other processes of rapid mass wasting are possible at present, they could prove hazardous to offshore development.

None of these potential hazards necessarily precludes development of hydrocarbon resources in the Georges Bank area. However, reasonable care must be taken to identify, characterize, and properly alleviate potential hazards at specific sites.

REFERENCES

Aaron, J.M., Butman, B., Bothner, M.H., and Sylwester, R.E., 1980, Maps showing environmental conditions relating to potential geologic hazards on the United States northeastern Atlantic Continental Margin: U.S. Geological Survey Miscellaneous Field Studies Map MF-1193.

Bothner, M.H., Spiker, E.C., Ferrebee, W.M., and Peeler, D.L., 1980, Texture, clay mineralogy, trace metals, and age of cored sediments from the North Atlantic Outer Continental Shelf, in Aaron, J.M., ed., Environmental geologic studies in the Georges Bank area, United States Northeastern Atlantic Outer Continental Shelf, 1975-1977: U.S. Geological Survey Open-File Report 80-240, p. 3-1 to 3-25.

Bothner, M.H., Spiker, E.C., Johnson, P.P., Rendigs, R.R., and Aruscavage, P.J., in press. Geochemical evidence for modern sediment accumulation on the Continental Shelf off southern New England: Journal of Sedimentary Petrology.

Bumpus, D.F., 1973, A description of the circulation on the Continental Shelf of the east coast of the United States: Progress in Oceanography, v. 6, p. 111-157.

Butman, B., and Noble, M., 1978, Long-term in situ observations of currents and bottom-sediment movement on Georges Bank [abstract]: Geological Society of America Abstracts with Programs, v. 10, p. 35.

Carlson, P.R., 1978, Holocene slump on the Continental Shelf off Malaspina Glacier, Gulf of Alaska: American Association of Petroleum Geologists Bulletin, v. 62, p. 2412-2426.

Emery, K.O., and Uchupi, E., 1972, Western North Atlantic Ocean: Topography, rocks, structure, water, life, and sediments: American Association of Petroleum Geologists Memoir 17, 532 p.

Folger, D.W., Butman, B., Knebel, H.J., and Sylwester, R.E., 1978, Environmental hazards on the Atlantic Outer Continental Shelf of the United States: Offshore Technology Conference, v. 4, p. 2293-2298.

Garrison, L.E., and Bea, R.G., 1977, Bottom stability as a factor in platform siting and design: Offshore Technology Conference, v. 3, paper 2893, p. 127-133.

Garrison, L.E., and McMaster, R.L., 1966, Sediments and geomorphology of the Continental Shelf off southern New England: Marine Geology, v. 4, p. 273-289.

Hathaway, J.C., Poag, C.W., Valentine, P.C., Miller, R.E., Schultz, D.M., Manheim, F.T., Kohout, F.A., Bothner, M.H., and Sangrey, D.A., 1979, U.S. Geological Survey core drilling on the Atlantic shelf: Science, v.

206, p. 515-527.

Jordan, G.F., 1962, Large submarine sand waves: Science, v. 136, p. 839-848.

Knott, S.T., and Hoskins, H., 1968, Evidence of Pleistocene events in the structure of the Continental Shelf off northeastern states: Marine Geology, v. 6, p. 5-43.

Lewis, R.S., Sylwester, R.E., Aaron, J.M., Twichell, D.C., and Scanlon, K.M., 1980, Shallow sedimentary framework and related potential geologic hazards of the Georges Bank area, in Aaron, J.M., ed., Environmental geologic studies in the Georges Bank area, United States Northeastern Atlantic Outer Continental Shelf, 1975-1977: U.S. Geological Survey Open-File Report 80-240, p. 5-1 to 5-25.

McIlvaine, J.C., 1973, Sedimentary processes on the Continental Slope of New England: unpublished dissertation, Massachusetts Institute of Technology and Woods Hole Oceanographic Institution, 211 p.

Roberson, M.I., 1964, Continuous seismic profile survey of Oceanographer, Gilbert, and Lydonia submarine canyons, Georges Bank: Journal of Geophysical Research, v. 69, p. 4779-4789.

Schlee, J.S., 1973, The Atlantic Continental Shelf and Slope of the United States--sediment textures of the northeastern part: U.S. Geological Survey Professional Paper 529-L, 64 p.

Schlee, J.S., Aaron, J.M., Ball, M.M., Klitgord, K.D., Grow, J.A., Butman, B., and Bothner, M.H., 1979, Summary report of the sediments, structural framework, petroleum potential, and environmental conditions of the United States northeastern continental margin: U.S. Geological Survey Open-File Report 79-674, 26 p.

Stanley, D.J., and Silverberg, N., 1969, Recent slumping on the Continental Slope off Sable Island Bank, southeast Canada: Earth and Planetary Science Letters, v. 6, p. 123-133.

Stewart, H.B., Jr., and Jordan, G.F., 1964, Underwater sand ridges on Georges Shoal, in Miller, R.L., ed., Papers in marine geology, Shepard commemorative volume: New York, MacMillan Co., p. 102-114.

Uchupi, E., 1967, Slumping on the continental margin southeast of Long Island: Deep-Sea Research, v. 14, p. 635-638.

Uchupi, E., 1970, Atlantic Continental Shelf and Slope of the United States--shallow structure: U.S. Geological Survey Professional Paper 529-I, 44 p.

U.S. Department of the Navy, 1954, Feasibility report on Texas Towers, part 1: unpublished report, Bureau of Yards and Docks.

Wilson, N.D., and Abel, W., 1973, Seafloor scour protection for a semi-submersible drilling rig on the Nova Scotian shelf: Offshore Technology Conference, v. 2, p. 631-646.

# Marine geologic studies
# of the inner continental shelf
# off Massachusetts

C. J. O'HARA
R. N. OLDALE

U.S. Geological Survey
Woods Hole, Massachusetts

## ABSTRACT

Since 1972, the U.S. Geological Survey, in cooperation with the Massachusetts Department of Public Works, has been investigating the geology, structural framework, and resource potential of the Inner Continental Shelf off southeastern Massachusetts. Objectives of the marine cooperative include assessments of the Commonwealth's offshore mineral resources (principally sand and gravel) and the environmental impact of mining these deposits and of dumping solid-waste material offshore. Additional studies have been conducted to delineate areas that may be suitable for disposal of large volumes of harbor dredge-spoil material with minimum damage to the environment, and to identify potential geologic hazards that could impede or possibly preclude development of the Massachusetts coastal zone.

Field data consist mostly of closely spaced high-resolution seismic-reflection profiles and vibratory cores. More than 4800 km of seismic profiles and 100 vibracores have been obtained from Cape Cod Bay, Buzzards Bay, Vineyard Sound, eastern Rhode Island Sound, Nantucket Sound, Massachusetts Bay, and waters off Cape Ann. Major products of our research include maps of the offshore geology and shallow structure and reports describing the geologic history of this part of the Atlantic Inner Continental Shelf. We have constructed isopach maps of significant geologic units, structure-contour maps of major contacts or unconformities, and geological and hazards maps of the sea floor, all of which will be useful in the economic evaluation and future utilization of the state's coastal resources.

## INTRODUCTION

The U.S. Geological Survey (USGS), in cooperation with the Massachusetts Department of Public Works (DPW), is conducting marine geological and geophysical studies in the waters adjacent to the Commonwealth of Massachusetts (Fig. 1). Major objectives of the marine cooperative include an assessment of offshore mineral resources (principally sand and gravel), evaluation of the environmental impact of offshore mining of mineral deposits and offshore disposal of solid-waste material, identification and mapping of the offshore geology and shallow structures, and determination of the geologic history of this part of the inner shelf.

Recently, as a result of increased interest in oil and gas exploration and production on the Outer Continental Shelf off Massachusetts and the potential effect of such activity and related developments on the coastal zone, program objectives have been expanded to evaluate possible pipeline corridors from offshore wells to processing facilities onshore. These evaluations will be based on the engineering or geotechnical properties of the sea-floor and shallow subbottom sediments, and on potential geological hazards or restrictions to pipeline emplacement, including areas of intense current scour, active sand-wave fields, unstable gas-charged sediments, texturally diverse buried channel deposits, outcrops of bed rock and coarse glacial debris, and shallow faults that could indicate recent seismic activity. Studies have also been expanded (in cooperation with the U.S. Army Corps of Engineers) to delineate offshore sites that may be suitable for disposal of large volumes of harbor dredge-spoil material at minimum damage to the environment.

Field studies consist mostly of closely spaced high-resolution seismic reflection profiling and vibracoring. Presently, more than 4800 km of seismic profiles and 100 vibracores (Fig. 2) have been obtained from Cape Cod Bay, Buzzards Bay, Vineyard Sound, eastern Rhode Island Sound, Nantucket Sound, Massachusetts Bay and waters off Cape Ann.

Geologic maps have been published for Cape Cod Bay (Oldale and O'Hara, 1975a) and Buzzards Bay (Robb and Oldale, 1977). Other publications that have resulted from the marine project are listed at the end of the paper.

## METHODS

### Seismic-Reflection Profiling

The high-resolution seismic profiling system used most often in the marine program consists of a surface towed EG&G unit Pulse Boomer[1] (300 joules; 400 Hz - 8 kHz frequency). Reflected acoustic energy is detected by a 4.6-m, 8-element hydrophone array, amplified, actively filtered (400 Hz - 4000 Hz bandpass), and graphically displayed on an EPC dry paper recorder. The electro-mechanical transducer is triggered every 0.5 seconds, and the sweep rate of the recorder is 0.25

---

[1] Trade names in this publication are used for descriptive purposes only, and do not constitute endorsement by the U.S. Geological Survey.

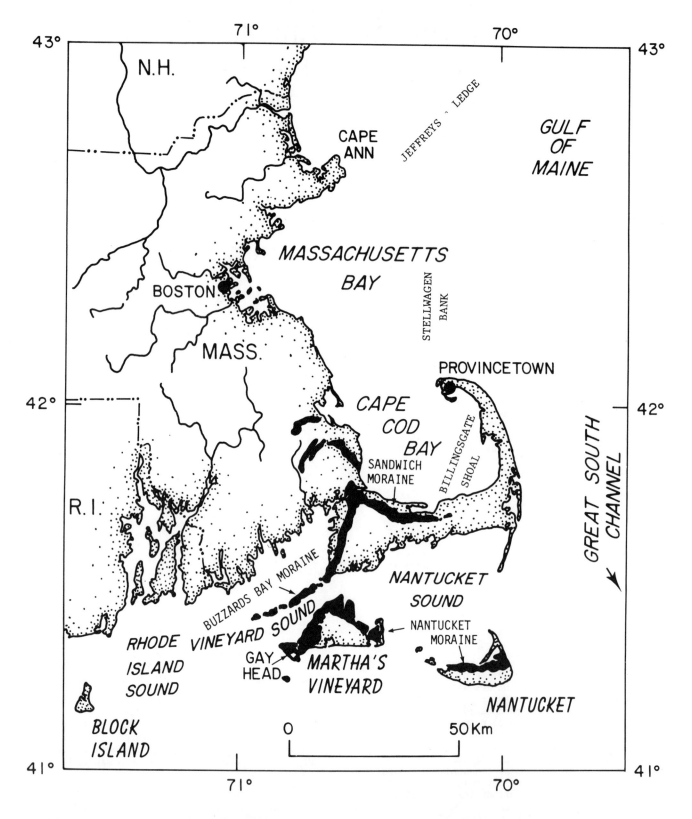

Figure 1. Physiographic index map of Massachusetts offshore region.

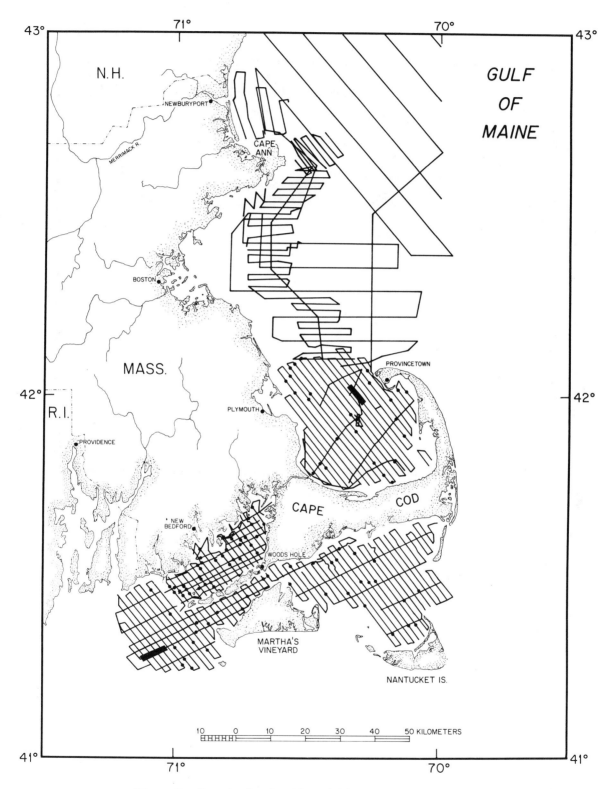

Figure 2. Map showing location of high-resolution seismic-reflection profile track lines (solid lines) and vibracore stations (dots). Heavy bars denote locations of selected seismic profiles shown in Figures 3 and 5.

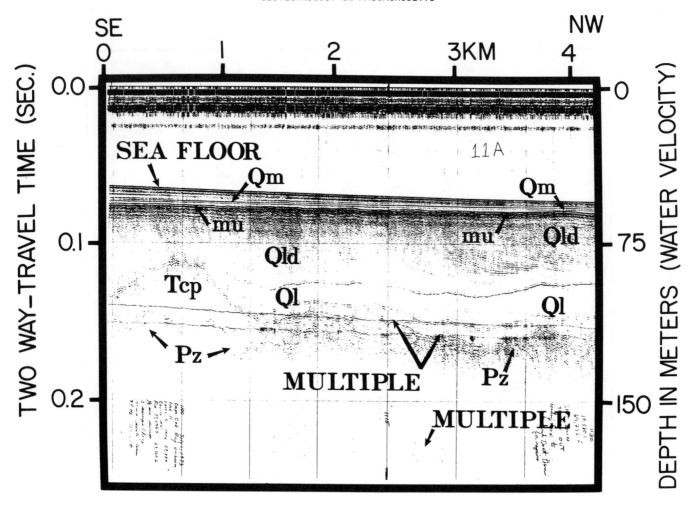

Figure 3. Seismic-reflection record from Cape Cod Bay showing pre-Mesozoic basement rocks (Pz) overlain by coastal-plain/continental-shelf strata (Tcp) of Tertiary age, glacial drift (Ql and Qld) of late Wisconsinan age, and well-stratified quiet-water marine deposits (Qm) of Holocene age. Reflector mu is postglacial marine unconformity. Location of seismic record is shown in Figure 2.

seconds. This system is capable of resolving sub-bottom reflectors as thin as 1 to 1.5 m and provides sediment penetration to depths of 75 to 100 m below the sea floor, which in most places includes the entire unconsolidated sedimentary section underlying the inner shelf of Massachusetts. Where the unconsolidated section is thicker, more powerful systems capable of deeper penetration are used. Navigational control is provided by Loran C (positional accuracy within 0.2 km), and track lines are generally spaced less than 2 km apart.

Vibracoring

As a result of glacial erosion and postgla-cial fluvial and marine erosion of the inner shelf of Massachusetts, older sedimentary deposits originally deeply buried now crop out on the sea floor or occur in the shallow subbottom in many places. Seismic-reflection records are initially examined to locate such sites so that they can be cored and the material identified. Vibracores designed to provide 9-cm-diameter cores as much as 12.2 m long in water depths of 11 to 70 m have been used, as they allow recovery of coarse sand and gravel and very compact sediments such as glacial tills. In the laboratory, the cores are visually examined to identify lithology and are sampled for petro-logic, palynologic, and paleontologic studies and radiocarbon dating. The core data, in combination with the acoustic units and major unconformities

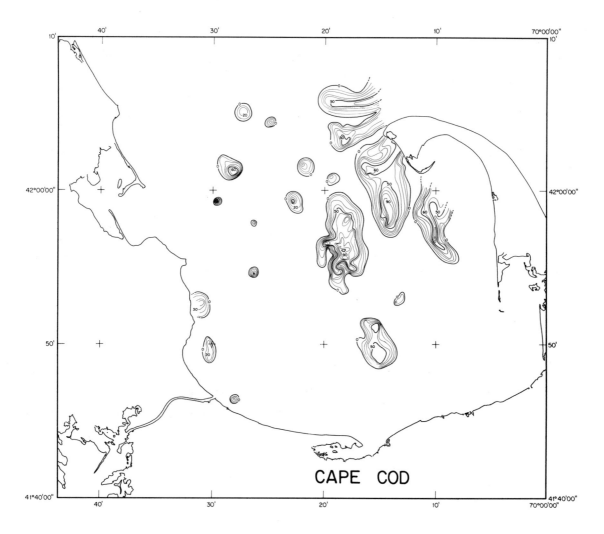

Figure 4. Isopach map showing distribution and thickness
of outliers of Tertiary (Eocene?) strata in Cape Cod Bay.
Contour interval is 10 m. Thickness based on inferred
compressional-wave velocity of 2.5 km/sec.

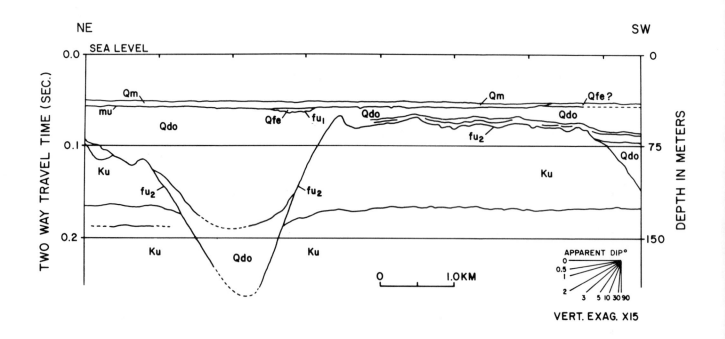

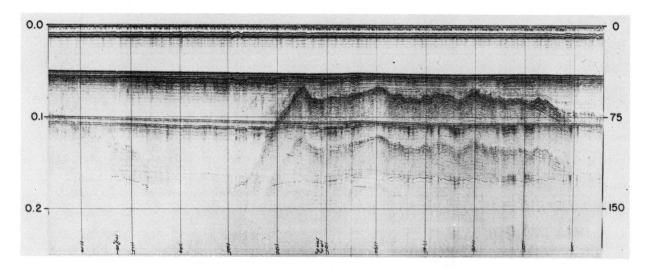

Figure 5. Seismic-reflection record and interpretive section from eastern Rhode Island Sound showing deeply eroded coastal-plain/continental-shelf strata (Ku) of mostly Late Cretaceous age overlain by glacial drift (Qdo) of late Wisconsinan age, and postglacial fluvial-estuarine (Qfe) and marine (Qm) deposits of Holocene age. Reflectors fu$_2$, fu$_1$, and mu represent late Tertiary-early Pleistocene fluvial unconformity, postglacial fluvial unconformity, and marine unconformity, respectively. Location of seismic record is shown in Figure 2.

defined by the seismic data, allow construction of isopach maps of important geologic units, structure maps showing the surface configuration of major seismic horizons or unconformities, and geologic and hazards maps of the sea floor.

## SUMMARY OF SCIENTIFIC RESULTS

The seismic-reflection and vibracore data have provided information on the geologic framework and late Mesozoic and Cenozoic development of the southeastern Massachusetts Inner Continental Shelf. The deepest observed acoustic reflector represents a regional unconformity of late Tertiary to early Pleistocene age that is underlain mostly by consolidated rocks of Proterozoic Z and early Paleozoic age, and to a lesser extent by unconsolidated to semi-consolidated continental-shelf rocks of Late Cretaceous to early Pleistocene age. In Massachusetts Bay and Cape Cod Bay (Fig. 3, unit Tcp), the unconformity is underlain locally by strata of possible Eocene age that occur as isolated erosional remnants (Fig. 4) (O'Hara and Oldale, 1976). Beneath much of eastern Rhode Island Sound, Vineyard Sound, and Nantucket Sound (O'Hara and others, 1976), this unconformity is underlain by strata (Fig. 5, unit Ku) of Late Cretaceous age (and some Tertiary?) that lie seaward of a deeply eroded cuesta (Fig. 6).

Glacial drift (till and proglacial outwash) of late Wisconsinan (Woodfordian?) age blanket the unconformity over most areas of the inner shelf. Radiocarbon dates (Oldale and O'Hara, 1980) of 12,000 to 13,000 years before present were obtained on freshwater basal peats cored atop the glacial drift; these dates suggest that the drift deposits offshore are no older than late Wisconsinan. Seismic profiles across the submerged parts of the Nantucket and Buzzards Bay moraines in Rhode Island Sound show reflectors believed to represent folding, faulting, and thrusting of preglacial and glacial sediments. This deformation and thrusting by ice is similar to that observed within the Gay Head Cliffs of Martha's Vineyard and within the nearby Elizabeth Islands and indicates that the coastal end moraines are in part glaciotectonic features (Oldale and O'Hara, 1978a).

The apparent structural nature of the moraine deposits suggests that deglaciation of southeastern Massachusetts was characterized by an oscillating ice front responding to short-term fluctuations of the Woodfordian glacial climate. Ice-front retreat is thought to have involved stagnation-zone retreat alternating with periods of vigorous ice advance, rather than a gradual and steady retreat in response to an ameliorating climate. Within Cape Cod Bay, the upper Wisconsinan drift is believed to be mostly of sublacustrine origin, deposited directly from the ice into deep water. Many imbricated northward-dipping reflectors are seen and are inferred to be basal tills deposited during ice readvances over sublacustrine drift. Off Provincetown, the drift

deposits are thought to consist of deep-water glaciolacustrine sediments (Fig. 3, unit Ql) and shallow-water foreset and bottomset sediments (Fig. 3, unit Qld) of large outwash-plain deltas (O'Hara and Oldale, 1976).

The glacial-drift surface off Massachusetts is locally incised by stream valleys. Within Cape Cod Bay (Oldale and O'Hara, 1975b), the postglacial fluvial drainage was northeastward toward the Gulf of Maine, whereas in Buzzards Bay, eastern Rhode Island Sound, Vineyard Sound, and western Nantucket Sound (Fig. 7), the drainage was southwestward toward Block Island Sound (O'Hara and others, 1976). The valleys are filled with mostly estuarine sediments (Fig. 5, unit Qfe), which were deposited as sea level rose and drowned the preexisting fluvially modified glacial drift surface. Ten radiocarbon dates obtained on shells and peats cored from these estuarine deposits allowed construction of a local Holocene sea-level-rise curve for the southeastern Massachusetts offshore area (Oldale and O'Hara, 1980). Approximately 12,000 years ago, relative sea level was 68 m below its present level and rose at a rate of 1.7 m/100 years until about 10,000 years ago. Between 10,000 years and 6,000 years ago, the rate of rise gradually slowed to about 0.3 m/100 years and remained at this rate until about 2,000 years ago. At that time, the rate of rise dropped to about 0.01 m/100 years.

A ubiquitous, nearly flat-lying reflector that caps the glacial drift and estuarine deposits filling the post-glacial valleys is thought to represent a planar marine unconformity (Figs. 3 and 5, acoustic reflector mu) cut during sea-level rise as the surf zone transgressed over the older deposits. Several Holocene marine deposits are found atop this wave-cut unconformity. In areas of active tidal-driven bottom currents, sand ridges, bars, tidal deltas, and sand wave fields are common; in areas of lesser tidal flow or deeper water, well-stratified deposits of silt and clay (Figs. 3 and 5, unit Qm) cap the marine unconformity. Adjacent to the coastal beaches, sand deposits are presently forming above the wave-cut surface.

## SUMMARY

The USGS/Massachusetts DPW marine cooperative has mapped a large part of the Massachusetts coastal zone. Additional seismic reflection surveys are scheduled in the State's coastal waters north of Cape Ann during the spring of 1980, and a vibracore sampling program in Massachusetts Bay is tentatively planned for the fall of 1980. Products of the marine program include isopach, structure, geologic, and hazards maps useful in the economic evaluation and development of the State's coastal resources. Most of the data collected during the program are available to other scientific investigators, consultants, and engineers. Unfortunately, all the cores that were collected by the marine cooperative were completely destroyed in a warehouse fire early in 1978.

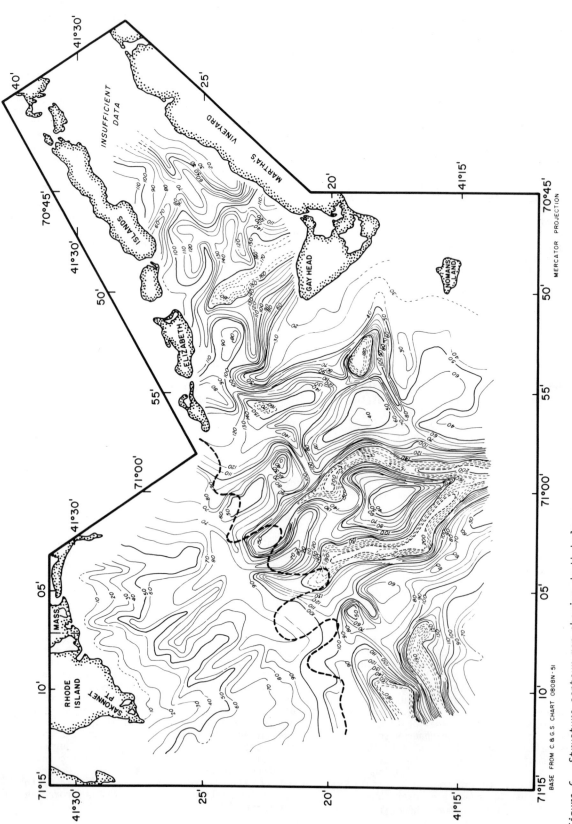

Figure 6. Structure-contour map showing depth below sea
level to basement (north of heavy dashed line) and submerged coastal-plain rocks (south of heavy dashed line) in
eastern Rhode Island Sound and Vineyard Sound. Heavy dashed line denotes approximate northernmost limit of cuesta
underlain by seaward-dipping strata of Late Cretaceous and
Tertiary(?) age. Contour interval is 10 m.

GEOTECHNOLOGY IN MASSACHUSETTS

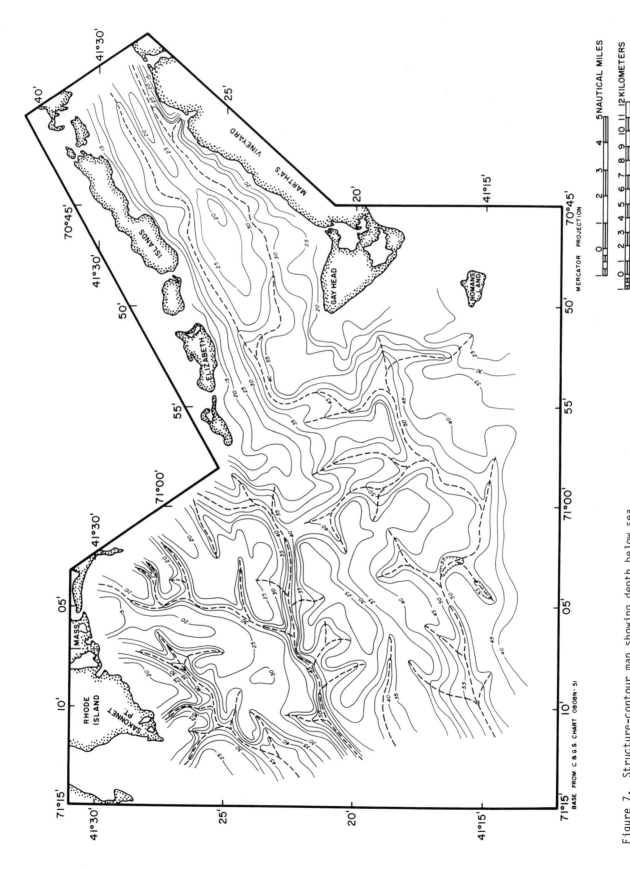

Figure 7. Structure-contour map showing depth below sea
level to top of glacial-drift surface in eastern Rhode
Island Sound and Vineyard Sound. Contour interval is 5 m.
Dashed lines show thalwegs of inferred postglacial streams.

- 547 -

PUBLICATIONS OF THE U.S.G.S./MASSACHUSETTS MARINE COOPERATIVE

(Open file reports with certain basic data are now available for inspection and may be examined at the Data Library, U.S. Geological Survey, Woods Hole, Massachusetts 02543. Microfilm copies can be purchased from the National Geophysical and Solar-Terrestrial Data Center (NGSDC), Boulder, Colorado 80302.

Butman, B., 1976, Hydrography and low frequency currents associated with the spring runoff in Massachusetts Bay: Société Royale des Sciences, Liège, Memoire ser. 6, v. 10, p. 247-275.

Butman, B., and Schlee, J.S., 1978, Bottom currents and bottom sediment distribution in Massachusetts Bay: U.S. Geological Survey Open File Report 78-369, 78 p.

Folger, D.W., Schlee, J.S., O'Hara, C.J., Butman, B., and Bumpus, D.F., 1971, Environmental factors affecting use of the Continental Shelf off Boston, Massachusetts [abs.]: Geological Society of America Abstracts with Programs, v. 3, no. 7, p. 569.

Folger, D.W., O'Hara, C.J., and Robb, J.M., 1975, Maps showing bottom sediments on the Continental Shelf of the northeastern United States--Cape Ann, Massachusetts, to Casco Bay, Maine: U.S. Geological Survey Miscellaneous Investigations Map I-839.

O'Hara, C.J., 1980, High-resolution seismic-reflection profiling data from the Inner Continental Shelf of southeastern Massachusetts: U.S. Geological Survey Open File Report 80-178, 2 p.

O'Hara, C.J., 1980, Side-scan sonograph data from eastern Rhode Island Sound and Vineyard Sound, Massachusetts: U.S. Geological Survey Open File Report 80-283, 3 p.

O'Hara, C.J., and Oldale, R.N., 1976, Basement morphology and pre-Holocene sedimentary structure of Cape Cod Bay, Massachusetts [abs.]: Geological Society of America Abstracts with Programs, v. 8, no. 2, p. 238-239.

O'Hara, C.J., Oldale, R.N., and Robb, J.M., 1976, Late Tertiary, Pleistocene, and Holocene development of the Inner Continental Shelf off southeastern Massachusetts [abs.]: Geological Society of America Abstracts with Programs, v. 8, no. 6, p. 1033.

O'Hara, C.J., and Meade, R.H., 1978, Suspended matter in Massachusetts Bay, September-October 1970, in Butman, B., and Schlee, J.S., Bottom currents and bottom sediment distribution in Massachusetts Bay: U.S. Geological Survey Open File Report 78-369, 78 p.

O'Hara, C.J., and Oldale, R.N., 1979, United States Geological Survey research in the Massachusetts coastal zone, in Aubrey, D.G., ed., Proceedings of a Workshop on Coastal Zone Research in Massachusetts, November 27-28, 1978: Woods Hole Oceanographic Institution Technical Report 79-40, p. 100-108.

O'Hara, C.J., and Oldale, R.N., in press, Geology and shallow structure of eastern Rhode Island Sound and Vineyard Sound, Massachusetts: U.S. Geological Survey Miscellaneous Field Studies Map MF-1186.

O'Hara, C.J., and Oldale, R.N., 1980, Geologic hazards on the Inner Continental Shelf off southeastern Massachusetts [abs.]: Geological Society of America Abstracts with Programs, v. 12, no. 2, p. 76.

Oldale, R.N., 1978, U.S.G.S. coastal zone studies in New England: in Coastal Zone '78--Proceedings of the Symposium on Technical, Environmental, Socioeconomic and Regulatory Aspects of Coastal Zone Management, ASCE/San Francisco, California, v. 3, p. 2137-2151.

Oldale, R.N., and O'Hara, C.J., 1975a, Preliminary report on the geology and sand and gravel resources of Cape Cod Bay, Massachusetts: U.S. Geological Survey Open File Report 75-112, 9 pl., scale 1:80,000.

Oldale, R.N., and O'Hara, C.J., 1975b, Postglacial fluvial erosion, marine planation, and marine deposition in Cape Cod Bay, Massachusetts [abs.]: Geological Society of America Abstracts with Programs, v. 7, no. 7, p. 1218-1219.

Oldale, R.N., and O'Hara, C.J., 1978a, Thrusted coastal end moraines and a Woodfordian fluctuating ice margin: evidence from Massachusetts onshore and offshore areas [abs.]: Geological Society of America Abstracts with Programs, v. 10, no. 2, p. 78.

Oldale, R.N., and O'Hara, C.J., 1978b, Postglacial sea levels on the Inner Continental Shelf of southern New England [abs.]: Geological Society of America Abstracts with Programs, v. 10, no. 2, p. 78.

Oldale, R.N., and O'Hara, C.J., 1978c, New radiocarbon dates from the Inner Continental Shelf off southeastern Massachusetts and a local sea-level rise curve for the last 12,500 years: in Proceedings of a Marine Geology Symposium dedicated to K.O. Emery by his colleagues and former students, Woods Hole Oceanographic Institution, p. 22.

Oldale, R.N., and O'Hara, C.J., 1980, New radiocarbon dates from the Inner Continental Shelf off southeastern Massachusetts and a local sea-level rise curve for the last 12,000 years: Geology, v. 8, no. 2, p. 102-106.

Robb, J.M., and Oldale, R.N., 1977, Preliminary geologic maps, Buzzards Bay, Massachusetts: U.S. Geological Survey Miscellaneous Field Studies Map MF-889.

Schlee, J.S., Folger, D.W., O'Hara, C.J., Butman, B., and Bumpus, D.F., 1971, Hydrology and sediments of the Continental Shelf: Cape Cod, Massachusetts to Portland, Maine [abs.]: Second National Coastal and Shallow Water Research Conference, p. 204.

Schlee, J.S., Folger, D.W., and O'Hara, C.J., 1973, Bottom sediments on the Continental Shelf off the northeastern United States--Cape Cod to Cape Ann, Massachusetts: U.S. Geological Survey Miscellaneous Investigations Map I-746.

Schlee, J.S., and Butman, B., 1974, Adjustments of inner shelf sediments to bottom currents off eastern Massachusetts: Institute de Geologie du Bassin d'Aquitaine Memoirs, v. 7, p. 75-80.

Tucholke, B.E., Oldale, R.N., and Hollister, C.D., 1972, Map showing echo sounding survey (3.5 kHz) of Massachusetts and Cape Cod Bays, western Gulf of Maine: U.S. Geological Survey Miscellaneous Investigations Map I-716.

Hors-texte

The eastern end of Cape Cod, Massachusetts, looking north from Chatham. Pleasant Bay occupies the foreground and Orleans the center. Wellfleet Harbor lies beyond, with Provincetown spit and Race Point in the far distance, some 30 miles away. The Cape Cod National Seashore stretches along the east coast for many miles, facing the Atlantic Ocean. (From Economic Geology in Massachusetts, O.C. Farquhar, ed., University of Massachusetts Graduate School, 1967, p. 520. Courtesy, Aerial Photos of New England.)

# Mass movement features and geomorphology of the continental slope off New Jersey

J. C. HAMPSON, JR.
J. M. ROBB
J. R. KIRBY

D. C. TWICHELL
U.S. Geological Survey
Woods Hole, Massachusetts

## ABSTRACT

Study of 2,250 km of high-resolution seismic profiles and core data in a 40 x 35-km segment of the Continental Slope and upper Rise between Lindenkohl and South Toms Canyons indicates that a complex of cut, filled, and recut Pleistocene deposits overlies a Pliocene (?) unconformity on the upper slope (130-800 m water depth) and middle slope (800-1500 m). Over most of the lower slope (1500-2150 m) Pleistocene deposits are absent (or very thin) and Miocene to Eocene deposits are exposed. The slope is dissected by numerous canyons and valleys which create a complex surface and localized areas of steep gradient. Five mass movement features were identified in this area; each of them appears to be associated with Pleistocene sediments. Individual surficial features in this environment can be easily misidentified as slumps or slides in seismic-reflection data unless closely spaced profiles with frequent tie lines and accurate bathymetry are used as a detailed three-dimensional basis for interpretation.

## INTRODUCTION

Because sediment mass movement has been identified as a potential hazard to petroleum development of the East Coast Continental Slope, the U.S. Geological Survey (USGS), in cooperation with the U.S. Bureau of Land Management (BLM), began a detailed study to identify and map mass-movement features on the Continental Slope between Lindenkohl and South Toms Canyons off New Jersey (Fig. 1). This 40 x 35-km area was chosen for study because it lies within an area of high interest for petroleum development (Lease sales 49 and 59), and because it includes several wells which provide stratigraphic control.

Mass movement of the sediments on the Continental Slope off the eastern United States has been identified by Rona and Clay (1967), Uchupi (1967), Rona (1969), and more recently by Embley and Jacobi (1977), McGregor and Bennett (1977), Knebel and Carson (1979), MacIlvaine and Ross (1979), and others. The reported slump features were identified by seismic profiling and range in area from about 2,000 km$^2$ (Embley and Jacobi, 1977) to perhaps 3 km$^2$ (estimated from data of Knebel and Carson, 1979).

These studies are largely topical, and there has been little detailed mapping of an entire slope segment in order to examine mass movement features in an areal perspective. To identify areas of mass movement and to understand their mode of occurrence it is necessary to understand the geologic setting. Our detailed analysis of the geomorphology and near-surface geology of a segment of the Continental Slope has provided insights into the geologic setting and has pointed to techniques and precautions that can be applied to future studies and other areas.

## METHODS

More than 2,250 km of seismic-reflection profiles (40 in$^3$-airgun, 800-J sparker, and 3.5-kHz echo sounder) were acquired in 1978 and 1979 aboard R/V COLUMBUS ISELIN (Robb, 1980b) and R/V JAMES M. GILLISS (Robb, 1980a). The data cover a 40 x 35-km area with a 900 x 1700-m grid (Fig. 2). Prime navigation for both cruises was LORAN-C. Satellite fixes and checks of water depths and subbottom reflectors at trackline crossing points indicate that positions are generally accurate to within 200 m. In order to aid interpretation, we also acquired 22 km of 97-kHz sidescan-sonar tracks (375-m swath) and 60 km of deep-towed hydrophone profiles (Robb and others, in press). Partial analysis of 550-km of mid-range sidescan sonar (5-km swath) acquired by the USGS in cooperation with the BLM and Lamont-Doherty Geological Observatory of Columbia University (LDGO) in September 1980 has also contributed to this report.

A bathymetric map (Fig. 2; Robb and others, 1981) was contoured from 3.5-kHz soundings. Points were digitized from profiles at time intervals of one-half minute or one minute of ship's travel (equivalent to about 60-m or 120-m distance). Because a wide-beam transducer was used for the echo-sounding system, migrations and diffractions from canyon walls obscure canyon floors, and the canyons appear to be V-shaped. More recent data obtained by means of the deep-towed hydrophone and the mid-range sidescan sonar have shown that most canyon floors are flat.

A geologic map (Fig. 3) was constructed using seismic-reflection profiles. Paleontological dates from six wells and 23 piston cores were used for stratigraphic control.

## TOPOGRAPHY

Because of the greater density of data, the bathymetric map (Fig. 2; Robb and others, 1981) shows the Continental Slope surface in consider-

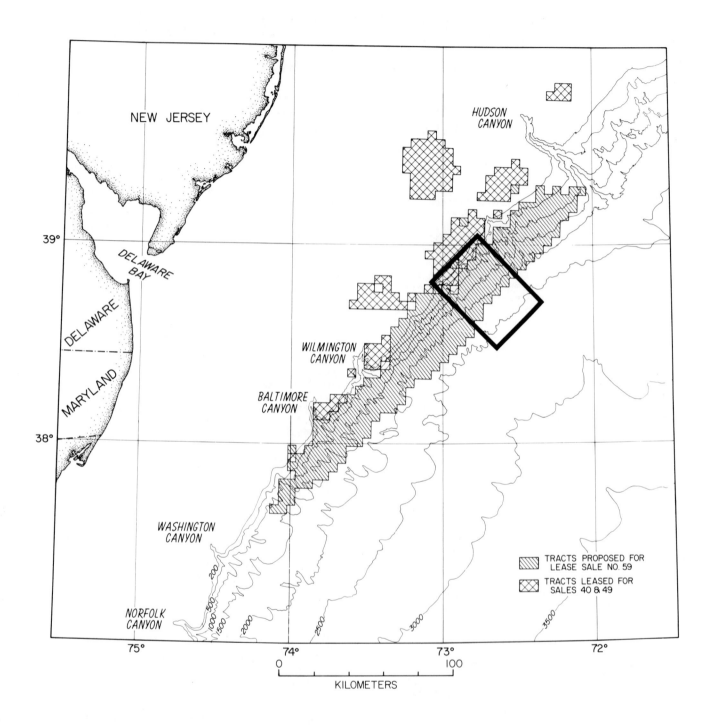

Figure 1. Map showing location of study area in relation
to tracts leased or proposed for lease.

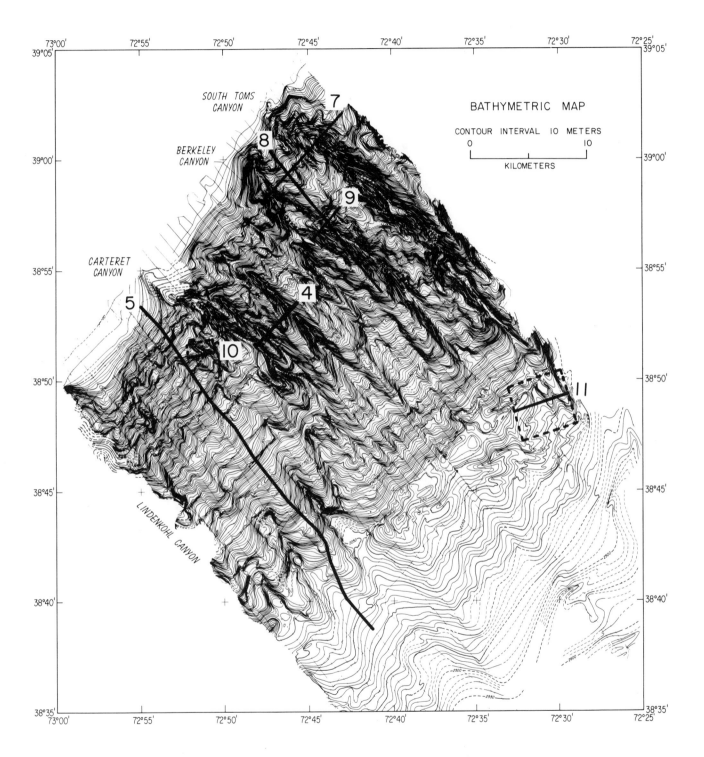

Figure 2. Bathymetric map showing seismic grid (light lines) and locations of illustrated profiles (numbers refer to figure numbers). From Robb, Kirby, and Hampson, 1981.

## A GEOLOGIC MAP OF THE CONTINENTAL SLOPE
## BETWEEN LINDENKOHL AND SOUTH TOMS CANYONS

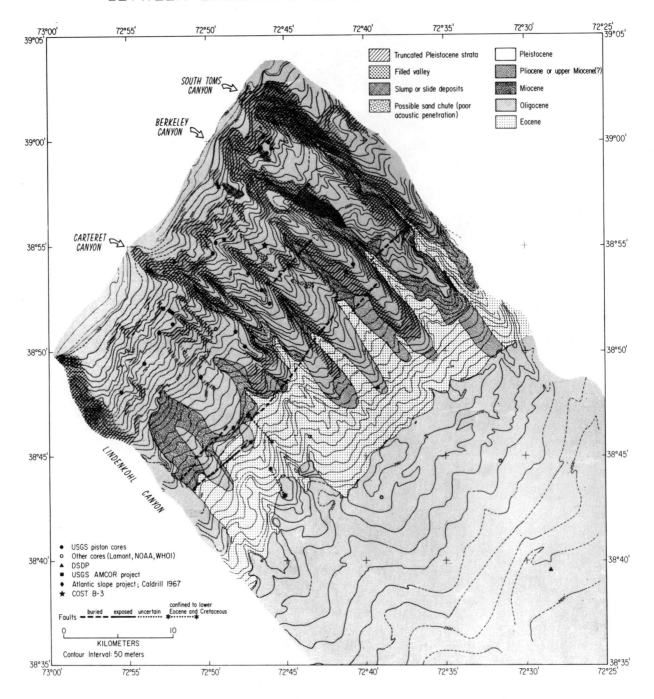

Figure 3. Geologic map of Continental Slope in the study area.

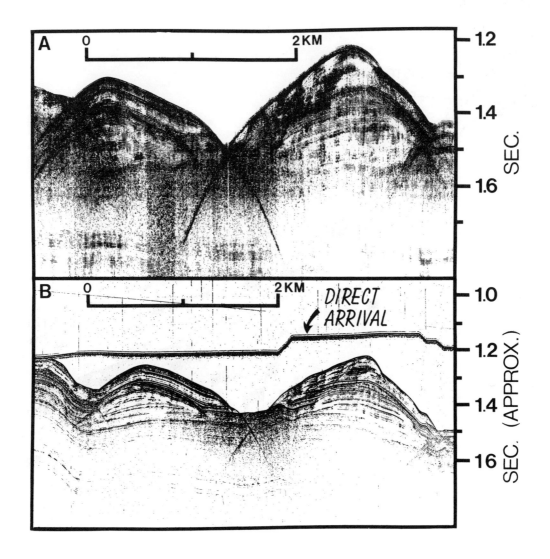

Figure 4. Comparison of (A) surface-towed hydrophone versus (B) deep-towed hydrophone record of minisparker signal across same area. Note flat-floored valley apparent in the deep-towed record. Location shown on Figure 2.

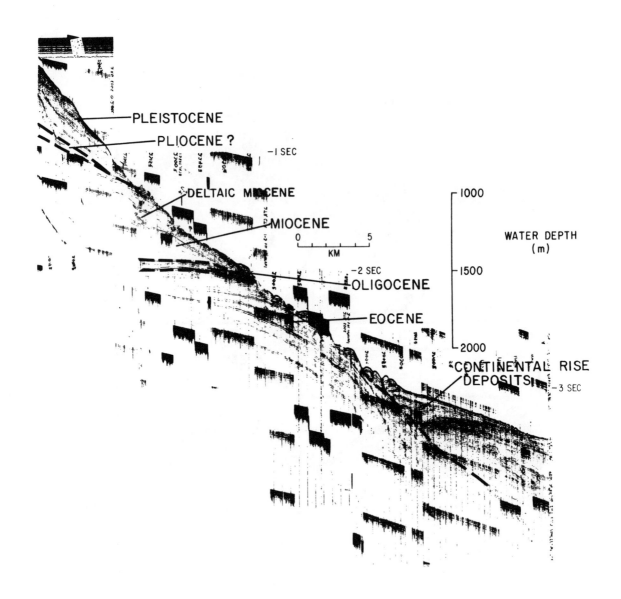

Figure 5. Airgun seismic-reflection profile (line 25) across Continental Slope. Vertical exaggeration 11x. Location shown on Figure 2.

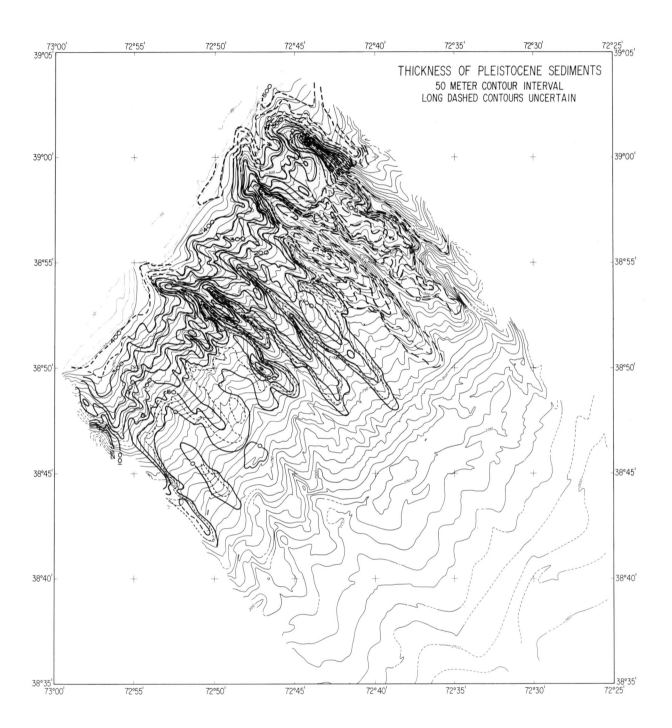

Figure 6.  Thickness of Pleistocene sediments.  Contour
interval is 50 m.

ably greater detail than is shown by older bathymetric maps of this area. The shelf break occurs near the 130-m isobath, and the base of the slope is at approximately 2,150-m water depth. Lindenkohl, Carteret, Berkeley, and South Toms Canyons are the major geomorphic features on the Continental Slope. They form a sigmoid pattern as they bend left then right in their downslope trend from an initial southerly direction nears the shelf edge. The surface of the upper Continental Slope between Lindenkohl and Carteret Canyons is smoother than the highly dissected area between Carteret and Toms Middle Canyons. Large numbers of small valleys or gullies are tributary to the submarine canyons on the upper slope. (To define terms for purposes of this report, canyons indent the edge of the Continental Shelf, whereas valleys do not; gullies are discontinuous, shallow valleys on the steep slopes of canyon walls.) The pattern of valley and canyon thalwegs is not dendritic, although gullies around some canyon heads may show a dendritic pattern. Canyons and valleys begin and terminate at various places on the Continental Slope; they do not always lead into a larger valley or extend to the Continental Rise. For example, Berkeley Canyon terminates at a depth of about 1,900 m on the Continental Slope whereas Lindenkohl Canyon extends across the Continental Rise.

The overall declivity of the Continental Slope ranges from 4° to 7°. The declivity of the Lindenkohl Canyon to Carteret Canyon area averages 7°, whereas the Carteret to South Toms area averages 4° to 5°. The general slope angle becomes a relatively meaningless figure for engineering or stability calculation, however, because of the complex relief. Slopes on canyon and valley walls are commonly 25° to 30°, and locally near vertical.

Measurements from the bathymetric map indicate that more than 17 percent of the Continental Slope in this area is steeper than 12°.

The axes of valleys and canyons appear sharp on the bathymetric map (Fig. 2). This is an artifact of diffractions from, and acoustic migration of, valley sidewalls (Krause, 1962). Figure 4 compares a surface-towed sparker profile with a simultaneous profile recorded by means of a hydrophone towed 100 m above the sea floor. Migration effects are minimal on the deep-towed hydrophone profile, and the valley floor can be seen to be flat. Mid-range sidescan-sonar records have shown that this is true of most canyon and valley axes.

STRUCTURE AND STRATIGRAPHY

Seismic profiles show strong, continuous, slightly seaward-dipping reflectors below the Continental Slope that are truncated and overlain by material having less continuous reflectors. A typical airgun profile, perpendicular to the regional contours, is shown in Figure 5. Paleontologic ages from boreholes, AMCOR 6021, ASP 13, ASP 14, and ASP 15 (Fig. 3) (Poag, 1979, 1980; Ruth Todd, oral comm., 1980) indicate that the

surficial deposits that dip generally parallel to the present slope surface are Pleistocene in age. The unconformity at their base may be of early Pleistocene or of Pliocene age. It truncates Miocene deposits below the middle slope (ASP 14 and ASP 15, Poag, 1979) and may truncate Pliocene deposits below the upper slope. Wash samples from the uncored, shallower parts of the COST B-3 well shown in Figure 3 contain Pliocene foraminifera (C.W. Poag, oral comm., 1980). A stratigraphically similar unconformity to the southwest, near Wilmington Canyon, was inferred to be of Pliocene age by McGregor and Bennett (1977).

Samples from piston cores show that the Holocene (post-Pleistocene) sediment cover is generally less than 2 m thick. Resolution of our seismic profiles (about 10 m) is therefore generally inadequate to distinguish them. Most piston cores in the area (average length about 6 m) penetrated sediments which contain foraminiferal faunas of Pleistocene age (C.W. Poag, written comm., 1979).

The Pleistocene sediments are about 450 m thick at the top of the Continental Slope and thin into lobate ridges extending down over the middle slope and parts of the lower slope (Figs. 3, 6). Seismic profiles show evidence of extensive cutting, filling, and recutting of valleys and canyons within the Pleistocene section (Fig. 7).

Tertiary sedimentary deposits make up the bulk of the material underlying the continental slope in this area (Poag, 1979). In seismic sections that have been processed to show true dip (Grow and others, 1979), these deposits are seen to occur in nearly flat-lying sequences that dip slightly seaward. A delta-front sequence of channeled and crossbedded sediments exists within the middle Miocene section (Poag, 1979); this sequence should not be confused in seismic outcrop with slump or slide deposits (Fig. 5). A zone of faulting is observed within the Tertiary sediments of the lower slope but does not appear to extend up through the pre-Pleistocene unconformity (Fig. 3); hence the faults probably do not consitute a present-day hazard. The faults displacing Tertiary deposits trend northeast. An older fault set, observed within the Cretaceous and lowermost Eocene sequences, appears to trend northwest.

MASS MOVEMENT

Detailed knowledge of the geology and surface morphology is necessary to identify and to map slope failures accurately. To date, many studies of slope areas have relied upon a small number of seismic profiles, oriented perpendicularly to the regional contours. Although many mass-movement features may be correctly identified in this fashion, the possibility for misidentification is great. For example, oblique crossings of canyons and valleys, filled channels, recut valleys, and conformable deposits on buried erosional topography can create reflection geometries which resemble slide scars, slump masses on a glide plane, offset bedding, or folded sediment layers. Such

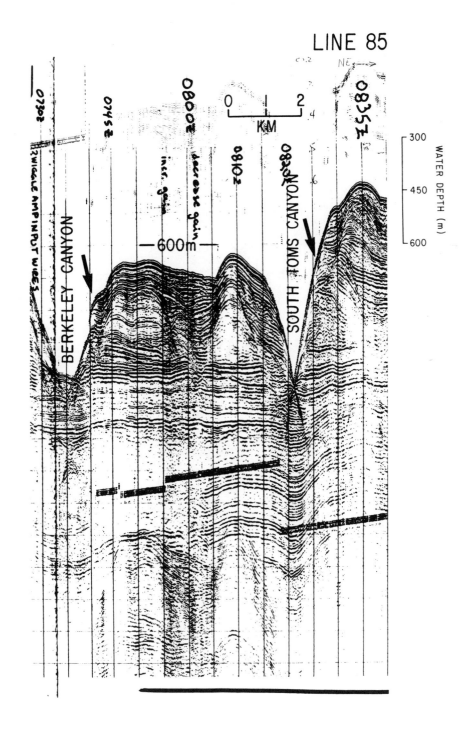

Figure 7. Airgun seismic-reflection profile showing filled valley in intercanyon area and recut valley-fill on canyon walls (arrows). Vertical exaggeration 12x. Location shown on Figure 2.

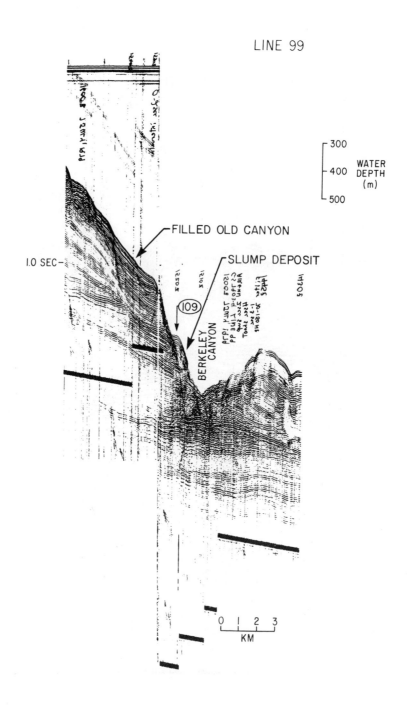

Figure 8.  Airgun seismic-reflection profile (line 99) across upper part of Berkeley Canyon showing slumped material on northeast wall.  Line 109 DH (Fig. 9) crosses as marked.  Vertical exaggeration 15x.  Location shown on Figure 2.

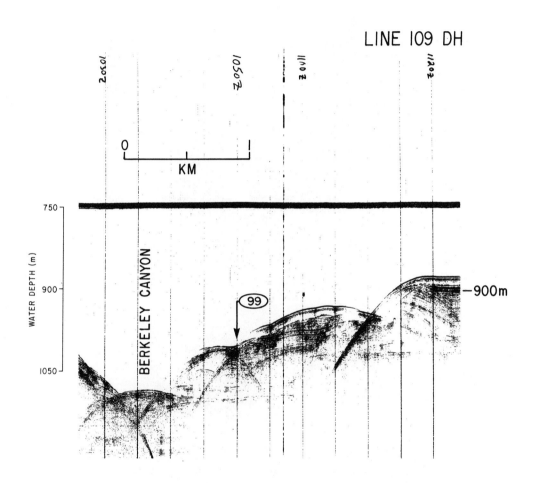

Figure 9. Deep-towed hydrophone, sparker reflection profile (line 109 DH) across slumped material in upper Berkeley Canyon. Line 99 (Fig. 8) crosses as marked. Vertical exaggeration 4x. Location shown on Figure 2.

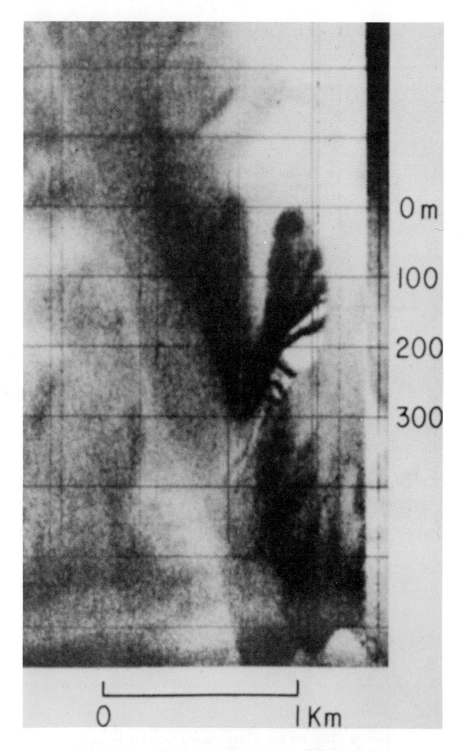

Figure 10. Sidescan sonograph of slide scar on wall of small valley on upper Continental Slope near 31°51'N., 72°51'W. (see Fig. 2). Valley runs from upper left to lower right of figure. Downslope direction is toward lower part of figure. At the base of the funnel-shaped slide scar there is a possible slide deposit, seen as a light area breaking the line of the valley axis.

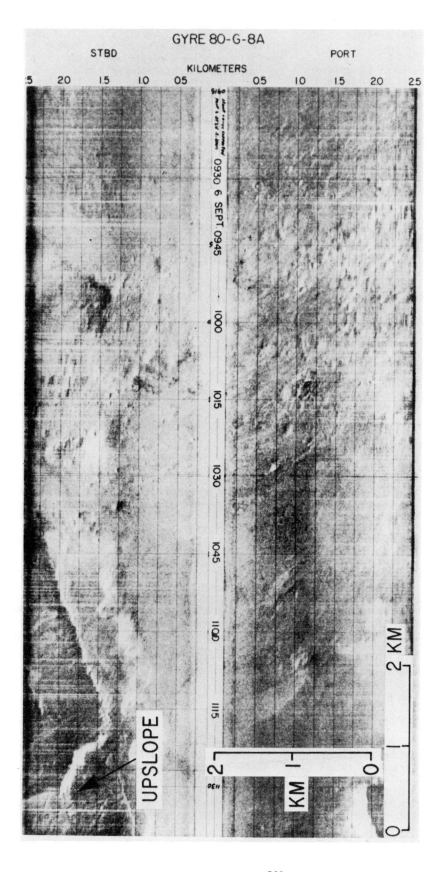

Figure 11. Mid-range sidescan sonograph of debris field(?) on upper Continental Rise below mouth of South Toms Canyon (for location see Fig. 2). This sonograph is corrected for slant range; width of swath is 5 km, 2.5 km either side of ship track at center line. Dark areas indicate strong reflections. The base of the slope is the line cutting the upper left corner near "UPSLOPE." The debris field covers most of the right side of the figure.

features can be more clearly identified by a grid of both normal-to-gradient and parallel-to-gradient profiles.

Most of the mass-movement features identified in this study are relatively small. The largest is intersected by three profiles within the survey grid. This feature is a slump in Berkeley Canyon (Figs. 8, 9). Here an old, filled, canyon intersects the present canyon, and part of that fill appears to have failed. The slumped material occupies about 5 km$^2$. Two smaller features were identified on the seismic profiles in intercanyon areas, and two additional mass-movement features were located on valley and canyon walls by means of sidescan sonar.

Using the primary data of this survey, a 900 x 1700-m profiling grid, the statistical probability of intersecting a single, quarter-mile circular target (a hypothetical single slump or slide) is 0.64 (calculated by the methods of McCammon, 1977). Intersecting such a target with two lines has a lower probability, and accurately identifying any target so intersected lowers the probability of discovery still more. However, features which slip through the grid may be identified with mid-range sidescan sonar. An example of such a feature is shown in Figure 10. Sidescan-sonar data can give more complete areal coverage, but sub-bottom profiles using seismic-reflection equipment are still required for sonograph interpretation.

Consideration must also be given to the resolution of the seismic system used in terms of the size features that can be identified. Slater (pers. comm., 1980) observed 1-m to 2-m scarps and blocks of clay, probably related to small-scale slumping, in the heads of Carteret and South Toms Canyons (water depths less than 360 m). Features of this size are too small for detection with conventional seismic-profiling systems. Their presence and importance would have to be determined on a site-specific basis by sidescan sonar, or by observation from a submersible.

In the study area, mass-movement features were identified only in deposits of Pleistocene sediments. We have not observed evidence in our seismic profiles of mass movement on slopes made up of Tertiary materials. However, some canyons have steep, possibly near-vertical walls in some places along their courses, and in those places there are probably slumping or failure of Tertiary outcrops. Dillon and Zimmerman (1970) and Ryan and others (1978) reported in situ observations of fresh, steep outcrops that may represent faces of slump scars deep in other East Coast submarine-canyon axes.

Scarps observed in canyons may be significant in light of recently acquired mid-range sidescan-sonar data which reveal a blocky surface deposit on the Continental Rise at the mouth of South Toms Canyon (Fig. 11). The material may have originated from a failure within the canyon, having been transported down onto the upper rise by debris flow or turbidity current.

We are unable to identify areas of creep (slow movement of surficial material downslope) from the present data. Strata identified as Pleistocene or older in age appear to be either conformable and undisturbed, or truncated on most surfaces within our resolution limit of about 10 m. However, the possibility of slow downslope movement should not be discounted from an overall hazards evaluation.

CONCLUSIONS

Our detailed survey of the Continental Slope between Lindenkohl and South Toms Canyons has revealed complex dissected topography and a Pleistocene sequence with many filled and recut valleys and canyons. Five mass-movement features were identified. Three of the features are located in intercanyon areas; these were found in conformable deposits often associated with gullies or small valleys, where local slopes were greater (Figs. 3, 10). Within the canyons, one 5-km$^2$ slump was identified on the side of Berkeley Canyon in re-excavated canyon fill. A small mass-movement feature was identified in Carteret Canyon (Fig. 3) by means of sidescan sonar. No massive (greater than 10 km$^2$) slumps were identified on this portion of the Continental Slope. No slumps or slides were identified in the Tertiary exposures on the lower slope. Hence Quaternary deposits and areas of steep slopes appear to have had the greatest number of failures, whereas seismic profiles of Tertiary sediments exposed in intercanyon areas show no evidence of failure.

The above conclusions imply that the bathymetric and geologic maps (Figs. 2, 3) may be used to predict areas of greatest potential for failure by identifying areas of steep slope and the distribution of Pleistocene sediments. In order to predict the degree of risk, however, a detailed engineering research program that included in situ geotechnical measurements to determine the present-day strength of the Pleistocene sediments would be necessary.

A combination of seismic profiling and high-resolution deep-towed systems, including mid-range sidescan sonar, provides a powerful tool for deep-water mapping. The sidescan aids in locating features missed by the seismic-profiling grid and resolves surface details, targeting areas for more detailed investigations with carefully sited cores and submersible dives.

Although the interpretive techniques and data-gathering methods used in this study are applicable to any slope study, interpretations based on the results of any detailed mapping should be extrapolated to other areas with great care. Regional studies of the Continental Slope between Georges Bank and Cape Hatteras, N.C. (Rona, 1969; Emery and Uchupi, 1972; McGregor, 1979) reveal that topography, thickness of surficial deposits, and possible mechanisms of deposition and erosion vary along the slope and with water depth. Off Georges Bank, for example, the Continental Slope has been subject to the rapid sedimentation rates associated with glacial deposits; hence, the distribution, thickness, and stability of Pleistocene sediment probably differs significantly from the area investigated in this study.

ACKNOWLEDGMENTS

Funding for this work was provided by the U.S. Bureau of Land Management (BLM) under Memoranda of Understanding AA551-MU8-21 and AA551-MU9-4 between the USGS and the BLM. We thank the officers and men of the R/V COLUMBUS ISELIN, R/V JAMES M. GILLISS, and R/V GYRE for their friendly cooperation and seamanship. W. B. F. Ryan (Lamont-Doherty Geological Observatory of Columbia University) provided the mid-range sidescan-sonar system. This study required the support of many people, both at sea and ashore, whom we thank for their hard work and dedication.

REFERENCES

Dillon, W.P., and Zimmerman, H.B., 1970, Erosion by biological activity in two New England submarine canyons: Journal of Sedimentary Petrology, v. 40, p. 524-547.

Embley, R.W., and Jacobi, R.D., 1977, Distribution and morphology of large submarine sediment slides on Atlantic Continental margins: Marine Geotechnology, v. 2, Marine Slope Stability.

Emery, K.O., and Uchupi, E., 1972, Western North Atlantic Ocean: Topography, rocks, structure, water, life, and sediments: American Association of Petroleum Geologists Memoir 17, 532 p.

Grow, J.A., Mattick, R.E., Schlee, J.S., 1979, Multichannel seismic depth sections and interval velocities over outer Continental Shelf and upper Continental Slope between Cape Hatteras and Cape Cod: in Watkins, J.S., Montadert, L., and Dickerson, P.W., eds., Geological and geophysical investigations of continental margins: American Association of Petroleum Geologists Memoir 29, p. 65-83.

Knebel, H.J., and Carson, B., 1979, Small scale slump deposits, middle Atlantic Continental Slope of eastern United States: Marine Geology, v. 29, p. 221-236.

Krause, D.C., 1962, Interpretation of echo sounding profiles: International Hydrographic Review, v. 34, no. 1, p. 65-123.

MacIlvaine, J.C., and Ross, D.A., 1979, Sedimentary processes on the continental slope of New England: Journal of Sedimentary Petrology, v. 49, p. 563-574.

McCammon, R.B., 1977, Target intersection probabilities for parallel-line and continuous grid types of search: Mathematical Geology, v. 9, p. 369-382.

McGregor, B.A., 1979, Variations in bottom processes along the U.S. Atlantic continental margin, in Watkins, J.S., Montadert, L., and Dickerson, P.W., eds., Geological and geophysical investigations of continental margins: American Association of Petroleum Geologists Memoir 29, p. 139-149.

McGregor, B.A., and Bennett, R.H., 1977, Continental slope sediment instability northeast of Wilmington Canyon: American Association of Petroleum Geologists Bulletin, v. 61, p. 918-928.

Poag, C.W., 1979, Stratigraphy and depositional environments of Baltimore Canyon Trough: American Association of Petroleum Geologists Bulletin, v. 63, p. 1452-1465.

Poag, C.W., 1980, Foraminiferal stratigraphy, paleoenvironments, and depositional cycles in the outer Baltimore Canyon Trough, in Scholle, P.A., ed., Geological studies of the COST No. B-3 well, United States Mid-Atlantic Continental Slope area: U.S. Geological Survey Circular 833, p. 44-65.

Robb, J.M., 1980a, High-resolution seismic-reflection profiles collected by the R/V JAMES M. GILLISS, cruise GS 7903-4, in the Baltimore Canyon Outer Continental Shelf area, offshore New Jersey: U.S. Geological Survey Open-file Report 80-934, 3 p.

Robb, J.M., 1980b, High-resolution seismic-reflection profiles collected by the R/V COLUMBUS ISELIN, cruise CI 7807-1, in the Baltimore Canyon Outer Continental Shelf area, offshore New Jersey: U.S. Geological Survey Open-file Report 80-935, 3 p.

Robb, J.M., Kirby, J.R., and Hampson, J.C., Jr., 1981, Bathymetric map of the Continental Slope and uppermost Continental Rise between Lindenkohl Canyon and South Toms Canyon, offshore eastern United States: U.S. Geological Survey Miscellaneous Field Investigation, MF 1270, 1 plate.

Robb, J.M., Sylwester, R.E., and Penton, R., in press, Simplified method of deep-tow seismic profiling: Geo-Marine Letters.

Rona, P.A., 1969, Middle Atlantic Continental Slope of the United States: deposition and erosion: American Association of Petroleum Geologists Bulletin, v. 53, p. 1453-1465.

Rona, P.A., and Clay, C.S., 1967, Stratigraphy and structure along a continuous seismic reflection profile from Cape Hatteras, North

Carolina, to the Bermuda Rise: Journal of Geophysical Research, v. 72, p. 2107-2130.

Ryan, W.B.F., Cita, M.B., Miller, E.L., Hanselman, D., Nesteroff, W.D., Hecker, B., and Nibbelink, M., 1978, Bedrock geology in New England submarine canyons: Oceanology Acta, v. 1, p. 233-254.

Uchupi, E., 1967, Slumping on continental margin southeast of Long Island, New York: Deep-Sea Research, v. 14, p. 635-639.

# Geotechnical properties and slope stability analysis of surficial sediments on the Atlantic continental slope in two regions—Georges Bank and Baltimore Canyon

J. S. BOOTH
U.S. Geological Survey
Woods Hole, Massachusetts

T. L. RICE
U.S. Geological Survey
Denver, Colorado

R. A. FARROW*
U.S. Geological Survey
*Deceased

## ABSTRACT

Potential geologic hazards on the Continental Slope off the northeastern United States are being investigated by the U.S. Geological Survey in co-operation with the U.S. Bureau of Land Management. As a part of this research program, the surficial sediments within the Georges Bank and Baltimore Canyon lease areas are being studied in order to establish their general geotechnical properties and potential for mass movement.

Piston cores collected from a variety of environments within these two areas are serving as the primary source of data. Analyses include shipboard vane shear measurements (undrained shear strength), a suite of index property tests, tri-axial tests (consolidated, undrained with pore pressure measurements), and, still in progress, consolidation tests (constant rate of strain).

Preliminary results indicate that the sediments sampled off Georges Bank on the Continental Slope tend to be highly plastic, inorganic silts and clays. These sediments also tend to be more sensitive ($\overline{St}$ = 5.2) and to have a higher shear strength ($\overline{S_u}$ = 9.5 kPa) than typical fine-grained surficial marine sediments. Analysis of two core sites suggested that approximately 10 meters and 40 meters of overburden may have been removed from the two sites, respectively. The sites may repre-sent mass movement scarps. Data also suggest that the cored surficial sediments on the Georges Bank Continental Slope are normally consolidated or overconsolidated and are relatively stable at present.

The area sampled within the Baltimore Canyon Continental Slope area appears to be a complex depositional environment. The saw-tooth nature of the shear strength profiles and the variability of the index properties support this suggestion. In general the sediments are inorganic sands, silts, and clays, and their plasticity ranges from low to high. These sediments tend to be more sensitive ($\overline{St}$ ~ 6) than typical fine-grained surfi-cial marine sediments; however, their average shear strength ($\overline{S_u}$ = 5.5 kPa) is typical for this class of sediment rather than higher, as was the case on Georges Bank. Slope stability analyses in the absence of pore pressure data indicate that generally stable conditions predominate in these sediments. However, indirect evidence suggests that the surficial sediment may be underconsoli-dated at some sites, and thus a metastable condi-tion may characterize a few areas.

## INTRODUCTION

### Georges Bank

The many recent investigations of the Conti-nental Slope off Georges Bank have brought into focus the depositional history, morphology, geo-logic processes, and other salient geologic char-acteristics of the area. These investigations have also served a dual purpose for hazards analysis: they have defined what appears to be the most serious geologic hazard, mass movement; and they have provided insight into the geotech-nical properties of the sediment, one of the pri-mary means for assessing the potential for mass movement.

Attention has been directed to mass movement as the preeminent hazard because it apparently has been widespread in the past. Aaron and others (1980), for example, reported that as much as 37 percent of the slope may have been affected by slump or slide phenomena. Mass-movement features were also identified by Uchupi (1967) and McGregor (1979); McIlvaine and Ross (1979) presented a de-tailed description of a slump in the area. Estab-lishing whether these events were caused by trig-gering mechanisms, such as oceanographic forces or earthquakes, or by inherent instability, such as that caused by rapid deposition, is, of course, relevant to our understanding of the present-day stability of the slope. And, although information on triggering mechanisms is unavailable, Emery and Uchupi (1972) have established that high rates of deposition did characterize the area in the past. In fact, these authors pointed out that during low stands of the sea, depositional rates were enhanced not only by greater proximity to drain-age systems, but by greater runoff from glacial melt as well.

This past rapid rate of sediment accumulation could have led to an underconsolidated sediment section and thus to a slope vulnerable to failure. Even though depositional rates are undoubtedly less at present (hemipelagic deposition and a small amount of shelf sediment spillover currently predominate (Doyle and others, 1979)), the under-consolidation effect of past rapid sedimentation may be within the sediment column, particularly if fine-grained sediments are involved. Fine-grained sediments do cover much of the Continental Slope off Georges Bank. Doyle and others (1979) showed that although grains of a wide variety of sizes exist--including sand and clasts of glacial origin--silt and clay predominate. This dominance of silt and clay is also reported by Keller and others (1979), who showed that the surficial sediments on the Continental Slope off Georges Bank are composed, on the average, of more than 80 percent silt and clay. Further, Hathaway and others (1976) found thick sections of fine sediments in several areas during drilling operations in the general vicinity of and within the Georges Bank lease area.

These fine sediments augment the effect of rapid deposition by trapping pore fluids more efficiently than sand or gravel. This trapping of pore fluid can result in a buildup of excess pore pressure and the creation of a high degree of underconsolidation (hence relative weakness) within the sediment column.

The relatively steep declivity of the Continental Slope off Georges Bank also is an important stability consideration. Keller and others (1979) reported that on the middle and lower slope gradients average 7°. Bathymetric data analyzed by Aaron and others (1980) indicate gradients as great as 10°. These rather steep slopes would warrant a careful hazards analysis even in the absence of the other factors mentioned. In planning the Georges Bank phase of the study, we were aware of this geologic setting and its geotechnical implications. Our objectives in this region were to verify the occurrence of past mass movement, provide more quantitative information on slope stability, and establish the general geotechnical properties of the sediments. Core sites were selected accordingly and included locations on the open slope, on possible mass-movement scars, and on possible mass-movement deposits (blocks) (Fig. 1). The limited sub-bottom penetration of piston coring (less than 6 m in this area) has necessarily restricted the scope of our investigation.

Baltimore Canyon

Evidence of a major episode of mass movement northeast of Wilmington Canyon reported by McGregor (1977) has underscored the need for research on potential geologic hazards in the Baltimore Canyon lease area as well. However, despite the fact that this mass-movement event has focused attention on the possibility of future events, it is not necessarily a precursor to them. That is, the central question of whether the slope is unstable may be answered on the basis of studies of current slope conditions rather than on the basis of studies of past events.

The geologic setting bears directly on the question of present conditions, and, as in the case of the geologic setting of Georges Bank, it has been thoroughly investigated. In addition to the aforementioned study by McGregor (1977), seismic studies by Emery and Uchupi (1972), Embley and Jacobi (1977), and Robb and others (1981) have shown that this part of the Continental Slope is relatively steep (gradients of 10° are common), is incised by numerous major canyons and lesser valleys, and contains a Pleistocene sediment sec-

tion as thick as a few hundred meters on the upper slope. In addition, the slope is commonly marked by evidence suggesting mass movement. As pointed out by Robb and others (1981), however, mass movement may not be as ubiquitous as some other studies have implied.

Rapid deposition, a common predecessor of mass movement, probably took place along the whole Mid-Atlantic Continental Slope area during times of lowered sea level just as it did on the Georges Bank Continental Slope. Also analogous to the Georges Bank sedimentation, the high rate of deposition, particularly as it involved the fine-grained sediments that characterize the area (Doyle and others, 1979; Keller and others, 1979), may have caused excess pore pressures within the sediment section and, hence, may have created a condition of instability on the slope. Although sedimentation rates are probably lower at present than they were during the past, the dissipation of these excess pore pressures may be incomplete. If excess pore pressures remain, the slope is still underconsolidated and thus is prone to fail, especially in areas having rather steep gradients.

Results of analyses of samples from Baltimore Canyon and adjacent slope areas are mixed. In an area south of Baltimore Canyon, for example, McGregor and others (1979) noted the presence of underconsolidated sediment and other conditions suggesting instability. Within the lease area itself, however, similar conditions have not been identified. Slope-stability analyses by Keller and others (1979) indicated that the surficial sediments were generally stable, and piston cores examined by Doyle and others (1979) showed no evidence of mass movement. Samples from a 300-m-deep drill hole (AMCOR 6021) near Toms Canyon also indicated stability (Sangrey and others, 1979); however, the analyses based on those samples did not take into account excess pore pressures that may be associated with the large quantities of methane found at that site. The massive slide deposit northeast of Wilmington Canyon, which is as much as 300 m thick and involves 11 km$^3$ of sediment (McGregor, 1977), has been examined by Bennett and others (1977) for its geotechnical properties. Their evidence does not refute the hypothesis that the feature is a slide deposit, and they presented additional evidence that creep is taking place upslope from the apparent mass-movement scar.

The previous acoustic and sampling studies established the framework for the research of hazard-related problems in the Baltimore Canyon lease area. Our objective in this phase of the research was to provide quantitative information regarding slope stability and other potential hazards and to establish the general geotechnical properties of the sediment. Site selection for the piston cores was based on the need to achieve geographic and geologic coverage and, thus, various environments from different locales were sampled. These included open slope areas, valley walls, valley floors, lobate sediment masses, and others. Locations are shown in Figure 2. The

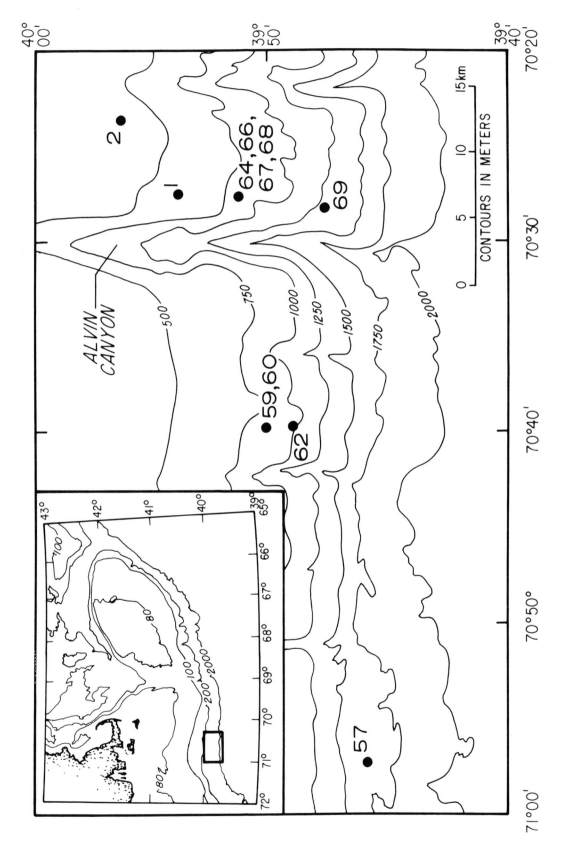

Figure 1. Core locations in Georges Bank lease area.

scope of our investigations is limited because piston cores generally penetrate less than 10 m in this area.

## METHODS OF INVESTIGATION

### Shipboard

The piston cores used for the geotechnical studies were collected aboard the R/V ENDEAVOR in August 1979 and October 1980. The coring system was designed to obtain cores with minimal mechanical disturbance because many geotechnical properties, especially those related to strength, are vulnerable to the effects of disturbance. The system thus differed from conventional systems in many respects. Core sample diameter was 89 mm, which is larger than the diameter of normal piston cores. This extra size not only reduces disturbance during the act of coring but, in the event of distortion on the core edge due to wall friction, permits removal of a relatively undisturbed inner core (subcore) for triaxial and consolidation testing. The liner was protected against collapse from differential pressure by a special sleeve and O-ring assembly at the joints between the outer barrels. The cutter unit had a cutting angle of less than 10°, which assured optimum penetration with a minimum of disturbance. Liner sections (as many as four 3-m-long sections per core) were taped at the ends in order to achieve a snug fit against the barrel and were beveled inside each end to promote a smooth piston action. By use of this system, 13 cores as long as 10 m were recovered in the Baltimore Canyon Slope region, and 11 cores as long as 5 m were recovered in the Georges Bank Slope region.

As during the sampling operation, avoiding disturbance was the prime consideration during core processing and storage. Once on board, the cores were cut into 1.5-m-long sections by using a tube cutter to sever the liner and a wire saw to part the sediments. Two 40-cm subsections were also cut for later triaxial testing, and a 15-cm subsection was removed for consolidation testing. All subsections, which were cut from the bottom parts of the cores, were X-rayed in order to judge the condition of the sample; only samples appearing to be relatively undisturbed were retained for later testing. Finally, the subsections were capped, taped, sealed with wax, and refrigerated. They were kept in the in situ position in specially fabricated boxes padded with foam rubber.

The remaining core sections were split lengthwise: one part of each section served as an archive half, the other as a working half. The archive half was placed in a D-tube and stored in a refrigerated van. The working half was taken to the shipboard laboratory for description, strength testing, and subsampling.

After a cursory description, "undisturbed" shear strength was measured. A four-bladed, 12.7-mm-square laboratory vane was used at

intervals of 0.50 m and at lithologic changes. Obvious sand layers, which are cohesionless and therefore inappropriate for this type of test, were avoided. The blade was inserted normal to the long direction of the core and buried at least 20 mm into the sample. In order to guard against sample drainage during the application of torque, a rotation rate of 0.0262 rad/s (90°/min) was used. Because of potential disturbance associated with prolonged exposure to ship motion and vibrations, this rapid rate also serves the function of allowing the test to be completed quickly, thus reducing the probability of this type of disturbance. The accuracy of the vane shear measurements is ± 0.30 kilopascals (kPa). We assumed on the basis of previous experience (Booth, 1979) that strength reduction due to the release of in situ stresses and mechanical disturbance is generally between 15 percent and 30 percent. Remolded strength (strength of thoroughly kneaded sample) was also determined by use of the vane apparatus. Subsamples for index property testing were taken at the locations of strength measurements, placed in plastic bags, and sealed in cans for later laboratory testing. These samples, and those taken for triaxial and consolidation testing, were transported to the laboratory in a refrigerated (4°C) van. Results of the lab shear-strength measurements are presented in Appendices I and II, along with the strength profiles for both Georges Bank and Baltimore Canyon cores.

### Laboratory

Index Properties. The suite of index property tests (bulk density, water content, liquid and plastic limits, and grain specific gravity) was conducted according to procedures recommended by ASTM (1977), with two exceptions. Grain specific gravity was measured by an air comparison pycnometer, and all water-content data were corrected for salt content. Precisions were: water content, ± 3 percent (relative); liquid limit, ± 3 percent (absolute); plastic limit, ± 2 percent (absolute); grain specific gravity, ± 1 percent (relative); and bulk density, ± 2 percent (relative). Derived from this basic data set were plasticity index, liquidity index, and porosity. The values of the index properties are presented in Appendices I and II, along with the vertical profiles of the limits for both the Georges Bank and Baltimore Canyon cores.

Triaxial Testing. Consolidated undrained triaxial tests with pore-pressure measurements were conducted in accordance with procedures given by Bishop and Henkel (1957). Briefly, for each set of tests, three specimens were cut from the prime core sample and trimmed to a right cylinder 50 mm in diameter and 100 mm in height. The specimens were then placed in triaxial cells, saturated, and consolidated to approximately 1.0, 2.0, and 4.0 times the assumed in situ overburden pressure. After consolidation was complete, the specimens were sheared, generally at a rate of 0.015 mm/min. Data from all phases of the tests were logged by an automatic data-acquisition system.

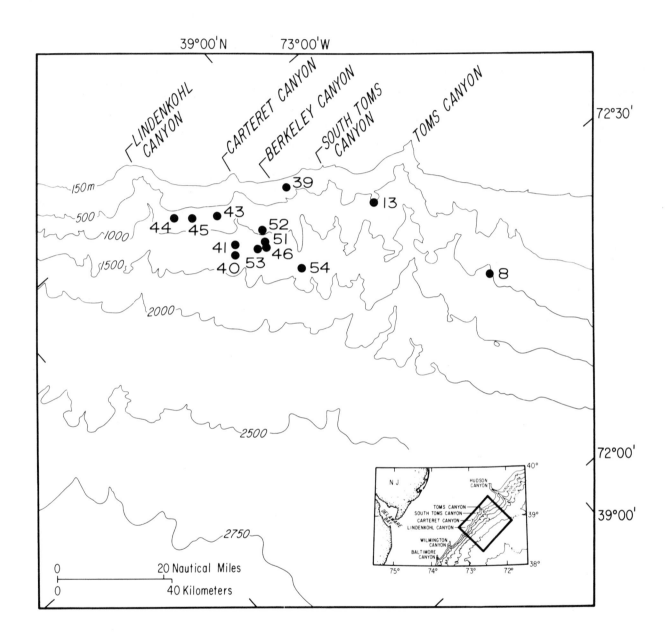

Figure 2.   Core locations in Baltimore Canyon lease area.

The angles of internal friction with respect to effective stress and cohesion, which are necessary for evaluating slope stability, were derived from p´-q diagrams. Specifically, a continuous plot of $p´ = (\sigma´_1 + \sigma´_3)/2$ versus $q = (\sigma_1 - \sigma_3/2)$ for each of the three levels of confining pressure results in three stress paths, where $\sigma_1$ and $\sigma_3$ are the major and minor principal stresses, and $\sigma´_1$ and $\sigma´_3$ are the major and minor effective principal stresses. The line that best encloses these stress paths is drawn, and its slope $\alpha$ and its intercept $a$ are calculated. The values of internal friction $\emptyset´$ and cohesion $c´$ are calculated from the following relationships: $\sin \emptyset´ = \tan \alpha$ and $c´ = a/\cos \emptyset´$.

## RESULTS AND INTERPRETATIONS

Analyses of the 24 cores recovered are still underway, as are the analyses of 28 additional piston cores recovered during cruise operations in 1980. The results presented herein are thus partial, and generalizations or interpretations based on them are subject to change. No consolidation test results are available at this time. The triaxial data and associated stress-path plots from the cores discussed in this report were given by Booth and others (1981a, b).

## Georges Bank

Shear Strength. In proportion to the average length of the cores (about 2.5 m), the shear-strength values in general are unusually high. As shown in the data summary (Table 1), the range is from 3.1 to 50.2 kPa, and the mean is 9.5 kPa. This average is about twice the strength that would be expected for normally consolidated fine-grained sediments and is higher than that reported by Keller and others (1979) for cores taken within the same general area. The highest single value measured, 50.2 kPa, was from a core (PC-57) taken on what appeared in seismic-reflection records to be a mass-movement scar. Approximately 0.5 m of considerably weaker sediment (less than 10 kPa) overlies the apparently over-consolidated material. Individual strength profiles for the cores are shown in Appendix I. Cores with less than three measurements were not plotted. The profiles generally display the strength increase expected with depth or, if values are initially high, as in the cores collected from apparent mass-movement scars, they generally remain at about the same high value (for example, PC-59) throughout the core. An exception to this general trend is PC-68 which shows a decrease in strength down the core. PC-68 was taken from a slump or slide block, and an atypical strength profile associated with such a feature has been

TABLE 1. SUMMARY OF GEOTECHNICAL DATA FOR GEORGES BANK

| Natural shear strength (kPa) | | | Sensitivity | | | Water content percent | | |
|---|---|---|---|---|---|---|---|---|
| min | avg | max | min | avg | max | min | avg | max |
| 3.1 | 9.5 | 50.2 | 1.5 | 5.2 | 15.0 | 36 | 53 | 65 |

| Bulk density (g/cm³) | | | Porosity percent | | | Liquid limit | | |
|---|---|---|---|---|---|---|---|---|
| min | avg | max | min | avg | max | min | avg | max |
| 1.66 | 1.75 | 1.91 | 49 | 59 | 64 | 40 | 56 | 65 |

| Plastic limit | | | Plasticity index | | | Liquidity index | | |
|---|---|---|---|---|---|---|---|---|
| min | avg | max | min | avg | max | min | avg | max |
| 21 | 26 | 30 | 18 | 30 | 36 | 0.50 | 0.90 | 1.14 |

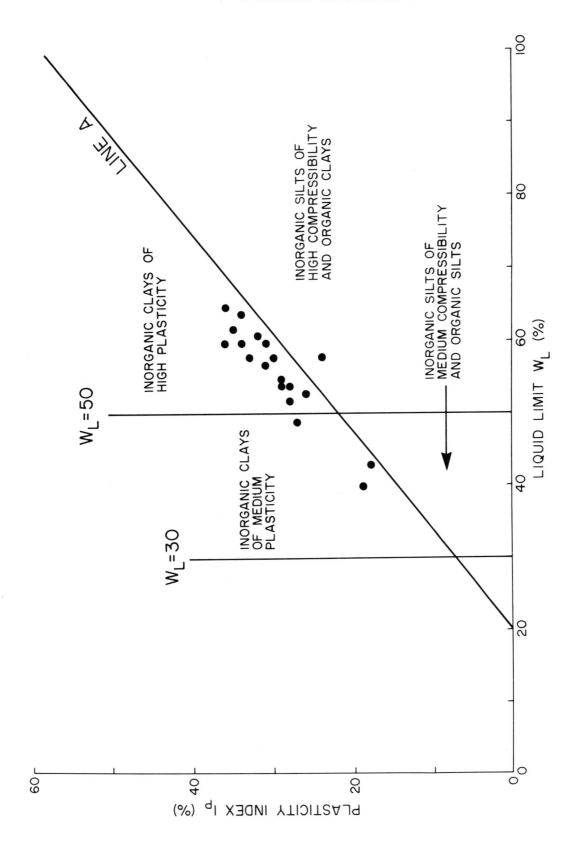

Figure 3. Classification of Georges Bank slope
sediment samples based on plasticity characteristics.

reported previously (for instance, McGregor and others, 1979).

Sensitivity, the ratio of natural to remolded shear strength of a sediment, is an important measure of the strength lost after disturbance, such as by shocks from earthquakes or other forms of loading. The mean sensitivity of these sediments is 5.2, which corresponds to an 84 percent reduction in strength (Table 1). According to the classification of Rosenquist (1953), these sediments, on the average, would be considered very sensitive, and they range from slightly sensitive to slightly quick. The most sensitive value (15.0) was associated with core PC-57, which also had the highest shear strength. Sediment in this core would lose more than 90 percent of its strength if it were shocked. Marine fine-grained sediments typically have sensitivities of 4 or less; thus, these sediments are slightly more sensitive than normal.

Index Properties. The combination of low water contents, low porosities, and high bulk densities is consistent with the abnormal shear strengths (Table 1). The extremes for these three variables are especially significant for surficial sediments. For example, the maximum water content of 65 percent is much lower than expected (typical values would generally be more than 90 percent), and a bulk density value of 1.91 g/cm$^3$ is far above the range of 1.50 to 1.60 g/cm$^3$ that is usually reported from surficial sediments. Relatively coarse grain sizes could force the typical values toward these extremes and, in fact, Keller and others (1979) reported that some sediments in this general area have significant sand contents. However, the unusual values reported here could also be attributed to the exhumation of once-buried, and thus more compacted, sediment. Size analyses from these cores are not yet available to provide further information on the relative effects of texture and overconsolidation. It is noteworthy, though, that the cores taken from apparent slump scars have the lowest water content, lowest porosity, and highest bulk density values.

Grain specific gravity, measured on 16 samples, averaged 2.70. This value is typical of fine-grained terrigenous sediment and is in accord with the value of 2.71 reported for the New England slope cores recovered by Keller and others (1979).

The plasticity data, which here include liquid and plastic limit, plasticity index (liquid limit minus plastic limit), and liquidity index (the ratio of natural water content minus liquid limit to plasticity index), provide a means for classifying sediments. One way this classification is accomplished is by using the plasticity chart devised by Casagrande (1948). The chart is divided into fields that embrace the different plasticity characteristics of various sediment types. Figure 3 is the plot of the samples from this study on such a chart. Note the fairly tight cluster that is basically confined to one field: inorganic clays of high plasticity. Here, fine-grained sediment of relatively high strength (in comparison with soils of lower plasticity) is indicated. In addition, a common clay-mineral suite is implied. The values shown in Figure 3 are typical of many terrestrial soils and, in fact, are quite similar to those found in adjacent coastal areas. The plasticity data are summarized in Table 1.

The vertical profiles of liquidity index, as represented by the relationship between natural water content and liquid limit, are shown in Appendix I. Note that of the four plots, only one (PC-64) shows a water content at or above the liquid limit throughout its length. The other cores show only water contents above liquid limits in the upper few centimeters, if at all. This pattern is uncharacteristic of many surficial muds, which typically have water contents above their liquid limits in the upper few meters rather than centimeters. This situation is, however, compatible with the suggestion that once-buried sediment may be represented within these cores. The average liquidity index for the sediments is 0.90 (Table 1), which supports the above suggestion. Further, it implies that, on the average, these sediments would behave as a plastic if remolded (by an earthquake, for example) rather than as a liquid.

The plasticity data also have implications regarding consolidation state and the presence of cements. They are discussed elsewhere in this report.

Triaxial Testing. The textural and mineralogical implications of the index tests are supported by the results of the triaxial analyses. One of the most important variables in that regard is the angle of internal friction ($\emptyset'$). Determination of this angle for cores PC-1 and PC-2 yielded values of 22.6° and 27.2°, respectively. The latter value is typical of marine sediments and reflects, as do the plasticity data, the presence of fine-grained material having a standard mineralogy (that is, containing no exotic or rare clay minerals). The value of 22.6° for PC-1 is slightly lower than would normally be expected.

Cohesion ($c'$) is the strength of the sediments at zero effective stress, that is, the strength due to interparticle attraction alone. The values of 9.9 kPa for PC-1 and 7.4 kPa for PC-2 are typical for marine sediment of the type sampled.

The stress-strain relationships indicate failure at 8 percent - 10 percent strain in both samples. Failure at 5 percent - 15 percent strain is common for most fine sediments, and thus these samples are typical. Plastic failure (no discrete failure planes) took place in both cores.

Baltimore Canyon

Shear Strength. The widespread occurrence of discrete sand layers, variable sand percentages, and other lithologic inconsistencies observed during cursory core descriptions indicate a complex depositional environment, which is reflected in the strength profiles. In particular, variations in sand percentage contribute to the sawtooth nature of some of the plots. Such textural variations can greatly influence the strength even within a basically cohesive sediment. Despite these variations, the usual strength increase with depth is seen in most of the cores. A lack of strength increase with depth is not unusual in such short cores, and we are not surprised that this relationship was not apparent in all cores. Although strength usually increases as depth increases, absolute strength values and the rates of strength increase in the tested cores are quite variable. As examples, cores PC-46 and PC-53 have an initial low shear strength and increase gradually to a strength of about 6 kPa.

The low rate of increase and the low absolute values indicate that these cores are abnormally weak. In contrast, core PC-8 shows a rapid increase in strength to 18 kPa at 4 m. This sediment is stronger than would normally be expected despite the fact that its surface strength is comparable to that of the previously mentioned cores. Overall, the shear strengths of these sediments span values from below the limit of accurate measurement (less than 0.5 kPa) to 46.7 kPa, as shown in Table 2. The average value of

5.5 kPa is typical for cohesive surficial marine sediments. Also, the mean sensitivity of these sediments is about 6, which corresponds to an 86 percent reduction in strength after remolding. According to the aforementioned classification of Rosenquist (1953), these sediments, on average, would be considered very sensitive, and they range from insensitive to slightly quick; thus, like the Georges Bank sediments, these sediments are slightly more sensitive than normal.

Index Properties. The water content, bulk density, and porosity data shown in Table 2 would usually be considered incompatible with the reported shear strength data. In fact, they also differ markedly from the average values for the Mid-Atlantic Slope reported by Keller and others (1979), who found higher water contents and porosities, and lower bulk densities, than are shown in Table 2. These differences can be attributed to the presence of sand in our cores. Cohesion and void space are reduced as the percentage of sand increases and, therefore, strength, water content, and porosity decrease as bulk density increases. Thus, just as sand is responsible, in part, for some of the erratic strength profiles, it also may be responsible for the unusual combination of water content, bulk density, and porosity and shear strengths noted here. Because the results of the textural analyses on these cores

TABLE 2.  SUMMARY OF GEOTECHNICAL DATA FOR BALTIMORE CANYON

| Natural shear strength (kPa) | | | Sensitivity | | | Water content percent | | |
|-----|-----|-----|-----|-----|-----|-----|-----|-----|
| min | avg | max | min | avg | max | min | avg | max |
| --- | 5.5 | 46.7 | 1.0 | 6.0[1] | 13.8[1] | 26 | 58 | 119 |

| Bulk density ($g/cm^3$) | | | Porosity percent | | | Liquid limit | | |
|-----|-----|-----|-----|-----|-----|-----|-----|-----|
| min | avg | max | min | avg | max | min | avg | max |
| 1.44 | 1.73 | 2.06 | 41 | 60 | 76 | 21 | 48 | 91 |

| Plastic limit | | | Plasticity index | | | Liquidity index | | |
|-----|-----|-----|-----|-----|-----|-----|-----|-----|
| min | avg | max | min | avg | max | min | avg | max |
| 15 | 23 | 40 | 8 | 25 | 60 | 0.73 | 1.42 | 2.20 |

[1] Because many samples were too weak to measure after remolding, these values are minimums.

are not yet available, the influence of sands in the cores cannot be evaluated beyond the level that simple core description permits.

Grain specific gravity, measured on 62 samples, averaged 2.70. This value is typical of fine-grained terrigenous sediment and is identical to the value reported for the Mid-Atlantic Slope cores recovered by Keller and others (1979). The plasticity chart shown in Figure 4 is the plot of the plasticity data from this area. Note the spread of data points along Line A. This spread indicates that a wide variety of sediment types is represented by the cores. Specifically, the sediments have a low organic content and include sands, silts, and clays. The fields marked as inorganic clays of low or medium plasticity also include sandy and silty clays (Keller and others, 1979). Approximately half the samples from this study fall into those two categories. This tendency toward coarse grain sizes is also reflected in the data summary (Table 2), which shows liquid limit, plastic limit, and plasticity index values slightly below those of a sediment totally dominated by fines. Compared to typical values of many types of terrestrial soils, these plasticity data do not imply any anomalous sediment types or extraordinary conditions. The spread of the data on the plasticity chart indicates a complex depositional environment, but the area is characterized by sediments having a common range in texture and common mineralogy.

The textural variability again manifests itself in the plastic limit-liquid limit-water content plots (Appendix II) that show the changes in the three variables down the core. An increase in the percentage of coarser grain sizes is commonly mirrored by a decrease in both plastic and liquid limit (the change in liquid limit generally being the most striking) and in the plasticity (shown in the figures as the distance between the two limits). Most cores show this effect to some degree, and some cores, for example PC-40, possibly manifest multiple changes in textural properties.

The vertical profiles of liquidity index, represented by the relationship between natural water content and liquid limit, are also shown in Appendix II. An example of a profile typical of most surficial sediments is that of core PC-08. The water content is above the liquid limit in the upper part of core PC-08, then it falls below the liquid limit for the remainder of the core. Although typical for most surficial sediments, this relationship is not typical of most of the cores in this study. Throughout the length of most cores, water-content values consistently match or exceed liquid limits. The average liquidity index of 1.42 (Table 2) underscores this relationship. Thus, upon remolding from a shock or other mode of disturbance, these sediments would behave more as a liquid than as a plastic, a fact that has implications regarding slope stability. Further, these data also have implications regarding the consolidation state of the sediments. These are discussed in the section on slope stability.

TABLE 3. SUMMARY OF SELECTED TRIAXIAL DATA FOR BALTIMORE CANYON CORES

| Core | c´ (kPa) | Ø´ |
|------|----------|------|
| PC-39 | 7.8 | 25.2° |
| PC-40 | 4.0 | 26.0° |
| PC-43 | 8.7 | 29.9° |
| PC-44 | 7.4 | 27.5° |
| PC-45 | 2.7 | 29.1° |
| PC-46 | 2.2 | 24.1° |
| PC-52 | 4.8 | 27.5° |
| PC-53 | 1.9 | 22.0° |
| PC-54 | 5.5 | 21.5° |
| Average | 5.0 | 25.9° |

Triaxal Testing. The results of the triaxal tests are given in Table 3. These data do not reflect any unusual sediment characteristics, although the angle of internal friction (Ø´) is somewhat low for cores PC-53 and PC-54. For the other cores, the Ø´ values are typical of essentially fine-grained marine sediments. The highest value (29.9°) is associated with PC-43. As inferred from the plasticity data, this core has relatively coarse grain sizes in its lower part. The presence of coarse grains is compatible with the higher friction angle noted here because Ø´ tends to increase as grain size increases. The slightly lower values of 22.0° and 21.5° for cores PC-53 and PC-54 may also indicate a textural effect; in these cores, the low values of Ø may be related to finer grain sizes. A change to a smectite-dominated clay mineral suite may also be responsible for the low values.

Cohesion (c´) represents the strength of the sediment at zero effective stress, that is, the strength due to interparticle attraction alone. The values shown in Table 3 are typical of the sediments discussed thus far.

The stress-strain relationships of the samples indicate that failure occurs generally between 2 percent and 20 percent strain. This large spread reflects the variety of sediment present. Generally, strains above 5 percent are common for cohesive sediments, and plastic failure (that is, no discrete failure plane(s)) is typical. Most sediments sampled did fail at strains greater than 5 percent. A few samples reached failure at less than 5 percent strain, however, indicating a less plastic sediment.

SLOPE STABILITY

Georges Bank

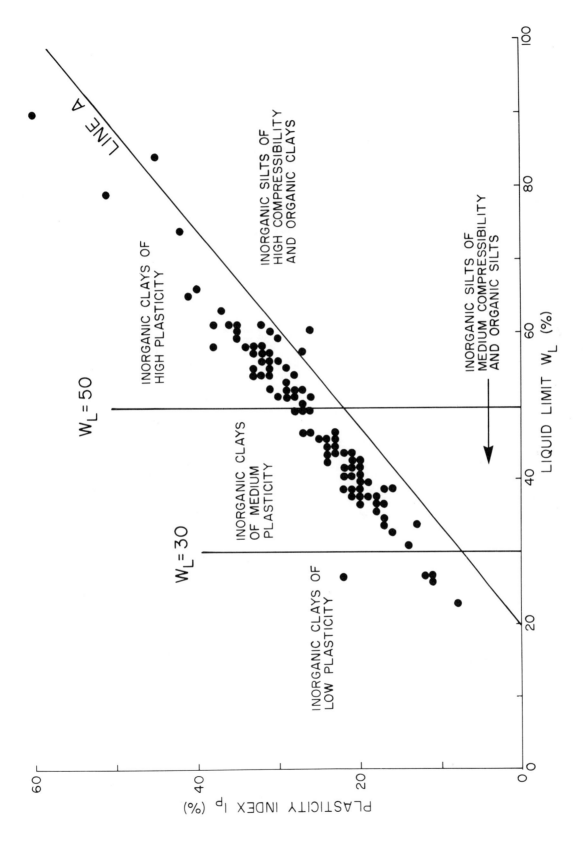

Figure 4. Classification of Baltimore Canyon slope sediment samples based on plasticity characteristics.

The mass-movement features tentatively identified on Georges Bank from seismic records were the focal points of the coring operation. The general purpose of sampling these sites was to verify that the features were the result of mass movement and were not depositional forms or artifacts of seismic profiling. If the samples were taken on scars left by mass movement, we would expect them to have a much greater shear strength than typical surface sediments. Cores PC-1, PC-57, PC-59, and PC-64 were targeted for scars, and PC-57 and PC-59 showed anomalously high shear strengths. Possibly PC-1 and PC-64 did not hit the intended target or, possibly, post-movement deposition prevented the piston core on the front reaching the scar. Whatever the reasons, the data do not show that a major strength anomaly (for instance, a scar) was sampled by cores PC-1 and PC-64. The other two cores showed shear strengths in the upper 0.5 m that were considerably in excess of normal expectations at this level. PC-57, in particular, which had a shear strength of 50 kPa near the top of the core, exemplifies what would be expected if a scar were cored.

Abnormally high strength at the surface is not unequivocal proof that mass movement has taken place; high strength may also be attributed to the presence of cements or to the removal of overburden by scour or other types of erosion. Criteria for recognizing the presence of cements in marine sediments have been developed by Nacci and others (1974). These criteria include liquidity indices greater than 1.5, sensitivities above a value of 4, and certain behavioral characteristics of the sediment during loading. As shown for PC-57 and PC-59, the natural water content is well below the liquid limit (the actual values of the liquidity index, as noted in Appendix I, range from 0.76 to 0.91 and 0.50 to 0.76, respectively). Further, if cements, and hence a rigid structure, were present, peak shearing resistance would typically develop early, at strains of less than 2 percent. However, strains of 8 percent to 10 percent were found in this study. These sensitivity values are in accord with the established criterion, and even though many of the values are marginal (Appendix I), the hypothesis that cements exist in these sediments cannot be ruled out on this basis. Their presence is unlikely because, as was discussed, other evidence is lacking.

Similarly, removal of material by scour seems unlikely. The site of PC-57, for example, is under 1,600 m of water in an intercanyon area where strong currents normally would not be expected. In fact, 0.5 m of rather soupy material is present above the stiff sediment, which implies an absence of scour, at least at present. The site of PC-59, which was taken farther upslope in 850 m of water, may be more vulnerable to scour, particularly at a time of lower sea level. This site, as was that of PC-57, is characterized by fine-grained sediment of low water content, and erosion would require a current of several tens of centimeters per second (Southard, 1974). Although no current data are available, current velocities of this magnitude would not be expected.

The anomalous shear strengths and index properties and the lack of significant evidence for cements or scour together suggest that some form of mass wasting took place at sites PC-57 and PC-59. Thus, the initial interpretations of the high-resolution seismic data that these sites are mass-movement scars is in accord with the geotechnical data.

By assuming that the overburden involved in the mass-wasting event was normally or underconsolidated, one may crudely estimate the thickness of the sediments involved in the mass wasting. In lieu of consolidation test results (not yet available), the formula of Skempton (1954) may be applied. It uses the plasticity index to predict the ratio of undrained shear strength to effective overburden ($S_u/\sigma'_v$) for cases of normal consolidation. Accordingly, these sediments should have a $S_u/\sigma'_v$ value of 0.22. Thus, the effective overburden values should exceed shear strength values by a factor of five. Assuming an average buoyant unit weight of 0.62 g/cm$^3$ (bulk density of 1.65 g/cm$^3$ minus seawater density of 1.03 g/cm$^3$), and using the strengths found at the two sites, we determined that approximately 10 m of overburden was removed from the PC-59 site and perhaps as much as 40 m from the PC-57 site. If substantial underconsolidation (and hence lower densities) were present in the original (pre-mass wasting) sediment column, these estimates could more than double.

The fact that mass movement has taken place in the past does not necessarily mean that it will take place in the future. In terms of hazard evaluations, the appropriate concern is the present stability of the slope. This concern may be addressed by using the infinite-slope method of stability analysis. The basic equation is:

$$F = (1 - u_e/\gamma'z \cos^2 \alpha) \tan \emptyset'/\tan \alpha$$

where F is the factor of safety against failure (< 1 is unstable, > 1 is stable), $u_e$ is the excess pore pressure (above hydrostatic), $\gamma'$ is the buoyant unit weight, z is the thickness of the sediment, $\alpha$ is the slope angle, and $\emptyset'$ is the angle of internal friction with respect to effective stress. In order to apply the equation, the excess pore pressure ($u_e$) must be known. For our cores, it is not known. A state of normal consolidation (that is zero excess pore pressure) must be assumed, therefore, which is a serious limitation to this type of analysis. The veracity of this assumption is discussed below. For a first approximation, however, the assumption is appropriate and instructional. If $u_e$ is zero, the equation may be rewritten as

$$F = \tan \emptyset'/\tan \alpha$$

Therefore, failure should take place only where the slope is equal to or greater than the angle of internal friction. For the two cores that are available for this type of analysis, the appropriate data are:

PC-1, $\alpha = 3°$, $\emptyset' = 22.6°$

PC-2, $\alpha = 2°$, $\emptyset' = 27.2°$

Thus, with factors of safety of 8 and 15, the surficial sediment on these sites should be stable.

The validity of assuming zero excess pore pressure can be judged by determining consolidation states. In particular, if a state of underconsolidation exists, excess pore pressure is implied and the calculated F values would be too high. For normally consolidated sediment, the strength to overburden ratio $(S_u/\sigma'_v)$ should be about 0.22, as mentioned above. At the bottom of PC-1 and PC-2, the values are 0.32 and 0.52, respectively. Thus, a state of overconsolidation is suggested by the data. The F values, therefore, err on the "safe" side, at least relative to positive excess pore pressure considerations.

In a similar fashion, consolidation states may be used to derive a general picture of slope stability and provide a crude check on the more formal infinite-slope method. Specifically, the $S_u/\sigma'_v$ values may be used to infer relative strength or weakness in a sediment column. Of the nine cores for which data are available, none have values less than 0.32, and values range up to 13. The sites represented by these cores are apparently overconsolidated to some degree. The masswasting scars, of course, are very much overconsolidated.

Evaluating the potential for a major mass-movement event (involving a thickness of several tens of meters, or more) is not possible because of the limited penetration of the piston corer. If rates of deposition were high at certain times in the past, however, as seems likely because slumps or slides apparently have taken place in the area, then thick sections of underconsolidated sediment could still exist. And, because of the associated excess pore pressures, marginally stable sediments may be present. Even given the likelihood that these excess pore pressures are dissipating under current conditions, the degree of dissipation, and hence the present-day stability of the slope, can only be surmised. Other factors, such as creep, interstitial gas, or occasional loading by earthquakes, further preclude a detailed slope-stability analysis at present.

Baltimore Canyon

The geotechnical evidence clearly suggests that the Baltimore Canyon area of the Continental Slope has been subjected to a complex and variable pattern of deposition in recent geologic time. It is an obvious hypothesis, therefore, that the mass-movement potential of the surficial sediments there is likewise variable. Again, using the infinite-slope model for stability analysis, we calculated F values. Table 4 shows the results of the calculations. The F values in all cases indicate that these sediments are inherently stable.

TABLE 4. FACTOR OF SAFETY, F, AGAINST MASS MOVEMENT FOR BALTIMORE CANYON CORE SITES [$F = \tan \emptyset'/\tan \alpha$]

| Core | $\alpha$ [1] | $\emptyset'$ [2] | F |
|------|------|------|---|
| PC-39 | 8° | 25.2° | 3.3 |
| PC-40 | 11° | 26.0° | 2.5 |
| PC-43 | 5° | 29.9° | 6.6 |
| PC-44 | 9° | 27.5° | 3.4 |
| PC-45 | 6° | 29.1° | 5.3 |
| PC-46 | 9° | 24.1° | 2.8 |
| PC-52 | 13° | 27.5° | 2.3 |
| PC-53 | 10° | 22.0° | 2.3 |
| PC-54 | 7° | 21.5° | 3.3 |

[1] Approximate slope angle.

[2] Angle of internal friction with respect to effective stress.

Thus, if they are normally consolidated or overconsolidated, mass movement would be unlikely under all but extreme circumstances. Analogous to the Georges Bank analyses, the absence of pore-pressure data for these sediments presents the one serious drawback in applying this type of analysis: a state of normal consolidation (no excess pore pressures) must be assumed. In particular, if a state of underconsolidation exists, excess pore pressure is implied, and the calculated F values would be too high. Consolidation state can also be used as an independent means for evaluating mass-movement potential because it can reflect the presence of abnormal strength or weakness in a sediment column. All other properties being equal, overconsolidation denotes a relatively high strength-stability under most circumstances, normal consolidation denotes standard strength-stability at typical slope angles and in the absence of outside forces, and underconsolidation denotes relative weakness and highest probability of sediment failure. Establishing a criterion for normal consolidation in the context of this study is the key step, because normal consolidation is the barometer for interpreting the other states.

By using the ratio of strength to overburden $(S_u/\sigma'_v)$, a state of normal consolidation may be recognized. Skempton (1954) has shown that, for normally consolidated sediment, the $S_u/\sigma'_v$ value is related to the plasticity index in the following manner:

$$S_u/\sigma'_v = 0.11 + 0.0037 I_p$$

If we use the plasticity indices from this study, an average value of 0.20 is predicted. The range is generally between 0.17 and 0.24. Thus, values within this range indicate normal consolidation, ratios below the minimum value indicate underconsolidation, and ratios above the maximum value indicate overconsolidation. Because the estimate of the $S_u/\sigma'_v$ range for normal consolidation is only approximate due to the effects of disturbance on the strength measurements ($S_u$ values), this criterion is restricted to qualitative assessment. In fact, this uncertainty about data accuracy prevents us from using the $S_u/\sigma'_v$ ratio in an undrained stability analysis.

The vane shear data ($S_u$) and computed overburden pressures (which were determined by summing buoyant bulk density values) were combined to get the $S_u/\sigma'_v$ values for the cores. Results of the comparison are shown in Table 5. The $S_u/\sigma'_v$ value for each core represents an average for the

TABLE 5. EVALUATION OF CONSOLIDATION STATES
FOR BALTIMORE CANYON CORE SITES

| Core | $S_u/\sigma'_v$[1] | Consolidation state[2] |
|------|------------|------------------------|
| PC-08 | 0.51 | Overconsolidated |
| PC-13 | 0.28 | Normally consolidated |
| PC-39 | 0.33 | Overconsolidated |
| PC-40 | 0.13 | Underconsolidated |
| PC-41 | 0.24 | Normally consolidated |
| PC-43 | 0.12 | Underconsolidated |
| PC-44 | 0.29 | Normally consolidated |
| PC-45 | 0.09 | Underconsolidated |
| PC-46 | 0.13 | Underconsolidated |
| PC-52 | 0.15 | Normally consolidated |
| PC-53 | 0.06 | Underconsolidated |

[1] $S_u$ = vane shear data = strength;

$\sigma'_v$ = overburden pressure.

[2] Determination criteria:

$S_u/\sigma'_v \leq 0.13$ indicates underconsolidation

$0.13 < S_u/\sigma'_v < 0.30$ indicates normal consolidation

$S_u/\sigma'_v \geq 0.30$ indicates overconsolidation

bottom meter or so. This comparison reduces the effects of the inconsistencies in lithology or undetected disturbance. Finally, the qualitative statements concerning consolidation state are intentionally conservative. That is, the core value had to be significantly below or above the stated range for normally consolidated sediment before a core was judged to be under- or overconsolidated. Significance was defined arbitrarily as more than

a 25 percent departure from the values of the end members of the range; thus, a value of 0.13 or less signified underconsolidation and a value of 0.30 or more signified overconsolidation. The analysis (Table 5) indicates that the expected variability of consolidation states is present. Of particular interest, however, is the possibility that five cores may be underconsolidated. These are PC-40, PC-43, PC-45, PC-46, and PC-53. The sites of these cores may be more vulnerable to failure than the other sites, at least in the upper few meters.

Skempton (1970) has shown that the relationship of liquidity index to overburden pressure may also be used to judge consolidation state. At the overburden pressure presumed for these cores, a liquidity index greater than 1.0 would indicate possible underconsolidation. This criterion was met by each of the five cores previously labeled as being underconsolidated. Accordingly, the factor of safety for these cores shown in Table 4 is too high.

In summary, the slope-stability and consolidation analyses suggest that the surficial sediments in the study area are essentially stable, although some sites may be marginally so. The fact that geophysical evidence indicates the absence of past large mass-movement events (Robb and others, 1981) may imply that the sediments, even during the periods of probable relatively rapid deposition, never reached a critical value of F. This past stability does not necessarily bear on the central question of present-day stability but, since we have assumed low rates of deposition for the past several thousand years, it does suggest that mass movement did not take place during the time that the slope would have been the most vulnerable to failure. Further, given lower rates of deposition and time, the excess pore pressures would tend to dissipate and the sediments would become increasingly stable. Until more evidence becomes available, as from a deep-drilling program in this area and Georges Bank, the exact condition of the sediments of this study must remain unknown.

CONCLUSIONS

Georges Bank

Analyses completed to date suggest the following tentative conclusions:

(1)  The surficial sediments on the Continental Slope off Georges Bank tend to be highly plastic, inorganic silts and clays. No exotic minerals or abnormal textures were indicated by the geotechnical data.

(2)  Measurements of shear strength and index properties and inferences concerning consolidation states suggest that the sites of cores PC-57 and PC-9 were once buried under a considerable amount of overburden. They may be mass-movement

scars. This finding is in accord with interpretations of high-resolution seismic-reflection data.

(3) Slope-stability analyses and indirect assessments of consolidation states suggest that the surficial sediments cored are stable with respect to mass movement.

Baltimore Canyon

The following conclusions are based on analyses completed to date:

(1) Erratic strength profiles and variability of index properties imply that the Baltimore Canyon Continental Slope is a complex depositional environment. The sediments are essentially inorganic sands, silts, and clays and range from low to high plasticity. No exotic minerals or abnormal textures were indicated by the geotechnical data.

(2) Slope-stability analyses without pore-pressure data indicate that the surficial sediments represented by the cores are stable. However, index properties and assessments of consolidation state suggest that excess pore pressures may exist in some areas and, thus, these areas may be only marginally stable. This conclusion applies to the sites of PC-40, PC-43, PC-45, PC-46, and PC-53.

(3) All possible consolidation states are represented by the cores, as judged from the strength and plasticity data.

REFERENCES

Aaron, J.M., Butman, B., Bothner, M.H., and Sylwester, R.E., 1980, Map showing environmental conditions relating to potential geologic hazards on the United States northeastern Atlantic Continental Margin: U.S. Geological Survey Miscellaneous Field Studies Map MF 1193.

American Society for Testing and Materials, 1977, 1977 Annual Book of ASTM Standards, Part 19, Natural Building Stones; Soil and Rock; Peats, Mosses, and Humus: Philadelphia, American Society for Testing and Materials, 494 p.

Bennett, R.H., Lambert, D.N., and Hulbert, M.H., 1977, Geotechnical properties of a submarine slide area on the U.S. Continental Slope northeast of Wilmington Canyon: Marine Geotechnology, v. 2, p. 245-261.

Bishop, A.W., and Henkel, D.J., 1957, The measurement of soil properties in the triaxial test: London, Edward Arnold, 225 p.

Booth, J.S., 1979, Recent history of mass wasting on the upper Continental Slope, northern Gulf of Mexico, as interpreted from the consolidation states of the sediment, in Pilkey, O. H., and Doyle, L. J., eds., Geology of Continental Slopes: Society of Economic Paleontologists and Mineralogists Special Publication 27, p. 153-164.

Booth, J.S., Farrow, R.A., and Rice, T.L., 1981a, Geotechnical properties and slope stability analysis of surficial sediments on the Baltimore Canyon Continental Slope: U.S. Geological Survey Open-File Report 81-733, 257 p.

Booth, J.S., Farrow, R.A., and Rice, T.L., 1981b, Geotechnical properties and slope stability analysis of surficial sediment on the Georges Bank Continental Slope: U.S. Geological Survey Open-File Report 81-566, 88 p.

Casagrande, A., 1948, Classification and identification of soils: American Society of Civil Engineers Transactions, v. 113, p 901-991.

Doyle, L.J., Pilkey, O.H., and Woo, C.C., 1979, Sedimentation on the eastern United States Continental Slope, in Doyle, L.J., and Pilkey, O.H., eds., Geology of Continental Slopes: Society of Economic Paleontologists and Mineralogists Special Publication 27, p. 119-129.

Embley, R.W., and Jacobi, R., 1977, Distribution and morphology of large submarine sediment slides and slumps on Atlantic continental margins: Marine Geotechnology, v. 2, p 205-228.

Emery, K.O., and Uchupi, E., 1972, Western North Atlantic Ocean--topography, rocks, structure, water, life, and sediments: American Association of Petroleum Geologists Memoir 17, 532 p.

Hathaway, J.C., Schlee, J.S., Poag, C.W., Valentine, P.C., Weed, E.G.A., Bothner, M.H., Kohout, F.A., Manheim, F.T., Schoen, R., Miller, R.E., and Schultz, D.M., 1976, Preliminary summary of the 1976 Atlantic Margin Coring Project of the U.S. Geological Survey: U.S. Geological Survey Open-File Report 76-844, 218 p.

Keller, G.H., Lambert, D.N., and Bennett, R.H., 1979, Geotechnical properties of Continental Slope deposits--Cape Hatteras to Hydrographer Canyon, in Doyle, L.J., and Pilkey, O.H., eds., Geology of Continental Slopes: Society of Economic Paleontologists and Mineralogists Special Publication 27, 131-151.

McGregor, B.A., 1977, Geophysical assessment of submarine slide northeast of Wilmington

Canyon: Marine Geotechnology, v. 2, p. 229-244.

McGregor, B.A., 1979, Variation in bottom processes along the U.S. Atlantic continental margin, in Watkins, J.S., Montadert, L., and Dickerson, P.W., eds., Geological and geophysical investigations of continental margins: American Association of Petroleum Geologists Memoir 29, p. 139-149.

McGregor, B.A., Bennett, R.H., and Lambert, D.N., 1979, Bottom processes, morphology, and geotechnical properties of the Continental Slope south of Baltimore Canyon: Applied Ocean Research, v. 1, p. 177-187.

McIlvaine, J.C., and Ross, D.A., 1979, Sedimentary processes on the Continental Slope of New England: Journal of Sedimentary Petrology, v. 49, p. 563-574.

Nacci, V.A., Kelly, W.E., Wang, M.C., and Demars, K.R., 1974, Strength and stress-strain characteristics of cemented deep-sea sediments, in Inderbitzen, A. L. ed., Deep-sea sediments: physical and mechanical properties: Marine Science, v. 2, p. 129-150.

Robb, J.M., Hampson, J.C., Kirby, J.R., and Twichell, D.C., 1981, Geology and potential hazards of the Continental Slope between Lindenkohl and South Toms Canyons, offshore

Mid-Atlantic United States: U.S. Geological Survey Open-File Report 81-600.

Rosenquist, I.Th., 1953, Considerations on the sensitivity of Norwegian quick clays: Geotechnique, v. 3, p. 195-200.

Sangrey, D.A., Booth, J.S., and Hathaway, J.C., 1979, The Atlantic margin coring project (AMCOR) of the USGS--geotechnical observations: International Conference on Port and Ocean Engineering under Arctic Conditions, 5th, Trondheim, 1979, Proceedings, p. 951-961.

Skempton, A.W., 1954, Discussion of the structure of inorganic soil: Journal of Soil Mechanics and Foundations Division, American Society of Civil Engineers, v. 80, no. 478, p. 19-22.

Skempton, A.W., 1970, The consolidation of clays by gravitation compaction: Geological society of London Quarterly Journal, v. 125, p. 373-411.

Southard, J.B., 1974, Erodibility of fine abyssal sediment, in Inderbitzen, A. L., ed., Deep-sea sediments: physical and mechanical properties: Marine Science, v. 2, p. 367-379.

Uchupi, E., 1967, Slumping of the continental margin southeast of Long Island, New York: Deep-Sea Research, v. 14, p. 635-639.

GEOTECHNOLOGY IN MASSACHUSETTS

Booth, Rice, Farrow

A P P E N D I X   I

GEORGES BANK REGION
Shear Strength Data Tables
Strength Profiles
Index Properties

Shear Strength Data

GEORGES BANK SAMPLES

[ND, no data--sample too weak for strength measurement]

| Core no. (length) | Penetration (m) | Shear strength (natural) (kPa) | Shear strength (remolded) (kPa) | Sensitivity |
|---|---|---|---|---|
| PC-1 (5.20 m) | 0.50 | 8.2 | 1.5 | 5.5 |
| | 1.00 | 5.9 | 1.0 | 5.9 |
| | 1.50 | 7.8 | 1.2 | 6.2 |
| | 2.00 | 9.2 | 1.2 | 7.3 |
| | 2.65 | 8.8 | 1.2 | 7.0 |
| | 3.00 | 9.4 | 1.5 | 6.2 |
| | 3.50 | 8.9 | 1.4 | 6.4 |
| | 4.50 | 10.4 | 1.8 | 5.9 |
| PC-2 (3.13 m) | .10 | 5.6 | 1.8 | 3.1 |
| | .50 | 5.4 | 1.2 | 4.4 |
| | 1.00 | 6.5 | .9 | 7.4 |
| | 1.80 | 7.2 | .9 | 8.2 |
| | 2.00 | 7.3 | 1.2 | 6.2 |
| | 2.50 | 9.3 | 1.2 | 7.4 |
| PC-57 (1.00 m) | .07 | 4.4 | ND | ---- |
| | .45 | 9.4 | .6 | 15.0 |
| | .53 | 50.2 | 4.5 | 11.1 |
| PC-59 (1.71 m) | .25 | 13.4 | 2.7 | 5.0 |
| | .50 | 15.6 | 1.8 | 8.6 |
| | .88 | 14.8 | 2.1 | 6.9 |
| PC-60 (1.91 m) | 1.02 | 8.3 | 2.4 | 3.5 |
| PC-62 (0.96 m) | .15 | 12.3 | 2.8 | 4.5 |
| | .50 | 9.2 | 3.3 | 2.8 |
| PC-64 (3.81 m) | .60 | 4.4 | 1.2 | 3.5 |
| | 1.00 | 7.1 | ND | ---- |
| | 1.50 | 4.8 | 1.1 | 4.2 |
| | 2.00 | 6.0 | 2.3 | 2.6 |
| | 2.50 | 5.8 | 1.5 | 3.8 |
| | 3.00 | 6.9 | 3.6 | 1.9 |
| PC-67 (2.16 m) | 1.00 | 5.1 | 2.7 | 1.9 |
| | 1.40 | 3.1 | 3.1 | 1.5 |
| PC-68 (2.45 m) | .14 | 9.7 | 3.5 | 2.8 |
| | .50 | 12.8 | 4.3 | 3.0 |
| | 1.13 | 12.2 | 5.2 | 2.3 |
| | 1.50 | 9.0 | 4.5 | 2.0 |
| | 1.80 | 8.1 | 4.4 | 1.8 |

GEORGES BANK

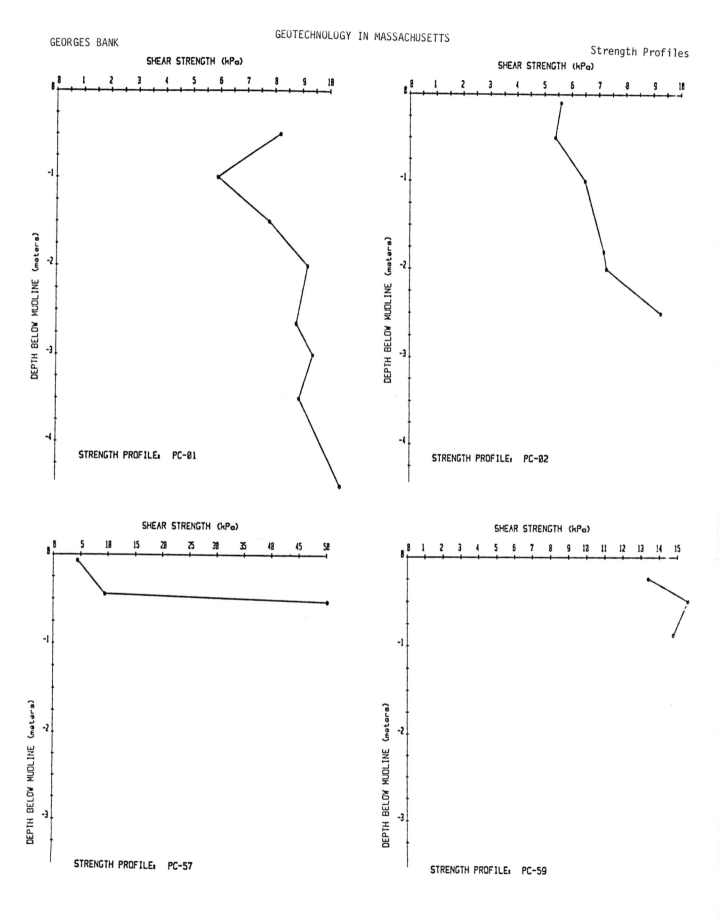

STRENGTH PROFILE: PC-01

STRENGTH PROFILE: PC-02

STRENGTH PROFILE: PC-57

STRENGTH PROFILE: PC-59

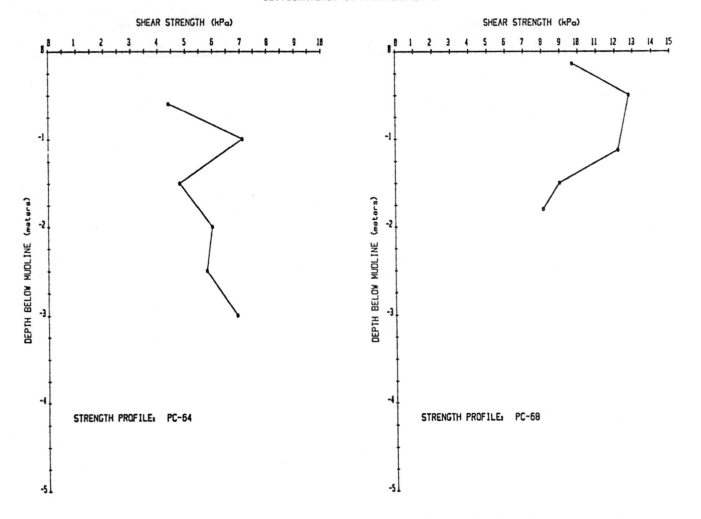

## Index Properties

### GEORGES BANK SAMPLES

| Core no. (length) | Penetration (m) | Water content (percent) | Bulk density (g/cm³) | Porosity | Liquid limit | Plastic limit | Plasticity index | Liquidity index |
|---|---|---|---|---|---|---|---|---|
| PC-57 (1.00 m) | 0.07 | 79 | 1.58 | 68 | 84 | 30 | 54 | .91 |
| | .45 | 62 | 1.67 | 62 | 70 | 28 | 41 | .84 |
| | .53 | 49 | 1.76 | 57 | 54 | 33 | 21 | .76 |
| PC-59 (1.71 m) | .25 | 40 | 1.87 | 52 | 58 | 28 | 30 | .50 |
| | .50 | 40 | 1.87 | 52 | 49 | 22 | 27 | .65 |
| | .88 | 36 | 1.91 | 49 | 40 | 21 | 19 | .76 |
| | 1.37 | 51 | 1.76 | 58 | 62 | 27 | 35 | .69 |
| PC-60 (1.91 m) | .18 | 57 | 1.72 | 61 | 64 | 30 | 34 | .79 |
| | 1.02 | 59 | 1.70 | 61 | 58 | 28 | 30 | 1.03 |
| PC-62 (0.96 m) | .15 | 52 | 1.75 | 58 | -- | -- | -- | ---- |
| | .50 | 42 | 1.85 | 53 | 43 | 25 | 18 | .93 |
| PC-64 (3.81 m)? | .60 | 62 | 1.68 | 63 | 61 | 29 | 32 | 1.04 |
| | 1.00 | 65 | 1.66 | 64 | 60 | 26 | 34 | 1.14 |
| | 1.50 | 59 | 1.70 | 61 | 55 | 26 | 29 | 1.12 |
| | 2.00 | 54 | 1.74 | 59 | 52 | 26 | 26 | 1.04 |
| | 2.50 | 57 | 1.72 | 60 | 54 | 26 | 28 | 1.08 |
| | 3.00 | 54 | 1.74 | 59 | 57 | 26 | 31 | .90 |
| | 3.30 | 58 | 1.71 | 61 | 60 | 29 | 31 | .81 |
| PC-67 (2.16 m) | 1.00 | 58 | 1.71 | 61 | 58 | 28 | 30 | 1.02 |
| | 1.40 | 59 | 1.70 | 61 | 65 | 29 | 36 | .85 |
| | 1.65 | 56 | 1.72 | 60 | 58 | 25 | 33 | .94 |
| PC-68 (2.45 m) | .14 | 58 | 1.71 | 61 | 55 | 26 | 29 | 1.13 |
| | .50 | 50 | 1.77 | 58 | 54 | 26 | 28 | .86 |
| | 1.13 | 50 | 1.77 | 57 | 54 | 26 | 28 | .86 |
| | 1.50 | 50 | 1.77 | 58 | 53 | 27 | 26 | .91 |
| | 1.80 | -- | ---- | -- | -- | -- | -- | ---- |
| | 2.11 | 54 | 1.74 | 60 | 60 | 24 | 36 | .83 |

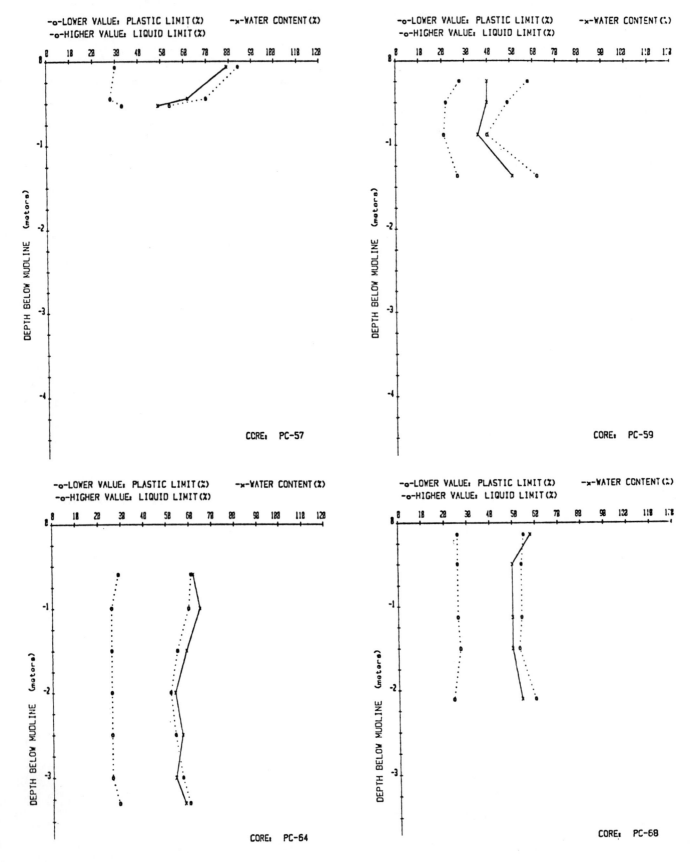

A P P E N D I X   I I

BALTIMORE CANYON REGION
Shear Strength Data Tables
Strength Profiles
Index Properties

Shear Strength Data

BALTIMORE CANYON SAMPLES

[ND, no data--sample too weak for strength measurement.  D, disturbed sample]

| Core no. (length) | Penetration (m) | Shear strength (natural) (kPa) | Shear strength (remolded) (kPa) | Sensitivity |
|---|---|---|---|---|
| PC-8 (5.85 m) | 0.25 | ND | ND | ---- |
| | .50 | 0.8 | ND | ---- |
| | 1.00 | 2.7 | 0.6 | 4.8 |
| | 1.50 | ND | ND | ---- |
| | 1.75 | 8.2 | 1.3 | 6.2 |
| | 2.00 | 7.7 | 1.1 | 6.8 |
| | 2.15 | 8.6 | .6 | 13.8 |
| | 2.50 | 13.6 | 3.1 | 4.3 |
| | 2.75 | 13.2 | 2.4 | 5.5 |
| | 3.50 | 15.0 | 1.9 | 7.7 |
| | 4.00 | 17.1 | 2.3 | 7.6 |
| | 4.25 | 11.9 | 2.0 | 5.9 |
| | 5.00 | 14.1 | 3.5 | 3.8 |
| | 5.50 | D | 2.4 | ---- |
| PC-13 (5.32 m) | .32 | 5.5 | 1.1 | 4.9 |
| | .50 | 6.8 | .8 | 8.3 |
| | 1.00 | 6.3 | 1.2 | 5.0 |
| | 1.50 | 6.3 | .6 | 10.1 |
| | 2.00 | 7.5 | .6 | 12.0 |
| | 2.50 | 8.4 | 1.32 | 6.4 |
| | 3.00 | 6.6 | 1.7 | 3.9 |
| | 3.50 | 6.8 | 1.1 | 6.0 |
| | 4.50 | 10.5 | 1.4 | 7.6 |
| | 5.00 | 8.3 | 1.5 | 5.5 |
| | 5.25 | D | 1.8 | ---- |
| PC-39 (5.72 m) | .25 | 1.4 | ND | ---- |
| | .50 | 1.9 | .7 | 2.8 |
| | 1.00 | 3.9 | ND | ---- |
| | 1.50 | 4.1 | .8 | 5.5 |
| | 2.00 | 2.5 | ND | ---- |
| | 2.50 | 4.1 | ND | ---- |
| | 2.70 | 4.1 | ND | ---- |
| | 3.00 | 5.7 | 1.0 | 5.7 |
| | 3.50 | 6.5 | 1.2 | 5.2 |
| | 3.90 | 11.8 | 1.7 | 7.0 |
| PC-40 (7.08 m) | 0.10 | ND | ND | ---- |
| | .50 | ND | ND | ---- |
| | 1.00 | ND | ND | ---- |
| | 1.50 | 2.8 | ND | ---- |
| | 2.00 | 2.0 | ND | ---- |
| | 2.47 | 3.4 | ND | ---- |
| | 3.00 | 3.1 | ND | ---- |
| | 3.50 | 2.3 | ND | ---- |
| | 3.96 | 3.6 | ND | ---- |
| | 4.50 | 4.8 | .6 | 7.6 |
| | 5.00 | 4.8 | ND | ---- |
| | 6.00 | 4.6 | .8 | 6.2 |
| | 6.32 | 6.0 | .6 | 9.6 |

Shear-Strength Data

BALTIMORE CANYON SAMPLES--Continued

| Core no. (length) | Penetration (m) | Shear strength (natural) (kPa) | Shear strength (remolded) (kPa) | Sensitivity |
|---|---|---|---|---|
| PC-41 (4.54 m) | .15 | 1.2 | ND | ---- |
| | .50 | 5.4 | 1.0 | 5.4 |
| | 1.00 | 3.6 | .5 | 7.2 |
| | 1.85 | 6.8 | 1.1 | 6.0 |
| | 2.35 | 3.4 | 1.1 | 3.0 |
| | 2.85 | 5.1 | 1.2 | 4.3 |
| | 3.20 | 6.3 | 1.5 | 4.2 |
| | 3.50 | 8.0 | .8 | 10.7 |
| | 3.90 | 5.3 | ND | ---- |
| PC-43 (9.42 m) | .50 | 2.8 | ND | ---- |
| | 1.00 | 2.6 | ND | ---- |
| | 1.50 | 2.9 | ND | ---- |
| | 2.00 | 3.3 | ND | ---- |
| | 2.50 | 4.0 | .7 | 5.7 |
| | 3.00 | 3.8 | .7 | 5.5 |
| | 3.25 | 6.3 | .8 | 8.3 |
| | 3.50 | 2.1 | ND | ---- |
| | 4.00 | 4.9 | ND | ---- |
| | 4.50 | 6.4 | 1.4 | 4.6 |
| | 4.70 | 4.6 | .9 | 5.3 |
| | 5.00 | 4.4 | ND | ---- |
| | 5.50 | 9.8 | ND | ---- |
| | 6.00 | 3.5 | ND | ---- |
| | 6.50 | 4.1 | ND | ---- |
| | 7.00 | 5.5 | .6 | 9.8 |
| | 7.40 | 6.6 | .8 | 8.2 |
| | 8.00 | 6.3 | .8 | 8.3 |
| | 8.50 | 7.8 | .8 | 9.6 |
| PC-44 (4.50 m) | 0.16 | 6.6 | 1.0 | 6.6 |
| | .50 | 5.9 | 1.2 | 4.7 |
| | 1.00 | 6.8 | 1.4 | 4.9 |
| | 1.53 | 8.3 | 1.2 | 6.6 |
| | 2.00 | 10.3 | 1.4 | 7.5 |
| | 2.47 | 9.0 | .9 | 10.3 |
| | 3.50 | 7.2 | 1.3 | 5.7 |
| | 3.85 | 4.8 | .9 | 5.1 |
| PC-45 (6.97 m) | .41 | 1.8 | ND | ---- |
| | 1.00 | ND | --- | ---- |
| | 1.50 | 2.1 | ND | ---- |
| | 2.00 | 2.1 | ND | ---- |
| | 2.50 | 3.4 | ND | ---- |
| | 3.00 | 4.8 | ND | ---- |
| | 3.50 | 12.8 | 2.5 | 5.1 |
| | 4.00 | 4.6 | ND | ---- |
| | 4.50 | 6.5 | .9 | 7.0 |
| | 4.90 | 3.1 | 1.1 | 2.8 |
| | 5.60 | 4.1 | 1.2 | 3.2 |
| | 6.00 | 3.8 | 1.8 | 2.1 |
| | 6.35 | 3.0 | 1.4 | 2.2 |

Shear-Strength Data

BALTIMORE CANYON SAMPLES--Continued

| Core no. (length) | Penetration (m) | Shear strength (natural) (kPa) | Shear strength (remolded) (kPa) | Sensitivity |
|---|---|---|---|---|
| PC-46 (7.05 m) | .50 | 1.1 | ND | ---- |
| | 1.00 | 2.0 | ND | ---- |
| | 1.50 | 1.2 | ND | ---- |
| | 2.00 | 2.1 | ND | ---- |
| | 2.50 | 3.4 | ND | ---- |
| | 3.00 | 6.6 | ND | ---- |
| | 3.50 | 3.9 | ND | ---- |
| | 4.00 | 4.3 | ND | ---- |
| | 4.50 | 5.2 | ND | ---- |
| | 5.00 | 4.2 | ND | ---- |
| | 5.50 | 5.9 | ND | ---- |
| | 5.70 | 5.0 | .8 | 6.7 |
| | 6.00 | 5.3 | .8 | 7.0 |
| | 6.45 | 5.6 | ND | ---- |
| PC-51 (0.17 m) | 0.05 | 15.5 | ---- | ---- |
| | .12 | 46.7 | ---- | ---- |
| PC-52 (6.73 m) | .50 | 3.1 | ND | ---- |
| | 1.00 | 3.3 | ND | ---- |
| | 1.50 | 4.6 | ND | ---- |
| | 2.00 | 4.8 | ND | ---- |
| | 2.50 | 4.3 | 0.6 | 6.9 |
| | 3.00 | 7.3 | 2.1 | 3.4 |
| | 4.00 | 6.1 | .8 | 8.2 |
| | 4.50 | 5.4 | 1.9 | 2.9 |
| | 5.00 | 6.8 | 1.6 | 4.3 |
| | 5.50 | 5.6 | .9 | 6.4 |
| | 6.00 | 3.8 | 1.2 | 3.0 |
| PC-53 (10.06 m) | .50 | 5.4 | .9 | 5.7 |
| | 1.10 | 1.7 | ND | ---- |
| | 1.50 | 1.9 | .6 | 3.0 |
| | 2.00 | 1.9 | ND | ---- |
| | 2.58 | 2.6 | .9 | 3.0 |
| | 3.00 | 2.1 | .6 | 3.4 |
| | 3.50 | 3.9 | .9 | 4.4 |
| | 3.91 | 1.9 | .8 | 2.5 |
| | 4.50 | 5.3 | .9 | 5.6 |
| | 5.00 | 4.9 | ND | ---- |
| | 5.60 | 5.7 | ND | ---- |
| | 6.00 | 5.5 | .9 | 5.9 |
| | 6.50 | 5.8 | ND | ---- |
| | 7.00 | 5.6 | ND | ---- |
| | 7.50 | 6.6 | .9 | 7.1 |
| | 8.00 | 5.0 | .9 | 5.7 |
| | 9.00 | D | 1.1 | ---- |
| | 9.40 | D | 1.1 | ---- |
| PC-54 (8.58 m) | .20 | 1.9 | 1.9 | 1.00 |
| | .55 | 2.7 | .6 | 4.30 |
| | 1.15 | 1.5 | ND | ---- |
| | 1.50 | 1.3 | ND | ---- |
| | 2.00 | .9 | ND | ---- |

## Shear-Strength Data

### BALTIMORE CANYON SAMPLES--Continued

| Core no. (length) | Penetration (m) | Shear strength (natural) (kPa) | Shear strength (remolded) (kPa) | Sensitivity |
|---|---|---|---|---|
| PC-54, continued (8.58 m) | 2.43 | 3.4 | ND | ---- |
| | 3.00 | 3.1 | ND | ---- |
| | 3.50 | 3.8 | ND | ---- |
| | 3.90 | 3.6 | ND | ---- |
| | 4.50 | 3.5 | ND | ---- |
| | 5.00 | 4.8 | ND | ---- |
| | 5.50 | 5.8 | ND | ---- |
| | 6.00 | 6.8 | ND | ---- |
| | 6.50 | 9.5 | ND | ---- |
| | 7.00 | 7.7 | .8 | 10.3 |
| | 7.50 | 8.6 | 1.1 | 8.0 |

BALTIMORE CANYON

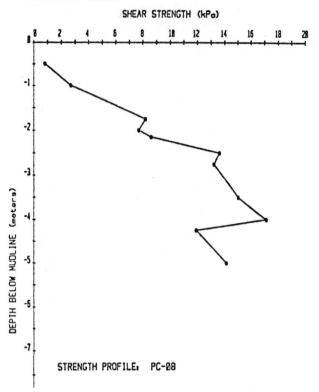

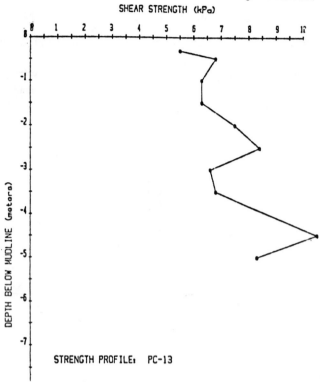

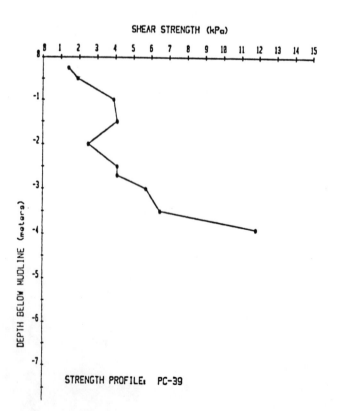

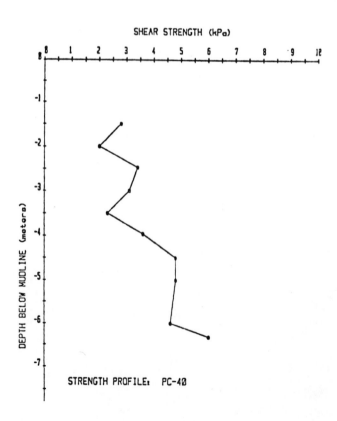

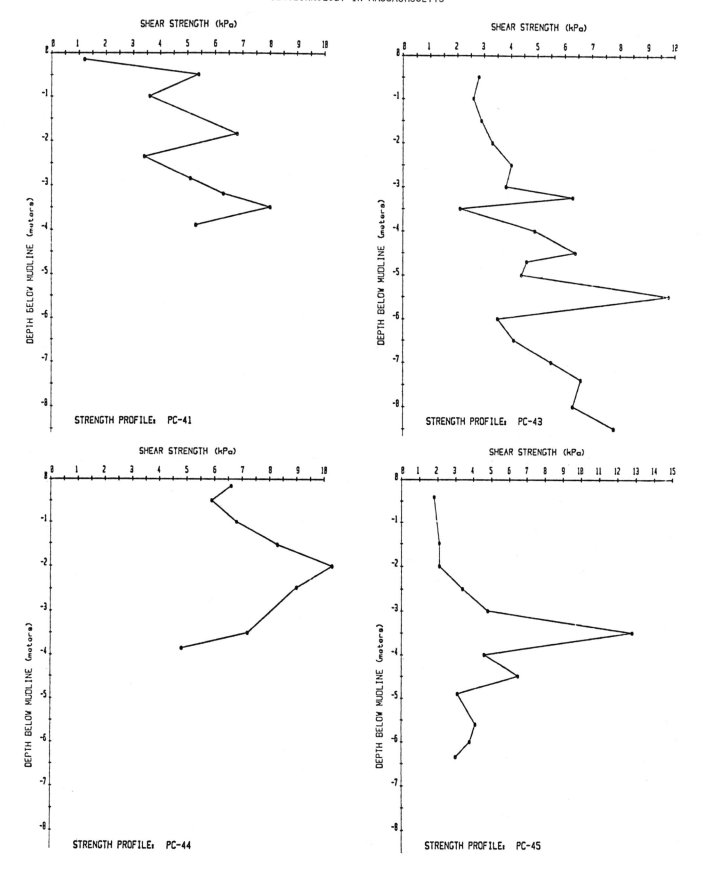

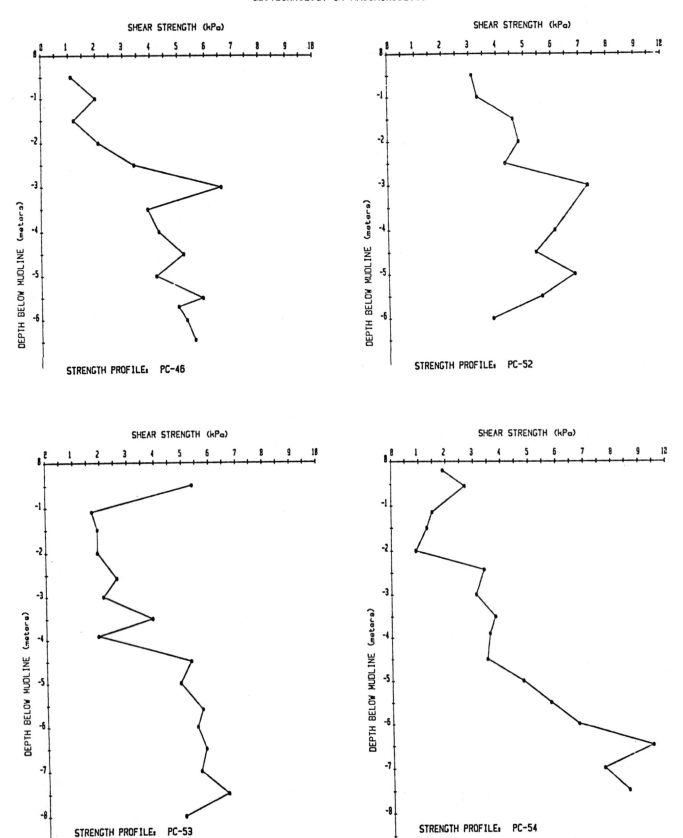

## Index Properties

### BALTIMORE CANYON SAMPLES

| Core no. (length) | Penetration (m) | Water content (percent) | Bulk density (g/cm³) | Porosity | Liquid limit | Plastic limit | Plasticity index | Liquidity index |
|---|---|---|---|---|---|---|---|---|
| PC-8 (5.85 m) | 0.25 | 119 | 1.44 | 76 | 85 | 40 | 45 | 1.76 |
| | .50 | 106 | 1.48 | 74 | -- | -- | -- | ---- |
| | 1.00 | 93 | 1.52 | 71 | 75 | 33 | 42 | 1.43 |
| | 1.50 | 66 | 1.66 | 64 | -- | -- | -- | ---- |
| | 1.75 | 57 | 1.72 | 61 | 55 | 27 | 28 | 1.07 |
| | 2.00 | 52 | 1.75 | 59 | 47 | 21 | 26 | 1.19 |
| | 2.15 | 56 | 1.72 | 61 | 51 | 24 | 27 | 1.19 |
| | 2.50 | 52 | 1.75 | 59 | 59 | 26 | 33 | .79 |
| | 2.75 | 52 | 1.75 | 59 | -- | -- | -- | ---- |
| | 3.50 | 51 | 1.76 | 58 | 57 | 27 | 30 | .80 |
| | 4.00 | 50 | 1.77 | 58 | 58 | 26 | 32 | .75 |
| | 4.25 | 50 | 1.77 | 58 | 59 | 26 | 33 | .73 |
| | 5.00 | 50 | 1.77 | 58 | -- | -- | -- | ---- |
| | 5.50 | 53 | 1.75 | 59 | 57 | 26 | 31 | .87 |
| PC-13 (5.32 m) | .32 | 63 | 1.67 | 63 | -- | -- | -- | ---- |
| | .50 | 36 | 1.91 | 50 | 27 | 15 | 12 | 1.75 |
| | 1.00 | 45 | 1.81 | 55 | 39 | 19 | 20 | 1.30 |
| | 1.50 | 41 | 1.86 | 53 | 39 | 19 | 20 | 1.10 |
| | 2.00 | 62 | 1.68 | 63 | 59 | 25 | 34 | 1.09 |
| | 2.50 | 58 | 1.71 | 61 | 51 | 24 | 27 | 1.26 |
| | 3.00 | 61 | 1.69 | 62 | 55 | 24 | 31 | 1.19 |
| | 3.50 | 52 | 1.75 | 59 | 53 | 22 | 31 | .97 |
| | 4.50 | 59 | 1.70 | 62 | 57 | 26 | 31 | 1.06 |
| | 5.00 | 60 | 1.69 | 62 | 62 | 24 | 38 | .95 |
| | 5.25 | 65 | 1.66 | 64 | 60 | 25 | 35 | 1.14 |
| PC-39 (5.72 m) | .25 | 62 | 1.68 | 63 | -- | -- | -- | ---- |
| | .50 | 57 | 1.72 | 61 | 51 | 24 | 27 | 1.24 |
| | 1.00 | 58 | 1.71 | 61 | 55 | 23 | 32 | 1.09 |
| | 1.50 | 60 | 1.70 | 62 | 53 | 26 | 27 | 1.26 |
| | 2.00 | 60 | 1.70 | 62 | -- | -- | -- | ---- |
| | 2.50 | 57 | 1.72 | 61 | 52 | 26 | 26 | 1.19 |
| | 2.70 | 57 | 1.72 | 61 | 46 | 23 | 23 | 1.22 |
| | 3.00 | 43 | 1.85 | 54 | 45 | 21 | 24 | .92 |
| | 3.50 | 50 | 1.77 | 58 | -- | -- | -- | ---- |
| | 3.90 | 43 | 1.85 | 54 | 43 | 19 | 24 | 1.00 |
| | 4.79 | 47 | 1.81 | 56 | 44 | 23 | 21 | 1.14 |
| PC-40 (7.08 m) | 0.10 | 78 | 1.59 | 68 | 57 | 27 | 31 | 1.68 |
| | .50 | 77 | 1.60 | 68 | 54 | 25 | 29 | 1.79 |
| | 1.00 | 77 | 1.60 | 68 | 52 | 23 | 29 | 1.86 |
| | 1.50 | 60 | 1.70 | 62 | 43 | 22 | 21 | 1.81 |
| | 2.00 | 65 | 1.67 | 64 | -- | -- | -- | ---- |
| | 2.47 | 68 | 1.65 | 65 | 46 | 22 | 24 | 1.88 |
| | 3.00 | 51 | 1.76 | 58 | 33 | 17 | 16 | 2.12 |
| | 3.50 | 54 | 1.74 | 60 | 36 | 18 | 18 | 2.00 |
| | 3.96 | 54 | 1.74 | 60 | 37 | 20 | 17 | 2.00 |
| | 4.50 | 54 | 1.74 | 60 | 40 | 20 | 20 | 1.70 |
| | 5.00 | 50 | 1.78 | 58 | 36 | 18 | 18 | 1.75 |
| | 6.00 | 56 | 1.73 | 60 | 45 | 21 | 24 | 1.46 |
| | 6.32 | 47 | 1.80 | 56 | 34 | 21 | 13 | 2.00 |
| | 6.56 | 48 | 1.79 | 57 | 39 | 19 | 20 | 1.45 |

Index Properties

BALTIMORE CANYON SAMPLES--Continued

| Core no. (length) | Penetration (m) | Water content (percent) | Bulk density (g/cm³) | Porosity | Liquid limit | Plastic limit | Plasticity index | Liquidity index |
|---|---|---|---|---|---|---|---|---|
| PC-41 (4.54 m) | .15 | 108 | 1.48 | 75 | -- | -- | -- | ---- |
| | .50 | 79 | 1.59 | 68 | -- | -- | -- | ---- |
| | 1.00 | 78 | 1.59 | 68 | -- | -- | -- | ---- |
| | 1.85 | 34 | 1.95 | 48 | 26 | 15 | 11 | 1.73 |
| | 2.35 | 29 | 2.02 | 44 | -- | -- | -- | ---- |
| | 2.85 | 40 | 1.87 | 52 | 37 | 19 | 18 | 1.17 |
| | 3.20 | 37 | 1.91 | 50 | 37 | 17 | 20 | 1.00 |
| | 3.50 | 37 | 1.91 | 50 | 34 | 17 | 17 | 1.18 |
| | 3.90 | 26 | 2.06 | 41 | 22 | -- | -- | ---- |
| | 4.22 | 27 | 2.04 | 42 | 27 | 16 | 11 | 1.00 |
| PC-43 (9.42 m) | .50 | 62 | 1.69 | 63 | -- | -- | -- | ---- |
| | 1.00 | 52 | 1.76 | 59 | 39 | 19 | 20 | 1.65 |
| | 1.50 | 52 | 1.76 | 59 | 41 | 20 | 21 | 1.52 |
| | 2.00 | 50 | 1.78 | 58 | 42 | 22 | 20 | 1.40 |
| | 2.50 | 55 | 1.74 | 60 | -- | -- | -- | ---- |
| | 3.00 | 67 | 1.65 | 65 | 56 | 25 | 31 | 1.35 |
| | 3.25 | 72 | 1.62 | 66 | -- | -- | -- | ---- |
| | 3.50 | 61 | 1.69 | 62 | -- | -- | -- | ---- |
| | 4.00 | 81 | 1.58 | 69 | 61 | 35 | 26 | 1.77 |
| | 4.50 | 73 | 1.62 | 66 | 57 | 26 | 31 | 1.52 |
| | 4.70 | 66 | 1.66 | 64 | 52 | 24 | 28 | 1.50 |
| | 5.00 | 76 | 1.60 | 67 | 60 | 25 | 35 | 1.45 |
| | 5.50 | 67 | 1.65 | 65 | 62 | 26 | 36 | 1.14 |
| | 6.00 | 66 | 1.66 | 64 | 52 | 22 | 30 | 1.47 |
| | 6.50 | 30 | 2.00 | 45 | 23 | 15 | 8 | 1.88 |
| | 7.00 | 36 | 1.92 | 49 | 31 | 17 | 14 | 1.36 |
| | 7.40 | 28 | 2.03 | 43 | 23 | 15 | 8 | 1.62 |
| | 8.00 | 27 | 2.05 | 42 | 21 | -- | -- | ---- |
| | 8.50 | 32 | 1.97 | 47 | -- | -- | -- | ---- |
| | 9.07 | 29 | 2.01 | 44 | 27 | 15 | 12 | 1.17 |
| PC-44 (4.50 m) | .16 | 43 | 1.84 | 54 | -- | -- | -- | ---- |
| | .50 | 43 | 1.84 | 54 | -- | -- | -- | ---- |
| | 1.00 | 38 | 1.90 | 50 | 35 | 18 | 17 | 1.18 |
| | 1.53 | 50 | 1.78 | 58 | 44 | 21 | 23 | 1.26 |
| | 2.00 | 44 | 1.83 | 54 | -- | -- | -- | ---- |
| | 2.47 | 46 | 1.81 | 56 | 42 | 21 | 21 | 1.10 |
| | 3.50 | 44 | 1.83 | 55 | 41 | 19 | 22 | 1.14 |
| | 3.85 | 46 | 1.81 | 56 | 46 | 21 | 25 | 1.00 |
| | 4.28 | 45 | 1.82 | 55 | 41 | 21 | 20 | 1.20 |

Index Properties

BALTIMORE CANYON SAMPLES--Continued

| Core no. (length) | Penetration (m) | Water content (percent) | Bulk density (g/cm$^3$) | Porosity | Liquid limit | Plastic limit | Plasticity index | Liquidity index |
|---|---|---|---|---|---|---|---|---|
| PC-45 (6.97 m) | .41 | 79 | 1.59 | 68 | 60 | 30 | 30 | 1.60 |
| | 1.00 | -- | ---- | -- | -- | -- | -- | ---- |
| | 1.50 | 62 | 1.69 | 63 | -- | -- | -- | ---- |
| | 2.00 | 62 | 1.69 | 63 | 44 | 22 | 22 | 1.82 |
| | 2.50 | 53 | 1.75 | 59 | 40 | 21 | 19 | 1.68 |
| | 3.00 | 42 | 1.85 | 53 | 40 | 20 | 20 | 1.10 |
| | 3.50 | 50 | 1.78 | 58 | 39 | 22 | 17 | 1.65 |
| | 4.00 | 74 | 1.61 | 67 | 67 | 27 | 40 | 1.18 |
| | 4.50 | 78 | 1.59 | 68 | 91 | 31 | 60 | .78 |
| | 4.90 | 82 | 1.57 | 69 | 80 | 29 | 51 | 1.04 |
| | 5.60 | 72 | 1.62 | 66 | 64 | 27 | 37 | 1.22 |
| | 6.00 | 67 | 1.65 | 65 | -- | 27 | -- | ---- |
| | 6.35 | 64 | 1.67 | 64 | 66 | 25 | 41 | .94 |
| | 6.60 | 55 | 1.73 | 60 | 58 | 27 | 31 | .90 |
| PC-46 (7.05 m) | .00 | 87 | 1.55 | 70 | 61 | 30 | 31 | 1.84 |
| | .50 | 70 | 1.64 | 65 | 50 | 23 | 27 | 1.74 |
| | 1.00 | 81 | 1.58 | 69 | 59 | 25 | 34 | 1.65 |
| | 1.50 | 80 | 1.58 | 69 | 53 | 25 | 28 | 1.97 |
| | 2.00 | 74 | 1.61 | 67 | -- | -- | -- | ---- |
| | 2.50 | 58 | 1.71 | 61 | 44 | 21 | 23 | 1.61 |
| | 3.00 | 62 | 1.68 | 63 | 50 | 22 | 28 | 1.43 |
| | 3.50 | 63 | 1.68 | 63 | 53 | 24 | 29 | 1.34 |
| | 4.00 | 67 | 1.65 | 65 | 58 | 25 | 33 | 1.27 |
| | 4.50 | 46 | 1.81 | 56 | 40 | 21 | 19 | 1.32 |
| | 5.00 | 43 | 1.84 | 54 | 38 | 19 | 19 | 1.26 |
| | 5.50 | 50 | 1.78 | 58 | 40 | 20 | 20 | 1.50 |
| | 5.70 | 44 | 1.83 | 55 | 35 | 18 | 17 | 1.53 |
| | 6.00 | 47 | 1.80 | 56 | 38 | 19 | 19 | 1.47 |
| | 6.45 | 45 | 1.82 | 55 | 38 | 18 | 20 | 1.35 |
| | 6.71 | 48 | 1.79 | 57 | 40 | 20 | 20 | 1.40 |
| PC-52 (6.73 m) | .50 | -- | ---- | -- | -- | -- | -- | ---- |
| | 1.00 | 51 | 1.77 | 58 | 38 | 17 | 21 | 1.62 |
| | 1.50 | 48 | 1.79 | 57 | 39 | 17 | 22 | 1.41 |
| | 2.00 | 47 | 1.80 | 56 | 38 | 18 | 20 | 1.45 |
| | 2.50 | 47 | 1.80 | 56 | 39 | 18 | 21 | 1.39 |
| | 3.00 | 56 | 1.73 | 60 | 53 | 24 | 29 | 1.10 |
| | 4.00 | 54 | 1.74 | 60 | 53 | 24 | 29 | 1.03 |
| | 4.50 | 51 | 1.77 | 58 | -- | -- | -- | ---- |
| | 5.00 | 52 | 1.76 | 59 | 55 | 22 | 33 | .91 |
| | 5.50 | 50 | 1.78 | 58 | 52 | 22 | 30 | .93 |
| | 6.00 | 53 | 1.75 | 59 | 45 | 22 | 24 | 1.36 |
| | 6.37 | 53 | 1.75 | 57 | 40 | 20 | 20 | 1.40 |
| PC-53 (10.06 m) | .50 | 65 | 1.67 | 64 | 56 | 27 | 29 | 1.31 |
| | 1.10 | -- | ---- | -- | -- | -- | -- | ---- |
| | 1.50 | 84 | 1.57 | 69 | 56 | 23 | 33 | 1.85 |
| | 2.00 | 89 | 1.54 | 71 | 58 | 26 | 32 | 1.97 |
| | 2.58 | 69 | 1.64 | 65 | 52 | 24 | 29 | 1.74 |
| | 3.00 | 58 | 1.71 | 61 | 42 | 20 | 22 | 1.73 |
| | 3.50 | 69 | 1.64 | 65 | 47 | 20 | 27 | 1.81 |
| | 3.91 | 53 | 1.75 | 59 | 37 | 20 | 17 | 1.94 |
| | 4.50 | 49 | 1.78 | 57 | 38 | 20 | 18 | 1.78 |
| | 5.00 | 51 | 1.77 | 58 | 37 | 20 | 17 | 1.82 |

Index Properties

BALTIMORE CANYON SAMPLES--Continued

| Core no. (length) | Penetration (m) | Water content (percent) | Bulk density (g/cm$^3$) | Porosity | Liquid limit | Plastic limit | Plasticity index | Liquidity index |
|---|---|---|---|---|---|---|---|---|
| PC-53, continued | | | | | | | | |
| (10.06 m) | 5.60 | 53 | 1.75 | 59 | 44 | 21 | 23 | 1.52 |
| | 6.00 | 51 | 1.77 | 58 | 39 | 23 | 16 | 1.77 |
| | 6.50 | 54 | 1.74 | 60 | 41 | 21 | 20 | 1.65 |
| | 7.00 | 55 | 1.74 | 60 | 43 | 23 | 20 | 1.60 |
| | 7.50 | 52 | 1.76 | 59 | 38 | 20 | 18 | 1.78 |
| | 8.00 | 51 | 1.77 | 58 | 40 | 21 | 19 | 1.58 |
| | 9.00 | 48 | 1.79 | 57 | 41 | 20 | 21 | 1.33 |
| | 9.40 | 51 | 1.77 | 58 | 43 | 22 | 21 | 1.38 |
| | 9.66 | 50 | 1.78 | 58 | 44 | 20 | 24 | 1.25 |
| PC-54 | | | | | | | | |
| (8.58 m) | .20 | 89 | 1.54 | 71 | 61 | 26 | 35 | 1.80 |
| | .55 | 76 | 1.60 | 67 | 62 | 27 | 35 | 1.40 |
| | 1.15 | 86 | 1.56 | 70 | 57 | 25 | 32 | 1.91 |
| | 1.50 | 89 | 1.54 | 71 | 54 | 25 | 29 | 2.20 |
| | 2.00 | 70 | 1.64 | 65 | 52 | 24 | 28 | 1.64 |
| | 2.43 | 76 | 1.60 | 67 | 59 | 27 | 32 | 1.53 |
| | 3.00 | 68 | 1.65 | 65 | 44 | 23 | 21 | 2.14 |
| | 3.50 | 65 | 1.67 | 64 | 45 | 22 | 23 | 1.87 |
| | 3.90 | 67 | 1.65 | 65 | 50 | 24 | 26 | 1.65 |
| | 4.50 | 66 | 1.66 | 64 | 47 | 24 | 23 | 1.83 |
| | 5.00 | 55 | 1.74 | 60 | 45 | 21 | 24 | 1.44 |
| | 5.50 | 58 | 1.71 | 61 | 44 | 23 | 21 | 1.67 |
| | 6.00 | 64 | 1.67 | 64 | 55 | 27 | 28 | 1.32 |
| | 6.50 | 64 | 1.67 | 64 | 58 | 31 | 27 | 1.22 |
| | 7.00 | 67 | 1.65 | 65 | 59 | 21 | 38 | 1.21 |
| | 7.50 | 70 | 1.64 | 65 | 58 | 27 | 31 | 1.39 |
| | 8.28 | 59 | 1.70 | 62 | 62 | 30 | 32 | .91 |

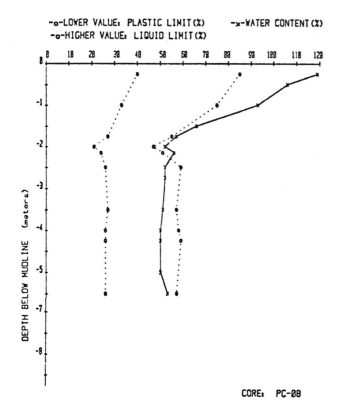

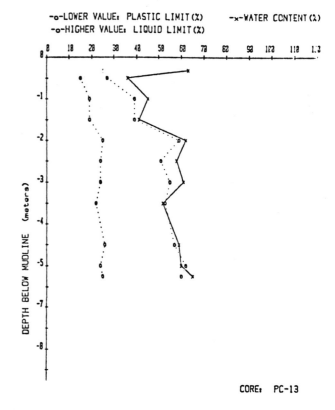

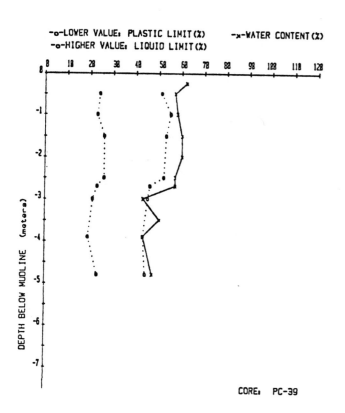

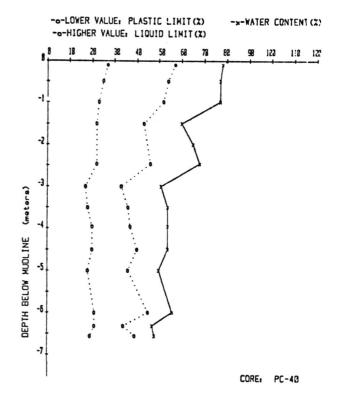

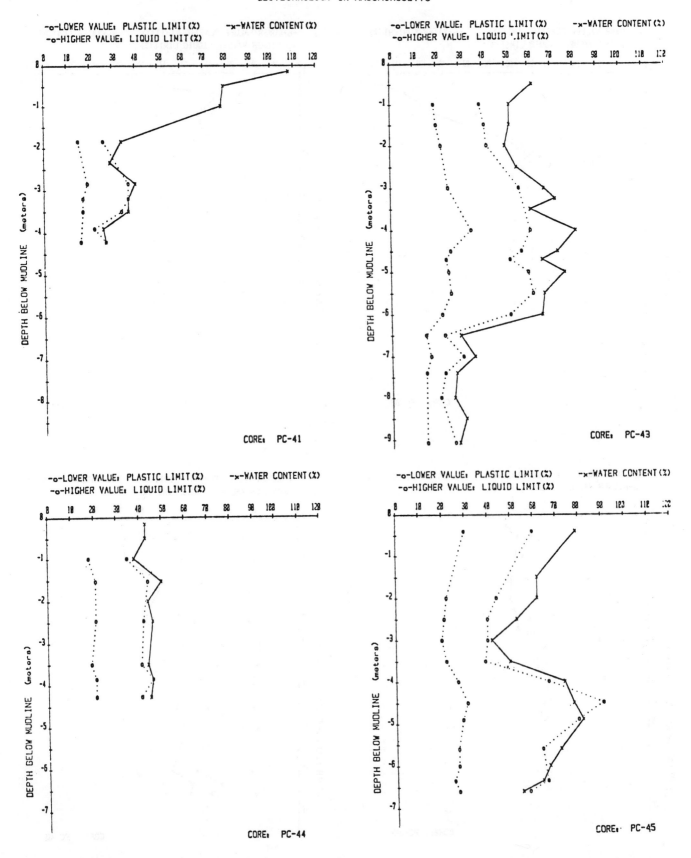

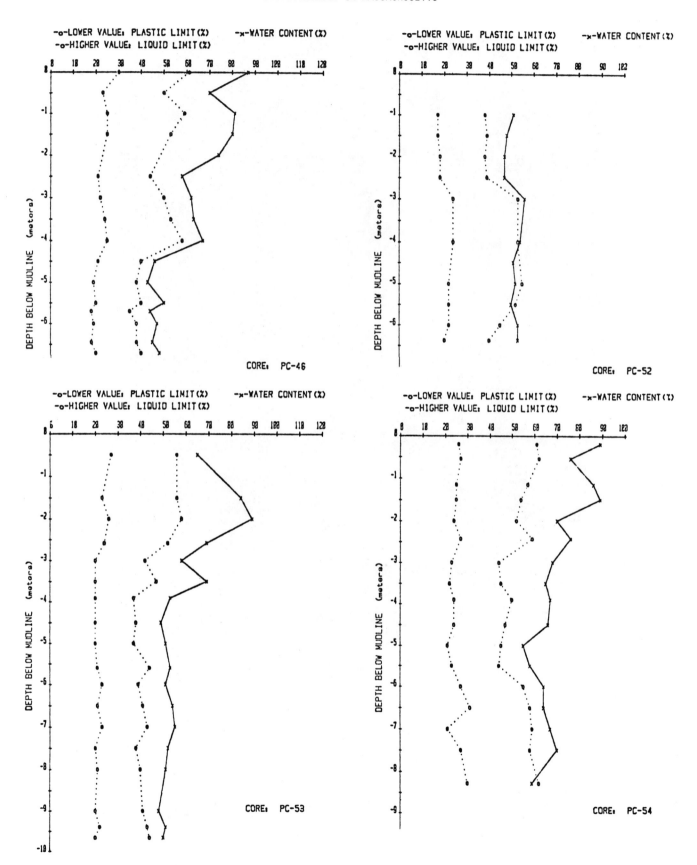

Narragansett Bay in southern New
England, from Rhode Island Sound.
(Courtesy, Aerial Photos of New
England.)

# Marine site investigations for bottom-seated structures

## J. A. FOCHT, JR.
## McClelland Engineers, Inc.

ABSTRACT

Most of the deep-penetration marine geotechnical soil sampling operations to date have been performed in connection with planning for petroleum drilling or production activities. The predominant kind of proposed facility has been the "fixed offshore platform," usually of the jacket-type supported by piles. In the last few years the gravity structure has been used for a number of drilling, production and storage projects, primarily in the North Sea. Other kinds of structures, such as tension leg platforms and guyed towers, have been proposed and will probably find acceptance in the near future. Concepts of submerged and seafloor structures for greater water depths are being considered. All of these structures, as well as the jack-up mobile drilling rigs, have the common need of some form of soil support. Consequently, engineering data on the characteristics and properties of the seafloor soils, often to considerable penetrations, are required for design of foundation elements of proposed structures.

The objective of this paper is to describe the procedures and techniques employed today in deep penetration soil sampling and engineering testing operations, more commonly called offshore foundation investigations, for bottom-seated structures with emphasis on deeper water locations. After a limited discussion of the onshore background of offshore exploration, attention will be given to the operating base from which soil sampling is performed, to geophysical studies that may be conducted prior to or concurrent with soil sampling, to details of sampling and in situ testing, and to testing of recovered samples to determine pertinent engineering properties. The final sections will be devoted to an outline of operational problems and a look at future developments in marine geotechnical investigations.

## ONSHORE BACKGROUND

In the early days of marine soil investigation, the procedures used were merely extrapolations from work on land. It seems appropriate, therefore, to examine some of the land-drilling-and-sampling techniques and tools and to trace their evolution as work progressed into the offshore environment.

### Drilling and Sampling

The actual hole drilling technique is little different onshore or offshore. Holes are usually advanced by ordinary wet rotary processes. Drilling fluid is pumped down through the bore of the drill pipe, and cuttings created by the bit are circulated out of the hole by upward flow of fluid in the annulus. Prepared drilling mud is used as necessary to condition the hole and combat drilling problems.

Soil borings on land commonly are fairly shallow, and samples are taken at selected depths using what are termed "conventional" methods. In conventional drilling and sampling operations, after a hole has been drilled to the depth desired for sampling, the drill pipe and bit are pulled out of the hole. Some type of soil sampler is substituted for the bit and the pipe is run back into the hole to take a sample by means of pushing, driving or rotating the drill pipe. After the sample has been taken, the pipe is again removed from the hole so that the sample can be retrieved. The bit is then substituted for the sampler and the pipe is reinserted to advance the boring to the next sampling depth. This requires two round trips of the drill pipe and, consequently, the procedure becomes slow and laborious with increasing depth. The offshore sampling technique, which will be described later, was designed to be a much faster operation.

### Sampling in Cohesive Soils

The most common method of sampling clay soils on land is to push a thin-walled tube into undisturbed soil below the bottom of a drilled hole in one fast, continuous motion. This procedure is standardized in D 1587-74 (American Society for Testing and Materials). Penetration is achieved by a mechanical or hydraulic pulldown system on the drilling rig. The tube diameter may range from 2 to 5 in., the wall thickness may range from 1/16 to 1/8 in., and the tube length is generally 10 to 15 times the diameter. The lower end of the tube is sharpened to provide a cutting edge and is slightly swaged to provide inside clearance between the sample and the inner wall of the tube.

Several factors contribute to the "undisturbed" quality of a clay sample. The tube should be clean and smooth; the area ratio of the tube, defined as the cross-sectional area of the metal divided by the gross cross-sectional area, should not exceed about 10 percent; the recovery ratio, the ratio of length of sample entering the tube to the length of push, should desirably be near 100 percent. These factors are particularly important in soils that are sensitive to strength loss with disturbance. A fixed piston can be incorporated in a thin-walled tube sampler to improve chances of obtaining an undisturbed sample in difficult or sensitive materials.

## Sampling in Granular Soils

Obtaining a true undisturbed sample in a cohesionless material such as sand is extremely difficult and expensive. Therefore, the most common procedure used in sampling sand is one that provides an indication of the in situ density and obtains a disturbed sample for examination and testing. This procedure is called the "Standard penetration test" and is described in D 1586-67 (American Society for Testing and Materials). It involves use of a split-barrel sampler having an outside diameter of 2 in. and an inside diameter at the shoe of 1-3/8 in. The sampler is first seated by driving 6 in. into the bottom of a drilled hole, using a 140-lb hammer dropped repeatedly a distance of 30 in. on top of the drill pipe. The sampler is then driven another foot and the number of blows required is called the penetration resistance (N). A small disturbed sample is recovered inside the barrel. The N value is used to judge the relative density of the sand. As will be noted later, offshore sampling in sand may involve the same sampler but not the same driving procedure.

## In Situ Testing

Onshore geotechnical studies occasionally employ in situ testing to evaluate engineering properties of the foundation materials. The shear strength of clay soils, particularly the weaker ones, can be measured in situ with a vane inserted into the undisturbed soil below the bottom of the borehole. Torque is applied to the vane causing it to rotate within the soil and induce shearing stresses on the rotational surface created by the vane edges. This tool has been used extensively in the highly sensitive soils of Scandanavia and Canada as well as in low strength alluvial soils of major U.S. river systems.

Cone penetrometers have been used extensively for many years in the lowlands of Northwest Europe to obtain soil penetration resistance which can be converted to soil strength. The original Dutch cone device measured only point resistance. A later version had a friction sleeve above the point; the point and sleeve were alternately advanced into the soil to obtain separate readings. In recent years another device called an electric cone has been widely used. This device simultaneously measures point resistance and friction as it is steadily advanced into the soil. The data from cone penetrometers are particularly useful for evaluation of sands and to determine boundary locations between sands and clays.

The pressure meter is another device designed to determine soil properties in situ. It uses an expanding cell to measure load-deformation characteristics. The cell is either driven into place or installed in a hole of carefully controlled dimensions. Readings, interpreted in terms of modulus of deformation and limit pressure, may be used to determine bearing capacity, settlement and other data.

In situ testing devices do not provide samples for inspection and examination. Therefore, they are used normally only in conjunction with sample borings.

## Geophysical Exploration

Borehole logging, refraction surveys, reflection surveys, and resistivity surveys are all types of geophysical tools that are being used in onshore geotechnical studies. Each has its advantages and disadvantages. In most instances, the geophysical exploration is intended to define stratigraphy and provide only a general indication of material properties. Nevertheless, geophysical data are extremely valuable to the geotechnical engineer in many onshore studies.

## Adaptation to Offshore

The utilization of onshore exploration techniques in offshore investigations has required modification to accommodate the physical problems of a moving base of operations, as well as economic constraints introduced by the large daily costs offshore and relatively slow production rates. Evolution of offshore procedures has been related primarily to changes in the base of operations for offshore geotechnical investigations to improve cost effectiveness.

## OPERATING BASE FOR OFFSHORE SOIL SAMPLING

Offshore soil exploration in the open waters of the Gulf of Mexico began in 1947. The water depths were shallow and the procedures adopted for supporting the soil boring equipment permitted direct use of land drilling and sampling methods.

## Fixed Platform

A small pile-supported platform served as the base for drilling in the early offshore investigations. All materials and equipment were loaded on a derrick barge along with the jacket and piling for the larger oil well structure to be erected. The coring platform was set first, and the coring equipment was placed aboard to begin the soil boring. In the very early years the jacket for the large structure was set immediately thereafter, and pile driving began. The art of pile design was not far advanced in those days; piles for the large platforms may have had a diameter of 24 to 30 in. and a uniform wall thickness of 3/8 in. Soon the soil boring programs began to be scheduled in advance of platform construction

Figure 1. The ship R.L. Perkins, used for drilling in the Gulf of Mexico. (McClelland Engineers).

(Also in the color section.)

to permit better use of the data obtained in platform design.

A small casing was set from the coring platform deck into the mudline after shallow soil samples had been taken. This casing provided hole reentry and permitted recirculation of drilling fluid from a tank built into the deck section. The casing was advanced as the boring progressed until a firm seal was obtained. After an early experience with a gas blowout and fire, a small manual blowout preventer was installed in the casing string. The drilling and sampling proceeded in the "conventional" manner used on land. Samples were taken at selected depth intervals and were tested at the site as soon as recovered. Results of tests were used to calculate required pile penetrations.

## Barge

Observation of the relative stability of derrick barges soon indicated that soil boring work could be done from floating equipment, using the same general techniques as from a fixed platform. The first such job was actually done from a derrick barge. Later, in order to be independent from a derrick barge, a large deck barge was used as a floating base. The barge had to be completely outfitted with mooring spread, quarters, galley, fresh water supply, generators, fuel tanks and over-the-side coring platform. The coring platform was usually somewhat elevated to accommodate tide change and wave motion, while keeping the top of the casing and the blowout preventer between the water surface and the underside of the drillng deck. Drilling mud circulated out of the casing and through a flexible hose into a mud tank suspended over the side of the barge. If the sea became too rough and the water was not too deep, the barge could be moved off location, leaving the casing standing so that the hole could be reentered later. As water depths increased beyond 100 ft, the capacity of the small casing to support its own weight plus the weight of a blowout preventer became marginal.

## Supply Vessel or Drill Ship

The change from barge drilling to boat drilling (Fig. 1) in the Gulf of Mexico came in 1962 when it was desired to conduct soil sampling in water depths down to about 600 ft. It was at the same time that drilling and sampling techniques changed to those that are in use today (described in a later section). These changes resulted in some sacrifices that seem justified by greater speed and versatility. The supply vessel was chosen because it was self-powered, had a fairly large deck space and had full living accommodations for personnel. A center well was installed through the boat hull so that drilling could be done at the point of least vessel movement, although drilling can also be done over the side. All that had to be added to the vessel were the mooring spread and the drilling equipment.

In recent years vessels specifically rigged and modified for geotechnical investigations have become available. The vessel size varies with the environmental conditions in which it will operate. Conventional supply boats about 165 ft in length work quite well in many marine regions, including the Gulf of Mexico, Arabian Gulf, southeast Asia, and Maracaibo. Larger vessels are required for more hostile areas such as the North Sea. Drill ships in North Sea service range in length from 240 to 325 ft with horsepower ratings of up to 2700.

Mooring or positioning of the coring vessel becomes increasingly difficult as water depth increases. Using readily available winches, cables and anchors, it is feasible to moor a vessel in up to 600 ft of water while providing a minimum desired anchor line scope of five times water depth. Except in relatively shallow water, about 100 ft or less, an auxiliary vessel with at least a 700-horsepower engine, usually the survey vessel, is needed to assist in setting anchors, unless the coring vessel is equipped with bow thrusters. In any event, the auxiliary vessel is needed for standby purposes. For deep water two different approaches to anchoring may be followed.

First, larger winches may be used to spool the needed length of cable. This procedure normally leads to use of a larger coring vessel, up to about 200-ft length, because of greater deck space and weight requirements for winches. The second approach is to retain the original mooring winches and lines and to preset a pattern of anchors, pendant lines and buoys to which the coring vessel anchor lines can be attached. The latter procedure definitely requires an additional vessel for anchor handling. The auxiliary vessel should be at least 150-ft in length and be equipped with an anchor handling winch. The preset anchor spread can be used in substantial water depth, probably as much as about 1500 ft. At some water depth a dynamic positioning system may become the only alternative for positioning. However, few vessels are so equipped and conversion is quite expensive.

## Large Mobile Platform

Many times a mobile drilling platform is on location where a soil boring is desired. To water depths of 300 ft the mobile platform may be of the self-elevating type; beyond this depth it will probably be either a semisubmersible or a drill ship.

If adequate space exists on the mobile platform, a soil boring can be made by placing a portable coring rig and necessary personnel aboard. In all other respects the boring operation follows the same procedures employed on a coring vessel.

If space is not available on the mobile platform, a soil boring may be made using the large rig on the platform. Geotechnical personnel are used to supervise the operation and work with the regular drill crews on the rig in accomplishing

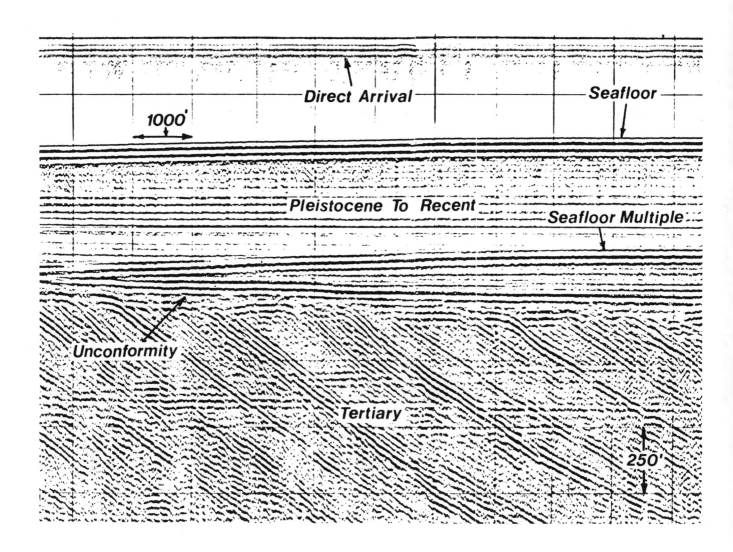

Figure 2. Optically stacked sparker record, Gulf of Alaska.

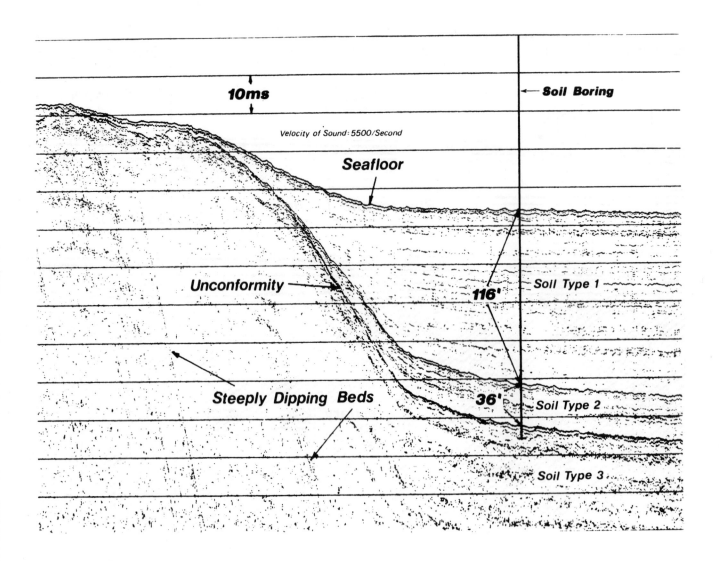

Figure 3.  Acoustipulse, Gulf of Alaska.

the boring. Obviously, this method cannot be used while the rig is engaged in well drilling operations. Consequently, a boring must be made before the well is spudded, or the platform or rig must be moved slightly to make a boring adjacent to the well location. About one day of rig time may be required to complete a normal boring; this may be quite expensive, depending upon the daily cost of the mobile drilling rig and its support equipment. However, if the boring is to be made in a remote area or in very deep water, this procedure may be the most expedient and economical. Close coordination is necessary to minimize rig time devoted to soil boring operations.

## HIGH RESOLUTION GEOPHYSICAL SURVEYS

The primary application of geophysical techniques to offshore foundation investigations is use of acoustical reflection systems. These systems permit determination of general stratigraphy and identification of pertinent anomalies at or below the seafloor. The intensity of an investigation or the degree of coverage is established by the stage of the project, whether pre-lease, pre-drilling, or pre-design. Most geophysical surveys use a multisensor array to obtain simultaneous coverage with subbottom profiling equipment, side scan sonar, fathometer and other devices. Individual survey systems and the information provided by them are described briefly in the following sections.

### Sparker

The high power, low frequency sparker is able to penetrate to 1500 ft or more below the seafloor in most areas. (Its specifications are 4 to 10 KJ and 80 to 200 hertz.) This part of the subbottom profile is missed by most deep seismic work oriented toward hydrocarbon discovery. The sparker provides a continuous cross-sectional display of formations below the seafloor that reflect the sound waves, as illustrated by Figure 2. The resolution is coarse, in the order of 20 to 30 ft, and this system does not provide definition of the shallow sediments. It must, therefore, be supplemented by another system to obtain needed detail at shallow penetrations beneath the seafloor.

### Shallow Profiler

Several electromechanical subbottom profiling devices such as the acoustipulse are designed to supplement the deeper sparker data and to give the needed resolution in shallow formations. Systems operate at 200 to 4000 hertz, penetrate to about 500 ft below the sea bottom, and provide a resolution within about 2 ft. An acoustipulse record showing the type of information obtained appears in Figure 3.

### Fathometer

The depth sounder or fathometer operates at a still higher frequency of about 40,000 hertz and is used primarily to provide a continuous profile of water depth. Fathometer records may be affected by changes in water salinity, temperature and suspended solids as well as other factors. Therefore, a fathometer should be calibrated for conditions existing in the survey area.

### Side Scan Sonar

The dual side scan sonar is used to provide a sonar picture of irregularities at the seafloor to either side of the track of the vessel towing the transducer or fish. The transducer is towed at a depth somewhat above the seafloor. The area of coverage can be varied by changing towing depth or scanning angle.

The side scan sonar fish is towed 800 to 1000 ft behind the survey vessel. The depth of the fish, currents and other factors combine to make accurate determination of the fish position very difficult. The best way to locate phenomena seen on the sonar record is to relate them to the same features seen on the fathometer, sparker or shallow profiler records. Precise navigation is also required.

### Uses of Geophysical Data

The various geophysical records can be converted into maps showing bathymetry, shallow structures, shallow isopachs, drilling and construction hazards and other features. An example of a drilling and construction hazard map is given in Figure 4. When information from examination and testing of bottom samples and soil boring samples is combined with geophysical results, other areal maps and cross-sections or profiles showing geological and geotechnical data can be developed. Figure 3 indicates how information obtained from a control soil boring may be used to correlate with geophysical data and permit extrapolation of stratigraphy from the control point.

In the case of an investigation for a specific structure location, the soil boring provides detailed information at the location; the geophysical data provide the opportunity to observe how stratigraphy may vary in the vicinity. The combination of bottom samples and geophysical records along a pipeline route provides a similar opportunity to observe soil types and their distribution. Detailed bathymetry and side scan records obtained as part of a geophysical study can be used to produce a drilling and construction hazards map (Fig. 4).

## SEAFLOOR SAMPLING

Sampling of soils right at the seafloor is frequently undertaken in connection with geophysical surveys and a few geotechnical studies. Samples to a penetration of a few feet can be obtained with a simple gravity drop sampler. Such samples are usually 2 to 3 in. in diameter

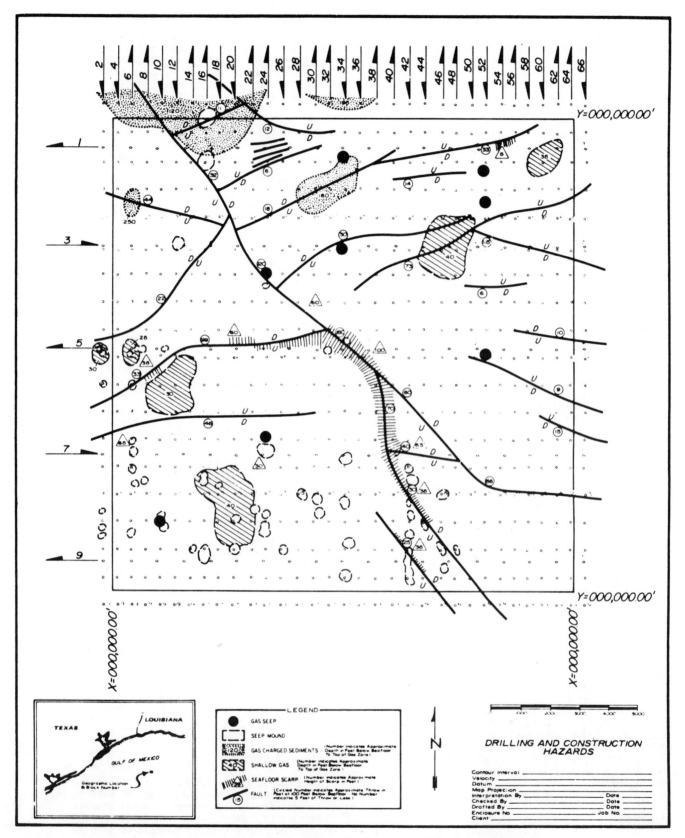

Figure 4. Drilling and construction hazards in the Gulf of Mexico.

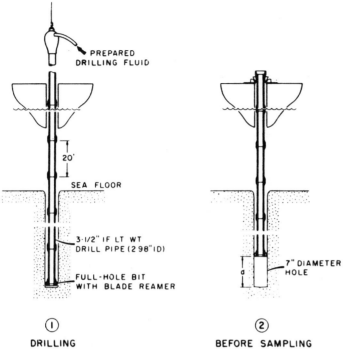

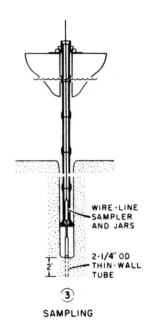

① DRILLING

-Rotary drill pipe, partially supported by draw-works line, moves vertically with drill boat.

-Drilling fluid and cuttings exit at seafloor

-Continuous re-supply of drilling fluid maintains a clean hole.

② BEFORE SAMPLING

-Drill pipe is set in slips at boat deck, with bit held off bottom a distance, d, which varies as boat moves with sea. Mean value of d is usually about 5-ft

-Hole diameter is about 7 in. Some cuttings accumulate at bottom

③ SAMPLING

-Sampler is lowered to rest on bottom, its depth monitored by wire-line revolution counter.

-Sample tube is driven to desired penetration, usually 18 to 24 in, by wire-line operation of jars attached to sampler head.

Figure 5.  Wire-line soil sampler.

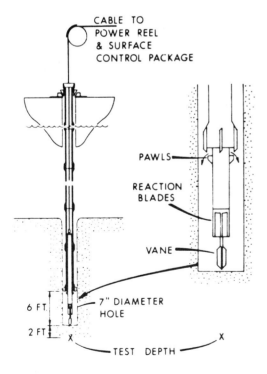

Figure 6.  Remote vane operation.

and have lengths of 2 to 4 ft.  Use of a gravity piston corer will permit recovery of fairly undisturbed samples to penetrations of 10 ft or slightly more.  With a vibracorer device penetrations of 20 to 30 ft are possible in soils of modest strength or density.  This device is placed on the seafloor, and penetration of the sampling tube is achieved by an electrically or hydraulically activated vibrator.  Samples recovered with most piston corers and vibracorers are 2 to 4 in. in diameter.

Greater penetration and sampling has been achieved with the giant piston sampler developed by Woods Hole Oceanographic Institution for deep sea sediment studies.  This sampler can recover samples 4.48 in. in diameter to penetrations approaching 100 ft.  To date the use of this sampler has been limited to research studies rather than to practical engineering problems.

DEEP PENETRATION SAMPLING

The drilling and sampling procedures being used offshore today differ in many respects from techniques used onshore.  The differences as mentioned in a previous section result from the necessity of working from a floating platform subject to some vertical motion and from the need to minimize operational time in order to reduce costs. Certain sacrifices, primarily related to the quality of cohesive samples, have resulted in the interest of cost-effective investigations. The following paragraphs describe the drilling and sampling methods commonly employed for marine investigations in water as much as 1500 ft deep.

## Drilling Equipment

The drilling equipment used for the majority of marine geotechnical investigations today is a unitized Failing 1500 rig with the diesel engine, mud pump, rotary, derrick and 3-drum drawworks mounted on a common skid as pictured in Figure 1. This size unit has an effective depth capability of about 1000 ft. The drilling system on the drill ships is usually not unitized but consists of separate pieces of equipment. On some a power swivel rotates the drill pipe rather than a rotary table.

The complement of drilling equipment normally includes a back-up of all drill pipe and downhole tools. Bumper subs may be used in the drill string to compensate for vessel heave, and drill collars are often necessary for drilling in hard formations. Desirably the drill pipe is in uniform even lengths, such as 20 ft or 30 ft, to avoid the need for measuring individual joints. Items such as mud tanks, mud mixing unit, sampling tools and field testing equipment round out the equipment complement.

## Drilling Method

Open hole drilling techniques are used for most offshore soil borings without provision for reentry. If drilling is interrupted by adverse weather, the drill pipe is pulled, and the boring has to be redrilled when work is resumed. In open hole drilling there is no recirculation of the drilling fluid, as indicated on Figure 5. The drill pipe is equipped with an open-center bit, which may have a wire-line center plug, and the drilling fluid is pumped down through the drill pipe. Cuttings from the formation created by the bit are carried up by the drilling fluid flow in the annulus around the drill pipe, and both cuttings and drilling fluid are wasted at the sea-floor.

The drilling fluid must have adequate gel properties to stabilize the borehole in granular formations. In some marine areas the boring can be drilled primarily with sea water, with prepared mud used only when circulation of drilling fluid is to be stopped. In most areas, however, mud of commercial salt water gel or suitable polymers is used throughout the boring. In addition, weight material such as barite is often required for protection against gas blowout, artesian flow of water, or heaving formations that might affect safety or sample quality.

## Wire-Line Sampling

When the boring has been advanced to the desired sampling depth, circulation of drilling fluid is stopped and the kelly or swivel is removed from the drill pipe. The pipe is supported by slips or elevators with the bit raised off the bottom of the hole (Fig. 5). The wire-line sampler is introduced through the bore of the drill pipe and the open-center bit to take a sample of undisturbed soil below the bottom of the drilled hole.

The sampler includes an upper hammer section usually weighing about 175 lbs, a central tele-scoping section of about 10-ft length and a lower adapter to which a sampling device is attached; the overall extended length is about 34 ft. There is no connection between the drill pipe and sampler. After the sampler is set on bottom, the hammer is actuated by the wire line to secure penetration of the sampling device. A 5-ft stroke of the downhole hammer is used for sampling; the remaining available stroke provides tolerance to vessel motion. In the event drilling and sampling are to be done from a fixed base such as a self-elevating platform, a latch-in sampler can be employed to take pushed samples in soft to firm clay soils.

The sampling device may consist of (1) a thin-walled tube sampler, (2) a sectional liner sampler, or (3) a split-barrel sampler with a core retainer. The thin-walled tube sampler is used in most sampling operations to recover both cohesive and cohesionless materials. To avoid disturbance caused by handling samples, the liner sampler is employed to obtain very soft clay soils having a shear strength less than about 500 psf. The split-barrel sampler with core retainer is used in cohesionless materials which are difficult to recover. At the end of the sampling operation, the sampler is retrieved with the wireline.

If materials too hard to sample by driving are encountered, a wire-line rotary rock core barrel can be used. The rock barrel includes an outer barrel or drill collar to which the bit is attached, and an inner barrel which latches into place inside the collar; the inner barrel is retrievable with a wire line and overshot. Use of a rock barrel is appropriate in any material sufficiently indurated to be classified as rock.

As mentioned earlier, some sacrifices are made in the interest of faster operations by the wire-line method. First, the sample tube is driven rather than being pushed in clay, and this results in some sample disturbance. Comparative sampling and testing have been done to evaluate the amount of disturbance and develop correction factors for specific engineering analyses. Secondly, the wire-line procedure in sand does not provide the "standard penetration resistance," although the same split-barrel sampler is used, but some general correlations have been made between the two driving procedures for nominal depths.

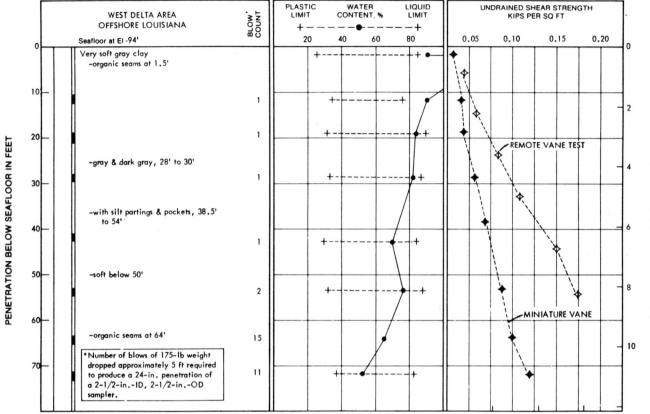

Figure 7. Partial boring log.

## IN SITU TESTING

As water depths and boring penetrations have increased, concern about validity and applicability of test results from recovered samples has also increased. For example, the effects of stress relief on sample properties, particularly shear strength, may be significant, especially for soils containing considerable gas. In situ testing with vane and penetrometer devices has begun to provide engineers with valuable data on properties measured in place without the effects of sampling, stress relief, and handling.

### Remote Vane

The remote vane shear probe was developed several years ago for Gulf of Mexico operations and has now been employed worldwide. Compatible with the wireline sampling method, it probably is the best means of determining in place the undrained shear strength of clay soils with shear strengths less than about 2.5 ksf. The probe is run through the bore of the drill pipe in lieu of a sampler (Fig. 6). Electrically operated pawls

are extended below the bit, and the weight of the drill pipe is used to push the vane and its reaction system into undisturbed soil below the bottom of the drilled hole. A down hole motor driving the vane is then actuated electrically, and results of the test are recorded digitally and graphically on the vessel. Strengths from remote vane tests are usually higher than strengths measured on recovered samples (Fig. 7). Recent modifications permit reversal of rotation and performance of cyclic tests.

### Cone Penetrometer

An electric friction cone penetrometer is an improvement of the mechanical friction cone, because it measures both point resistance and sleeve friction simultaneously as the unit is pushed into a foundation formation. The measured point resistance and sleeve friction may be used to estimate end bearing and friction values for piles. The ratio of point resistance to sleeve friction is used to evaluate soil type. The cone data have primary application in evaluating the relative density of sands but are also useful in all soil types. The continuous penetration record is very valuable in delineating thin and variable soil layers.

Reliable interpretation of cone data requires a uniform rate of penetration. Therefore, the most successful use of cone penetrometers offshore has come from two units that operate at the seafloor. The first of these units is the "seacalf," which is a remotely operated hydraulic unit that is lowered to the sea floor with a fixed length of cone rod. Cone penetration is limited either by the length of the rod or refusal under the weight of the reaction system. The seacalf has been used extensively in the North Sea for over four years.

A second generation seafloor cone system, called the "stingray" and developed by McClelland Engineers, has several advantages. The seafloor jack is used with drill pipe and can be used as a reentry system for drill pipe. The electric cone assembly is lowered on a wire line into the drill pipe and latches in just above the bit. The jacking unit can clamp on to the drill pipe, and then through a second set of jacks force the cone assembly into the sea bottom or the soil below the bottom of a boring. Clamping devices in the cone assembly alternately grip and release the cone rod as the cone is jacked down by the jacking unit, operated hydraulically from a control unit on the drilling vessel. After several strokes of the jack, the cone assembly can be retrieved and the hole advanced by drilling to be followed by another cycle of cone testing. The stingray system was operated successfully in the North Sea during the summer of 1977.

The stingray system also permits taking of pushed thin-wall tube samples, which are much less disturbed than driven samples. In addition, a newly developed push-in-type pressure meter can be used with the stingray system and was given initial trials in 1979. The current limitation of both the seacalf and the stingray is the requirement for a large vessel with a 3-m square moonpool, heavy hoisting equipment, and motion compensator gear. Vessels capable of handling these marine cone penetrometers are presently working only out of North Sea ports.

## LABORATORY TESTING OF SAMPLES

Testing of recovered samples to determine their engineering properties is a vital part of a geotechnical site investigation. The most significant property to be evaluated is the soil shear strength and its variation with penetration below the sea floor, reflected in part by the data presentation on boring logs like Figure 7. As in onshore studies, various tests are utilized depending upon the soil conditions and the design problem. However, in a marine investigation some tests need to be performed in a shipboard laboratory to guide the scope of the investigation as it proceeds. These are primarily simple undrained strength tests and soil classification tests. Accurate and complete visual descriptions of soil

samples with dimensional measurements are a vital part of the field laboratory activity.

### Shipboard Tests

Testing in a shipboard laboratory is usually limited to determination of undrained strength properties of cohesive soils by relatively simple tests. Estimates of shear strengths should be obtained by simple hand-held devices such as the "torvane" or pocket penetrometer. More reliable strength data are secured using a fall cone device, a miniature vane shear device, and/or unconfined compression testing equipment. Under some circumstances unconsolidated-undrained triaxial tests, Atterberg limit tests and water content tests may be performed in a shipboard laboratory.

Dimensional measurements are an important component of shipboard handling of recovered samples. Weight measurements in the field followed by subsequent measurements in the onshore laboratory will reveal moisture losses that would affect test results. Observations of sample growth due to stress release and indications of soil structure are significant data to be used in interpretation of other information. Careful handling and packaging of samples complete the shipboard laboratory activity.

### Onshore Tests

The testing program in the onshore laboratory will include the full range of geotechnical tests, beginning with necessary identification and classification tests. These are usually visual examination, water content, unit weight, Atterberg limits and grain size tests. Color photographs and radiographs are frequently useful for evaluation of natural soil structure.

Strength tests on cohesive samples currently are predominantly directed at total stress analyses and include tests on remolded as well as undisturbed samples. Miniature vane and unconfined compression tests are repeated in the onshore laboratory; triaxial tests tend to be of the unconsolidated-undrained type with a few consolidated-undrained tests. Tests on reconstituted sand samples are usually of the consolidated-undrained multiple-stage type. In all tests stress-strain data are acquired.

With increased efforts to apply effective stress procedures to marine foundation analyses, triaxial tests with pore pressure measurements, sometimes with anisotropic consolidation, are now being performed for particular studies. The impact of dynamic and cyclic loads on foundation materials is being evaluated by cyclic triaxial, simple shear and direct shear tests. Resonant column tests are also used to determine dynamic properties.

Consolidation tests may be required to measure compressibility characteristics or to assist in the evaluation of stress history of the foundation formations. Other tests such as relative density determinations of granual materials are occasionally needed for particular problems. Special test procedures may be devised to represent as closely as possible those conditions that will actually exist in the field.

## OPERATIONAL PROBLEMS

### Water Depth and Tide

Accurate determination of water depth is very important to a platform designer. The measurement of water depth is particularly difficult in deep water, strong currents, significant tides, soft mudline conditions, and a sloping sea floor. A close approximation of water depth can frequently be obtained using a sounding weight attached to a wire line and using a calibrated wire line counter to measure the length of line. Probably the most accurate method involves the use of a pressure sensitive device projecting slightly below the drill bit to indicate when the drill bit touches the sea floor. Such a device can be run down through the drill pipe on an electrical conductor cable after the bit is thought to be close to the sea floor. These observations should be compared to depths measured with a fathometer or a pressure transducer; both of the methods are affected by variations in water density. The accuracy of the water depth measurement should be within one percent of the depth. Accurate and reproducible location data are obviously vital to water depth measurement where the water depth varies.

Tidal changes may be quite significant in some offshore areas; sampling depths and stratum changes can be incorrect by several feet if tidal changes are not taken into account. Depth readings versus time and comparisons with tidal charts should be considered in adjusting drilling depth measurements to a common datum.

### Difficult Formations

Hole stability in the absence of casing that can be advanced through difficult formations is dependent on an appropriate mud program. Cohesionless soils tend to cave unless stabilized by a suitable drilling mud. Certain soft cohesive soils have a tendency to squeeze and close the bore hole; in rare cases, flow of very soft soil up into the drill pipe has occurred after pumping was stopped. Combatting this problem requires use of weight material in the drilling fluid. The mud weight must be kept low enough to avoid hydrofracture of the formation.

### Formation Gas

There have been many encounters with shallow gas in offshore oil activities that have resulted in loss of equipment and life. Fortunately, indication of gas can frequently be obtained from high resolution acoustical records secured in advance of drilling.

In the open hole drilling method, an appropriate mud program is the only way to protect against a blowout. As a minimum the mud weight program should provide reasonable assurance that a blowout will not occur under normal conditions. If the presence of gas is expected from geophysical records or prior experience, special care and attention are required.

### Weather and Sea State

Because deep water geotechnical investigations are usually well offshore, the coring vessel must be sufficiently seaworthy that it does not have to seek safe harbor from moderately bad weather or unfavorable sea conditions. If drilling and sampling are interrupted by rough weather of limited duration, the vessel should be able to remain in the vicinity until the weather abates. Most vessels in current use for marine site investigations can drill and sample in a 6 to 8-ft sea, provided the bow is oriented into the sea. Larger drill ships can accommodate slightly more adverse weather conditions.

## FUTURE DEVELOPMENTS

The boat drilling approach to offshore geotechnical drilling and sampling for deep penetration studies is expected to remain the most viable method. For water depths much in excess of 1000 ft, dynamic positioning will probably supersede conventional mooring. Use of a seafloor jacking system, like the stingray, will improve sample quality but with an increase in costs. Efforts will be made through development of new samplers to minimize effects of pressure changes on recovered samples. Increased emphasis will be placed on in situ measurement of soil properties with the remote vane and the cone penetrometer. Other investigation techniques such as push-in piezometers and the push-in pressure meter may become important for evaluation of in situ effective stress conditions. With the support and encouragement of the oil industry, geotechnical consultants will in the future as in the past meet and overcome the continuous challenges of deeper water, different structures and new problems.

## REFERENCES

American Society for Testing and Materials, 1974, Standard method for penetration test and split-barrel sampling of soil: D 1586-67, reapproved 1974.

American Society for Testing and Materials, 1974, Standard method for thin-walled tube sampling of soils: D 1587-74.

## ADDITIONAL READING

American Society of Civil Engineers, 1976, Subsurface investigation for design and construction of foundations of buildings: Manual 56.

Ardus, D.A., 1979, Offshore site investigation: Conference proceedings, Society of Underwater Technology and Institution of Civil Engineers, Graham and Trotman, Ltd., London, 650 p.

de Ruiter, J., 1975, The use of in-situ testing for North Sea soil studies: Offshore Europe 75, Aberdeen, Scotland.

de Ruiter, J., and Fox, D.A., 1975, Site investigations for North Sea Forties Field: Proceedings, 7th Offshore Technology Conference, Houston, v. 2, p. 21-36.

Doyle, E.H., McClelland, B., and Ferguson, G.H., 1971, Wireline vane probe for deep penetration measurements of ocean sediment strength: Proceedings, 3rd Offshore Technology Conference, Houston, v. 1, p. 21-32.

Emrich, W.J., 1979, Performance study of soil sampler for deep-penetration marine borings: Sampling of soil and rock, American Society for Testing and Materials, STP 483, p. 30-50.

Ferguson, G.H., McClelland, B., and Bell, W.D., 1977, Seafloor cone penetrometer for deep penetration measurements of ocean sediment strength: Proceedings, 9th Offshore Technology Conference, Houston, v. 1, p. 471-478.

Focht, Jr., J.A., and Kraft, Jr., L.M., 1977, Progress in marine geotechnical engineering: Journal, Geotechnical Engineering Division, American Society of Civil Engineers, v. 103, GT10, p. 1097-1118.

Focht, Jr., J.A., Ehlers, C.J., Kraft, Jr., L.M., and Young, A.G., 1980, Advantages of using in situ vane for marine soil investigations: International Symposium on Marine Soil Mechanics, Mexico City. In press.

Kraft, Jr., L.M., Ahmad, N., and Focht, Jr., J.A., 1976, Application of remote vane results to offshore geotechnical problems: Proceedings, 8th Offshore Technology Conference, Houston, v. 3, p. 75-96.

LeTirant, P., 1979, Seabed reconnaissance and offshore soil mechanics for the installation of petroleum structures: Editions Technip and Graham and Trotman, Ltd., London, 508 p.

McClelland, B., 1972, Techniques used in soil sampling at sea: Offshore, v. 32, no. 3, March, p. 51-57.

McClelland, B., 1975, Trends in marine site investigations--a perspective: Proceedings, Offshore Europe 75, University of Aberdeen, v. 220, p. 1-9.

Perkins, R.L., 1957, Floating rig takes core samples in deep swift water: Engineering News-Record, September 12, p. 60-62.

Zuidberg, H.M., 1975, Seacalf, a submersible, cone penetrometer rig: Marine Geotechnology, v. 1.

# PARTICIPANTS

## Conference on
## Geotechnology in Massachusetts

(addresses in March 1980, some abbreviated)

John M  Aaron
USGS
Office of Marine Geology
Woods Hole MA  02543

David Acheson III
46 Tremont St Apt 1
Brighton
MA  02135

Cheryl Alderman
Univ of Mass
54 Meadow St
Amherst MA  01002

Paul Aldinger
C E Maguire
31 Canal St
Providence RI  02903

Barry Alexsavich
Boston Univ  PO Box 271
Boston Univ Station
Boston MA  02215

Robert E  Allen
Schiavone Construction Co
28 Dwight Ave
Spring Valley NY  10977

S A Alsup
2344 Commonwealth
Suite 1-2
Newton MA  02166

Jorge Alva-Hurtado
28 Marston Hall
Univ of Mass
Amherst MA  01003

Fred J  Anders
Blaisdell House
Univ of Mass
Amherst MA  01003

Bob Andrews
Dept of Geology
Univ of Conn
Storrs CT  06268

Mike Angieri
Hayden  Harding & Buchanan
1340 Soldiers Field Rd
Boston MA  02135

William B  Armstrong
Box 27
Arlington
MA  02174

David D  Ashenden
Metropolitan District Comm
Belchertown
MA  01007

James W  Ashley
Vt Dept of Water Resources
RFD
W Danville VT  05873

Frederick G  Aufiero
S E A Consultants
54 Canal St
Boston MA  02114

Richard Ayache
Science Dept
Needham H S
609 Webster St
Needham MA  02192

John Ayres
Goldberg Zoino
30 Tower Rd
Newton Upper Falls MA  02164

Chris Bade
Boston College
35 Graycliffe Rd
Newton Center MA  02159

Sher Bahadur
Acres American
Clark Building Suite 329
Columbia MD  21044

John J  Balco
Water Resources Council
2120 L Street NW
Washington DC  20000

Ari Barjosef
Haley & Aldrich
238 Main St
Cambridge MA  02142

Patrick J  Barosh
Weston Observatory
Concord Rd
Weston MA  02193

William Barton
US Bureau of Mines
201 West Amherst Rd
Sterling VA  22170

Matthew Barvenik
Goldgerg Zoino
311 Kendrick St
Newton MA  02158

P  Beal
Hanover Water Dept
Hanover
MA  02339

Lawrence Beals
BSC Engineering
263 Summer St
Boston MA  02210

Michael Beck
Hubbardston Rd
Princeton
MA  01541

Francis Bellini
Yankee Atomic Electric Co
149 Bradford St
Lexington MA  02173

Stanley Bemben
Goldberg  Zoino
Shattuck Rd
Hadley MA  01035

Jeffrey Benoit
Dept of Envir Qual Eng
DEQE Lakeville Hospital
Lakeville MA  02346

Susan Bianchetti
GCA Technology Div
Burlington Rd
Bedford MA  01730

Audrey Bickford
Univ of Mass
Apt C5 Cliffside
Sunderland MA  01375

Marland P Billings
Harvard University
Dept of Geological Sciences
24 Oxford St
Cambridge MA  02138

Thomas E Billups
United Engineers & Constructors
108 North St
Medford MA  02155

Claes Bjork
Skanska USA
8330 Old Courthouse Rd
Vienna VA  22180

Mark Blackey
Univ of Mass
454 Patterson House
Amherst MA  01003

Edwin A Blackey Jr
Corps Engineers NED
62 King Philip Rd
Sudbury MA 01776

Don Blanchard
NE College
Foster Hill Rd
Henniker NH 03242

Zenas Bliss
Haley & Aldrich
238 Main St
Cambridge MA 02142

Fred Bodholt
Geology Dept
New England College
Henniker NH 03242

Jane Bolton
709 Bl Brown
Univ of Mass
Amherst MA 01003

Bill Bombard
Greenman Pederson Assoc
63 Lincoln St
Worcester MA 01605

William A Bonin
NH Dept of Res & Econ Devel
PO Box 856
Concord NH 03301

Ralph Borjeson
Stone & Webster
589 Franklin St
Duxbury MA 02332

Bob Bouchard
GCA Technology Div
Burlington Rd
Bedford MA 01730

Lawrence J Boudreau
Univ of Mass
89 Northwood Apts
Sunderland MA 01375

Bruce Bouley
Callahan Mining Corp.
CBT Plaza
1120 Post Road
Darien CT 06820

Donovan Bowley
DEQE Room 2000
100 Cambridge St
Boston MA 02202

Edward Bradley
Star Rte
Manchester Rd
Steep Falls ME 04085

Olin C Braids
Geraghty & Miller
6800 Jericho Turnpike
Syosset NY 11791

Benno Brenninkmeyer SJ
Dept of Geology
Boston College
Chestnut Hill MA 02167

Thomas Brewer
Boston City College
19 High St
Holliston MA 01746

Eugene Brickman
Corps Engineers NED
172 River St
Waltham MA 02154

Darinka Zigic Briggs
Univ of Michigan
3451 Burbank Dr
Ann Arbor Mich 48105

Randolph W Bromery
Dept of Geology
Univ of Mass
Amherst MA 01003

Arthur H Brownlow
Dept of Geology
Boston University
Boston MA 02215

Donald Bruehl
Metcalf & Eddy
50 Staniford St
Boston MA 02114

Dan Bubly
C E Maguire
31 Canal St
Providence RI 02903

Linda Burnett
Boston University
2160 Commonwealth Ave
Auburndale MA 02166

Eric E Butler
Guild Drilling Co
100 Water St
E Providence RI 02914

Rebecca E Buxton
Dept of Geology
Boston College
Chestnut Hill MA 02167

Richard M Cadwgan
Environmental Research & Tech
696 Virginia Rd
Concord MA 01742

Tom Cambareri
Cape Cod Planning Comm
Rte 6A
Barnstable MA 02630

Nicholas Campagna
Goldberg Zoino
86 Countryside Lane
Norwood MA 02062

Hugh Caspe
Kaiser Engineers
6 St James Ave
Boston MA 02116

Leona Champeny
Terrain Investigation
South Great Rd
Lincoln MA 01773

Rudy Chlanda
USDA Soil Conservation Service
23 Kettle Pond Rd
Amherst MA 01002

Clara Chow
EPA Water Supply Branch
JFK Building
Boston MA 02203

Richard G Christian
Camp Dresser & McKee
9 Oak Grove Rd
Randolph MA 02368

Steen Christiansen
C E Maguire
31 Warren Ave
Somerville MA 02143

Cathleen Clark
Univ of Mass
Civil Engineering Dept
Amherst MA 01003

D Theodore Clark
Dunn Geoscience Corp
5 Northway Lane North
Latham NY 12110

James M Cleary
Box 541
Falmouth
MA 02541

Richard Clingan
US Geological Survey
1725 K Street NW
Washington DC 20006

Tim Connors
Univ of Mass
100 Jackson Hill Rd
N Leverett MA 01054

David Cook
GCA Technology Div
Burlington Rd
Bedford MA 01730

David Corkum
United Engineers & Constructors
Box 700
Seabrook NH 03874

Cheryl Cornwell
29 Clifton Ave
Hull
MA 02045

Chancellor Robert A Corrigan
Harbor Campus
Univ of Mass
Boston MA 02125

Anthony D Cortese
Dept of Env Quality Engin
100 Cambridge St - 20th Floor
Boston MA 02202

Antonio da Costa
Room 48-209
MIT
Cambridge MA 02139

Timothy R Cullen
Bechtel Inc
58 Day St
Somerville MA 02144

William E Cutfliffe
Dunn Geoscience Corp
5 Northway Lane North
Latham NY 12110

John F Cysz
Robert G Brown & Assoc
Berkshire Common - Third Floor
Pittsfield MA 01201

Donna L B D'Amore
Camp Dresser & McKee
One Center Plaza
Boston MA 02108

Lee Dane
Terrain Investigation
South Great Rd
Lincoln MA 01773

Alton P Davis
1 Kenilworth Rd
Arlington
MA 02174

Robert Davis
Univ of New Hampshire
Dept of Earth Sciences
James Hall
Durham NH 03824

Duane D Day
DOE
150 Causeway St
Boston MA 02114

Susan Dayan
EPA
Falmouth Town Hall
Falmouth MA 02545

Steven L Dean
Whitman & Howard
49 Ontario Dr
Hudson MA 01749

Richard J Defieux
Environmental Research & Tech
696 Virginia Rd
Concord MA 01742

Margaret Dein
Univ of Rhode Island
435 Graduate Village
Kingston RI 02881

Helen L Delano
National Park Service
75 Central St
S Weymouth MA 02190

Michele Dermer
Univ of Mass
24A Nutting Ave
Amherst MA 01002

John Dick
Public Works
Town Hall
Danvers MA 01923

Jeffrey E Dieriks
Camp Dresser & McKee
One Center Plaza
Boston MA 02108

Charles Wm Dimmick
Central Ct St College
1718 Milldale Rd
Cheshire CT 06410

Richard Dinitto
GCA Technology Div
Burlington Rd
Bedford MA 01730

Francis Dittami
Perini Corp
73 Mt Wayte Ave
Framingham MA 01701

Mary-Frances Doiron
Boston College
66 Old Stage Rd
Chelmsford MA 01824

Kevin Donahue
Algonquin Gas Transmission
1284 Soldiers Field Rd
Boston MA 02135

Jim Dowd
Boston State College
41 Summit Ave
Brookline MA 02146

John Drobinski
Weston Geophysical
PO Box 550
Westborough MA 01581

Herman C Duecker
W R Grace & Company
62 Whittemore Ave
Cambridge MA 02140

John Dugan
Haley & Aldrich Inc
238 Main St
Cambridge MA 02142

Normand G Duphily
Univ of Mass
24 Mill Hollow Apt
Amherst MA 01002

Herbert Einstein
Room 1-330
MIT
Cambridge MA 02139

Jane Elmer
Morrison Geotech Engin
RFD 3 China Rd
Winslow ME 04901

Bruce Ey
Schofield Brothers
1071 Worcester Rd
Framingham MA 01701

Oswald C Farquhar
Dept of Geology
Univ of Mass
Amherst MA 01003

Charles N Faulstich Jr
Raytheon Service Co
14 Flagg Circle
Waltham MA 02154

W S Febiger
New England River Basins Comm
53 State St
Boston MA 02109

Lawrence Feldman
Goldberg Zoino
30 Tower Rd
Newton Upper Falls MA 02164

Antonio Ferreira
Electric Power Research Inst
c/o Neplan
174 Brush Hill Ave
W Springfield MA 01089

Ralph Fine
62 Wade St
Newton Highlands
MA 02161

Dennis Finn
Salem State College
182 Lafayette St
Salem MA 01970

James D Fitzgerald
Univ of Mass
112 Northwood Apt
Sunderland MA 01375

Mark L Flagg
Univ of Mass
66 Mill Hollow Apts
Amherst MA 01002

Kathleen Flynn
791 E 4th St
So Boston
MA 02127

John A Focht Jr
McClelland Engineers
6100 Hillcroft Avenue
Houston TX   77081

David Foster
Normandeau Assoc
25 Nashua Rd
Bedford NH   03102

Brian K Fowler
Pike Industries
RFD 7 - Box 159
Gilford NH   03246

Sandra Franz
Univ of Mass
175 Amherst Rd
#3 Green House
Sunderland MA   01375

Michael H Frimpter
USGS Water Resources Div
150 Causeway St
Boston MA   02114

Ted Gabel
Univ of Mass
114 Leverett Rd
Shutesbury MA   01072

Charles E Gale
Gale Engineering Company
8 Washington Place
Braintree MA   02184

Lester Gaynor
S E A Consultants Inc
54 Canal St
Boston MA   02114

Robert G Gerber
Ash Point Rd
So Harpswell
ME   04079

Richard P Gillespie
Stone & Webster
164 Harris Rd
Nashua NH   03062

Michael Goetz
N E River Basins Comm
53 State St
Boston MA   02109

Sylvie Olney Gorman
Old Nook Rd
Manchester
MA   01944

Mark Gould
S E A Consultants Inc
54 Canal St
Boston MA   02114

Lois Grady
Univ Mass
375 Shays St
Amherst MA   01002

Edward Greco
Metcalf & Eddy
50 Staniford St
Boston MA   02114

Lee Grubman
Leggette Brashears Graham
72 Danbury Rd
Wilton CT   06897

Gary Guazzo
Kaiser Engineers
6 St James Ave
Boston MA   02116

James D Gustin
Law Engineering Testing Co
1561 Sprayberry Dr
Marietta GA   30066

Jutta L Hager
Bentley College
100 Memorial Dr   Apt 11-23A
Cambridge MA   02142

David Haines
Univ of Mass
24 West St
Hadley MA   01035

James Haker
Salem State College
95 Kidder Ave
Somerville MA   02144

Leo M Hall
Dept of Geology
Univ of Mass
Amherst MA   01003

William John Hall
Dunn Geoscience Corp
20 Albright Ave
Albany NY 12203

Joseph H Hartshorn
Univ of Mass
1150 Bay Rd
Amherst MA   01002

Stephen K Harvey
Algonquin Gas Transmission
1284 Soldiers Field Rd
Boston MA   02135

Allen W Hatheway
Haley & Aldrich
238 Main St
Cambridge MA 02142

Michael Havenen
15 Ryder St
Arlington
MA   02174

Michael S Healy
Geotechnical Engineers
1017 Main St
Winchester MA   01890

Heeley (after Smith)

Craig Heindel
Wagner Heindel & Noyes
301 College St
Burlington VT   05401

Bruce A Heise
USGS Conservation Div
Suite 204
1725 K Street NW
Washington DC   20006

Edward Hellier
22 Cushing Ave
Hingham
MA   02043

Nancy Hellier
22 Cushing Ave
Hingham
MA   02043

Karl N Hendrickson
56 Berkshire Terrace
Amherst
MA   01002

Zoltan Hershkowitz
The Analysts/Schlumberger
1600 Ocean Parkway
Brooklyn NY   11223

Patrick J Hester
Algonquin Gas Transmission
1284 Soldiers Field Rd
Boston MA   02135

Janice Hight
Haley & Aldrich
238 Main St
Cambridge MA   02142

Richard Hight
181 E Main St
Northboro
MA   01532

Carol T Hildreth
135 Washington St
Holliston
MA   01746

Michael J Hobson
Acres American
Clark Building   Suite 329
Columbia MD   02144

Jeffrey R Holt
Clough Associates
24 Aviation Rd
Computer Park
Albany   NY   12205

D K Holway
W R Holway Associates
41111 South Darlington Ave
Tulsa OK   74135

Robert E Hoops
Robert G Brown
Berkshire Common Third Floor
Pittsfield MA   01201

John Hubert
Dept of Geology
Univ of Mass
Amherst MA  01003

John T Humphrey
Haley & Aldrich
195 West St
Reading MA  01867

Dorothy Hunnewell
600 Washington St    Room 320
Boston
MA  02111

Peter Jacobson
Univ of Mass
629 Main St
Amherst MA  01002

J Richard Jones
Boston State College
Dept of Regional Studies
Boston MA  02115

Peter Kallio
Woods Hole Oceanographic Inst
Woods Hole
MA  02543

John Henry Kalmbach
First National Bank of Boston
100 Federal St
Boston MA  02110

William B Kerfoot
K-V Associates
281 Main St
Falmouth MA 02540

John F Kick
Box 6
Dunstable
MA  01877

President David C Knapp
Univ of Mass
250 Stuart Street
Boston MA  02116

Steve Koorse
EPA
JFK Building
Boston MA  02203

Michael Kupferman
Northeastern Univ
Dept of Civil Engineering
Boston MA  02115

Normand Laberge
PO Box 151
Eastport
ME  04631

Andrew Lacroix
6440 Hillcroft
Houston
TX  77487

Winslow Ladue
VT Health Dept
60 Main St
Burlington VT    05401

Robert Laidlow
Phelps Dodge Exploration East
PO Box 1046
Bangor ME  04401

David M Lane
Home Oil
5204 Varsity Drive NW
Calgary Alberta T3A 1A6
Canada

Richard M Lane
NH Public Works & Highways
107 Pembroke Hill Rd
Pembroke NH  03301

Fred Larsen
Norwich Univ
9 Slate Ave
Northfield VT  05663

Jeffrey T Lawson
Weston Geophysical
PO Box 550
Westborough MA  01581

Denis R LeBlanc
US Geological Survey WRD
279 Winter St
Waltham MA  02154

G Leblanc
Weston Geophysical
PO Box 550
Westborough MA  02155

Fred M Levine
Weston Geophysical
PO Box 550
Westboro MA  01701

Margaret Lidback
Framingham State College
26 Oak St
Natick MA  01760

Elizabeth London
USGS
Stop 928
Reston VA  22092

Taylor H Loop
New England College
PO Box 55
Warner NH  03278

Henry Lord
Metcalf & Eddy
50 Staniford St
Boston MA  02114

Harro Lorenzen
PB-KBB Inc
6756 W Magnolia Blvd
Harahan LA  70123

Frederick Luckey
Univ of Mass
Apt 314
435 North Pleasant St
Amherst MA  01002

Lee Lyman
Lycott Environmental Research
Box 535
Sturbridge MA  01566

Stephen J Mabee
Sasaki Associates
64 Pleasant St
Watertown MA  02172

William F MacLean
Univ of Rhode Island
97 Lafayette Rd
North Kingston RI  02852

Anthony Maevsky
94 Browne St
Brookline
MA  02146

Andrew Magee
Boston Univ
173 Shirley Street #6
Winthrop MA  02152

Denis L Maher Jr
The Maher Corp
107 Mishawum Rd
Woburn MA  01801

William J Mallio
109 Mass Ave
Lexington
MA  01890

Lesley Manent
Smithsonian Institution
National Air & Science Museum
Room 3101
Washington DC  20560

Arnis Mangolds
Foster Miller
350 2nd Ave
Waltham MA  02154

Sandra Marsh
78 Possum Rd
Weston
MA  02193

Leo Martin
Stone & Webster
683 Main St
Watertown MA  02172

Peter Matonis
455 Read St
Seekonk
MA  02771

Tom McCrory
Univ of Mass
130 Upper Rd
West Deerfield MA  01342

Thomas McElroy
Univ of Mass
704 Main St
Amherst MA  01002

Tim McElroy
Mass Dept Env Quality Eng
W Mass Public Health Center
Univ of Mass
Amherst MA  01003

George E McGill
Univ of Mass
Dept of Geology
Amherst MA  01003

Robert McGlashan
Con-Tec Inc
16 South St
Concord NH  03301

William A McIlvride
Univ of Mass/Amherst
175 Amherst Rd
Sunderland MA  01375

William R McMenimen
Board of Health
Town Hall
Tewksbury MA  01876

Michael McVay
Univ of Mass
28 Marston Hall
Amherst MA  01003

Lance Meade
Geomapping Assoc
PO Box 133
Pittsford VT  05763

Henry J Miller
5 Amy Todt Dr
Monroe
NY  10950

James Monk
NE Power Co
25 Research Drive
Westover MA  01581

Lillian Morgenstern
MA Exec Off of Energy Resources
73 Tremont Street
Boston MA  02116

J Theodore Morine
D L Maher
71 Concord St  PO Box 127
No Reading MA  01864

Garrett Morrison
Morrison Geotech Engin
RFD 3  China Rd
Winslow ME  04901

John A Moser
Arch Associates
161 Hallet St
Yarmouth Port MA  02675

Ward S Motts
Geology Dept
Univ of Mass
Amherst MA  01003

Walter S Mulica
IEP Inc
Wayland
MA  01778

Mary L Murdock
Northeastern University
180 Market St  #308
Lynn MA  01901

Tom Murphy
EPA
JFK Federal Building
Boston MA  02203

Vincent Murphy
Weston Geophysical
PO Box 550
Westborough MA  02155

Anthony Murtaugh
1715 Comm Ave
Brighton
MA  02135

A Scott Nagel
Metcalf & Eddy
50 Staniford St
Boston MA  02114

Richard S Naylor
103GR Earth Sciences
Northeastern University
Boston MA  02115

Thom L Neff
Portland State University
PO Box 8082
Portland OR  97207

Eric Nelson
Stone & Webster
176 Topsfield Rd
Boxford MA  01921

Donald W Nickerson
Wentworth Inst of Tech
478 Rogers St
Tewksbury MA  01876

Michael A Nicoloro
Algonquin Gas Transmission
1284 Soldiers Field Rd
Boston MA  02135

Walter Nold
Walter Nold Co
24 Birch Rd
Natick MA  01760

Richard F Norton
Gale Engineering
8 Washington Place
Braintree MA  02184

Jeff Noyes
Wagner Heindel & Noyes
301 College St
Burlington VT  05401

Charles J O'Hara
UGGS
Office of Marine Geology
Woods Hole MA  02543

Robert O'Laskey
Univ of Mass
21 Mt Toby Apts
Sunderland MA  01375

Gerard O'Shea
S E A Consultants
54 Canal St
Boston MA  02114

Bernie Paquin
Dana F Perkins & Assoc
125 Main St
Reading MA  01867

William C Paris
Bechtel Assoc Prof Corp
2831 Lone Oak Dr
Ann Arbor MI  48103

Harold Patch
DEQE
6 Linwood St
Saugus MA  01906

Thomas Pawlina
S E A Consultants
54 Canal St
Boston MA  02114

Carl A Pearson
Univ of Rhode Island
45 Jefferson Drive
E Greenwich RI  02818

John H Peck
Stone & Webster
66 Austin Rd
Sudbury MA  01776

J M Pecoraro
DOE
150 Causeway St
Boston MA  01938

Michael A Penzo
SUNY/Binghamton
126 Burr Ave
Binghamton NY  13903

Hank Petranik
Home Oil
2300 Home Oil Tower
324 8th Ave
Calgary Alberta T2P 2Z5  Canada

Leonard Phillips
Room 10-140
MIT Tech Review
Cambridge MA  02139

Susan Pierce
Metcalf & Eddy
50 Staniford St
Boston MA   02114

William Pitt
Geotechnical Engineers
1071 Main St
Winchester MA   01890

Robert B Pojasek
Energy Resources Co
185 Alewife Brook Parkway
Cambridge MA   02138

Catherine S Pope
Pike Industries
246 N Main St
Apt #7 Concord NH   03301

Bran Potter
Univ of Mass
130 Sugarloaf St
South Deerfield MA   01373

Asaf Qazilbash
17 Myopia Rd
Hyde Park
MA   02136

Arthur L Quaglieri
Raytheon Service
65 Robinwood Rd
Norwood MA   02062

Sidney Quarrier
Conn Geological Survey
State Office Building
Hartford CT   06115

Gloria J Radke
Salem State College
30 Surfside Rd   Apt 10
Lynn MA   01902

John R Rand
Cundy's Harbor
RD2-210A
Brunswick
ME   04011

Donald Reed
1093 Main St
Norwell
MA   02061

Kenneth Richards
Boston College
48 Atherton Rd
Brookline MA   02146

John Risitano
Metcalf & Eddy
50 Staniford St
Boston MA   02114

John Rivard
Guild Drilling
100 Water St
E Providence RI   02914

Ben Rizzo
Fish and Wildlife Services
162 Virginia Rd
Waltham MA   02154

Peter Robar
Mass Dept Env Quality Eng
W Mass Public Health Center
Univ of Mass
Amherst MA   01003

James Robb
USGS
Office of Marine Geology
Woods Hole MA   02543

Joan Roberts
US Geological Survey
1725 K Street NW
Washington DC   20006

Peter Robinson
Univ of Mass
Dept of Geology
Amherst MA   01003

Brian Rogan
Univ of Mass
Cliffside Apts   J-8
Sunderland MA   01375

Paul Ross
S E A Consultants
54 Canal St
Boston MA   02114

Henry A Russell
26 Love Rd
Holbrook
MA   02343

Joseph S Russo
Div of Waterways
100 Nashua St   Room 532
Boston MA   02114

Barbara J Ryan
US Geological Survey
150 Causeway St
Suite 1001
Boston MA   02114

John S Schlee
USGS
Office of Marine Geology
Woods Hole MA   02543

Carolyn Schneider
Harbor Campus
Univ of Mass
Boston MA   02125

Robert P Schreiber
CDM/Resource Analysis
235 Wyman St
Waltham MA   02154

William Schwalbaum
Univ of Mass
245 Lincoln Apts
Amherst MA   01002

Walter Schwarz
Mass Dept Env Quality Eng
W Mass Public Health Center
Univ of Mass
Amherst MA   01003

Norman E Scott
Falmouth Sewer Advisory Comm
198 Sippewissett Rd
Falmouth MA   02540

Ernest T Selig
Civil Engineering
Univ of Mass
Amherst MA   01003

Ralph N Shaver
Charles T Main
10 Longmeadow Rd
Westford MA   01886

James Sicuso
St Dominic Savio HS
10 Dawes St
Revere MA   02151

Joseph A Sinnott
267 Salisbury St
Worcester
MA   01609

James W Skehan SJ
Boston College
Weston Observatory
Weston MA   02193

Stuart Skinner
K-V Associates Inc
281 Main St
Falmouth MA   02540

Lester B Smith Jr
MA Coastal Zone Management
100 Cambridge Street
Boston MA   02202

Philip G Smith
58 Foster St
Brighton
MA   02135

Richard W Heeley
Lycott Environmental Research
44 Chandler St
Belmont MA   02178

Lars Söderberg
Skanska Cementgjuteriet
8330 Old Courthouse Rd
Vienna VA   22180

Franklin M Stephens
Exxon Corporation
1251 Ave of the Americas
Room 4280
New York NY   10020

Robert H Stewart
Camp Dresser & McKee
8 Pilgrim Rd
Waban MA   02168

Byron Stone
US Geological Survey
MS 928
Reston VA  22092

Janet Stone
US Geological Survey
MS 928
Reston VA  22092

John Stone
US Geological Survey
1725 K Street NW
Washington DC  20005

Carol Sweet
Metcalf & Eddy
50 Staniford St
Boston MA  02114

James B Thompson Jr
Harvard Univ
202 Hoffman Lab
Cambridge MA  02138

Stuart N Thompson
Acres American
48 Jefferson Dr
Lockport NY   14044

Chris Tilden
DEQE
218 Furnace St
Marshfield MA  02050

Franklin S Tirsch
Univ of Mass
50 Meadow St  #26
Amherst MA  01002

Timothy Toomey
Weston Geophysical
PO Box 550
Westborough MA  01581

Charles H Trautmann
235 Forest Home Dr
Ithaca
NY  14850

Patricia Trombly
Conservation Dept
Room I - 52 Sanborn St
Reading MA  01867

Martha W Vaccaro
Town of Falmouth
Box 245
W Falmouth MA  02574

Alan Van Arsdale
DEQE
100 Cambridge St
Rm 2000
Boston MA  02202

Frank Vetere
52 Colby St
Bradford
MA  01830

David Vine
Hayden Harding & Buchanan
1340 Soldiers Field Rd
Boston MA  02135

Phil Wagner
Wagner Heindel & Noyes
301 College St
Burlington VT  05401

Sarah K Walen
Geology Dept
Univ of Mass
Amherst MA  01003

Barbara Walsh
EPA
JFK Federal Building - Rm 1903
Boston MA  02203

William  Walsh
Raytheon
11 Coolidge Rd
Acton MA  01720

Everett Washer
355 Sudbury Rd
Stow
MA  01775

Robert Weimar
Camp Dresser & McKee
One Center Plaza
Boston MA  02108

Barbara Weiss
Worcester Polytech
79 Spiers Rd
Newton MA  02159

Ken Wenger
EPA
JFK Federal Building
Boston MA  02203

David Westcott
C E Maguire
31 Canal St
Providence RI  02903

Karl S Westermann
Mueser Rutledge
415 Madison Ave
New York NY  10017

Owen L White
Ontario Geological Survey
77 Grenville St
Toronto Ontario M7A 1W3
Canada

Allan Wicklund
Univ of Mass
100 Jackson Hill Rd
N Leverett MA  01005

Jacquelyn Wilkins
DEQE
43 Allen St
Brockton MA  02041

Donald U Wise
Geology Dept
Univ of Mass
Amherst MA  01003

Richard Witt
Town of Falmouth
295 Hatchville Rd
East Falmouth MA  02536

Fred Wolf
EPA
JFK Building
Boston MA  02203

Jo Ann Wolf
24 Haverhill St
Andover
MA  01810

I H Wong
Ebasco Service
World Trade Center #2
91st Floor
New York NY  10048

David Woodhouse
Goldberg Zoino
104 Randall St
N Easton MA  02356

Robert S Young
North American Exploration
PO Box 7584
Charlottesville VA  22906

William S Zoino
Goldberg Zoino
30 Tower Rd
Newton MA  02158

*the discussion*
*the light at the end*